LIBRARY
STATE UNIVERSITY
OF NEW YORK
DELHI, NEW YORK

D1536033

SPORES
THEIR DORMANCY AND GERMINATION

SPORES

THEIR DORMANCY AND GERMINATION

ALFRED S. SUSSMAN

UNIVERSITY OF MICHIGAN

HARLYN O. HALVORSON

UNIVERSITY OF WISCONSIN

HARPER & ROW, *Publishers*

NEW YORK *AND* LONDON

 For information address Harper & Row, Publishers, Incorporated, 49 East 33rd Street, New York, N.Y. 10016.

Library of Congress Catalog Card Number: 66-11271

To our wives
for knowing when
to persevere or prod;
and to our children
for being.

PREFACE

THIS BOOK is intended as a reference work in the basic principles of the dormant state in biology. The initial research was begun some 13 years ago when we were both faculty members (Botany, Bacteriology) at the University of Michigan. The research interests in our two laboratories on the physiology and nature of spores in *Neurospora* and in *Bacillus* led to numerous discussions with students and colleagues as to whether common principles determined the dormant state. The intervening years have supported the notion that dormant systems may share basic mechanisms and this view was supported in 1958 by Professor D. Keilin in his lecture on "The Problem of Anabiosis or Latent Life." Further evidence was summarized in 1960 in the fifth Oholo Conference in Israel on "Cryptiotic Stages in Biological Systems."

Five years ago we started the preparation of a monograph to highlight the common denominators in biological dormancy. Inspection of the literature in this field led us not only to expand the treatment to a book, but also to sharply define the limits of discussion. To retain an historic as well as introspective analysis, this book is largely restricted to discussions of dormancy in microbial systems in which biochemical aspects have been analyzed in some detail. An important, but unfortunately necessary, omission has been that of references to the literature on spore formation. We hope that a detailed analysis of the maintenance and breaking of the dormant state will provide an informative background against which the morphogenic conversion of a vegetative cell to a dormant spore can be measured. The differential activation of the genome, the qualitative changes in the types of proteins produced, the new physiological functions accompanying the origin of structures are all properties of sporulation which will undoubtedly hold the attention of experimentalists for years to come. We hope only to draw attention to this conversion as a model system for study of the regulation of intracellular differentiation. Spores are formed at the peak of the differentiation of many microorganisms, as the culmination of a series of major morphological and biochemical changes. Therefore, to this extent, they represent an endpoint in the morphogenesis of these organisms.

That they are a beginning, too, is shown by their embryonic capacity in serving as initiators of the development of the vegetative organism after dormancy has been broken. Differentiation in metazoans and higher plants involves simultaneous changes in tissues, as well as sequential ones, so it is likely that regulatory mechanisms of a kind not found in microbes exist. Moreover, cells of functions unknown to microbes, such as nerves and those producing acid, keratin, hormones, and other substances must undergo biochemical changes which differ from those to be discussed for spores. Nevertheless, the successes of the comparative biochemical and developmental approach are manifest and it is possible that the mechanisms suggested for spores may have generality for resting stages like seeds, cysts, and others.

One unavoidable difficulty attendant upon writing is that scientific discoveries are not arrested awaiting a "sifting and winnowing" of available data. After three successive attempts to "update" and predict the basis of dormancy, we are forced by the nature of things to close the literature as of early 1965.

Our thanks are gratefully extended to the following, who furnished illustrations: Drs. T. Beale, N. Dombrowski, P. Fitz-James, P. Gerhardt, Audrey M. Glauert, H. Iisuka, R. J. Lowry, A. Miller, W. Murrell, C. Robinow, A. Takagi, R. D. Tresner, and O. Wyss. Moreover, we would like to acknowledge the help provided by Drs. G. Mandel, A. Marr, and L. Campbell in reading and criticizing the manuscript. Finally, we would like to thank Mrs. Carol Nimke for her conscientious and intelligent help in preparing the manuscript for publication.

CONTENTS

SPORES
THEIR DORMANCY AND GERMINATION

CHAPTER 1

Types of Dormancy

THE IDEA that the earth was originally inseminated by forms of life that arrived from other worlds, after passage through outer space, has intrigued biologists and laymen alike. According to one proponent of this theory (Wagner, 1874), "the atmospheres of the heavenly bodies, and also the swirling cosmic mists may be regarded as eternal repositories of living forms, as perpetual plantations of organic germs." Because of the requirement that such "organic germs" be enduring of severe environmental stress, and of small size to permit ready propulsion even by the pressure of light "Radiopanspermie" (Arrhenius, 1910), microbial spores have been used as examples of the form in which life could exist in the "swirling cosmic mists" (Nagy, 1963). These beings can survive boiling, submergence in concentrated acid, and the extremes of cold and vacuum which can be developed by man. The unlifelike tolerance of these durable organisms, the nature of the dormant condition, and the mechanism for breaking the dormant state will be the subjects of this book.

Periods of rest or dormancy are not unique with microorganisms; in fact, they are common in plants and animals. In this condition, organisms can withstand environmental upsets of prolonged duration. Among animals such as insects and bears, the period of diapause, or hibernation, may be an important ecological adaptation which enables these organisms to survive extreme temperatures and restricted food supplies. The characteristics and control of mammalian hibernation have been the subject of a recent symposium (Lyman and Dawe, 1960). The resistance of seeds to unfavorable environmental conditions makes possible storage of grains and other important crop plants which are the basis of agriculture.

There are two types of dormancy for seeds (Toole et al., 1956), one of which is retained only as long as the seed remains dry, whereas the other is independent of moisture. Buds of plants, which normally remain dormant only during winter, may on occasion remain latent during most of the life of the plant and develop shoots under conditions which are little understood (Ferry and Ward, 1959). Prolonged dormancy is also characteristic of eggs such as those of worms and insects (Grossowicz et al., 1961). For example, dry larvae can survive heating to 100°C or exposure to liquid air temperatures (Hinton, 1960). Analogous examples of dormancy are found in the case of dehydrated vegetative cells, cysts of protozoa, and spores of bacteria. Dormancy, then, is widespread in nature and, judging from experience with other biological systems, it is likely that there are parallel mechanisms by which dormancy can be explained, no matter how disparate the organisms. This was recently the subject of a symposium on "Cryptobiotic Stages in Biological Systems" (Grossowicz et al., 1961). With this possibility in mind, we have undertaken to outline the types of dormancy found in microorganisms and to explore mechanisms, wherever possible, in search of the parallels that may generalize these observations.

Interest in spores was first generated by practical considerations. The function of spores as dormant cells is greatly aided by their resistance, thereby making for special problems in applied microbiology. What biologist is not familiar with the need for sterile technique in maintaining the purity of cultures, or with the fact that heating foods to pasteurization temperature does not kill all of the cells in this medium? Moreover, the canning industry's preoccupation with the recalcitrant "last spore" has generated practical interest in them. Recent development of an irradiation sterilization procedure has led to renewed interest in determination of sterilization doses of spores.

The role of spores in nature as well as the factors controlling their formation and germination will be stressed in this book. Dormant spores are both an end point and a beginning in biology. They represent the end of the development of many organisms and in this sense are the climax of their life history. This is illustrated by the finding that the spore has a specialized and complex structure whose formation involves a morphogenetic change in vegetative growth. In addition, spores are frequently associated with sexuality and the subtle metabolic controls upon which this process is based.

At the same time, the spore is endowed with the capacity for rapid and sustained growth and mitotic activity. Spores are embryonic in function and possess many attributes in common with totipotent cells of higher organisms. This versatility, and the key role played by the spore in the life cycle of organisms, has suggested the need for this summary of their biology.

Nomenclature of Metabolic States

> But above and beyond there's still one name left over,
> And that is the name that you never will guess;
> The name that no human research can discover—
> BUT THE CAT HIMSELF KNOWS, and will never confess.
> —T. S. Eliot (1939)

A spectrum of metabolic states between active and vigorously metabolizing vegetative organisms and those that show no perceptible metabolism is known. The state that is imposed by temperatures low enough to vitrify the contents of cells has been referred to as *latent life*, or *abiosis* by Schmidt (1948), or as *anabiosis* by Preyer (1891). Anabiosis has been widely used in this sense but was originally proposed by Preyer to describe the resurrection of completely lifeless but visible organisms ("Wiederbelebung"). Schmidt (1955), in his important treatise which uses this term in its title, introduced *abiosis* as a substitute for anabiosis, but the prior application of this term to problems in the origin of life has argued against its acceptance. For these reasons, Keilin (1959) has proposed the term *cryptobiosis* as an alternative and this term will be adopted here. An outline of the interrelations of these terms, and others to be discussed later, is provided below:

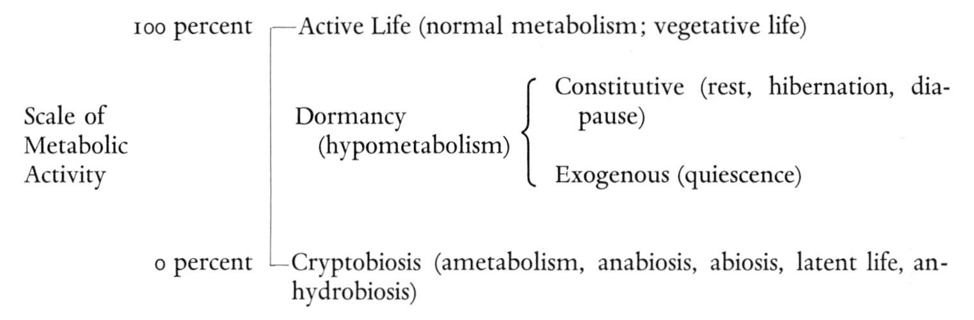

Dormancy and Stages in Germination

That two classes of phenomena influence dormancy was perceived early by Doran (1922) who labeled them as the "internal" and "external" factors. Included among the internal ones are the maturity of the spore, its longevity and "animation" and "a poorly understood factor which may be called vitality. . ." External factors include temperature, light, water, oxygen, nutrients, and toxic substances. Although it is obvious that these elements are related to the extent that any environmental stimulus is received and interpreted through the complex of constitutional factors which comprise the organism, there is heuristic value in maintaining such a dichotomy. The definitions which follow are taken from Sussman (1965) and compelling arguments for the maintenance of the dichotomy which has been outlined are presented by Mandels and Norton (1948).

Dormancy—any rest period or reversible interruption of the phenotypic development of an organism.

Constitutive dormancy—a condition in which development is delayed due to an innate property of the dormant stage such as a barrier to the penetration of nutrients, a metabolic block, or the production of a self-inhibitor.

Exogenous dormancy—a condition in which development is delayed because of unfavorable chemical or physical conditions of the environment.

Maturation—the complex of changes associated with the development of the resting stage of dormant organisms or of the germinable stage in those without a dormant period.

Activation—the application of environmental stimuli which induce germination.

Germination—a process which leads to the first irreversible stage which is recognizably different from the dormant organism, as judged by physiological or morphological criteria.

The example of *Phytophthora cactorum* (Blackwell, 1943) will serve to make the distinction between these terms clearer. The oospores of this phycomycete will not germinate immediately upon being shed but require a 3–4 week delay or maturation period until nuclear fusion is accomplished. A further period of after-ripening of from 6–7 months succeeds the latter, and, in contrast to the immature prefusion phase, this dormant phase may be reduced by freezing the spores. Consequently maturation is a preliminary to after-ripening which, in turn, can be shortened by activating the spores with low-temperature treatment. Dormancy is a condition between maturation and germination and it may coincide with the after-ripening period if the stimulus which induces germination is applied immediately after maturation. On the other hand, it may be of much longer duration if this stimulus is delayed. In contrast to the situation in *P. cactorum*, maturation is accomplished before the spores are shed, as in the case of many of the meiospores of ascomycetes and basidospores. Moreover, the after-ripening period may be very short, or extend over a period of several years, as described by McKay (1935, 1939) for *Peronospora schleideniana*.

Dormant periods have been found in a wide variety of organisms and diverse approaches have been used in their study. An example of the stages in formation and breaking of dormancy in bacterial systems, as well as the terminology employed, is given in Chapter 2. Different terms have been used which appear to describe similar biological phenomena. Such is the case for the two types of dormancy described previously, as the terms listed in Table 1.1 reveal. It can be seen in this table that botanists have used a similar, but not identical classification to the one proposed in this text. Thus, in the botanical literature, rest (constitutive dormancy) is distinguished from quiescence (exogenous dormancy). However, dormancy induced by permeability barriers is considered a type of quiescence (Vegis, 1965), whereas in our interpretation of constitutive dor-

Table 1.1 Nomenclatorial Equivalents in the Description of Dormancy

Term	Organisms	Reference
Constitutive Dormancy		
True dormancy, physiological rest	Higher plants	Hill and Campbell, 1949
Rest	Higher plants	Chandler, 1907; Samish, 1954
"Wahre," or "Wirkliche" Ruhe	Higher plants	Vegis, 1965
Hibernation, aestivation	Vertebrates	Bartholomew and Hudson, 1960
Diapause	Arthropods	Lees, 1955
Exogenous Dormancy		
Imposed rest	Higher plants	Hill and Campbell, 1949
Quiescence	Higher plants	Hill and Campbell, 1949; Samish, 1954
"Zwangsruhe," "aufgezwungene Wachstumsruhe"	Higher plants	Vegis, 1965
Hypothermia	Vertebrates	Lyman and Dawe, 1960
Quiescence	Arthropods	Lees, 1955

mancy, any restraint upon the development of the cell which is imposed by factors related to the cell's own structure or function should be included in this category. To draw a distinction between constitutive factors which are inside, or within the metabolic apparatus of the cell, and those concerned with the wall would seem to be overly arbitrary. A corollary of the broad interpretation of dormancy is that any cell (or organism) that can germinate after environmental upsets of some duration may be considered to have had a period of dormancy. A prerequisite for such cells is the ability to survive the rigors of a physical and chemical environment that would be lethal to the organism at other stages in its development. Furthermore, it is not to be expected that constitutive dormancy would be found to exist in ephemeral organisms; that is, selection in nature must inevitably favor, among organisms lacking resistance, those which germinate with relative ease and rapidity.

There are many kinds of resistant cells. Among the bacteria, even vegetative cells may survive drastic conditions of temperature, atmospheric and osmotic pressure (Gaughran, 1947; Johnson, 1957). However, it is the endospores of these organisms that are responsible for the survival of bacteria under the most drastic conditions. The vegetative mycelium of fungi can also serve as a resistant stage (Zimmerman, 1925; Hawker, 1957). Survival of the vegetative organism may be effected without change in its structure or, as in the cases discussed by Hawker, alterations may occur, in response to environmental pressures, which make the organism more able to survive. Still, the most usual way by which fungi persist is through the production of special resistant stages. These may be modified cells of the mycelium, as in the case of the "dauerzellen" of yeasts, or the chlamydospores of several fungi, including *Fusarium* sp. and *Mucor racemosus*. Furthermore, aggregates of hyphae, such as sclerotia, rhizomorphs, and even parts of fruiting bodies, may serve to perpetuate the fungi. But, as in the case of the bacteria, spores of several types are usually the most resistant of the stages in the fungus life history and it is to these cells that most attention will be devoted.

REFERENCES

ARRHENIUS, S. 1910. *L'Evolution des Mondes. La Vie dans l'Univers*. Paris, 236 pp.

BARTHOLOMEW, G. A., and V. A. HUDSON. 1960. *Bull. Museum Comp. Zool., Harvard Coll.* 124:193–208.

BLACKWELL, E. 1943. *Trans. Brit. Mycol. Soc.* 26:71–89.

CHANDLER, W. H. 1907. *Missouri Univ. Agr. Exp. Sta. Bull.* 74.

DORAN, W. L. 1922. *Bull. Torrey Botan. Club.* 49:313–314.

ELIOT, T. S. 1939. *Old Possum's Book of Practical Cats*. Faber and Faber Ltd., London, and Harcourt, Brace & World Inc., New York, 49 pp.

FERRY, J. F., and H. S. WARD. 1959. *Fundamentals of Plant Physiology*. MacMillan, N.Y., 288 pp.

GAUGHRAN, E. R. L. 1947. *Bacterial Rev.* 11:189–225.

GROSSOWICZ, N., S. HESTRIN, and A. KEYNAN, Eds. 1961. *Proc. Symp. Cryptobiotic Stages in Biological Systems*. Elsevier, Amsterdam, N.Y., London, 232 pp.

HAWKER, L. E. 1957. in *Microbiol. Ecology, 7th Symp., Soc. Gen. Microbiol.* Cambridge Univ. Press, London, pp. 238–258.

HILL, A. G. G., and G. K. G. Campbell. 1949. *J. Exp. Agr.* 17:259–264.

HINTON, H. E. 1960. *Proc. Roy. Entomol. Soc. (London)* C25:7.

JOHNSON, F. H. 1957. in *Microbial Ecology, 7th Symp., Soc. Gen. Microbiol.* Cambridge Univ. Press, London, pp. 134–167.

KEILIN, D. 1959. *Proc. Roy. Soc. (London) Ser. B* 150:150–191.

LEES, A. D. 1955. *The Physiology of Diapause in Arthropods*. Cambridge Univ. Press, London, 115 pp.

LYMAN, C. P., and A. R. DAWE. 1960. *Mammalian Hibernation. Bull. Museum Comp. Zool., Harvard Coll.* 124, 549 pp.

MCKAY, R. 1935. *Nature* (London) 135:306.

MCKAY, R. 1939. *J. Roy. Hort. Soc.* 64:272–285.

MANDELS, G. R., and A. B. NORTON. 1948. *Quart. Gen. Labs. Res. Rept. Microbial Ser.* 11:1–50.

NAGY, B. 1963. *Ann. N.Y. Acad. Sci.* 108:615.

PREYER, W. 1891. *Biol. Zentr.* 11:1–5.

SAMISH, R. M. 1954. *Ann. Rev. Plant Physiol.* 5:183–201.

SCHMIDT, P. 1955. *Anabioz. Izd. AN SSR.* Moscow and Leningrad.

SUSSMAN, A. S. 1965. In *Encyclopedia of Plant Physiology*. Vol. 15. Anton Lang, Ed., Springer-Verlag, Berlin, pp. 933–1025.

TOOLE, E. H., S. B. HENDRICKS, H. A. BORTHWICK, and V. K. TOOLE. 1956. *Ann. Rev. Plant Physiol.* 7:299–324.

VEGIS, A. 1965. In *Encyclopedia of Plant Physiology*. A. Lang, Ed., Springer-Verlag, Berlin, pp. 498–668.

WAGNER, M. 1874. *Augsberger Allgem. Z., Beilage.* Oct. 6, 7, and 8.

ZIMMERMAN, A. 1925. *Zentr. Bakteriol. Parasitenk. Abt.* 65:311–418.

CHAPTER 2

The Structure and Formation of Dormant Cells

Types of Spores

THE TERM *spore* in this book will be used to describe any reproductive structure found in microbes. Frequently, multicellular propagules also are called spores, especially in the fungi, but they may be considered groups of one-celled spores because each cell can usually produce a germ tube. A prefix denoting the manner of origin of the spore, or the name of its container, completes the term used to describe such propagules. This is illustrated in the case of bacterial *endo*spores, fungal *asco*spores (formed within asci), *basidio*spores (formed on basidia), and so on. Sometimes, as when only one type is formed in a particular group, it may simply be called the spore, as in the myxomycetes (slime molds) and ustilaginales (smuts).

BACTERIA

At least three types of reproductive bodies are formed by bacteria, including endospores, cysts, and conidia. Endospores occur among the gram-positive spore-forming rods of the genera *Bacillus* and *Clostridium*, as well as in the coccus, *Sporosarcina* (MacDonald and MacDonald, 1962) and in *Mycobacterium* (Csillag, 1963), and perhaps *Spirillum* (Delaporte, 1964). As can be seen in Figures 2.1 and 2.2, endospores are formed within cells, usually are very heat resistant, and are of complex internal structure. Further details of the structure of these spores will be discussed in Chapter 5.

Another kind of propagule formed by bacteria is the cyst, such as that formed by *Azotobacter*. Detailed studies of the structure and formation of this structure have recently been reported (Socolofsky and Wyss, 1961; Tchan et al., 1962; Layne and Johnson, 1964). Figure 2.3 reveals that these cysts are spherical, with a

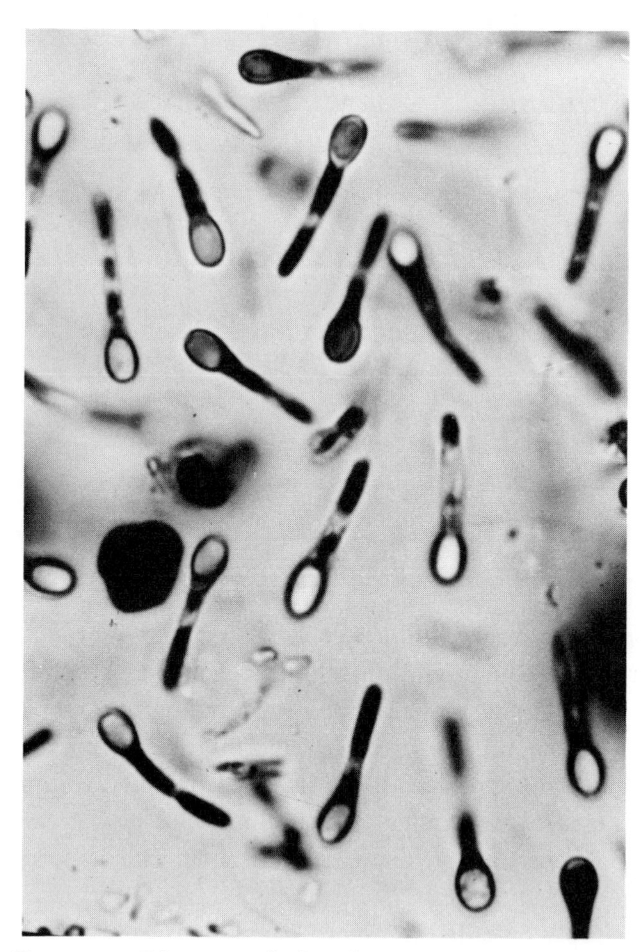

Figure 2.1 Edospores of *Clostridium pectinovorum* in a raw culture on rice, in tap water. Stained with Lugol's iodine to show granulose. ×3600. (Robinow, 1960, courtesy Academic Press, Inc., Publishers.)

contracted cytoplasm and a thick contoured wall. Cysts are formed by myxobacteria as well, including those of *Sporocytophaga* (Grace, 1951) and *Myxococcus* (Voelz and Dworkin, 1962). In addition, Bisset (1950) discusses microcyst formation in other bacteria as well, although very little is known of their role and manner of formation.

The spores (conidia) of actinomycetes are formed by the fragmentation of the ends of aerial mycelial strands and appear as in Figure 2.4 (see also Chapter 5). They may appear warty, spiny, smooth, as well as forming spirals, or cottony masses as described in the work of Tresner et al. (1961). The detailed morphology of one such spore can be seen in Figures 5.11 and 5.15 from which comparisons can be made with the structure of cysts and endospores. A summary of such comparisons, as well as those based upon other characters, is presented in

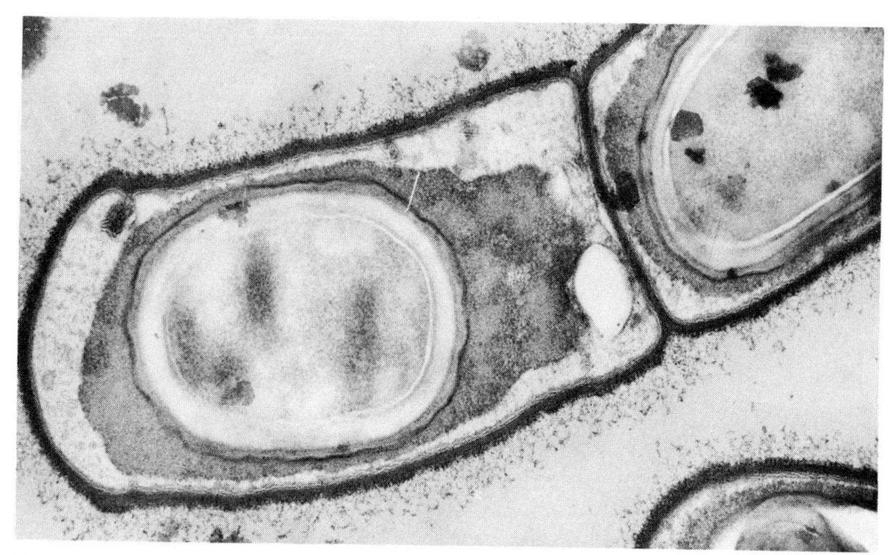

Figure 2.2 Completion of sporulation in *Bacillus megaterium*. Note beginning of sporangial lysis. Osmium-uranyl fixed and stained by prolonged exposure to PbOH. ×75,000. (Courtesy of P. C. Fitz-James.)

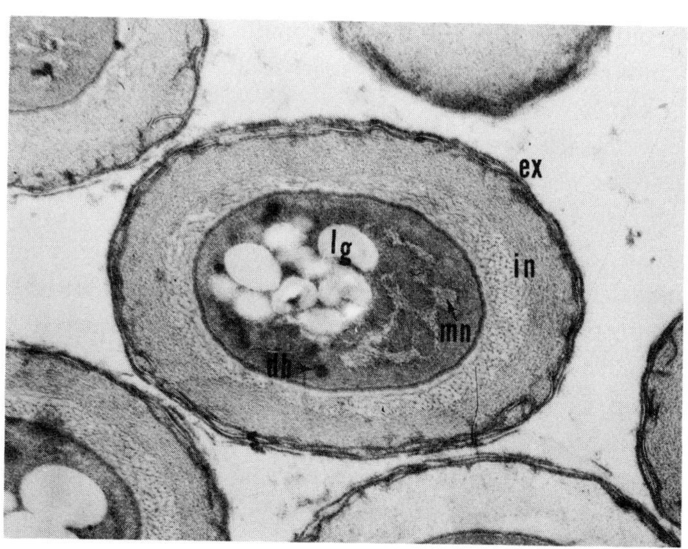

Figure 2.3 Cysts of *Azotobacter agilis*. Legend: db, electron-dense body; ex, exine; in, intine; lg, lipoidal globule; nm, nuclear material. ×47,000. (Courtesy of O. Wyss.)

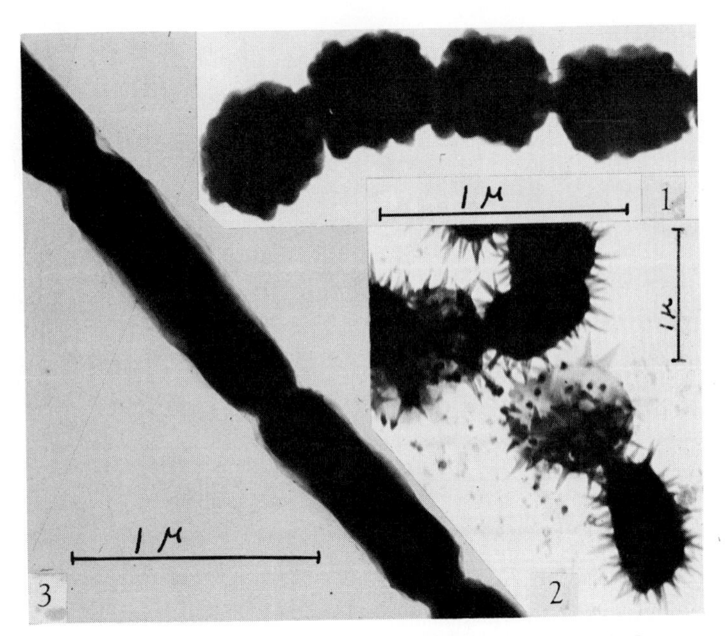

Figure 2.4 Actinomycete spores. 1. *Streptomyces olivaceus* ATCC 12019, Led. AH-415, showing "warts." (Courtesy of H. D. Tresner.) 2. *Streptomyces* sp., showing spines. (Courtesy of Pearl Chen.) 3. *Streptomyces phaeochromogenes*, Led. AC-474. Heyden #406, showing smooth and elongate spores. (Courtesy of H. D. Tresner.)

Table 2.1. Details of the development of conidia of *Streptomyces* are provided by Glauert and Hopwood (1961), Tresner et al. (1961), and Rancourt and Lechevalier (1964).

FUNGI

There are many different types of propagules among the fungi, many of which are not dormant and others which are not spores in the sense used here. Thus, many types of propagules are ephemeral and appear to function as gametes, or in ways other than as resistant cells. Furthermore, as was discussed in Chapter 1, structures that are functionally similar to spores but which are resistant masses of hyphae, such as sclerotia, are found in many fungi.

Fungus spores may be produced asexually, on the vegetative organism, or sexually, as a result of nuclear fusion. Among the former are included the following:

Conidia—any asexual spore produced at the ends of mycelia and not enclosed within a specialized cover.

Uredospores (urediniospores)—dikaryotic rust spores that are usually freed through the broken epidermis of the host.

Aeciospores (aecidiospores)—dikaryotic spores of rusts which, upon germination, may lead to the formation of uredospores or teliospores.

Resting Spore—any spore that cannot develop immediately after formation. In certain of the phycomycetes such structures may function as spores or as sporangia, as in *Phytophthora*. In other cases, as in *Physoderma*, such resting spores always release spores and are therefore more properly called resting sporangia.

Sexual spores among the fungi include:

Zygospores—spores resulting from the conjugation of like gametes or like gametangia, in the phycomycetes.

Oospores—the product of the fertilization of the egg in the phycomycetes.

Ascospores—spores produced as a result of meiosis in the ascomycetes.

Basidiospores—spores produced as a result of meiosis in the basidiomycetes.

Teliospores (teleutospores)—spores within which nuclear fusion in the rusts occurs.

Table 2.1 Summary of some of the Differences Between Types of Bacterial Spores

Endospores	Cysts (*Azotobacter*)	Conidia (Actinomycetes)
Very heat-resistant	Lack heat-resistance, *A. agilis* Very heat-resistant, *A. chroococcum*	Mildly heat-resistant
DPA present[a]	Lack DPA	Lack DPA
Resist desiccation	Resist desiccation	?
Formed singly	Formed singly	Formed in chains
Formed within vegetative cell	Formed within vegetative cell	Formed on aerial hyphae
Cortex present	Lack cortex	Lack cortex
Nuclear region not visible	Nuclear material may be visible	Nuclear region visible
Appearance under phase-contrast differs from vegetative	Same appearance as vegetative under phase-contrast	Same appearance as vegetative under phase-contrast
Resist ultrasonic treatment	Resist ultrasonic treatment much better than vegetative cells	?

[a] DPA = dipicolinic acid.

The varied appearance of the several types of fungus spores is illustrated in Figure 2.5.

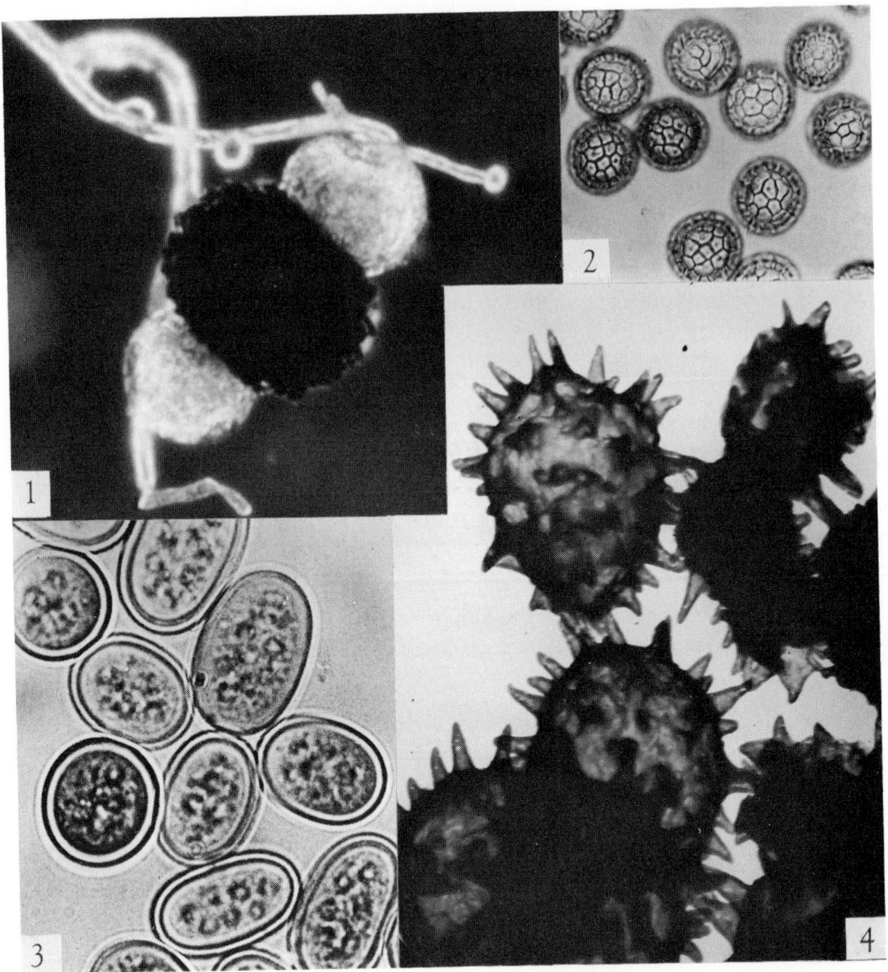

Figure 2.5 Various fungus spores. 1. Zygospores of *Rhizopus sexualis*. × 1250. (Courtesy of Hiroshi Iizuka.) 2. Spores of *Tilletia caries*. × 3000. (Courtesy of G. Fischer.) 3. Spores of *Phycomyces blakesleeanus*. × 3500. (Courtesy of H. Rudolph.) 4. Conidia of *Aspergillus aculeatus*. × 15,000. (Courtesy of Hiroshi Iizuka.)

The Structure, Formation, and Chemistry of Dormant Cells

STRUCTURE OF BACTERIAL SPORES

Examination with the light microscope revealed initially the complexity of the structure of bacterial endospores (Cook, 1932). With the advent of electron microscopy it has been possible to study the fine structures of the bacterial spore (for general review see Robinow, 1960). Studies of this type have documented the origin of the components during sporulation (Tokuyasu and Yamada, 1959;

Young and Fitz-James, 1959), provided a basis for examining the germination process (Levinson and Wrigley, 1960), and also aided in taxonomic description of the genus *Bacillus* (Bradley and Franklin, 1958).

The conversion of a vegetative cell into the dormant state is accompanied by fundamental changes in cellular structure. Details of this transition, as well as the elucidation of the fine structure, have been obtained by electron microscopy of ultrathin sections. Detailed morphological studies on sporulation have been reported in *B. megaterium* (Chapman, 1956), *B. subtilis* (Takagi et al., 1956; Tokuyasu and Yamada, 1959), *B. anthracis* (Suzuki et al., 1957; Takagi et al., 1956), *B. mesentericus* (Takagi et al., 1956), *B. thiamenolyticus* (Suzuki et al., 1957), *B. polymyxa* (Holbert, 1960), *B. cereus* (Chapman, 1956; Young and Fitz-James, 1959; Hashimoto et al., 1960; Norris and Watson, 1960), *Clostridium sporogenes* (Hashimoto and Naylor, 1958), *C. perfringens* (Smith and Ellner, 1957), and *C. butyricum* and *C. botulinum* (Takagi et al., 1960).

From the elegant studies of the process of sporulation in *Bacillus* and *Clostridium* by Fitz-James (1960, 1962*a,b*) and in *Bacillus* by Ohye and Murrell (1962), the role of internal membranes in the sporulation process has become evident. In the early stages of sporulation, an infolding of the cytoplasmic membrane occurs, leading to the formation of a double-stranded membrane (forespore) which

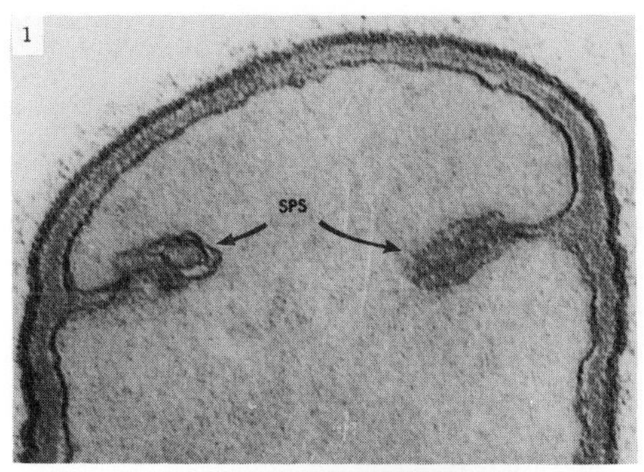

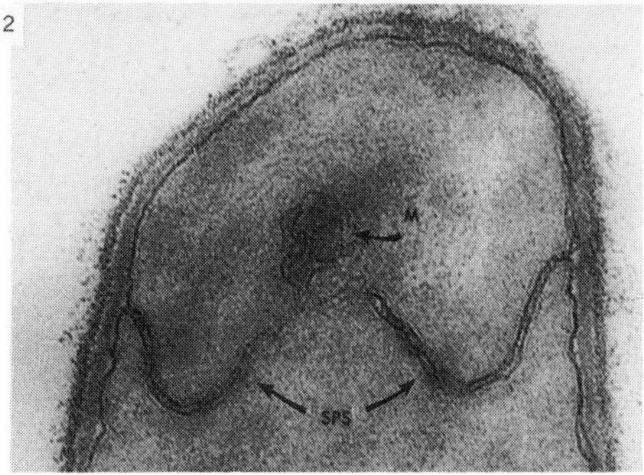

Figure 2.6 Electron micrographs of early stages in the development of the spore septum (1) and a later stage in the completion of the spore septum (2) in *Bacillus coagulans*. Note the double unit membrane nature of the septum. × 140,000. From Ohye and Murrell, 1962. Legend: M, mesosome; SPS, spore septum.

eventually surrounds the nuclear spore material. This process appears to be under the control of membranous organelles called mesosomes (Figure 2.6). Over-all sporulation is not controlled by mesosomes since, when committed cells are converted to protoplasts, the interior of the mesosome is lost without diminishing sporulation (Fitz-James, 1964). The cortex develops between the layers of the forespore, whereas the spore coat is formed peripherally to the outer forespore membrane (Fitz-James, 1962*a*).

The mature spore has a complex structure which contains a number of layers about which there is considerable disagreement. For example, two layers have been reported in spores of *B. megaterium* (Chapman, 1956) and six in spores of *B. polymyxa* (Holbert, 1960).

Exosporium

The outermost envelope surrounding the spore is called the *exosporium*. This is a thin, delicate covering which lies outside of the spore coat. In some spores, such as *B. cereus*, it exists as a loose covering which is closely connected to the sides of the spore but extends beyond the poles. In other spores, such as *B. polymyxa* and *B. megaterium*, the exosporium is tight fitting and stretched over the surface of the spore coat (Robinow, 1960; Dondero and Holbert, 1957 and Figure 2.7). Gerhardt et al (1961) and Gerhardt and Ribi (1964) have reported the

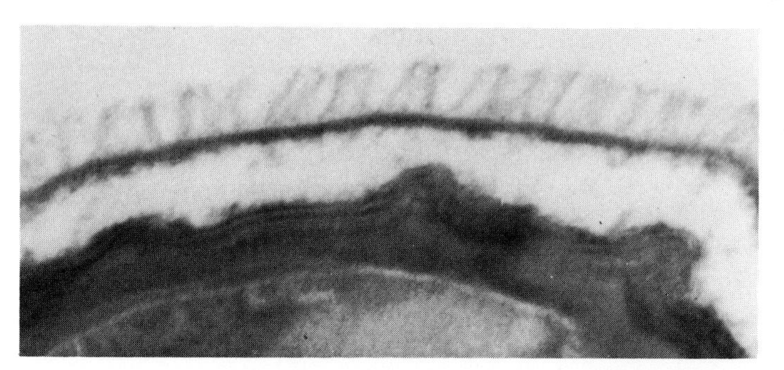

Figure 2.7 Portion of a spore of *Bacillus anthracis*, in which a longer and more apparent nap occurs on the exosporium. (From Gerhardt and Ribi, 1964.)

isolation of exosporium in reasonably pure form (Table 2.2) from disrupted spores by density-gradient centrifugation. In the electron micrograph this material appeared as a lamellar substructure, having hexagonal fragments resembling a crystalline configuration. An ordered crystalline structure was confirmed by x-ray diffraction analysis.

It has often been assumed that the exosporium is a remnant of the wall of the sporangium. Hannay (1956), employing ultrathin sectioning techniques with *B. thuringiensis*, observed that the exosporium was formed *within* the bacterial

Table 2.2 Chemical Composition of Exosporium of *Bacillus cereus*

	μg/mg
15 Amino acids	373
Glucosamine	113
Carbohydrate	104
Lipid	174
Teichoic acids	20
Organic acids	21
DPA	2
Nucleic acids	(12)
Nonhydrolyzable	180
Total recovery	987

SOURCE: Data from L. Matz and P. Gerhardt, unpublished.

cell at the time of sporulation. Similar conclusions were derived from studies with *B. cereus* (Chapman, 1956), *B. cereus* var. *alesti* (Young, 1958; Norris and Watson, 1960) and *B. cereus* strain T (Hashimoto et al., 1960). This conclusion is supported by serological comparisons of spores and vegetative cells. One of the first of these was the finding of spore-specific antigens (Mellon and Anderson, 1919; Howie and Cruickshank, 1940; and Lamanna, 1940). Vennes and Gerhardt (1957) showed that isolated spore coats or the surface of spores of *B. megaterium* do not contain antigens in common with the cell wall or other structures of the vegetative cell. Tomcsik and Baumann-Grace (1959) and Tomcsik et al. (1959) found in a study of 51 strains of *B. megaterium* that antisera prepared against spores, exosporium, and spore coats did not cross-react against vegetative cells. Five types were obtained from a study of 36 strains. Lamanna and Eisler (1960) have recently demonstrated, by agglutination tests with *B. anthracis* and *B. cereus*, the presence of antigens specific to the spore phase. Finally, in experiments employing prelabeled cell walls (α-diaminopimelic acid-C^{14}), Vinter (1963) observed that there was no transfer of radioactivity to spores during sporulation, as might be expected if vegetative cell walls were not incorporated into one of the spore structures.

Spore Coat

Beneath the exosporium lies a layer or layers, the spore coat, which gives rise to the characteristic structure of the spore. Bradley and colleagues (1957, 1958), employing the technique of carbon replicas, have demonstrated that the surfaces of spores have different patterns. They may contain grooves, ridges, or be dimpled. The spore coat may be composed of more than one layer (van den

Hooff and Aninga, 1956; Robinow, 1953; Dondero and Holbert, 1957; Hashimoto and Naylor, 1958; Holbert, 1960; Mayall and Robinow, 1957; Takagi et al., 1960; Tokuyasu and Yamada, 1959) and the layers are themselves composed of a laminated structure (Holbert, 1960; Smith and Ellner, 1957; Tokuyasu and Yamada, 1959, Ohye and Murrell, 1962). As seen in Figure 2.2, the spore coat of *B. megaterium* is composed of three layers, the middle layer consisting of 5–8 lamellae of thin membranes and interspores, both about 20–25 A thick. The inner layer of the spore coat is separated from the spore cortex by a thin membrane. Fitz-James (1962*a*) reported a similar situation in spores of *Clostridium pectinovorum.*

The Cortex

The region below the inner spore coat is characterized by low electron density and was named by Robinow (1953) as the cortex. This region, which occupies approximately half of the spore volume within the outer coat of *Bacillus megaterium* (Mayall and Robinow, 1957), is evident in the electron micrographs of thin sections of spores of both aerobic and anaerobic bacteria (van den Hooff and Aninga, 1956; Dondero and Holbert, 1957; Franklin and Bradley, 1957; Hashimoto and Naylor, 1958; Fitz-James, 1959, and others). When the thin sections of acid-treated spores are treated with lanthanum nitrate (Mayall and Robinow, 1957), the density of the cortex is increased, and the cortex can be seen to be composed of concentric layers of fine fiberlike bundles (Figure 2.8). During germination the cortex breaks down.

Since its initial description, numerous suggestions have been made that the cortex was the site of dipicolinic acid (DPA) (Rode et al., 1962), minerals (Knaysi, 1961), and mucopeptide (Ohye and Murrell, 1962). The early complexity of the cortex was indicated by the finding that conditions which lead to depletion of DPA can leave spores with the characteristic cortical zone (Hashimoto et al., 1960; Hashimoto and Gerhardt, 1960). Isolation of the cortex or of coat fragments with adhering, fibrous cortex material has permitted direct chemical and enzymatic analysis of its constituents. Ohye and Murrell (1962) heat-killed spores of *B. coagulans* to inactivate endogenous degradative enzymes and then disrupted the spores with glass beads, yielding a coat preparation rich in cortex material. This material is rich in diamino pimelic acid (DAP) and mucopeptides which are released following treatment with lysozyme or an enzyme from spores (Warth et al., 1962). Hitchins and Gould (1964) recently found that when spores of *B. subtilis* were mechanically disrupted below *p*H 4.2 the spore core could be separated from the broken coats and separated as a bright body. Separation of the core from the coat fraction solubilized almost all of the DPA and most of the mucopeptide—as would be expected if these resided in the intervening cortex material. Supporting evidence has been provided by

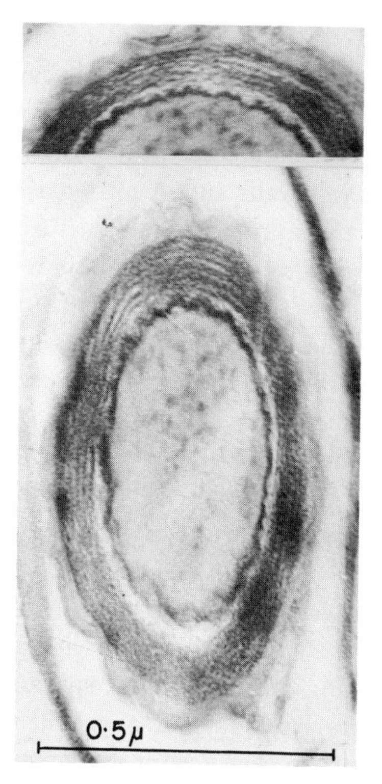

Figure 2.8 Two sections of acid-treated spores of *Bacillus megaterium*. Staining with lanthanum has revealed a concentric array of fine fibrils in the cortex. Facing the inner surface of the cortex is the dense, much folded spore wall. On the outside are two separate spore coats. (From Mayall and Robinow, 1957, courtesy Academic Press, Inc., Publishers.)

the studies of FitzJames (1962*b*) on a cortexless mutant of *B. cereus*. During sporulation, DPA and DAP hexosamine peptides are produced normally; however, these are released to the medium during the lysis period accompanying sporulation. The resulting spore has little or no cortex, DPA or DAP hexosamine peptide.

Spore Wall

The chemistry of the wall of vegetative cells and spores is reviewed by Salton (1964). The dormant cytoplasm is separated from the cortex by a thin membrane called the spore wall (Hashimoto and Naylor, 1958).

The spore wall is also of a low electron density and is often not visible unless sections of acid-treated spores are employed (Mayall and Robinow, 1957). During germination, the spore wall becomes the cell wall of the newly formed vegetative cell (Takagi et al., 1960; Mayall and Robinow, 1957; Robinow, 1960).

Cytological studies on the process of sporulation in bacteria have led to the conclusion that the spore envelope (exosporium and spore wall) is composed of distinct layers and that these layers are not derived from vegetative cell membranes. One might assume, however, that the synthesis of the spore envelopes is a special type of *in situ* cell wall synthesis involving the cell wall synthesizing system of the vegetative cell. Since the original isolation of homogeneous wall fractions from bacteria by differential centrifugation (Salton and Horne, 1951), the chemical and physical properties of walls from vegetative cells have been described in considerable detail (Strange, 1959; Salton, 1960). These studies on vegetative cells have provided a background against which the uniqueness of the spore envelopes could be determined.

The advent of methods of isolation of bacterial cell walls and of protoplast membranes has enabled an anatomical approach to the immunological structure of the bacterial cell. Thus with vegetative cells of *Bacillus*, Tomcsik and Guex-Holzer (1954) and Vennes and Gerhardt (1956) have shown that antiserum against protoplast membranes does not react significantly with cell walls or intact cells. As discussed earlier (page 15), serological differences exist between vegetative cells and spores. In some cases, such as the findings of Tomcsik and Baumann-Grace (1959), a serological component specific for the exosporium in *B. megaterium* has been identified. From studies like these, and those of Norris and Wolf (1961) on the spore, somatic, and flagellar antigens, it is clear that not only do the cell walls of vegetative cells and spore envelopes differ, but there are a number of specific components present in the spore envelopes.

The initial studies on the chemistry of the spore envelopes began with a description of the soluble materials released during germination of spores. Powell and Strange (1953) observed that germinating spores of *B. megaterium* excreted 30 percent of their dry weight into the medium. The germination exudate contained free amino acids, a nondialyzable peptide, protein (10–15 percent) and a compound which absorbed ultraviolet light (50 percent). The latter has been isolated and identified (Powell, 1953) as the calcium salt of pyridine 2,6, dicarboxylic acid.

Dipicolinic acid, whose structure is shown in Figure 2.9, has been found to occur in all aerobic and anaerobic spores examined to date. The peptide has been isolated from spore exudates (Strange and Powell, 1954) and found to have a molecular weight of about 15,000 (Record and Grinstead, 1954) and on acid hydrolysis to yield D-glutamic acid, D- and L-alanine, α- ε-diamino pimelic acid (DAPA) (in the molar ratio of 1:3:1), acetyl glucosamine, and an amino sugar. The amino sugar has been identified (Strange and Kent, 1959) as muramic acid (3-O-α-carboxyethyl hexosamine) and probably exists in the spore as the *N*-acetyl derivative (Figure 2.9). The peptide-amino sugar complex (mucopeptide) has been found in both spore coats and vegetative cell walls (Strange and Dark, 1956; Salton and Marshall, 1959) and undoubtedly represents a basic cell wall structure common to most, if not all, bacteria (Salton, 1960, 1964).

Studies on the cell walls of vegetative cells have added considerably to our knowledge of the composition of spore coats. Thus, teichoic acid, a ribitol phosphate polymer (Figure 2.9) which comprises 50 percent of the weight of the cell walls of vegetative cells (Armstrong et al., 1961) appears also to be present in spore coats.

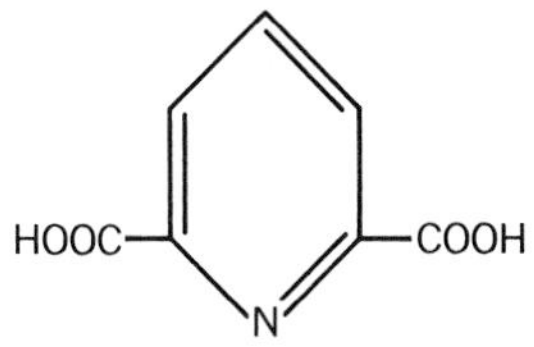

Dipicolinic Acid (DPA)

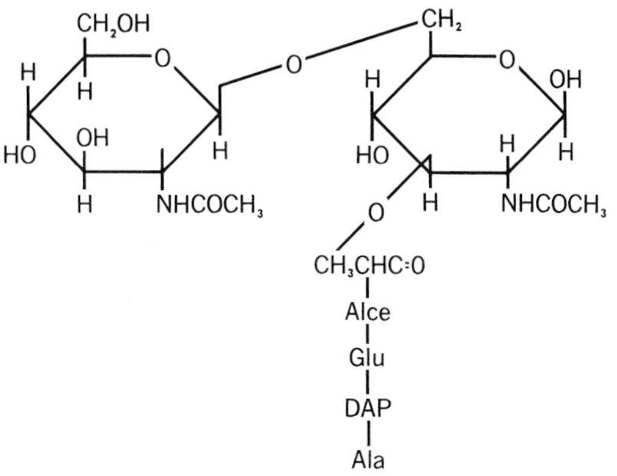

Muramic Acid

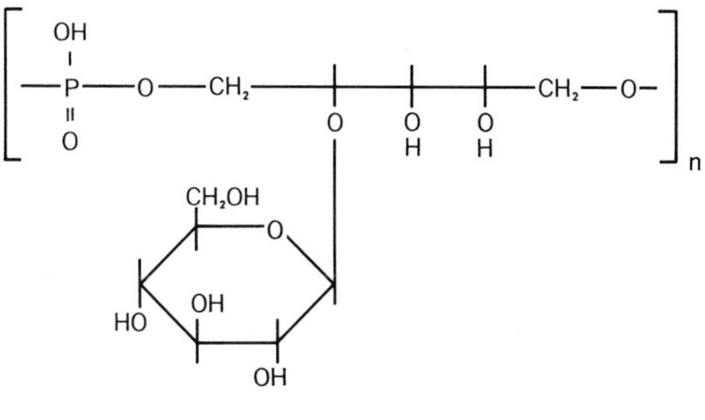

Teichoic Acid
(From Lactobacillus Arabinosus)

Figure 2.9 Chemical formulae of spore components.

The chemical composition of purified cell walls from vegetative cells and spore coats shows a number of significant differences (Salton, 1960). Some of these are summarized in Table 2.3. Although the spore wall preparations contain the components characteristic of the walls of vegetative organisms, namely mucopeptide and teichoic acid (Hunnell, 1961; Strange and Powell, 1954; Strange and

Kent, 1959; Armstrong et al., 1959), these represent only a minor part of the spore wall. α-ε-diamino pimelic acid is a constituent of the mucopeptide of spores and usually of vegetative cells of *Bacillus*. There is one interesting exception, however, where Powell and Strange (1957) observed in three strains of *B. sphaericus* that the vegetative cells contained no DAP, whereas sporulating cells and spores contained normal amounts.

The lipid content of walls from gram-positive bacteria is generally very low (Salton, 1960; Work, 1961; Strominger, 1962). The level of lipid in walls from spores is variable and can only in part be accounted for as *O*-ester groups (Table 2.3). Spores differ also in the distribution of the lipid. Douglas (1957), in an analysis of the effect of enzymes on bacterial spores, and from studies on their electrophoretic mobilities, concluded that the surfaces of spores of *B. megaterium* and *B. subtilis* differed significantly. Both spores contain significant quantities of the mucopeptide in their outer surface. However, in spite of the similarities in lipid content (Table 2.3), the surface of *B. subtilis* spores was essentially carbohydrate while *B. megaterium* spores had largely a surface lipid. The presence of surface lipids is probably the basis for the hydrophobic character which is characteristic of many types of bacterial spores.

Probably the most significant difference between walls of vegetative cells and spores is the higher content of nitrogen in the latter (Table 2.3). Whereas the

Table 2.3 Analysis of Spore Walls and Walls of Vegetative Cells

Constituent	*B. subtilis*[a]		*B. subtilis*[b]	*B. megaterium*[b]	*B. cereus*[b]
	Veg. Cell	Spore	Spore	Spore	Spore
Total N	4.6	12.9	13.1	12.8	13.2
Total P	4.2	1.4	1.6	0.3	1.2
Hexosamine	10.7	2.2	1–2	10 15	2–3
Glucosamine	7.9	1.5	1–4	1.0	4
Muramic acid	2.3	0.6	—	—	—
DAPA	5.6	—	—	—	—
Lipid	0.7	3.0	1.1	0.95	0.9
O-ester groups (as *o*-acetyl)	0.255	0.255	0.027	—	—

[a] Salton, 1960.
[b] Salton and Marshall, 1959.

mucopeptide comprises the bulk of the nitrogen of walls of vegetative cells, the walls of spores of *B. cereus*, *B. subtilis*, and *B. megaterium* contain a variety of amino acids in addition to the mucopeptide-teichoic acid complex (Strange and Dark, 1956). The teichoic acid from walls of *B. subtilis* was identified as a polymer, composed of nine D-alanyl glucosyl ribitol 5-phosphate subunits, which is associated ionically with the mucopeptide (Armstrong et al., 1960). A comparison of the amino acid distribution in walls of vegetative cells and spores of *B. subtilis* is shown in Table 2.4. The spore coat is composed largely of protein, which possesses structural and biochemical functions, rather than just the mucopeptide-teichoic acid complex. This same structure is rich in cystine (Vinter, 1960) and probably also in metaphosphate (Fitz-James, 1955).

Analysis of the spore coats is complicated by the fact that the preparations are often mixtures of exosporium and spore coats. This difficulty may account for conflicting data on the composition of spore coats. Bernlohr and Novelli (1960) noted a correlation between the synthesis of the peptide antibiotic, bacitracin, and sporulation in *Bacillus licheniformis* and suggested that the antibiotic may be incorporated into newly formed spores. Supporting evidence was furnished by Bernlohr and Sievert (1962) who isolated spore coats and found they were nearly identical to bacitracin in amino acid composition. However, from isolated spore coats of the same organism, Snoke (1964) failed to find a similarity between the amino acid composition of bacitracin and spore coats and could not detect a constituent of bacitracin, ornithine, in spore coats. In a similar test, the branched cyclic decapeptide antibiotic, polymyxin B, is produced by cells of *B. polymyxa* but is not incorporated into the spore coat (Brenner et al., 1964).

Table 2.4 The Amino Acid Composition of Cell Walls of *B. subtilis*

AA	Molecular proportions:[a] Veg. Cells	Spores
Lysine	0	6
Glycine	0	5
Serine	Trace	4
Alanine	4	4
Glutamic acid	2	3
Valine/methionine	Trace	2
Leucine/isoleucine	Trace	2
Tyrosine	0	1.5
Aspartic acid	0	1
DAPA	1	1
Threonine	0	1

[a] Salton, 1960.

STRUCTURE AND CHEMISTRY OF FUNGAL SPORE STRUCTURES

Structure of spore wall

Considerable information of a descriptive kind is available on fungus spores because of the use of differences in spore wall markings in taxonomy. Recently, the electron microscope has opened new vistas to the descriptivist, as well as furnishing the means for the correlation of structure and function at the molecular level. Ingress to recent literature in this field can be gained through the review by Moreau (1958). Examples of fungi in which the surface structures of

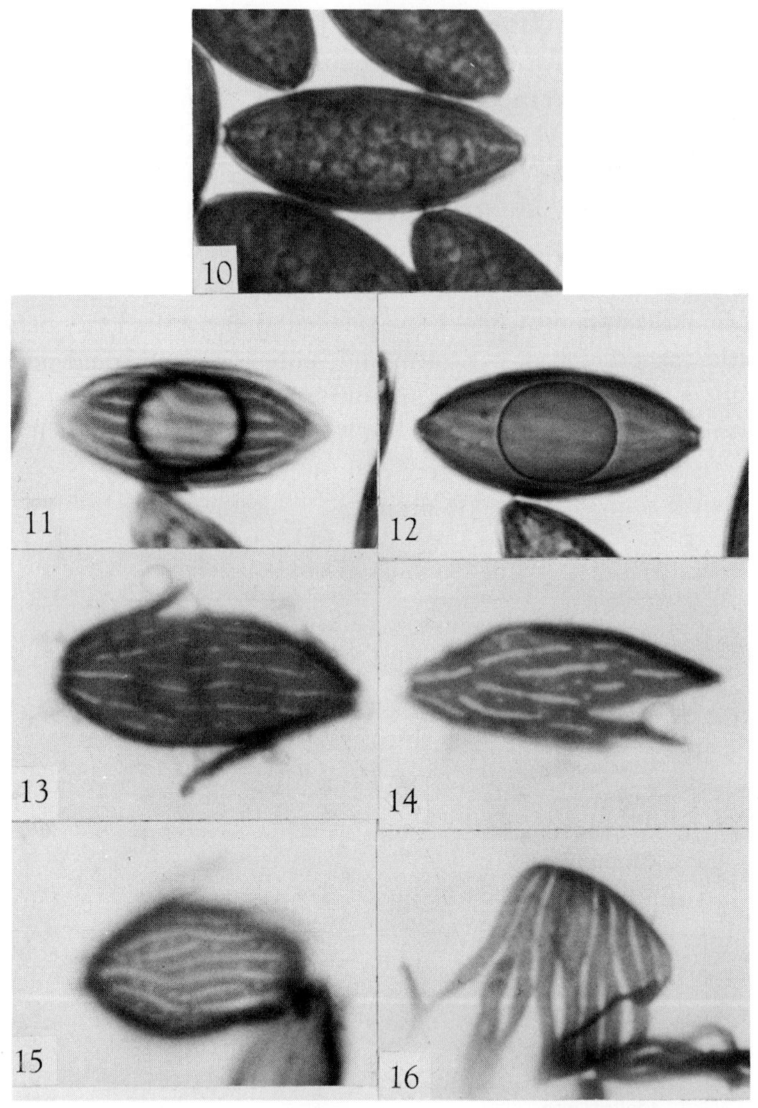

Figures 2.10–2.16 Fig. 2.10 Untreated ascospores of *Neurospora tetrasperma*. Fig. 2.11 Ribs on surface of untreated spores. Photograph was taken by focussing on the upper surface of the spore. Fig. 2.12 Same cell as in Fig. 2.13 except that it was photographed in median optical section. Figs. 2.13–2.16 Ribbed layers removed from ascospores by action of sodium hypochlorite, and stained in 0.4 percent gentian violet. × 2000.

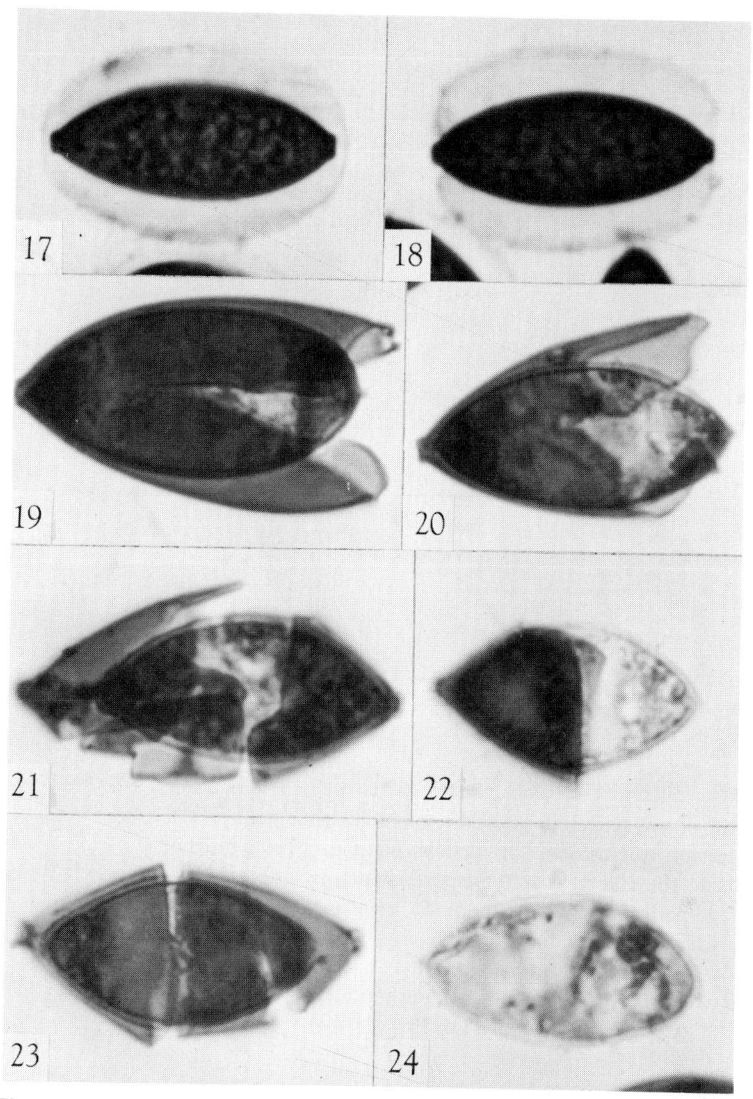

Figures 2.17–2.18 Ascospores treated with sodium hypochlorite in order to swell the ribbed layer. It has been swollen so that the germ pore is revealed. Figs. 2.19–2.24 Progressive stages in the removal of the melanized wall of ascospores of *Neurospora tetrasperma*. × 2000.

spores have been studied through the electron microscope include the slime mold *Didymium* (Schuster, 1964), *Neurospora* (Miller, unpublished; Lowry and Sussman, 1965), *Ustilago* sp. (Hilles and Brandes, 1956), several rusts (Mielke and Cochran, 1952; Hess and Schantz, 1956), some gasteromycetes (Gregory and Nixon, 1950), several aspergilli (Iizuka, 1955), and *Pithomyces chartarum* (Bertaud et al., 1963).

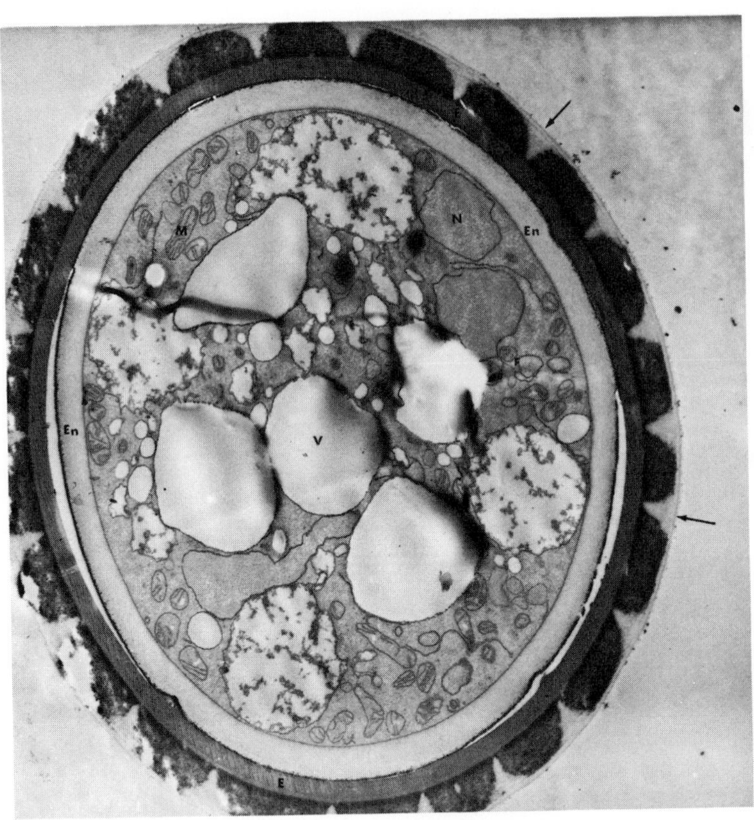

Figure 2.25 Section of an activated ascospore of *Neurospora tetrasperma* viewed with an electron microscope. The arrows point to a layer on the surface that is outside the ribbed coat (perispore) which is visible by its furrowing. Within the perispore is the epispore (E), a melanized coat that is very rigid, within which is the endospore (En), the wall layer that surrounds the protoplast. Nuclei (N), mitochondria (M), and vacuoles (V) are visible along with endoplasmic reticulum and other inclusions. × 9000. (Courtesy of Dr. R. J. Lowry.)

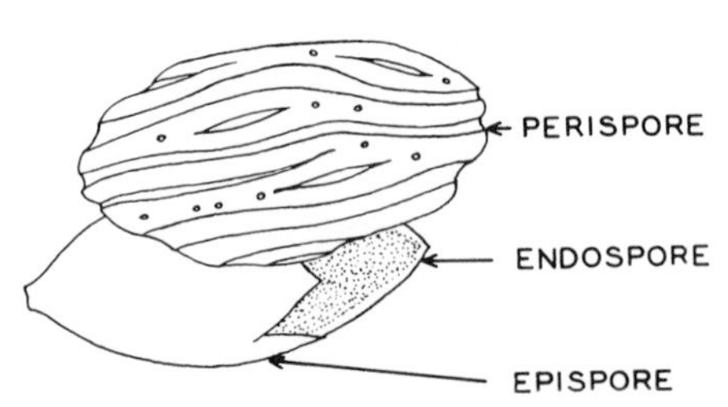

Figure 2.26 Diagrammatic representation of ascospore wall of *Neurospora tetrasperma* according to the terminology of Le Gal (1947).

The surface of ascospores of *Neurospora tetrasperma* has been studied in considerable detail by Lowry and Sussman (1958) and their findings are discussed below. As Figures 2.10–2.26 reveal, the surface of this dormant cell consists of at least three elements, including a ribbed layer, a melanized and rigid intermediate layer, and an inner wall which surrounds the protoplast. This interpretation is corroborated by the work of Lowry and Sussman (1965), who have sectioned these spores and viewed them with the aid of the electron microscope (Figure 2.25). This work reveals the presence of a fourth layer which is outside the ribbed layer and is too small to be seen by the light miscroscope.

In view of the increasing importance that the detailed structure of walls is assuming in physiological as well as descriptive studies, it is well that the nomenclature of the surface layers be clarified. The system that is suggested is that described in detail by Le Gal (1947) on the basis of previous work by Mattirolo (1921) and Malençon (1928). Accordingly, the following structures comprise the surface of ascospores of *Neurospora:*

1. Endospore wall—that which is the most internal surface structure of the spore and which surrounds the protoplast.
2. Epispore wall—the layer which immediately surrounds the endospore. This includes, with the endospore, the essential elements of the spore. The epispore and endospore walls provide support and rigidity to the spore and maintain its shape.
3. Perisporic structures ("formations perisporiques")—these include all the layers, or all other elements of the spore, which surround the spore proper and which can be absent without interfering with the functioning of the spore. The perisporic structures include the subperisporic layer, which is often so narrow as to be inconspicuous, on the surface of which is a membranous pellicle, the *perispore*.

An interpretation of the structure of the surface of *Neurospora* ascospores, based upon the preceding description, is offered in Figure 2.26. Thus, the innermost wall is considered to be the endospore, the melanized intermediate one is called the epispore, and the ribbed layer would seem to be analogous with the "pellicule membranaire" of Le Gal, which is the perispore. Further details of the walls of these spores as well as descriptions of their formation are to be found in the work of Lindegren and Scott (1936) and of Dodge (1957).

A comparison between the wall of ascospores and conidia of *Neurospora* is meaningful because of the different roles played by the two types of spores in the life cycle of this organism. Figures 2.10–2.24 and 2.27 permit such a comparison to be made in the case of conidia of *N. crassa* and ascospores of *N. tetrasperma,* and it can be seen that there are considerable differences between the two walls. First, the ribbed coat is lacking in conidia, as is the melanized epispore, both of which are found in the ascospore. Instead, the wall of the conidium resembles the endospore in texture and thickness. The nature of these differences is reflected in the physiology of these cells and in their role in nature, as will be discussed later. The work of Shatkin (1959) and of Shatkin and Tatum (1959) on

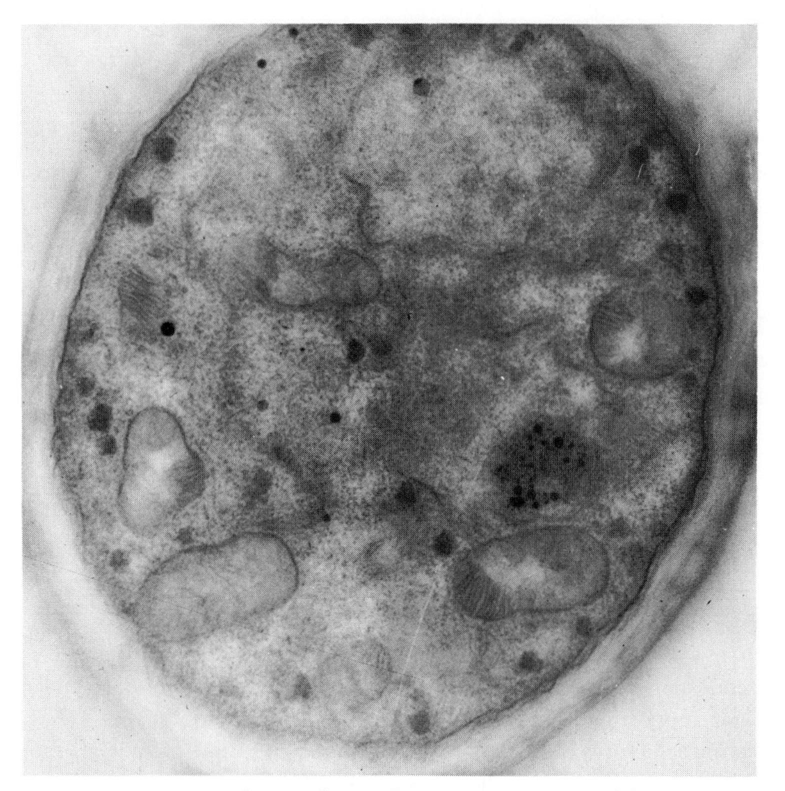

Figure 2.27 Section of a conidium of *Neurospora crassa* (wild type, strain 1A). Note fibrous elements in wall and the arrangement of the "cristae mitochondriales". × 50,000. (Photograph obtained through the courtesy of A. Miller.)

the vegetative mycelium of *Neurospora* reveals that its wall resembles that of conidia in appearance. This comparison, as well as the one made above, will have more meaning when the chemical constituents of the walls have been analyzed. Unfortunately, little work has been done on this subject (see page 27).

Although it is not possible at this time to analogize the structure of the wall of *Neurospora* and those of the discomycetes studied by Le Gal with those of other groups of fungi, certain parallels exist within the ascomycetes. For example, Rhoads (1918) has described a colorless "exospore" in *Daldinia concentrica* which dehisces after being treated with dilute alkali, and Yu (1954) illustrated a "perispore" in *Ascobolus stercorarium* which had been swollen by treatment of a similar kind. These observations are similar to those of Le Gal (1947) and Lowry and Sussman (1958) because in both cases sodium hypochlorite was found to swell the perispore. In fact, in the latter case, prolonged exposure to this reagent resulted in its dehiscence, just as in the case of *Daldinia*. Whereas a detailed comparison of the walls of these ascomycetes remains to be made, a chemical similarity in at least one coat is suggested by these data. As for other groups of fungi, it is clear, as in the case of the ascomycetes, that the wall of dormant spores consists of two or more layers. Thus, Blackwell (1943) reported that the wall of oospores of the phycomycete, *Phytophthora cactorum*, consists of a substance removable by chlorine water and NaS_2O_3, a cellulose layer, and a framework after the other layers are removed. In addition, Blackwell has shown (1935) that the wall of *Peronospora schleideni* is a complex of several layers. Recent work on the teliospore of the dwarf-bunt organism, *Tilletia contraversa* (Graham, 1957), reveals the presence of three separate layers whose chemistry will be discussed later. Finally, many observations in other basidiomycetes attest to the presence of one or more coats in addition to a dark coat in species like *Coprinus stercorarius* (Buller, 1922), so that these structures may ultimately be shown to be widely distributed throughout the fungi.

Chemistry of the Spore Wall of Fungi

The study of the chemistry of the walls of fungi began with the over-all analysis of their constituents and progressed to the use of qualitative tests for distinguishing between complex polymers like chitin, cellulose, and hemicellulose. In view of the structural complexity of spore walls which, as was shown, may consist of several distinct layers, it is clear that the older methods of analysis were inadequate to describe their organization satisfactorily. Therefore, not only is it necessary to isolate and purify the walls, but it is also necessary to analyze the separate layers as well as the cementing materials of these complex structures.

In addition to these structural problems which arise in the study of the polymers that comprise wall materials, chemical difficulties have also arisen. Even analysis by means of x-ray powder diagrams, exploited so successfully by Frey (1950) and others, has been made more difficult by the masking of reflections from hexosamines by materials such as fats. Some of these difficulties have been overcome by the techniques developed by Kreger and Meeuse (1952), but distinction between related hexosamines is not possible by this method. Furthermore, it has become increasingly apparent from recent work on the vegetative stages of fungi, just as in the bacteria, that the chemistry of cell walls can no longer be described solely in terms of the generic names chitin and cellulose. Thus, the former may consist of hexosamine units containing glucose, mannose or other hexoses, or mixtures thereof. The distinction between these substances has only recently become possible, so much of the older work is inadequate in this respect. Moreover, carbohydrates of other types have been described, including a glucomannan-protein complex from yeast cell walls (Northcote and Horne, 1952; Kessler and Nickerson, 1959), a complex glucan in *Penicillium* sp. from which at least two other hexoses have been isolated, in addition to amino acids (Koffler, 1961). A glucan associated with chitin has also been found in a phycomycete, *Allomyces macrogynus* (Aronson and Machlis, 1959), so that such materials appear to be widely distributed. Although these data bear upon vegetative hyphae only, it is likely that similar, or greater, complexity will be found to exist in the walls of spores.

This possibility is suggested by the work of Horikoshi and Iida (1964), who separated and analyzed the spore "coat" (epispore ?) and cell wall (endospore ?) of conidia of *Aspergillus oryzae*. The coats contained phosphate, nucleic acid, ash, protein, and a polysaccharide of glucose, galactose, mannose, and glucosamine, as well as a β-1,3-linked laminarin-like substance. Although the cell walls resembled the coats in chemical composition, they contained 50 percent glucosamine, compared to 20 percent in the latter. Moreover, the walls had only 5 percent protein in contrast to about 19 percent in the coats.

Although the complete analysis of even a single spore's wall has not yet been accomplished, promising beginnings have been made. Thus, Graham (1957) has reported that mature teliospores of *Talletia contraversa* have a wall consisting of several morphologically distinct and separable layers. The outer one is soluble in alcoholic potash and is digested by pectinase while an intermediate layer, which is reticulate, is reported to consist of a pectin-protein-hemicellulose-chitin complex. Unfortunately, few details of the methods have been reported, and the sugars in the "pectin," "chitin," and so forth, have not been isolated, so that it is difficult to evaluate these results. The isolated perispore of *Neurospora* ascospores has been analyzed by Sussman (unpublished) and found to consist mainly, if not entirely, of hexuronic acid residues. This conclusion was based upon elemental analysis, and the liberation of carbon dioxide upon hydrolysis. Chitin has been shown to be present in the zygospores and azygospores of *Empusa muscae* (Schweizer, 1947), and in many other fungi (see Young, 1958 for a review) but the bulk of the work has been done with vegetative states of the life cycle (Frey, 1950; Roelefsen and Hoette, 1951; Kreger, 1954; Blank, 1954, and others).

Internal Structure of Fungus Spores

A generalization that holds for many of the fungi studied concerns the paucity of endoplasmic reticulum in ungerminated spores. These include the spores of *Blastocladiella emersonii* (Cantino, Lovett, Leak, and Lythgoe, 1963), sporangiospores of *Rhizopus* (Hawker and Abbott, 1963), conidia of *Botrytis* (Hawker and Hendy, 1963), uredospores of *Puccinia graminis tritici* (Williams and Ledingham, 1964), and ascospores of *Neurospora tetrasperma* (Lowry and Sussman, 1965). In the latter case, an unusual membrane complex, which may play a role in the generation of endoplasmic reticulum, is formed after activation. Thus, one of the important ultrastructural events associated with the germination of fungus spores is the formation of endoplasmic reticulum.

Another characteristic of some dormant spores is the possession of relatively few and large mitochondria, as compared with those in germinating spores.

Such is the case for sporangiospores of *Rhizopus* (Hawker and Abbott, 1963), conidia of *Botrytis cinerea* (Hawker and Hendy, 1963), and ascospores of *Neurospora tetrasperma* (Lowry and Sussman, 1965). This tendency reaches its maximum expression in the remarkable zoospores of *Blastocladiella emersonii* wherein only one very large mitochondrion is to be found (Cantino et al., 1963). Recent work by Lowry and Sparrow (unpublished) established that zoospores of *Physoderma*, another phycomycete, also possess a single mitochondrion. Further studies of the structure and development of fungus spores is indicated for, as the above review indicates, there are interesting generalizations that should be checked, as well as rich diversity. For example, the ultrastructure of conidia of *Neurospora crassa* appears to be much more like that of the vegetative cell (Weiss, 1963) than that of ascospores, as might be expected from the different functions of the two types of spores.

Physiology of the Spore Surface

PERMEABILITY OF BACTERIAL SPORES

From the first recognition of bacterial spores, considerable doubt was raised as to the permeability of this biological system. This conclusion was based on the finding that dry vegetative cells were about as heat-resistant as spores and also that spores were nonstainable, highly refractive, and often nonwetable. The early prevailing view was that spores were dry and impermeable to water (Fischer, 1877). Since spores can be stained peripherally with basic dyes (Burke, 1923), it was concluded that the inner core of the spore was impermeable to water and solutes.

Many attempts have been made to measure the water content of spores, often with conflicting results. Based on the high optical density of the spore, Davenport and Castle (1895) concluded that spores had a low content of water. Employing more sensitive methods with an interference microscope, Ross and Rilling (1957) found that spores and vegetative cells have significantly different refractive indices, 1.51 to 1.54 and 1.39 to 1.40, respectively. The refractive indices of spores were comparable to those found for almost completely dehydrated proteins—suggesting that spores contain very little water. Assuming that the protoplasm has a specific gravity of 1.33 (predominantly protein) they calculated from refractive index measurements that the water contents were 14.0 to 26.0 gm/100 ml and 72.5 to 78.0 gm/100 ml for spores and vegetative cells, respectively.

Murrell and Scott (1957) examined the relative resistance of spores heated under conditions of varying water activity. They found that when spores with a water activity below 0.9 were heated, differences in heat-resistance usually evident between various species disappeared, thus supporting the hypothesis that there is a low water content in spores.

A number of attempts have been made to directly measure water and bound water of spores and vegetative cells. Friedman and Henry (1938) attempted to measure the bound water in spores and vegetative cells on the basis of cryoscopic methods. By these methods they concluded that spores contained twice as much bound water as vegetative cells. On the basis of hygroscopic properties, Virtanen and Pulkki (1933) concluded there was no difference between spores and vegetative cells. More recently, Waldham and Halvorson (1954) reported that until the moisture content of spores drops to a low value, the equilibrium vapor pressure of water in spores is practically the same as that of pure water. However, in vegetative cells the equilibrium vapor pressure drops below that of pure water, even though the moisture content of the cell is relatively high. The vegetative cells are more strongly hygroscopic than spores and, in fact, will cause the removal of water from spores if stored in a closed system. Waldham and Halvorson (1954) concluded that the polar groups of the spore proteins were unavailable or bound in some way so that the proteins of the spore, although accessible to water, were not readily wetted. This conclusion was supported by the experiments of Murrell and Scott (1958). In experiments with D_2O they observed that the isotope exchanged freely with almost all (96 percent or more) of the spore water. If a dry region of the spore exists, it must therefore contain less than 1 percent of the total water. Murrell and Scott (1958) estimated from their experiments that the dry spore, depending upon assumptions of density, could occupy approximately 30–40 percent of the volume of the spore. There are apparently negligible quantities of nonexchangeable water, which is evident from the fact that only 0.2 percent of the hydrogen of the spore exchanged with D_2O (Murrell and Scott, 1958). Marr (1960), in studies on the infrared spectrum of spores soaked in D_2O, also concluded that there is negligible exchange between D_2O and the amide hydrogen atoms.

The view proposed by Lewith (1890) that a part of the spore is in an anhydrous state has been more recently considered as one of the more likely explanations for the properties of the spore (Powell and Strange, 1953; Fitz-James and Vance, 1955; Rode and Foster, 1960; Black, 1960; Lewis et al., 1960). Several laboratories have attempted to directly test this hypothesis by measuring the volume of the spore which is accessible to solutes. Although this method has a number of well-known limitations, it has provided some interesting information on the permeable volume of the spore, provided that accurate estimates are made of the volume of a spore and of the interstitial space in centrifuged spore packs. The latter is generally measured by the use of large molecular weight substances, such as dextran, which are normally impermeable. Employing this technique, Gerhardt and Black (1961*a*) estimated that glucose permeates 40 percent of the weight or 51 percent of the volume of spores of *Bacillus cereus*, apparently by free diffusion since its uptake was relatively independent of environmental variables. The uptake of a large variety of compounds was examined and their permeability was found to depend upon their charge, lipid solubility, and molecular weight. Molecules of molecular weights up to 160,000 were able to penetrate the spore. Compounds with molecular weights of 400 to 160,000 were taken up in inverse proportion to their molecular weights (Figure 2.28). From these data it was estimated that the surface of the spore contained pores varying in diameter from 100 to 200 A.

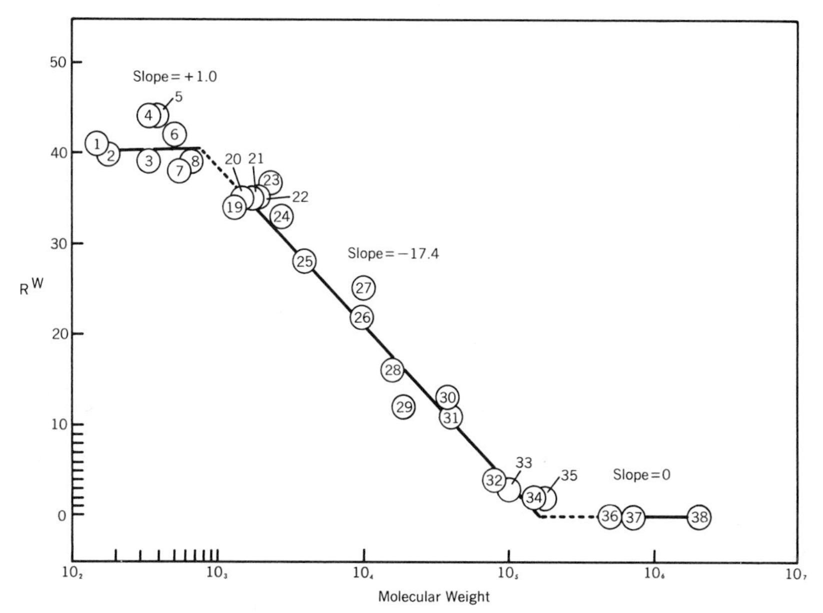

Figure 2.28 Correlation between solvent molecular weight and the uptake of glycols and polyglycols by dormant spores. The numbered points correspond to the following compounds: 1. ribose, 2. glucose, 3. sucrose, 4. melibiose, 5. maltose, 6. raffinose, 7. melezitose, 8. stachyose, 9. glucosamine, 10. glucuronate, 11. acetylglucosamine, 12. erythritol. 13. sorbitol, 14. glycerol. 15. glycerol monoacetate, 16. glycerol diacetate, 17. glycerol triacetate, 18. inulin, 19. dextran, 20–38. dextrans in order of increasing molecular weight. The lines were plotted by the method of least squares, with the points weighted according to the number of determinations. R^w corresponds to the corrected space value. (From Gerhardt and Black, 1961*b*.)

Germination is accompanied by swelling, decreases in dry weight, and the loss of refractility. These changes are accompanied by an increase in the weight fraction (R^w) available to water (Table 2.5). The water volume fraction (R^v) is not significantly altered. These findings favor the conclusion that a part of the spore is anhydrous.

An interesting question is how an anhydrous region of the spore can be created in an aqueous environment. Von Darányi (1927, 1930) suggested that colloidal shrinkage could lead to a loss in water content. More recently, Lewis et al. (1960) postulated that a compressive contracture of the cortex would lead to an expression of spore water. Based on studies with synthetic copolymers, they pro-

Table 2.5 Comparison Between Dormant and Germinated Spores of Water Content and Uptake

Measure[a]	Spore type: Dormant	Germinated
Density (gm/ml)	1.28	1.11
Dry weight (percent)	35.2	27.0
Water uptake (R^w)	66.6	75.6
Water uptake (R^v)	86.0	83.9

SOURCE: Data from S. H. Black, 1960.
[a] Spore of *Bacillus cereus* strain T.

posed that during sporogenesis the accumulation by active transport across a membrane of ions, DPA, peptides, and so forth, leads to changes in chemical potential which in turn cause a contraction of the protoplasm underlying the cortical region. The continued pressure maintains the anhydration of the core, and the spores have heat-resistance comparable to that of lyophilized cells. The release of internal pressure, by mechanical means or physiological stimulation, leads to a disintegration of the cortex and the entry of water.

PERMEABILITY OF FUNGUS SPORES

A reasonable conclusion on the basis of the data that are available at present is that dormant and vegetative stages of bacteria and fungi differ most clearly in the structure of the cell surface. Therefore, analysis of the physiology of the wall, as well as of its chemistry, is necessary before an understanding of dormancy in microbes can be achieved. An obvious function of this part of the cell is associated with the entrance of metabolites and, as a consequence, it seems possible that the permeability of dormant spores differs from that of other stages in the life history.

Ascospores of *Neurospora tetrasperma* have been studied with this in mind and the evidence suggests that cations do not penetrate dormant cells but remain attached to the surface instead. This conclusion is supported by the following data:

1. The kinetics of uptake of cations, including Ag^+, Th^{++++}, UO_2^{++}, and Cu^{++}, as well as of organic ones such as methylene blue, polymyxin B, and phenyl chloromercuri-

benzoate resemble those for adsorption isotherms (Figure 2.29; Sussman and Lowry, 1955; Lowry et al., 1957).

2. Such uptake is little affected by killing the cells, or by lowering the temperature to 4°C (Sussman and Lowry, 1955; Lowry et al., 1957).

Uptake of cations occurs in the presence of isolated cell walls (Lowry and Sussman, 1956).

4. Uptake of cations is a function of ascospore concentration and that of the starting solution (Figure 2.29).

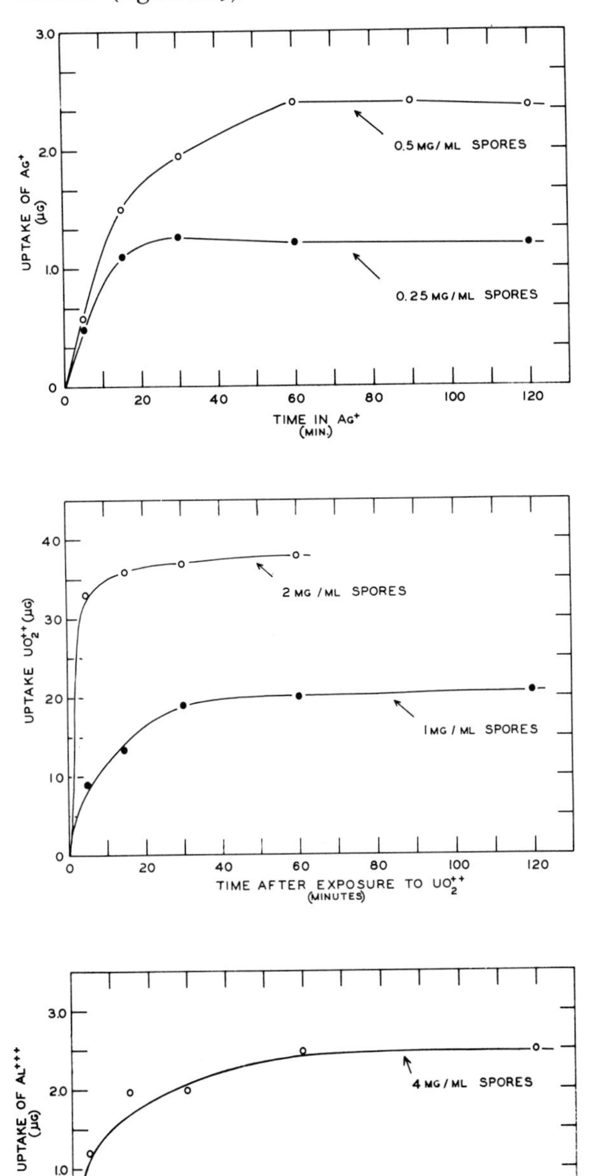

Figure 2.29 Uptake of cations by dormant ascospores of *Neurospora tetrasperma*. A starting concentration of 50 μg per milliliter of the cation was used in all cases. The suspending medium contained only water in addition. (From Lowry et al., 1957, courtesy of *Mycologia*, New York Botanical Garden.)

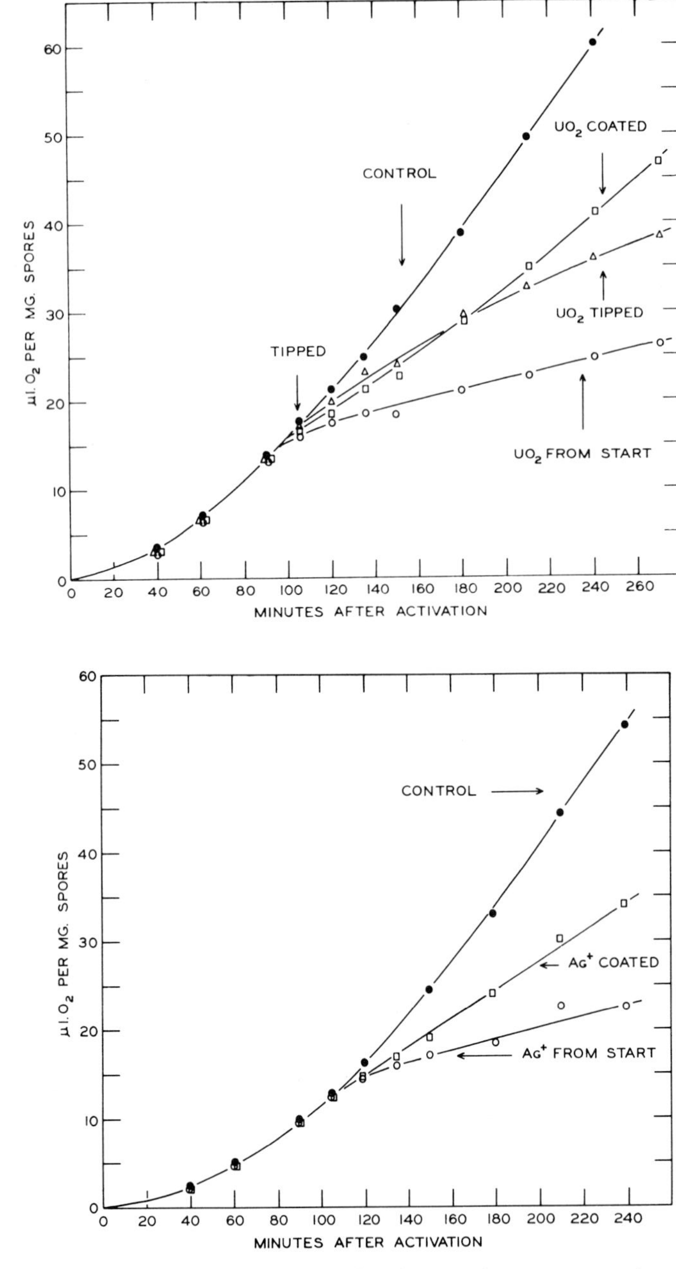

Figure 2.30 Effect of UO_2^{++} and Ag^+ upon the oxygen uptake of ascospores of *Neurospora tetrasperma*, whose dormancy was broken at 0 time by a heat shock. "Coated" ascospores were prepared by treatment with 1×10^{-2} *M* UO_2^{++} for 24 hours, after which they were washed free of the residual metal by repeated centrifugation in distilled water. Final concentration of UO_2^{++} in the manometer vessels was 1×10^{-2} *M* when incubated from the start with spores, or when tipped at 100 minutes after the start of the experiment. Conditions for Ag^+ were as for UO_2^{++}. (From Sussman et al., 1957.)

5. Decreasing the *p*H of the cation solutions results in a marked reduction in uptake (Sussman and Lowry, 1955).

6. The order of relative affinity of cations for the surface resembles the Hofmeister (lyotropic) series (Sussman and Lowry, 1955).

7. Elution of cations is possible by the use of other cations, chelating agents, and other basic substances (Sussman and Lowry, 1955).

8. It is possible to retard or prevent uptake of cations such as methylene blue by pre-

Table 2.6 Reversal of Metal Toxicity by Various Substances

Reversing Compound	Percentage Germination — Concentration Tested (*M*)									
	Ag^{+}		UO_2^{++}		PBC[a]		Cu^{++}		Ce^{+++}	
	10^{-2}	10^{-3}	10^{-2}	10^{-3}	10^{-2}	10^{-3}	10^{-2}	10^{-3}	10^{-2}	10^{-3}
Thioglycollate	90	90	—	90	—	94	—	0	—	80
Cysteine	91	93	—	0	—	94	95	93	—	23
Dihydroxy-phenylalanine (dopa)	92	90	17	4	88	0	85	75	13	21
p-aminobenzoate	0	—	70	—	0	—	26	—	88	—
Arginine	50	—	51	—	0	—	26	—	61	—
Glycine	0	—	2	—	0	—	93	—	23	—
Ethylenediamine -tetraacetate	0	—	72	—	91	—	97	—	92	—
Histidine	0	—	16	—	16	—	93	—	—	—
Adenosine triphosphate	97	—	—	—	—	—	92	—	—	—
Na^{+}	0	—	0	—	0	—	6	—	—	—
K^{+}	0	—	0	—	0	—	16	—	—	—
Mg^{++}	0	—	0	—	0	—	41	—	—	—
Ca^{++}	0	—	0	—	0	—	82	—	—	—
Control (coated)	0		0		0		16		0	
Control in water	91		94		93		94		92	

SOURCE: Data from Lowry et al., 1957.

Dormant ascospores of *N. tetrasperma* were shaken with an equal volume of 2×10^{-2}M of the metal for 30 minutes except for PBC which was used at 2×10^{-3}M. After being washed free of the cation the coated ascospores were shaken in solutions containing various concentrations of the substances to be tested. Activation and incubation of ascospores was accomplished after the reversing materials were removed from the ascospores by centrifugation in four changes of distilled water.

[a] Phenyl Chloromercuribenzoic acid.

treatment of cells with basic proteins (protamine), peptides (polymyxin B), or inorganic bases with high charge density (cobalt hexammine, hexol nitrate) (Sussman and Lowry, 1955; Sussman et al., 1957).

9. The respiration of dormant ascospores is unaffected by heavy metals and other inhibitory cations whereas that of germinating ones is strongly inhibited by such compounds (Figure 2.30; Sussman et al., 1957).

Furthermore, treatment of dormant ascospores with toxic cations, followed by the removal of the remaining inhibitor in the suspending medium by thorough washing, leaves a residuum on the spore. Although such coated ascospores, when maintained in the dormant state, are unaffected by the presence of the cation, the percentage germination of activated ascospores and their respiration are markedly inhibited about 100 minutes after activation and incubation at 26°C. The reversibility of the attachment of these materials to the spores is demonstrated by the data in Table 2.6 which show that several metabolites, as well as ethylenediamine–tetraacetic acid (EDTA), can effect the uncoating of the dormant spores. In contrast, however, the inhibition of germinating spores by cations cannot be reversed in this way.

Efflux of cations from the dormant ascospore of *Neurospora* does not seem to occur under normal circumstances. Thus, there is no measurable release of inorganic cations from such spores incubated for days in distilled water (Table 2.7; Sussman, 1954). However, shortly before germination, about 85 percent of the cell's Na^{+} and a considerable part of its Ca^{++} are released into the medium.

Table 2.7 Concentration of Cations in the Supernatant Fluid Recovered from Dormant, Activated, and Germinating Ascospores of *Neurospora tetrasperma*

Time after Activation (measured in Minutes)	Concentration (mg/gm ascospores) of Cations in Supernatant: Ca^{++}	Mg^{++}	Na^{++}	K^{+}
Incubated in H_2O				
Dormant controls	0	0	0	0
0	0	—	—	—
60	0.06	—	—	—
150	0.56	0	0.6	0
Incubated in EDTA				
Dormant controls	0	0	0	0
0	0	0	0	0
150	0.6	0	1.16	11.2

SOURCE: Data from Sussman, 1964.
The spores were incubated in deionized water, or in 0.028*M* ethylenediamine tetraacetic acid (EDTA) and the samples ionized by a flame spectrophotometer after removal of the spores by centrifugation.

Even in the presence of EDTA, no cations are released into the medium by dormant cells but germinating ones lose K^+ in addition to the cations mentioned.

Those anions that can be absorbed by dormant ascospores are taken up over a period of hours and the kinetics of uptake are linear (Sussman et al., 1958). Only acids of small size, such as hydrazoic and hydrofluoric acids penetrate the dormant ascospore rapidly. Anionic compounds which contain two carbon atoms approach the limit of size beyond which no penetration is effected so that acetate and certain of its analogs penetrate slowly and poison after 24 hours. Propionate, phosphate, and larger molecules do not penetrate even after this time (Sussman et al., 1958). Moreover, those toxic acids which penetrate, such as hydrofluoric, hydrazoic, and fluoroacetic acids, inhibit the respiration of dormant ascospores, as well as prevent the germination of activated ones, thus suggesting that these substances penetrate to sensitive sites within the cell at once. In these cases, however, it should be noted that entrance is probably effected by the undissociated molecule, rather than the anions (Sussman et al., 1958).

On the other hand, the uptake of cations by the conidia and mycelium of

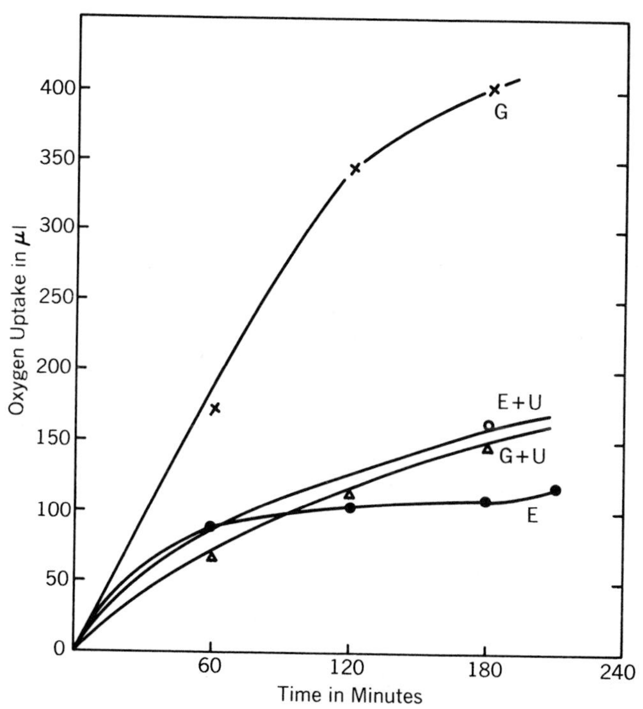

Figure 2.31 Effect of UO_2^{++} on the endogenous respiration of conidia of *Neurospora sitophila* and upon the respiration in the presence of glucose. Legend: G, 20 μM glucose; U, uranyl nitrate (3.7 μg per 10^5 spores); E, endogenous respiration. Each flask contained $MgCl_2$ (0.003M). (Redrawn from Cochrane and Tull, 1958, courtesy of *Phytopathology*.)

Table 2.8 Comparison of the Permeability Characteristics of Different Stages in the Life-Cycle of *Neurospora*

Ascospores of *N. tetrasperma*: Dormant	Germinating	Conidia of: *N. sitophila*	*N. crassa*
Cations such as UO_2^{++}, Cu^{++}, Cd^{++}, polymyxin-B taken up by cells without affecting respiration	Cations such as UO_2^{++}, etc., inhibit respiration	Cations such as Ag^{+}, Zn^{++}, Ce^{+++}, Cd^{++}, Hg^{++}, inhibit or stimulate respiration depending upon concentration	—
Cations bound to cell wall of intact cell, as well as to isolated walls	As in dormant ascospores	Very little attachment of cations to wall; mostly bound on intracellular particles	Rb^{+}, K^{+}, and Na^{+} bound intracellularly
Cations bound to dead cells	As in dormant ascospores	Uptake abolished by killing cells	Uptake abolished by metabolic inhibitors
Uptake of cations repressed by pretreatment with densely charged basic substances	As in dormant ascospores	Uptake affected variously, depending on nature of pretreatment	Intracellular binding repressed by deoxycorti-costerone
Acids larger than two carbon atoms enter slowly or not at all; glucose enters slowly	Glucose and other sugars enter; acids taken up	Glucose and Krebs cycle acids enter	—
Lowry et al., 1957; Sussman et al., 1958; Budd et al., 1965		Kunkel, 1913; Cochrane and Tull, 1958; McCallan, Miller and Weed, 1954; Miller and McCallan, 1956; Owens and Miller, 1957; Owens, 1955	Lester and Hechter, 1958, 1959

Neurospora follows a more usual course, that is, these substances appear to penetrate soon after introduction to the cells. Some of the differences between the permeability to cations of ascospores and other stages are outlined in Table 2.8 and Figure 2.31. Thus, it seems clear that the ability of ascospores to bind cations on the surface, without permitting their entrance to the cell, is unique for this stage in the life cycle of *Neurospora*. Moreover, a comparison between Figures 2.30 and 2.31 reveals that UO_2^{++} has no effect upon the respiration of

Table 2.9 Comparison of the Toxicity of Ag^{+} and Cu^{++} for Conidia and Ascospores of *Neurospora*

Toxicant Organism	ED_{50} (Germination) (μg/gm spores)	Uptake (μg/gm spores)	Reference
Ag^{+}			
Conidia (*N. sitophila*)	165	—	Miller and McCallan, 1956
Ascospores (*N. tetrasperma*)			
dormant	—	8300[a]	Lowry et al., 1957
germinating	216	—	Lowry et al., 1957
Cu^{++}			
Conidia (*N. sitophila*)	1650	—	McCallan et al., 1954
Ascospores (*N. tetrasperma*)			
dormant	—	2730[a]	Lowry et al., 1957
germinating	1905	—	Lowry et al., 1957

[a] There is no measurable effect of the cation upon dormant ascospores.

dormant ascospores, whereas that of conidia is inhibited immediately upon the addition of the toxicant. A difference in the metabolism of activated ascospores and conidia can be perceived when the data in Figures 2.30 and 2.31 are compared in that the endogenous respiration of the former is strongly inhibited by UO_2^{++} whereas that of conidia is little affected. Some data on the sensitivity of these different stages to inhibitors are summarized in Table 2.9 which reveals a striking parallel in the ED_{50} (μg of toxicant required to inhibit 1 gm of cells) for germinating ascospores and conidia of *Neurospora*. Furthermore, it is clear from these data that the failure of dormant ascospores to respond to these poisons is not due to insufficient uptake because fifty times more than is necessary to inhibit germination 50 percent is adsorbed by such cells.

Regrettably, such data as are available for *Neurospora* have been obtained by the use of different species. However, similar results to those obtained by the use of conidia of *N. sitophila* have been obtained with those of *Monilinia fructicola, Aspergillus niger, Alternaria oleracea, Glomerella cingulata, Venturia pyrina, Rhizopus nigricans,* as well as yeast (Miller, 1957) so that the effects described seem generally applicable to this spore type at least. On the other hand, the results of Goldsworthy and Greene (1936) with conidia of *Monilia (Sclerotinia) fructicola,* when Cu^{++} uptake was studied, are more in accord with the data obtained with dormant ascospores in that the toxic action of this metal was not manifested until germination began. Similarly, Cu^{++} adsorbed by conidia of *Cochliobolus* (*Ophiobolus*) *myabeanus* could be eluted in acid solution with little effect upon viability (Akai and Itoi, 1954). Unfortunately, these differences cannot be resolved at present but it seems reasonable to conclude that the permeability of dormant ascospores of *Neurospora* is far more restricted than that of conidia of this organism and of the several other fungi studied.

Before concluding this section, it is pertinent to ask how the characteristics of the walls of the dormant cells discussed here bear upon the survival of organisms in nature. That heavy metals are excluded from such cells is clear for, even if traces were adsorbed on the surface, they would probably be eluted by the larger amounts of alkaline earth metals in the soil. In fact, it has been shown (Sussman, 1954) that germinating ascospores of *Neurospora* will tolerate even 0.2 *M* K^{+} or Na^{+} without being inhibited, so that the elements in the highest concentration in the usual habitats of this organism have little effect upon it. Furthermore, it seems unlikely that, at the range of *p*H values found in nature, acids will penetrate. The conclusion must be that ascospores are closed to most, if not all, exogenous supplies of chemicals until shortly before they germinate. Inasmuch as these cells contain enough substrates to last for years (Lingappa and Sussman, 1959), it is likely that the exclusion of metabolites from them is of survival value as a protective device against the incorporation of toxicants such as antibiotics.

The Fungus Wall as a Light Filter

Another aspect of the protection afforded some dormant cells by the wall is its function as a light filter. This was observed first by Fulton and Coblentz (1929) who found that of 27 species exposed to ultraviolet irradiation, the more resistant fungi were those having dark walls. Then, Weston (1931) was able to show that dark-colored uredospores of *Puccinia graminis tritici* survived such treatment better than lighter colored ones. Similar results were obtained with conidia of *Ophiostoma* (Fries, 1946), *Glomerella cingulata* (Markert, 1953), and *Cochliobolus sativus* (Tinline et al., 1960). In addition, Rabinovitz-Sereni (1932) found that dark, thick-walled conidia, such as those of *Helminthosporium gibberosporum*, *Coniosporum bambusae*, and *Epicoccum purpurescens*, resisted exposure to ultraviolet light for 180 minutes. On the other hand, slightly olivaceous conidia, like those of *Microascus styeanus*, and *Penicillium crustaceum*, withstood a similar dose for only 25 minutes; hyaline conidia of *Clonostachys araucaria* and *Fusarium martii*, and pycnospores of *Deuterophoma tracheiphila* survived 10 minutes. Finally, a comparison between the survival of *Alternaria* sp., a black-walled species, with that of several hyaline-walled ones, yielded in the experiments of English and Gerhardt (1946) results which are similar to those just described. Therefore, these data lend support to the suggestion of Buller (1934) that the survival value of the black wall of spores of coprophilous fungi, including *Coprinus, Panaeolus, Anellaria, Sordaria* and others, which are in an exposed position on vegetation for some time, is related to the protection afforded against excessive insolation.

In the above cases, the pigment usually involved probably is melanin, a comparatively inert group of substances whose chemical nature is poorly defined (Pearse, 1961). Durrell (personal communication) has shown that a synthetic melanin, prepared by the oxidation and polymerization of some phenols, prevented damage to unpigmented spores of *Gliocladium roseum* when used as a screen between the spores and an ultraviolet light source. Melanin may act as an electron acceptor, thereby controlling the free radical concentration of the cell, or by maintaining a constant rH, according to recent work (Dain et al., 1964). However, not all pigments protect against ultraviolet light, for it was shown by Masago (1959) that certain colorless strains of *Serratia marcescens* are less sensitive than pigmented ones to such radiations, and Durrell and Shields (1960) have shown that the black spores of *Aspergillus niger* are not resistant. In neither of these cases is the pigment involved melanin.

It should be noted that the thickness of the wall of spores also may be a factor in protection against radiation damage, but there is little information on this point.

REFERENCES

Akai, S., and S. Itoi. 1954. *Botan. Mag.* 67:787–788.

Armstrong, J. J., J. Baddiley, J. G. Buchanan, A. L. Davison, M. V. Kelemen, and F. C. Neuhaus. 1959. *Nature* (London) 184:247–249.

Armstrong, J. J., J. Baddiley, and J. G. Buchanan. 1960. *Biochem. J.* 76:610–621.

Armstrong, J. J., J. Baddiley, and J. G. Buchanan. 1961. *Biochem J.* 80:254–261.

Aronson, J. M., and L. Machlis. 1959. *Am. J. Botany* 46:292–300.

Baumann-Grace, J. B., and J. Tomcsik. 1957. *J. Gen. Microbiol.* 17:227–237.

Berger, J. A., and A. G. Marr. 1960. *J. Gen. Microbiol.* 22:147–157.

Bernlohr, R. W., and G. D. Novelli. 1960. *Arch. Biochem. Biophys.* 87:232–238.

Bernlohr, R. W., and C. Sievert. 1962. *Biochem. Biophys. Res. Comm.* 9:32–37.

Bertaud, W. S., I. M. Morice, D. W. Russell, and A. Taylor. 1963. *J. Gen. Microbiol.* 32:385–395.

Bisset, K. A. 1950. *The Cytology and Life-History of Bacteria.* E. S. Livingstone, Edinburgh, 136 pp.

Black, S. H. 1960. Ph.D. Thesis, Univ. of Michigan.

Blackwell, E. 1935. *Nature* (London) 135: 546.

Blackwell, E. 1943. *Trans. Brit. Mycol. Soc.* 26:71–89.

Blank, F. 1954. *Can. J. Microbiol.* 1:1–5.

Bradley, D. E., and J. G. Franklin. 1958. *J. Bacteriol.* 76:618–630.

Bradley, D. E., and D. J. Williams. 1957. *J. Gen. Microbiol.* 17:75–79.

Brenner, M., E. Gray, and H. Paulus. 1964. *Biochim. Biophys. Acta* 90:401–403.

Budd, K., A. S. Sussman, and F. I. Eilers. 1965. *J. Bacteriol.* In press at time of publication.

Buller, A. H. R. 1922. *Researches on Fungi* vol. 2. Longmans, Green, London, 492 pp.

BULLER, A. H. R. 1934. *Researches on Fungi* vol. 6. Longmans, Green, London, 513 pp.

BURKE, G. S. 1923. *J. Infect. Diseases*. 32:433–438.

CANTINO, E. C., J. S. LOVETT, J. V. LEAK, and J. LYTHGOE. 1963. *J. Gen. Microbiol.* 31:393–404.

CHAPMAN, G. B. 1956. *J. Bacteriol.* 71:348–355.

COCHRANE, V. W., and D. L. W. TULL. 1958. *Phytopathology* 48:623–628.

COOK, R. P. 1932. *Biol. Rev. Biol. Proc., Cambridge Phil. Soc.* 7:1.

CSILLAG, ANNA. 1963. *J. Gen. Microbiol.* 30:21–27.

DAIN, A., G. A. KERKUT, R. C. SMITH, K. A. MUNDAY, and T. H. WILMSHURST. 1964. *Experientia* 20:76–78.

DARÁNYI, J. VON. 1927. *Zentr. Bakteriol. Parasitenk. Abt. II Orig.* 71:353–357.

DARÁNYI, J. VON. 1930. *Biol. Zentr.* 50:471–478.

DAVENPORT, C. B., and W. E. CASTLE. 1895. *Arch. Entwick. Organismen* 2:227.

DELAPORTE, B. 1964. *Ann. Inst. Pasteur* 107: 246–262.

DODGE, B. O. 1957. *Bull. Torrey Botan. Club* 84:182–188.

DONDERO, N. C., and P. E. HOLBERT. 1957. *J. Bacteriol.* 74:43–47.

DOUGLAS, H. W. 1957. *J. Appl. Bacteriol.* 20: 390–403.

DURRELL, L. W., and LORA M. SHIELDS. 1960. *Mycologia* 52:636–641.

ENGLISH, H., and F. GERHARDT. 1946. *Phytopathology* 36:100–111.

FISCHER, A. 1877. *Vorlesungen über Bakterien.* Gustav Fischer, Jena.

FITZ-JAMES, P. C. 1955. *Can. J. Microbiol.* 1:502–519.

FITZ-JAMES, P. C. 1959. *J. Bacteriol.* 78:765–768.

FITZ-JAMES, P. C. 1960. *J. Biophys. Biochem. Cytol.* 8:507–528.

FITZ-JAMES, P. C. 1962*a*. *J. Bacteriol.* 84:104–114.

FITZ-JAMES, P. C. 1962*b*. *8th Intern. Congr. Microbiol.* p. 16.

FITZ-JAMES, P. C. 1964. *J. Bacteriol.* 87:667–675.

FITZ-JAMES, P. C., and VANCE. Unpublished data, quoted by Fitz-James. 1955. *Can. J. Microbiol.* 1:525.

FRANKLIN, J. G., and D. E. BRADLEY. 1957. *J. Appl. Bacteriol.* 20:467–472.

FREY, R. 1950. *Ber. Schweiz. Botan. Ges.* 60:199–230.

FRIEDMAN, C. A., and B. S. HENRY. 1938. *J. Bacteriol.* 36:99–105.

FRIES, H. 1946. *Svensk Bot. Tidskr.* 40:127–140.

FULTON, H. R., and W. W. COBLENTZ. 1929. *J. Agr. Res.* 38:159–168.

GERHARDT, P., E. A. BANNAN, and E. RIBI. 1961. *Bacteriol Proc.*, p. 77.

GERHARDT, P., and S. H. BLACK. 1961*a*. in *Spores II.* H. O. Halvorson, Ed. Burgess Pub. Co., Minneapolis, pp. 218–228.

GERHARDT, P., and S. H. BLACK. 1961*b*. *J. Bacteriol.* 82:750–760.

GERHARDT, P., and E. RIBI. 1964. *J. Bacteriol.* 88:1774–1789.

GLAUERT, A. M., and D. A. HOPWOOD. 1961. *J. Biophys. Biochem. Cytol.* 10:505–516.

GOLDSWORTHY, M. C., and E. L. GREEN. 1936. *J. Agr. Res.* 52:517–533.

GRACE, JOYCE B. 1951. *J. Gen. Microbiol.* 5:519–524.

GRAHAM, S. O. 1951. *Phytopathology* 47:522.

GREGORY, P. H., and H. L. NIXON. 1950. *Trans. Brit. Mycol. Soc.* 33:359–363.

HANNAY, C. L. 1956. *6th Symp. Soc. Gen. Microbiol.* 6:318–340.

HASHIMOTO, T., and N. B. NAYLOR. 1958. *J. Bacteriol.* 75:647–653.

HASHIMOTO, T., and P. GERHARDT. 1960. *J. Biophys. Biochem. Cytol.* 7:195–196.

HASHIMOTO, T., S. H. BLACK, and P. GERHARDT. 1960. *Can. J. Microbiol.* 6:203–212.

HAWKER, LILIAN E., and PATRICIA MC. V. ABBOTT. 1963. *J. Gen. Microbiol.* 37:295–298.

HAWKER, LILIAN E., and R. J. HENDY. 1963. *J. Gen. Microbiol.* 33:43–46.

HESS, G. E., and E. J. SCHANTZ. 1956. *Science* 123:983–984.

HILLES, M., and J. BRANDES. 1956. *Phytopathol. Z.* 28:104–109.

HITCHINS, A. D., and G. W. GOULD. 1964. *Nature* 203:895–896.

HOLBERT, P. E. 1960. *J. Biophys. Biochem. Cytol.* 7:373–376.

HORIKOSHI, K., and S. IIDA. 1964. *Biochem. Biophys. Acta* 83:197–203.

HOWIE, J. W., and J. CRUICKSHANK. 1940. *J. Pathol. Bacteriol.* 50:235–242.

HUNNELL, J. W., and Z. J. ORDAL. 1961. in *Spores II.* H. O. Halvorson, Ed. Burgess Pub. Co., Minneapolis, pp. 101–108.

IIZUKA, H. 1955. *J. Gen. Appl. Microbiol., Tokyo* 1:10–17.

KESSLER, GIAN, and W. J. NICKERSON. 1959. *J. Biol. Chem.* 234:2281–2285.

KNAYSI, G. 1961. *J. Bacteriol.* 82:556–563.

KOFFLER, H. 1961. *Bacteriol Proc.*, p. 95.

KREGER, E. R. 1954. *Biochim. Biophys. Acta* 13:1–9.

KREGER, E. R., and B. J. D. MEEUSE. 1952. *Biochim. Biophys. Acta* 9:699–700.
KUNKEL, O. 1913. *Bull. Torrey Botan. Club* 40:625–639.
LAMANNA, C. 1940. *J. Infect. Diseases* 67:193–205.
LAMANNA, C.,and D. EISLER. 1960. *J. Bacteriol.* 79:435–441.
LAYNE, J. S., and E. J. JOHNSON. 1964. *J. Bacteriol.* 87:684–689.
LEGAL, M. 1947. *Bull. Trimestr. Soc. Mycol. France* 62:241–245.
LESTER, G., and O. HECHTER. 1958. *Proc. Nat. Acad. Sci. U.S.* 44:1141–1149.
LESTER, G., and O. HECHTER. 1959. *Proc. Nat. Acad. Sci. U.S.* 45:1792–1801.
LEVINSON, H. S., and A. S. WRIGLEY. 1960. *Science* 131:1382.
LEWIS, J. C., N. S. SNELL, and H. K. BURR. 1960. *Science* 132:544–545.
LEWITH, S. 1890. *Arch. Exp. Pathol.* 26:341–354.
LINDEGREN, C. C., and M. A. SCOTT. 1936. *La Cellule* 45:359–371.
LINGAPPA, Y., and A. S. SUSSMAN. 1959. *Am. J. Botany* 46:671–678.
LOWRY, R. J., and A. S. SUSSMAN. 1956. *Arch. Biochem. Biophys.* 62:113–124.
LOWRY, R. J., and A. S. SUSSMAN. 1958. *Am. J. Botany* 45:397–403.
LOWRY, R. J., A. S. SUSSMAN, and B. VON BÖVENTER-HEIDENHAIN. 1957. *Mycologia* 49:609–622.
MACDONALD, R. E., and S. W. MACDONALD. 1962. *Can. J. Microbiol.* 8:795–808.
MALENÇON, G. 1928. *Ann. Cryptogamie Exotique* 1:58–74.
MARKERT, C. L. 1953. *Exptl. Cell Res.* 4:427–435.
MARR, A. G. 1960. in *The Bacteria*. I. C. Gunsalus and R. Y. Stanier, Eds., vol. 1. Academic Press, N.Y., pp. 443–465.
MASAGO, H. 1959. *Ann. Phytopathol. Soc. Japan* 24:97–103.
MATTIROLA, O. 1921. *Atti Accad. Nazl. Lincei. Mem. Classe Sci. Fis. Mat. Nat.* 30:149–160.
MAYALL, B. H., and C. F. ROBINOW. 1957. *J. Appl. Bacteriol.* 20:333–341.
MCCALLAN, S. E. A., L. P. MILLER, and R. M. WEED. 1954. *Contrib. Boyce Thompson Inst.* 18:39–68.
MELLON, R. R., and L. M. ANDERSON. 1919. *J. Immunol.* 4:203–208.
MIELKE, J. L., and G. W. COCHRAN. 1952. *Mycologia* 44:325–329.
MILLER, L. P. 1951. *J. Agr. Food Chem.* 5:116–122.
MILLER, L. P., and S. E. A. MCCALLAN. 1956. in *Peaceful Uses of Atomic Energy*. Proc. Internat. Conf. in Geneva, Aug. 1955. vol. 12. United Nations, N.Y.
MOREAU, F. 1958. *Bull. Soc. Botan. France* 105:363–429.
MURRELL, W. G., and W. J. SCOTT. 1957. *Nature* (London) 179:481–482.
MURRELL, W. G., and W. J. SCOTT. 1958. *Proc. 7th Intern. Congr. Microbiol., Stockholm* p. 26.
NORRIS, J. R., and D. H. WATSON. 1960. *J. Gen. Microbiol.* 22:744–749.
NORRIS, J. R., and J. WOLF. 1961. *J. Appl. Bacteriol.* 24:42–56.
NORTHCOTE, D. H., and R. W. HORNE. 1952. *Biochem. J.* 51:232–236.
OHYE, D. F., and W. G. MURRELL. 1962. *J. Cell Biol.* 14:111–123.
OWENS, R. G. 1955. *Contrib. Boyce Thompson Inst.* 18:125–144.
OWENS, R. G., and L. P. MILLER. 1957. *Contrib. Boyce Thompson Inst.* 19:177–188.
PEARSE, E. A. G. 1961. *Histochemistry, Theoretical and Applied*. Little, Brown, Boston, 998 pp.
POWELL, J. F. 1953. *Biochem. J.* 54:210–211.
POWELL, J. F., and R. E. STRANGE. 1953. *Biochem. J.* 54:205–209.
POWELL, J. F., and R. E. STRANGE. 1957. *Biochem. J.* 65:700–708.
RABINOVITZ-SERENI. 1932. *Boll. R. Staz. Patol. Veg. N.S.* 12:115–144.
RANCOURT, MARTHA W., and H. A. LECHEVALIER. 1964. *Can. J. Microbiol.* 10:311–316.
RECORD, B. R., and K. H. GRINSTEAD. 1954. *Biochem. J.* 58:85–87.
RHOADS, A. S. 1918. *Mycologia* 10:277–284.
ROBINOW, C. F. 1953. *J. Bacteriol.* 66:300–311.
ROBINOW, C. F. 1960. in *The Bacteria*. I. C. Gunsalus and R. Y. Stanier, Eds., vol. 1. Academic Press, N.Y., pp. 207–248.
RODE, L. J., and J. W. FOSTER. 1960. *Proc. Nat. Acad. Sci. U.S.* 46:118–128.
RODE, L. J., C. W. LEWIS, and J. W. FOSTER. 1962. *J. Cell Biol.* 13:423–435.
ROELEFSEN, P. A., and I. HOETTE. 1951. *Antonie van Leeuwenhoek, J. Microbiol. Serol.* 17:293–313.
SALTON, M. R. J. 1960. in *The Bacteria*. I. C. Gunsalus and R. Y. Stanier, Eds., vol. 1. Academic Press, N.Y., pp. 97–151.
SALTON, M. R. J. 1964. *The Bacterial Cell Wall*. Elsevier, Amsterdam, N.Y., London, 293 pp.

SALTON, M. R. J., and R. W. HORNE. 1951. *Biochim. Biophys. Acta* 7:177–197.

SALTON, M. R. J., and B. MARSHALL. 1959. *J. Gen. Microbiol.* 21:415–420.

SCHUSTER, F. 1964. *J. Protozool.* 11:207–216.

SCHWEIZER, G. 1947. *Planta* 35:132–176.

SHATKIN, A. J. 1959. *Trans. N.Y. Acad. Sci.* 21:446–453.

SHATKIN, A. J., and E. L. TATUM. 1959. *J. Biophys. Biochem. Cytol.* 6:423–426.

SMITH, A. G., and P. D. ELLNER. 1957. *J. Bacteriol.* 73:1–7.

SNOKE, J. E. 1964. *Biochem. Biophys. Res. Com.* 14:571–574.

SOCOLOFSKY, M. D., and O. WYSS. 1961. *J. Bacteriol.* 81:946–954.

STRANGE, R. E. 1959. *Bacteriol. Rev.* 23:1–7.

STRANGE, R. E., and F. A. DARK. 1956. *Biochem. J.* 62:459–465.

STRANGE, R. E., and F. A. DARK. 1957. *J. Gen. Microbiol.* 16:236–249.

STRANGE, R. E., and L. H. KENT. 1959. *Biochem. J.* 71:333–339.

STRANGE, R. E., and J. R. POWELL. 1954. *Biochem. J.* 58:80–85.

STROMINGER, J. L. 1962. in *The Bacteria.* I. C. Gunsalus and R. Y. Stanier, Eds., vol. 3. Academic Press, N.Y., pp. 413–470.

SUSSMAN, A. S. 1954. *J. Gen. Physiol.* 38:59–77.

SUSSMAN, A. S., and R. J. LOWRY. 1955. *J. Bacteriol.* 70:675–685.

SUSSMAN, A. S., B. VON BÖVENTER-HEIDENHAIN, and R. J. LOWRY. 1957. *Plant Physiol.* 32: 586–589.

SUSSMAN, A. S., R. HOLTON, and B. VON BÖVENTER-HEIDENHAIN. 1958. *Arch. Mikrobiol.* 29:38–50.

SUZUKI, T., T. TANINO, W. MOCHIZUKI, F. NOKA, and Y. SHIGEMATSU. 1957. *Electron-Microscopy (Tokyo)* 6:82–85.

TAKAGI, A., T. KAWATA, T. KUBO, Y. NAKATA, and M. IWATANI. 1956. *Electron-Microscopy (Tokyo)* 5:35–37.

TAKAGI, A., T. KAWATA, and S. YAMAMOTO. 1960. *J. Bacteriol.* 80:37–46.

TCHAN, Y. T., A. BIRCH-ANDERSEN, and H. L. JENSEN. 1962. *Arch. Mikrobiol.* 43:50–66.

TINLINE, R. D., J. F. STAUFFER, and J. G. DICKSON. 1960. *Can. J. Botany* 38:275–282.

TOKUYASU, K., and E. YAMADA. 1959. *J. Biophys. Biochem. Cytol.* 5:129–133.

TOMCSIK, J., and S. GUEX-HOLZER. 1954. *J. Gen. Microbiol.* 10:317–324.

TOMCSIK, J., and J. B. BAUMANN-GRACE. 1959. *J. Gen. Microbiol.* 21:666–675.

TOMCSIK, J., M. BOUILLE, and J. B. BAUMANN-GRACE. 1959. *Z. Allgem. Pathol Bakteriol.* 22:630–637.

TRESNER, H. D., M. C. DAVIES, and E. J. BACKUS. 1961. *J. Bacteriol.* 81:70–80.

VAN DEN HOOFF, A., and S. ANINGA. 1956. *Antonie van Leeuwenhoek, J. Microbiol. Serol.* 22:327–330.

VENNES, J. W., and P. GERHARDT. 1956. *Science* 124:535–536.

VENNES, J. W., and P. GERHARDT. 1957. *Bacteriol. Proc.*, p. 105.

VINTER, V. 1960. *Folia Microbiol.* 5:217–230.

VINTER, V. 1963. *Folia Microbiol.* 8:147–155.

VIRTANEN, A. I., and L. PULKKI. 1933. *Arch. Mikrobiol.* 4:99–122.

VOELZ, H., and M. DWORKIN. 1962. *J. Bacteriol.* 84:943–952.

WALDHAM, D. G., and H. O. HALVORSON. 1954. *Appl. Microbiol.* 2:333–338.

WARTH, A. D., D. F. OHYE, and W. G. MURRELL. 1962. *8th Intern. Congr. Microbiol.*, p. 16.

WEISS, B. 1963. *J. Gen. Microbiol.* 39:85–94.

WESTON, W. A. R. DILLON. 1931. *Sci. Agr.* 12:81–87.

WILLIAMS, P. G., and G. A. LEDINGHAM. 1964. *Can. J. Botany* 42:1503–1508.

WORK, E. 1961. *J. Gen. Microbiol.* 25:167–189.

YOUNG, I. E. 1958. Ph.D. Thesis, Univ. of Western Ontario.

YOUNG, I. E., and P. C. FITZ-JAMES. 1959. *J. Biophys. Biochem. Cytol.* 6:483–498.

YU, C. C. C. 1954. *Am. J. Botany* 41:21–30.

CHAPTER 3

Longevity and Survivability of Spores

IT HAS BEEN said (P. Becquerel, 1950*a*):

"En effet, que le froid envahisse un jour notre planête, soit par l'éloignement du soleil, l'absorption de ses radiations ou par leur extinction, à la suite de certains événements astronomiques, notre atmosphère se liquéfierait, comme cela est déjà arrivé pour celles de Jupitre, Uranus, Neptune, Pluton. Le monde végétal et le monde animal disparaîtraient. Seuls longtemps subsisteraient en vie suspendue, les spores, les oeufs, les animalcules reviviscents, prêts à une nouvelle évolution, si des conditions cosmiques favorables revenaient."

Thus, according to this point of view, which is shared by other scientists, if most of life were destroyed by a holocaust of natural, or man-made origin, a residuum in the form of spores, cysts, or seeds might remain to serve as the raw material of further evolution. The data upon which these conclusions are based will be reviewed in this chapter.

Longevity of Spores

RECORDS OF LONGEVITY IN ANCIENT MATERIALS

Spectacular reports have appeared which claim that living microorganisms can be isolated from ancient materials of terrestrial origin. Recently, for example, paleozoic salt from the Kali and Zechstein deposits of Germany was investigated by Dombrowski (1960, 1961) who found pseudomonads and several strains of

Bacillus circulans, a bacterium that is not commonly isolated elsewhere in that region (Figure 3.1). Elaborate precautions were taken to exclude contaminants, including rigorous washing, ultraviolet irradiation, and surface heating. Even after numerous repetitions of certain of these techniques, living organisms were recovered. Dombrowski (1960) also was able to isolate from salt springs at Bad Nauheim halophilic pseudomonads which are similar to organisms recovered

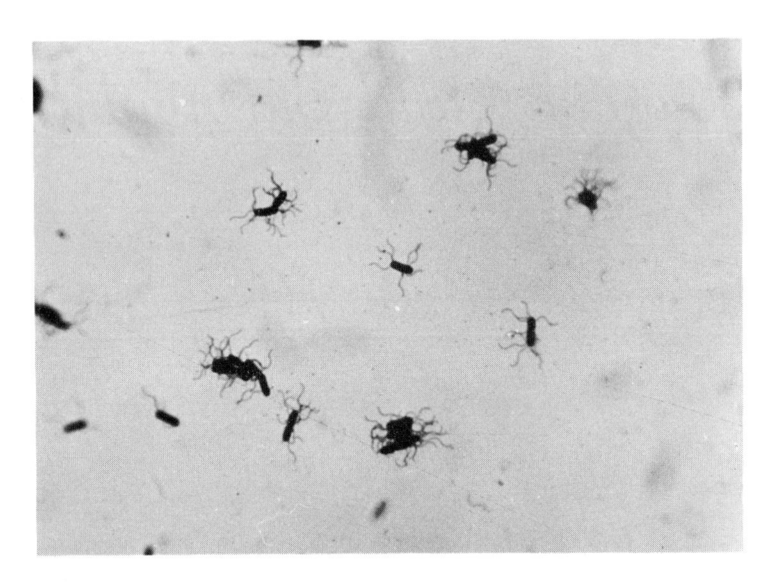

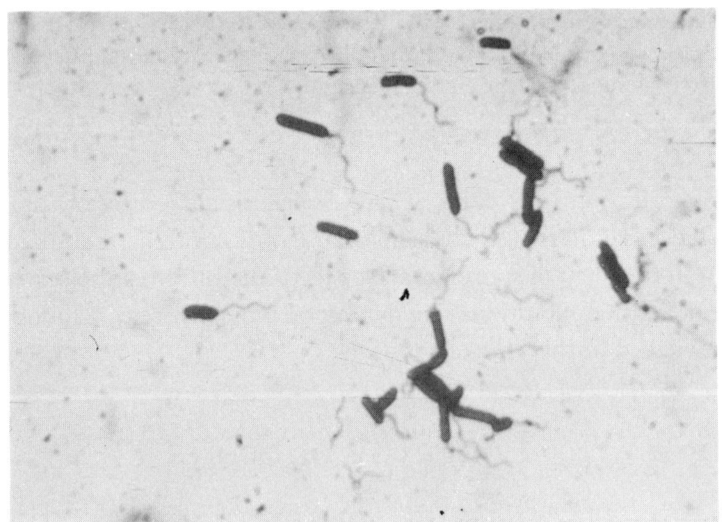

Figure 3.1 Bacteria recovered from Zechstein salt deposits (NaIBr). *Top: Bacillus circulans* about 180 million years old. × 1000. *Bottom: Pseudomonas halocrenaea* about 180 million years old. × 1200. (These photographs were obtained through the courtesy of H. Dombrowski, Institüt für physikal. Medizin, Justus Liebig-Univ. Giessen, Bad Nauheim, Germany.)

from the Zechstein deposits. Comparisons between three isolates of *B. circulans* from the salt and three strains of recent origin revealed that the former possessed more saccharolytic activities than did one of the modern strains.

Other reports of the survival of microorganisms for millennia include those of Lipman (1928, 1931) who alleged that living bacteria were recoverable from the interior of pre-Cambrian rocks from the Algonkian in Canada, from the Grand Canyon in Colorado, and from anthracite coal and other materials. As in Dombrowski's case, Lipman exerted great care in the attempt to avoid contamination from the outside during the grinding of the rocks and the plating procedures. As far as could be determined, the bacteria he isolated were identical to present-day ones. In addition, Omelyanskii (1911) found several species of bacteria in broth cultures prepared from the mucosa and other tissues of the trunk of the Sauga Yurakh mammoth. Algae, fungi, and crustacea, in addition to bacteria, were claimed by Kapterev (1936, 1938) to be present at a depth of 2–7 meters in soil. By contrast, other investigators have failed to recover living things from ancient materials. Thus, no cultivable bacteria were found in salt crystals by Müller and Schwartz (1953) or by Rippel (1935), although numerous examples of fossil forms were described. Furthermore, the former workers used several types of media, with varying salt concentrations, which should have permitted the growth of halophiles. It should be noted that Müller and Schwartz used salt from some of the Zechstein deposits, as did Dombrowski, so that in this case the results are in direct contradiction.

Another contradiction stems from Lipman's findings, which appeared to show the presence of living bacteria in coal and other ancient materials. These experiments were repeated in another laboratory (Farrell and Turner, 1932) but no viable organisms were recovered from anthracite that was intact before use. However, bacteria were obtained from coal that had been fractured, thereby being exposed to the penetration of bacteria by diffusion from the surroundings. Furthermore, the microorganisms found in such materials were plentiful in the waters and salt of the mine and were similar to those found by Lipman.

As for terrestrial materials of relatively more recent origin, the contents of a sealed canopic jar (c. 1800 B.C.), found in the tomb of Tutankh-Amen were examined by Dickson (1936). Here also, no living organisms could be isolated, even though the contents were not toxic to a few microorganisms that were tested. Admittedly, the nature of the preservative used could have changed over the centuries, and so the conclusions derived from this experiment can only be tentative.

More recently, Sneath (1962) has examined two types of fecal material, both of which contained the fatty acid patterns of fecal lipids. One was human feces from the Meso de Guajo culture (c. 1500 B.C.) that had been preserved in dry caves, the second from some intestines from a peat burial (c. 1000 A.D.). In neither case could microorganisms be detected. By contrast, Patočka and Šefrna (1944) were able to isolate *Clostridium tertium*, *C. sordelli*, and *C. novyi* from the abdomens of well-preserved mummies found in the catacombs of the town of Klatovy in Bohemia. None of these strains was found in swabs from the skin of the mummies, or from the coffins and the ground around them. These data and other evidence support the conclusion that these bacteria survived from 180 to 250 years at about 8–10° C, the temperature of the crypt in which the mummies were stored.

REQUIREMENTS FOR HUNTING VIABLE CREATURES IN ANCIENT AND EXTRATERRESTRIAL MATERIALS

Although a priori reasons can be assembled for denying the sustained existence of living creatures in ancient materials, enough uncertainty over the possibility exists to warrant experimental test. Some of the investigators mentioned previously, notably Lipman (1932) and Oparin (1957) have provided criteria for judging the effectiveness of the techniques to be used in such studies. Others, like Fitch and Anders (1963) and Sall (1964) have discussed techniques for investigating extraterrestrial materials. These criteria and others are outlined below.

Exclusion of Contaminants

It is a *sine qua non* of work in this field that all possible precautions be taken to exclude contaminants. Contamination may occur before, during, or after the isolation of organisms is attempted. The conditions imposed by the study of materials in soil and water would appear to increase the possibility of chance contamination. For example, in the studies of Omelyanskii on the Sauga Yrakh mammoth and in those of Kapterev (1936, 1938) with soil at great depths, the inocula were prepared from materials after their transportation to the investigators.

An analogous problem is encountered with mineral materials of terrestrial or extraterrestrial origin. It is difficult, if not impossible, to obtain specimens which have not been in contact with the earth and water, or which have not been contaminated by excessive handling. Because stony meteorites are porous and absorb water (Roy, 1935), the possibility that bacteria have diffused into rocks is not easily ruled out. It is likely that the results of Lipman (1928, 1931) and others are ascribable to contamination of this sort.

In addition to rigorously excluding contaminants, care must be taken that the sterile techniques used do not kill organisms that may have survived in ancient materials. Therefore, protracted heating or submergence in antiseptics may result in spurious negative results.

Proper Isolation Medium

Specialized media may be required for the isolation of organisms from ancient materials such as salt. In fact, it is a logical possibility that extraterrestrial microbes may escape detection because of growth requirements that are insufficiently understood. Conditions of growth, such as temperature, gas environment, and so forth, must be considered before negative results can be accepted without reserve.

Characterization of the Organisms Isolated

Although it is difficult to be specific about the characteristics that ancient microorganisms might be expected to demonstrate, some general properties might be predicted. For one, the considerable fossil microbial flora reveals the presence of organisms whose morphology is similar to that of present-day organisms (Müller and Schwartz, 1953). Therefore, if viable microbes are obtained from ancient materials, striking changes in morphology are not likely to be found, although evolutionary offshoots of unique morphology may have been deposited.

Prior History of Sample Investigated

Since rocks are porous, they are expected to be infiltrated with water from the environment from which collections are made. Also, small cracks or fissures may occur, through which organisms can penetrate to the interior of samples. The data of Farrell and Turner (1932) are pertinent in this connection insofar as they demonstrated that only previously fractured anthracite coal yielded microorganisms. As Roy (1935) has pointed out, rocks with an intact crust offer promise that the ingress of surface contaminants has been restricted and that the materials within the interior are more likely to be retained in their original form. Finally, any handling of samples, by being a potential source of contamination, can confuse results.

Life may have had more than one independent origin. Consequently, there may be environments such as those under the surface of the earth, or on other planets, in which forms of life flourish which are very different from those with which we are familiar. Not only might we not know how to elicit their growth in culture, due to ignorance of their physiology, but the recognition that they are living organisms might present real difficulties. As will be mentioned later, this problem is faced in a more acute form when extraterrestrial life is considered.

Under favorable conditions, how long can organisms survive? From the preceding discussion it is not clear whether or not microorganisms can survive for thousands of years on earth. Recent data, such as those of Dombrowski (1960, 1961), suggest the possibility that viable forms may be found in ancient materials. Becquerel (1950*a*), from a study of the effect of temperature on survival curves, estimated that near absolute zero microorganisms could survive for millions or billions of years. While chemical breakdown may not be important in these cases, as pointed out by Sneath (1962), irradiation from the decay of cellular potassium-40 may be the determining factor and provide upper limits of about 10^9 years for survival. As will be shown later in the chapter, some organisms are extraordinarily resistant to environmental hazards such as heat, cold, and desiccation for more limited survival periods.

RECORDS OF LONGEVITY IN MODERN MATERIALS

The data in Table 3.1 reveal that microbes can survive for more than 5 years in soil under natural conditions. In addition, the survival of organisms has been studied in inoculated soils. Katznelson (1940) found that whereas *Bacillus cereus*, *B. megaterium*, *Trichoderma* sp., *Penicillium* sp., *Aspergillus* sp., *Cunninghamella* sp., and some actinomycetes survived more than 230 days, *Helminthosporium sativum*

Table 3.1 Longevity of Spores and Vegetative Cells and the Conditions Under Which They Survive

Organism	Stage	Longevity	Conditions of Storage	Reference
Bacillus anthracis	Spores	47 years	Sealed vials and test tubes	Bosco, 1960*a*
		60 years	Soil, room temp.	Wilson and Russell, 1964
		68 years	Sealed vials	Jacotot and Virat, 1954
Thermophilic bacillus	Spore	118 years	Canned meat	Wilson and Shipp, 1938
Bacillus species	Spores	37 years	Dry soil, room temp., dark	Sneath, 1962
Clostridium sporogenes	Spores	46 years	In alcohol	Bulloch, 1928
65 strains of nonspore-forming bacteria	Vegetative	16–48 years	Room temp., dark	Bosco, 1960*b*
Eberthella typhosa	Spores	28 months	In ice cream (−20°C)	Prucha and Brannon, 1926
Rhizobium meliloti	Vegetative	30–45 years	Autoclaved soil	Jensen, 1961
Neisseria gonorrhoeae	Vegetative	18 years	Freeze-dried, stored *in vacuo*	Elser et al., 1935
67 species of bacteria	Vegetative	21 years	Dry *in vacuo* 10°C	Miller and Simons, 1962
Actinomyces violaceus	Spores	> 10 years	Dry soil, room temp.	Berestneff, 1907
Nocardia sp., *Streptomyces* sp., *Micromonospora* sp.	Spores	10–14 years	Autoclaved soil	Jensen, 1961
Dictyostelium discoideum	Spores	8 years	Lyophilized 4°C	Raper, 1951
		19 years		Raper, unpublished
Polysphondylium violacium	Spores	8 years	Lyophilized 4°C	Raper, 1951
		19 years		Raper, unpublished
Physarum cinereum, *Fuligo septica*, *Hemitrichia clavata*, *Stemonitis ferruginea*, *Didymium squamulosum*, *Diachea leucopoda*	Spores	> 30 years	Herbarium collection	Smith, 1929

Table 3.1 (*Continued*)

Organism	Stage	Longevity	Conditions of Storage	Reference
Trichia scabra	Spores	> 27 years	Herbarium collection	Smith, 1929
Hemitrichia clavata	Spores	75 years	Herbarium collection	Erbisch, 1961
Lycogala flavofuscum	Spores	68 years	Herbarium collection	Erbisch, 1961
Rhizopus nigricans	Conidia	22 years	Dried in sealed tubes	McCrea, 1923
Absidia sp., *Mortierella* sp., *Haplosporangium* sp., *Phycomyces* sp.	Conidia	> 2 years, 8 months	On agar at 7°C	Hesseltine, 1947
Peronospora schleideni	Oospores	3–4 years	Dry	McKay, 1935
Empusa muscae	Conidia	3–5 days	—	Schweizer, 1947
E. muscae	Zygospores Azygospores	> 1 year	On host	Schweizer, 1947
Candida albicans	Vegetative	21 years	Dry *in vacuo* 10°C	Miller and Simons, 1962
Erysiphe graminis	Perithecia	> 2 years	On plant	Cherewick, 1944
Endoconidiophora fagacearum	Ascospores	232 days	24°C, 10 percent relative humidity	Merek and Fergus, 1954
Caliciopsis pseudotsugae	Ascospores	2 years	2–5°C	Funk, 1963
	Spermatia	3–4 weeks	Room temp.	Funk, 1963
Endothia parasitica	Ascospores	1 year	Dry, in bark	Anderson and Rankin, 1954
Omphalia flavida	Gemmae	<26 hours	Dry air	Buller, 1934
Neurospora crassa	Conidia	2–3 years	5°C, on agar	M. Mitchell, 1960
N. crassa	Ascospores	> 10 years	5°C, on agar	M. Mitchell, 1960
Pyrenophora bromi	Ascospores	7 months	In perithecia	Chamberlain and Allison, 1954
Cronartium ribicola	Basidiospores	5–6 days	Air-dried	Spaulding and Rathbun-Gravatt, 1926
C. ribicola	Aeciospores	8 weeks	—	Spaulding, 1922
Puccinia triticina	Teliospores	2 years	5–7°C	Prasada, 1948
P. triticina	Uredospores	44 days	−8 to −9°C, on plant	Abe, 1933
Coleosporium solidaginis	Aeciospore	143 days	8°C, over $CaCl_2$	Fergus, 1959
Sphaerobolus stellatus	Basidiospores	10 years	Dry, in gleba	Buller, 1933
Tilletia foetida	Basidiospores	> 25 years	Herbarium	Fischer, 1936
Ustilago nuda	Mycelium	> 11 years	In barley seed	Porter, 1955
Psilocybe mutans	Basidiospores	> 9 years	Herbarium	McKnight, 1960
Schizophyllum commune	Fruit body and spores	35 years	0.1 mm Hg and 3 weeks at −190°C	Bisby, 1945
	Basidiospores	52.5 years	*In vacuo*	Ainsworth, 1964
Verticillium albo-atrum	Microsclerotia	13 years	In field or culture	Wilhelm, 1955
Aspergillus niger	Conidia	> 12 years	Covered test tubes, room temp.	Roberg, 1948
Aspergillus sp., *Penicillium* sp., *Fusarium* sp.	Conidia	8–10 years	Unsealed tubes	McCrea, 1931
Helminthosporium sativum	Conidia	20 months	Soil in field	Chinn and Ledingham, 1958
Penicillium brevicaule, *P. luteum*, *P. camemberti*	Conidia	< 12 years	Covered test tubes, room temp.	Roberg, 1948
Phymatotrichum omnivorum	Sclerotia	> 5 years	20–40 percent water, in soil	Taubenhaus et al., 1936
Beauveria bassiana	Conidia	128 weeks	Refrigerator	Steinhaus, 1960
Fusarium oxysporum	Chlamydospores	> 17 years	Sterile soil, 4°C	McKeen and Wensley, 1961

lasted somewhat less than 167 days and *Pseudomonas fluorescens* less than 83 days. These data on *Helminthosporium* conflict with those in Table 3.1, revealing that varying soil conditions may influence longevity. The survival of soil organisms is reviewed in detail by Menzies (1963).

Many microorganisms can survive in cultures for 15–40 years or longer (Table 3.1). The organisms that are included in this category represent the bacteria and each of the major groups of fungi, except the ascomycetes. From the known heat-resistance of many ascospores it is the paucity of data, rather than inherent evanescence, that accounts for this difference. Furthermore, it is likely that the records for longevity presented in Table 3.1. are minimum estimates, in that germination was still obtained in many of the cases listed.

Several types of propagules other than spores are represented on this list, including vegetative bacteria, sclerotia, gemmae, and, in the case of *Ustilago nuda*, mycelium of surprising persistence in barley seeds. This instance of an enduring mycelium is not exceptional because *Phytophthora infestans* is known to overwinter and to survive several weeks of hot weather in stems of potatoes (Hickman, 1958), while mycelium of some powdery mildews is capable of overwintering in the buds of host plants (Yarwood et al., 1954). Moreover, Zimmerman (1925) reviews several cases where rust mycelium has been found in the host after winter and Hawker (1957) refers to other cases as well. Among the most resistant of spores are those of the myxomycetes, several of which survive for more than 50 years in herbaria.

Variation in the longevity of the different spore types within a single organism is also illustrated in Table 3.1. Thus, conidia of *Neurospora crassa* are much less durable than are ascospores of this organism. Other examples of this kind include *Empusa muscae* in which the azygospores and zygospores are much more long-lived than conidia, and the teliospores of rusts, which are usually the most resistant of the several types of spores produced by these fungi.

Among the evanescent stages are found the basidiospores (sporidia) of rusts, conidia of *Empusa muscae*, the powdery mildews of *Pyrenophora bromi*, and gemmae of *Omphalia flavida*. It is interesting to note that in all these fungi there are other stages that are persistent, thereby ensuring the organism's survival. Fennell (1960) has recently reviewed the conditions under which fungus cultures may be stored.

Considerable data exist for the survival of bacteria in culture. Thus, of the 2700 strains maintained by the National Collection of Type Cultures (England) which were dried over phosphorus pentoxide, fully 83 percent were viable after 14 years (Rhodes, 1950). Miller and Simons (1962) recently reported that of 202 cultures of vegetative cells, representing 67 different species, which had been dried in vacuum and stored at 10°C, 94 percent were viable after 21 years. Moreover, records of extreme longevity are provided in Table 3.1, where it is seen that some spore-forming rods survive over 40 years when dry or in alcohol. A bibliographic list of bacteria which survive long periods of time is provided by Bosco (1960*a*), and others are discussed in the review by Menzies (1963).

What is the maximum time that microorganisms can survive? Although some microorganisms can survive over 50 years (Table 3.1), few survival curves have been followed over prolonged periods; Sneath (1962) attempted to answer this question by measuring the number of microorganisms present in the soil dried on the roots of plants from botanical collections of the Royal Botanical Gardens and the British Museum. The plants, some of which were over 300 years old, were kept constantly dry and some were treated with mercuric chloride. It therefore seems reasonably certain that the multiplication of microorganisms was unlikely. The viable microorganisms present in the various soil samples are shown in Figure 3.2. Almost all of the microorganisms present in the older

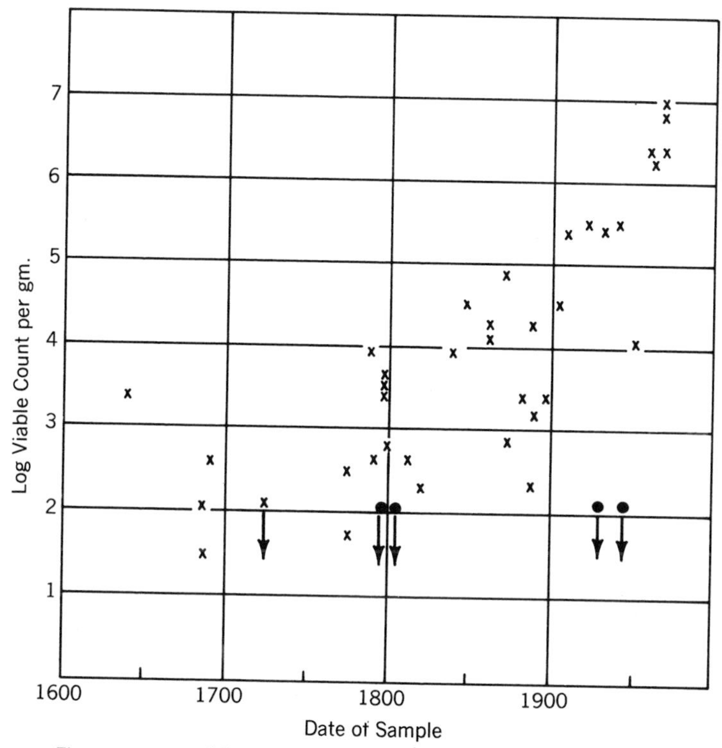

Figure 3.2 Viable counts of soils on aerobic nutrient agar. The circles indicate counts on materials used as controls, for example, leaves, florets, paper. (From Sneath, 1962.)

samples were identified as various species of *Bacillus*. Investigations of fungi and streptomycetes showed that few survived over 50 years. From these data Sneath (1962) estimated that after the first few years 90 percent of the organisms die every 50 years initially (or 100 years for a more resistant fraction). From the latter figure, and using the commercial standards for sterilization, a kilogram of soil would be sterilized after about 10^3 years.

A comparison of the longevity of other organisms with that of bacteria and fungi is possible when the data in Table 3.2 are compared with those in Table 3.1.

Table 3.2 Longevity of Certain Animals, Plants, and Viruses

Organism	Stage	Longevity	Conditions of storage	Reference
Insects				
Polypedilum vanderplanki	Larvae	>11 hours	Dry at 68.5°C	Hinton, 1951
Eburia quadrigeminata	Larvae	40 years	Dry wood	Hinton, 1953
Nematodes				
Anguina tritici	Larvae	28 years	Dried	Steiner and Albin, 1946
Tylenchus polyhypnus	Larvae and mature females	39 years	Dried	Goodey, 1923
Annelids				
Ascaris sp.	Ova	>8 years	In 4 percent formalin	Witenberg, 1961
Tardigrada				
Several species	Cysts	7–13 years	Dried	Keilin, 1959
Rotifera				
Several species	Cysts	7–13 years	Dried	Keilin, 1959
Bryophyta				
Riella sp.	Spores	25 years	Dried	Maks, 1933
Oedipodium sp.	Spores	20 years	—	Chalaud, 1932
Pteridophyta				
Marsilea fournieri	Sporocarps	>68 years	Herbarium	Allsopp, 1952
Asplenium serra	Spores	48 years	Herbarium	Fischer, 1911
Phanerogams				
Several legumes	Seeds	Up to 90 years	Dried	Turner, 1933
Nelumbo nucifera	Seeds	800–1000 years (?)	In peat	Ohga, 1923; Chaney, 1951
Rumex crispus, Oenothera biennis, Verbascum blattaria	Seeds	>80 years	In soil	Darlington and Steinbauer, 1961
Protozoa				
Colpoda duodenaria	Cysts	7 years	Room temp., 10^{-6} mm	van Wagtendonk, 1955

Table 3.2 (*Continued*)

Organism	Stage	Longevity	Conditions of storage	Reference
Haematococcus pluvialis	Cysts	8 years	Dry	Doflein and Reichenow, 1953
Didinium nasutum	Cysts	10 years	Sealed in hay infusion	Beers, 1937
Virus				
Nuclear polyhedrosis	—	>20 years	Sealed tubes	Steinhaus, 1960
Tobacco mosaic	—	52 years	Dried leaves	Spector, 1956
Sugar beet curly top	—	8 years	Plant tissue	Spector, 1956

Seeds of higher plants have been recorded to possess the greatest longevity but it may be that the availability of stored material of known origin has made it easier to accumulate information on these organisms over longer time periods. In any case, certain insects, nematodes, tardigrades, and rotifers are capable of surviving over 10 years when dried, although it is doubtful that the latter three groups of animals can exist much beyond this time (Keilin, 1959). The astonishing case of the lotus (*Nelumbium nucifera*), which is a sacred plant in China and other Asiatic nations, is worthy of mention because, if anything, the figure for its longevity given in the table is an underestimate. Seeds from an old dried-up lake in Manchuria were successfully germinated and estimates of their age vary from 800 to 50,000 years. The most recent information, based upon C^{14}-dating of a few seeds, suggests that the lower figure is probably correct (Libby and Arnold, 1951; Chaney, 1951). When one considers the events in history that have transpired during the dormancy of this seed, even accepting the lower figure, this is still a remarkable example of longevity in a resting structure. These and other examples of longevity are discussed in the recent book by Mamikunian and Briggs (1965).

Factors Influencing Survival of Spores

HIGH TEMPERATURE

The great variation in the resistance of microorganisms to high temperatures is illustrated by the data in Table 3.3. Among the most resistant of all are the anaerobic spore-formers, such as *Clostridium botulinum* which produces a lethal toxin. Almost equally resistant are the conidia of the thermophilic actinomycete, *Micromonospora vulgaris*, and spores of *Bacillus larvae*. None of the fungi that have been studied is as resistant to high temperatures as are these bacteria. The ascospores of *Byssochlamys fulva* and of *Neurospora*, and the winter sporangia of *Synchytrium endobioticum* are the most enduring in this group. Resistance to high temperature is not restricted to the spores of fungi, for the mycelia of several of the wood-rotting basidiomycetes (*Lenzites* sp., and so on) and of *Colletotrichum lini* are surprisingly durable when exposed to 55°C. Sclerotia can also be very resistant, as in a species of *Penicillium* isolated from spoiled canned goods by Williams et al. (1941), and in *Verticillium albo-atrum* where they persist longer at 50°C than do conidia (Nelson and Wilhelm, 1958).

Of the stages in the life cycle of a single organism, the spores are usually most resistant. Spores of some flat-sour bacteria will withstand steam under pressure at 115°C for over 3 hours, whereas the vegetative cells of most species are killed after a few minutes between 55 and 60°C (Curran, 1952). Vegetative cells of *Clostridium perfringens* are killed in 10 minutes at 80°C but 25 percent of spores

Table 3.3 Effect of Heat (Wet) upon Various Microorganisms

Organism	Stage	Time needed to kill at: 50°C	55°C	60°C	100°C	Reference
Bacillus larvae	Spores				160 minutes	Calesnick and White, 1952
Clostridium botulinum	Spores				240–360 minutes	Hampil, 1932
Thermophilic bacteria	Spores				788–834 minutes	Bigelow, 1922
Pasteurella pestis	Vegetative			60 minutes		Hampil, 1932
Aerobacter aerogenes	Vegetative			30 minutes		Spector, 1956
Nocardia sebivorans	Spores				3 minutes	Erikson, 1955
Micromonospora vulgaris	Spores				30–100 minutes	Erikson, 1955
Actinomyces bovis	Spores			10 minutes		Spector, 1956
Synchytrium endobioticum	Winter sporangia			8 hours		Glynne, 1926
Phytophthora infestans	Sporangia	Seconds				Taylor et al., 1955
Neurospora tetrasperma	Conidia	30 minutes			5 minutes	Y. Lingappa and Sussman, 1959
N. tetrasperma	Ascospores			4 hours		Y. Lingappa and Sussman, 1959
Monilia sp. (*Neurospora*)	Conidia			1 hour	30 seconds	Tokugawa and Emoto, 1924
Mycosphaerella musicola	Ascospores	1 hour				Frossard, 1962
Byssochlamys fulva	Ascospores				10 minutes	Hull, 1939
Lenzites sepiaria, L. lepideus, Trametes scialis, T. carnea	Mycelium in wood		12 hours			Snell, 1923
Botrytis cinerea	Spore-bearing mycelium	Few minutes				Jensen, 1948
Penicillium chrysogenum	Conidia		3 days		5 minutes	Groom and Panisset, 1933
Cercospora cryptomeriae	Conidia			5 minutes		Kitasima, 1916
Colletotrichum lini	Mycelium		3–4 days			Tochinai, 1926
Verticillium albo-atrum	Conidia, hyphae, and sclerotia	10 minutes				Nelson and Wilhelm, 1958
Fusarium lini	Mycelium		10 minutes			Tochinai, 1926

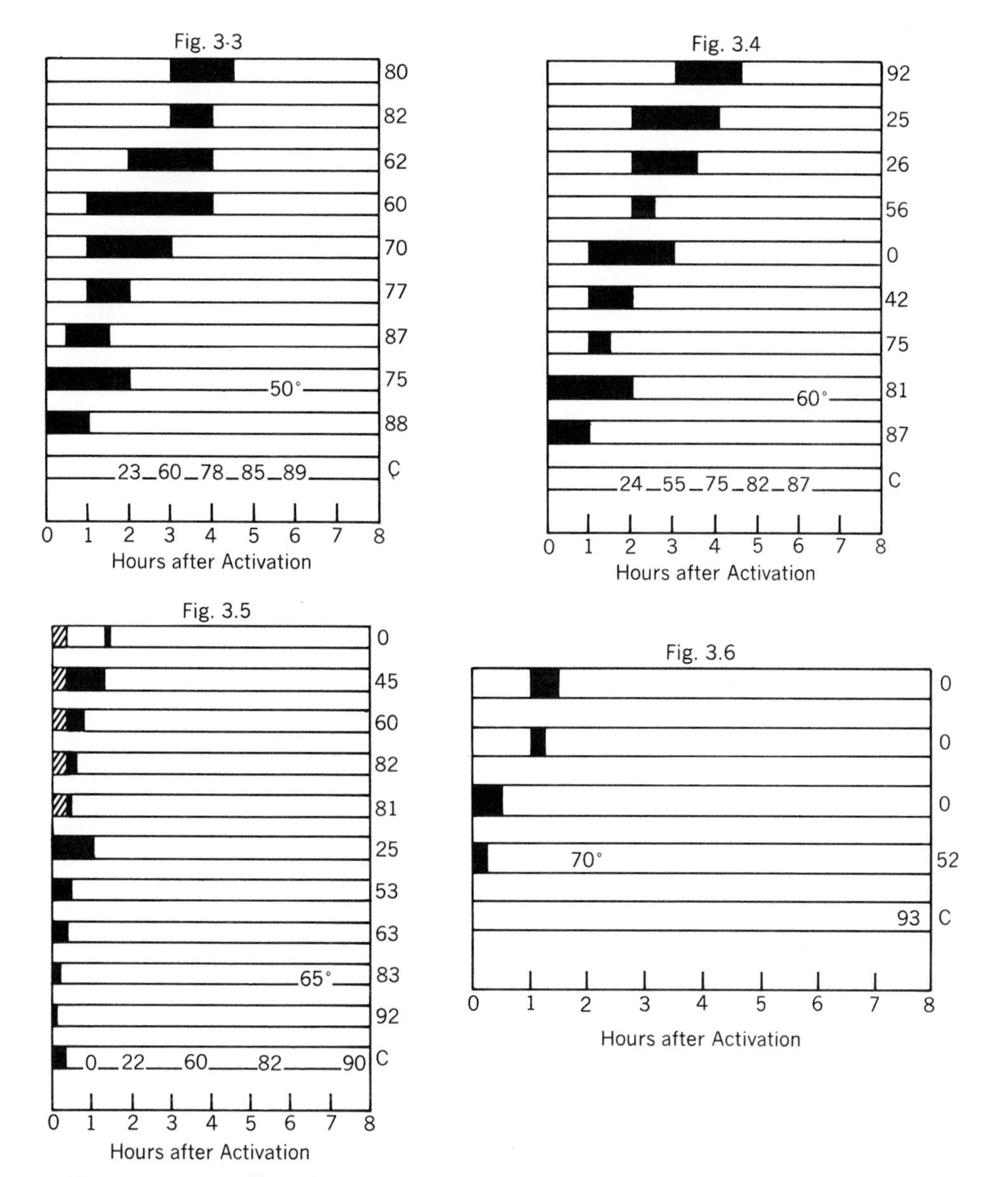

Figures 3.3–3.6 Effect of exposure to high temperature upon germination of ascospores of *Neurospora tetrasperma*. Ascospores were activated at 60°C for 20 minutes, before the start of the experiment, except for some of those used as outlined in Fig. 3.5. Periods of incubation at 27°C are indicated by the clear spaces and exposures to higher temperatures by the black ones. The letter *c* along the ordinate refers to the control which was incubated throughout at 27°C, and the numbers along this axis represent the percentage germination 8 hours after the start of the incubation. The numbers within the control box are the germination percentages at the times indicated below on the abscissa. Fig. 3.3 Heat-treatment at 50°C. Fig. 3.4 Heat-treatment at 60°C. Fig. 3.5 Heat-treatment at 65°C. The gray spaces indicate exposure to 60°C for 20 minutes, and the black, exposure to 65°C. No activation treatment, other than exposure to 65°C, was provided the other spores used in this experiment. Exposures of 5, 10, 20, 30, and 60 minutes were provided. Fig. 3.6 Heat-treatment at 70°C.

of certain strains survive (Canada et al., 1964). In fungi the asporogenous mycelium of *Botrytis cinerea* survives only a few minutes at 40°C whereas the spore-bearing mycelium survives at least an hour (Jensen, 1948). Furthermore, the data in Table 3.3 reveal that the ascospores of *Neurospora* are more resistant than the conidia of the same species, and Hull (1939) has shown that the same is true for *Byssochlamys fulva*. The ascospores of both of these organisms have dormant periods that can be broken by a heat shock.

The heat-resistance of certain spores is known to change during the course of germination. An example of this is shown in the case of ascospores of *Neurospora tetrasperma*. The spores were initially heat shocked at 60°C for 20 minutes to break dormancy (Y. Lingappa and Sussman, 1959) and then tested for their subsequent resistance to temperatures from 50–70° C. The results (Figures 3.3–3.6) show that after 1 hour of incubation at 27° C, a marked decrease in heat-resistance occurs in activated cells. Two hours at 60° C reduces germination by only 10 percent but the same treatment, after the spores have been kept at 27° C for 1 hour, prevents germination entirely. These results are even more striking when incubation of activated spores at 27° C is interrupted by a 5-minute heat-flash at 65° C. In this case, germination is completely stopped. If spores are exposed twice as long to this temperature immediately after activation, germination is affected only slightly. Decreases in the heat-resistance of *Neurospora* ascospores have been observed after as little as 5 minutes' incubation at 27° C.

A loss in heat-resistance is characteristic of the germination of bacterial spores.

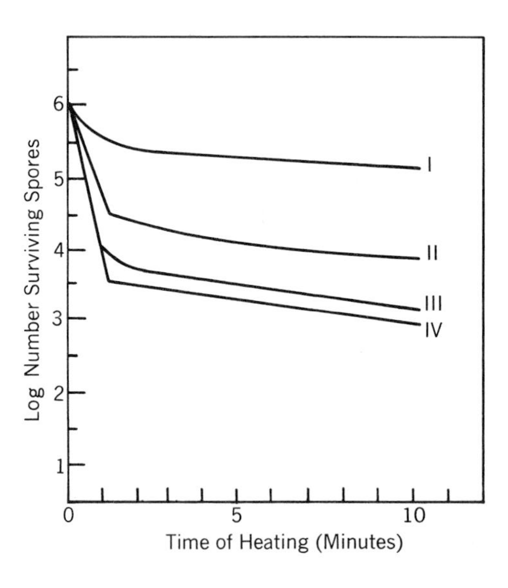

Figure 3.7 Heat-inactivation rates of *B. cereus* p2. The spores were incubated in a medium containing adenosine (40 μmoles/liter) and L-alanine (2 mmoles/liter) as activators for certain times and subsequently heated to 70°C. Curves I–IV: incubated for 1, 2, 5, and 10 minutes, respectively, in activating medium. Reproduced from Fig. 2. *Biochem. Biophys. Acta* 22: 242, 1956.

An example of this is shown in Figure 3.7. for spores of *Bacillus cereus*. The spores were germinated in response to adenosine and L-alanine, and tested for their resistance to heat. Spores survive 10 minutes' exposure to 70°C, whereas vegetative cells are rapidly killed at this temperature. The loss in heat-resistance as a function of germination is so well characterized in bacteria that it is used as one of the criteria of germination (Schmidt, 1955).

Numerous factors influence heat-resistance, some of which will be discussed later. One of the most important of these is humidity. For example, Tokugawa and Emoto (1924) found that wet conidia of *Neurospora* were killed in less than 30 seconds at 100°C but dry conidia survived for 100 minutes at this temperature. Similar results have been obtained for sporangia of *Synchytrium endobioticum* (Glynne, 1926), oospores of *Sclerospora graminicola* (Tsaugi, 1933), the mycelium of several basidiomycetes (Snell, 1923), spores of *Tilletia contraversa* (Dewey and Tyler, 1958) and other organisms (Curran, 1952; Rahn, 1932). In bacteria some spores survive dry heating at 300°C for 30 minutes, whereas moist steam will kill most such organisms in the same time (Curran, 1952).

In the later sections of this chapter other factors which influence heat-resistance will be discussed. These include conditions of sporulation, chemical composition, nature of the medium in which the spores are heated, and the nutritional requirements for recovery of viable spores. In addition, the density of the suspension influences the survival of spores. In *Micromonospora vulgaris* (Erikson, 1955) dense suspensions are more thermoresistant than thin ones. Amaha (1952) observed similar results with *Bacillus natto* spores and found that fivefold differences in survival time resulted from varying the concentration of spores.

Kinetics of Heat Inactivation

The order of death by heating has been treated extensively by Rahn (1932) who concluded that exponential kinetics were followed. These conclusions were supported by Amaha (1952) who worked with several bacilli, but were criticized by Vas and Proszt (1951) who claim that the order of destruction of spores of *Bacillus cereus* by heat is sigmoidal, if allowances are made for the heterogeneity of cell populations and for certain experimental difficulties. Similar disagreements are reviewed by Schmidt (1955), Reynolds and Lichtenstein (1952), and Halvorson (1958) and it is possible that their resolution may lie in the suggestion of the latter that the initial lag is due partly to heat-activation of dormant spores and partly to "multi-hit" inactivation. In fact, Shull and Ernst (1962) have demonstrated that heat-activation can be responsible for much of the initial lag in thermal death curves of *B. stearothermophilus* but it is still not clear exactly how much of the lag can be attributed to activation. More recent work (Shull et al., 1963) suggests that the techniques of measurement must be improved by minimizing temperature changes during the experiment before this problem can be satisfactorily resolved.

Another influence upon the shape of thermal death curves has been suggested by Alderton et al. (1964) who found that spores of *B. megaterium* gain increased heat-resistance during the process of heating. Such heat-adaptation can be minimized if equilibration to high temperatures is rapid. It is worth noting that no such adaptation to heat has been reported for vegetative cells of bacteria. These workers point out that the efficiency of killing of spores by heat should be enhanced by storage at low temperatures prior to heating, and by the use of high lethal temperatures (for shorter times) because of the much higher Q_{10} of the killing process as compared to that for heat-adaptation. Wang and co-workers (1964) used a tubular flow reactor to equilibrate spores of *B. stearothermophilus* within a fraction of milliseconds. They showed that logarithmic killing was only approximated in the tail or high-kill region of the curve.

Factors Which Alter Heat-Resistance

Recent reviews have considered factors which alter the heat-resistance of non-sporulating organisms (Hansen and Riemann, 1963) and of spores (Ordal, 1964). These factors may be classified as follows:

1. Inherent (intrinsic)
   a. genotypic—strain, species, and genetic variation
   b. phenotypic—state of activation of spores, or of adaptation to temperature; age
2. Environmental
   a. during growth and spore formation—components of medium, *p*H, temperature, and so forth
   b. after spore formation but before heating—see 2a above; antibiotics, chemicals
   c. during heating—see 2a above; time of equilibration to temperature; density of suspension; chemicals of various kinds
   d. after heating—the recovery medium; chemicals other than ordinary nutrients

Only a few of these factors will be reviewed in detail because of the existence of good reviews and the selection of material which bears on spores.

One approach to an understanding of the nature of dormancy has been to search for agents which decrease, or in some cases increase, the resistance of spores. This approach has been motivated primarily by the desire to improve the preservation of perishable foods. The list of compounds which have been tested for effects on the thermoresistance of anaerobic (Amaha and Sakaguchi, 1954; Le Blanc et al., 1953; Schmidt, 1955; Michener et al., 1959) and aerobic (Vas and Proszt, 1955; Anderson and Michener, 1950; Simidu and Veno, 1954; Amaha and Sakaguchi, 1957) spore-forming bacteria is by now quite large and the data often contradictory. Only a few agents were found to be effective. For example, out of 650 substances tested (Michener et al., 1959), only 26 were found to significantly reduce the viable count of heated spores of *Clostridium* sp. strain PA 3679. Subtilin, nisin, 12 sulfur compounds, long-chain fatty acids, and a number of bacterial and bacteriostatic compounds were effective. However, at least two phases are involved in the measurement of resistance: (a) the effect of a given agent on the survival of a spore and (b) the ability of the surviving spore to germinate, divide, and produce a recognizable colony. A number of compounds originally presumed to reduce the heat-resistance of spores have affected step (b). Thus, subtilin has been shown to become attached to spores and to kill heated spores only when they start to germinate (Michener, 1955; O'Brien et al., 1956). Vas and Proszt (1955) have extended this to show that a number of chemical agents are effective only in the post-heat-treatment period.

The enhanced sensitivity of germinating spores is not surprising in that biosynthetic reactions are sensitive to inhibition; also, the outer membranes of the newly emerged germ tube are more exposed to surface-active agents. It is well known, in perhaps an analogous situation, that disinfectants and surface-active agents react rapidly against protoplasts of *Bacillus* (Tomcsik, 1955). Similarly, unsaturated fatty acids have been thought to be sporocidal, but Foster and Wynne (1948) showed that these agents inhibited the germination of spores and that this inhibition could be overcome by the addition of starch. Roth and Halvorson (1952) demonstrated that the inhibitory effect of these fats on germination was due to the production of peroxides. Finally, the nutritional requirements for germination and outgrowth are frequently increased in spores which have undergone prolonged heat-treatment (Curran and Evans, 1945; Wynne and Foster, 1948). Because an analysis of the effect of an agent on viability assumes quantitative recovery of the cells, the results are therefore dependent upon the recovery medium employed.

Heating a spore in the presence of any given agent would be expected to increase the rate of any chemical interaction between the two. This can be seen in a number of ways. When spores and a dye are heated together, the uptake of stain is greater than if the spores are preheated and then incubated at a lower temperature with the dye (Murrell, personal communication). The increase in bacteriostatic effects of disinfectants with increasing temperature (Simidu and Veno, 1954, 1955, 1956) probably has a similar explanation. Direct interactions between the dormant spore and highly reactive molecules such as ethylene oxide, mustards, and mutagenic agents (Michener et al., 1959) are frequently encountered. In these cases the effects on the spore are probably nonspecific and may involve structural elements. It has been well known from the studies of surface fine structure of a number of *Bacillus* spores (Bradley and Williams, 1957; Franklin and Bradley, 1957; Bradley and Franklin, 1958; Fitz-James and Young, 1959*b*) that equatorial ridges or grooves are commonly found encircling the spore. During germination (Levinson and Wrigley, 1960), or following heat-treatment (Franklin and Bradley, 1957), the spores become somewhat swollen, and the spore case cracks along the ridge. Since similar splits occur when spores are mechanically disrupted (Levinson and Wrigley, 1960), it follows that this is a zone of weakness in the spore case. Chemical agents may well be expected to weaken this structure further and therefore to affect the heat-resistance of a dormant spore.

Mechanisms of Heat-Resistance

A number of mechanisms have been proposed to explain heat-resistance (Hansen and Riemann, 1963; Koffler et al., 1957). These may be divided into two categories including one which depends upon an innate property of the sensitive locus itself, and the other which suggests that resistance derives from naturally occurring materials, or from an organization state of the cell.

1. *"Derived" Heat-Resistance.* Organizational states of the cell, as determined by the amount of water, or the properties of osmotic barriers, for instance, have been claimed to influence the heat-resistance of organisms. A second type of phenomenon included under this heading is the protective effect of certain substances upon cells undergoing heat stress.

THE ANHYDROUS THEORY. The absence of water has long been recognized as a means of increasing the resistance of a biological system to elevated temperatures. For example, Zamenhof (1960) recently demonstrated that in the dried state *in vacuo*, vegetative cells of *Escherichia coli* are almost as heat-resistant as the spores of *Bacillus subtilis*. Cohn (1876) and Lewith (1890) first proposed that the nature of the heat-resistance of the bacterial spore was due to the existence of a dehydrated cytoplasm. Several lines of evidence support this view, as summarized in Chapter 2, but not all the known facts can be accommodated by the anhydrous theory.

PROTECTION BY MINERALS. An experimental approach to the basis of thermoresistance was suggested by Williams (1929) who observed that a number of factors, including the incubation temperature and composition of the sporulation medium, could influence heat-resistance. Certain salts, iron, calcium, magnesium, and phosphate were necessary for high heat-resistance. These results were confirmed and extended by Curran et al (1943) and Levinson and Hyatt (1964) and Alderton et al. (1964). In a spectrochemical study of 12 different species of bacilli, they observed that the spores were richer in calcium, copper, and manganese than the vegetative cells from which they were derived. Spores contained 4 percent calcium, whereas only 0.5 percent was found in vegetative cells. Similar results have been reported in *B. megaterium* (Grelet, 1952; Cohen and Wiener, 1954; Vinter, 1956), *B. cereus* (Vas and Proszt, 1957), *B. coagulans* (Amaha and Ordal, 1957), and *Clostridium botulinum* (Sugiyama, 1951). In fact, elevated levels of divalent metals, particularly calcium, are associated with all thermostable spores that have been examined. When sporulation is carried out in a calcium-free medium only a few heat-sensitive spores are produced (Grelet, 1952). Similar "defective" spores were observed in *Bacillus megaterium* by Vinter (1956, 1957) in calcium-free medium or when sporulation was carried out in

10^{-4} *M* cystine. In this case the spores contained the same amount of calcium as vegetative cells. These results, taken together with the high calcium content of normal spores, and the excretion of calcium DPA during germination (Powell and Strange, 1953) support the view that calcium is specifically associated with heat-resistance.

Supporting evidence has been furnished from studies in which the metal content of the spores has been varied by the use of different growth and sporulation media. Slepecky and Foster (1959) found that the calcium of *B. megaterium* could be replaced by Mn^{++}, Zn^{++}, Ni^{++}, Co^{++} and Cu^{++}. These spores, in which the calcium was replaced to various extents, had the same morphology, staining characteristics, refractivity, and resistance to killing by desiccation and phenol. The substitution of various metals for calcium was not quantitative and only the calcium-enriched spores were thermoresistant. DPA levels of these spores were not measured, but might have provided interesting information as to the connection between this substance and thermoresistance. Halvorson (1961) has recently studied the effect of varying concentrations of calcium in the medium on the concentrations of calcium in the spores of *B. cereus* strain T. Increasing the calcium concentration raised both the level of Ca^{++} and DPA in the spore in an equimolar fashion. Recent studies by Walker et al. (1961) suggest that, in addition to DPA and calcium, magnesium is also involved in heat-resistance.

Protection by DPA. Church and Halvorson (1959) found a relationship between DPA content, viability, and heat-resistance. They produced spores with low DPA content by changing the carbon sources in a calcium-rich medium. The rate of heat-inactivation varied considerably with the DPA content of the spores. Above 1 percent DPA, the spores were all viable and their heat-resistance was proportional to their DPA content. Below 1 percent DPA, viability decreased and a closer correlation between heat-resistance and DPA was found. Black et al. (1960), working with endotropically produced spores, found that these spores had low levels of DPA, were heat-labile, and germinated slowly. They studied the effect of salts added to the distilled water used for endotropic sporulation and found that when calcium was used the spores produced were normal in DPA content and heat-resistant.

Sporulation at elevated temperatures has long been recognized to increase thermoresistance of spores. Lechowich (1959) has recently examined the chemical changes associated with temperature-induced thermoresistance in *B. coagulans* and *B. subtilis*. The DPA and calcium contents increased correspondingly with increase in thermoresistance in spores of *B. subtilis*, whereas in spores of *B. coagulans* there was a decrease in total DPA, but their cation concentration remained fairly constant as their resistance to thermal destruction increased. He concluded from these studies that the cation concentration played a dominant role in thermoresistance.

There are several mechanisms which might be proposed for the interrelationship of calcium and DPA in heat-resistance.

1. Calcium could play a catalytic function in the synthesis of DPA, the DPA being necessary for heat-resistance.
2. DPA may be required for calcium accumulation, the calcium being required for heat-resistance.
3. DPA and calcium might both be required in heat-resistance, the mechanism being the particular type of binding between DPA, calcium, and spore protein which renders them more resistant to denaturation by heat.

Several observations rule out the first possibility. Normal DPA synthesis can be obtained when calcium is replaced by strontium. The spores thus produced are heat-sensitive (Halvorson, 1961; Black et al., 1960). When these spores are soaked in calcium, part of the strontium is replaced by calcium, and increased heat-resistance is observed.

A number of attempts have been undertaken to locate DPA in spores. From the experiments of Berger and Marr (1960) and Lechowich (1959), it was concluded that the majority of the DPA is associated with the cytoplasm rather than the spore coats or exosporium. Numerous suggestions have been advanced for the location of DPA in the spore, such as the cortex region, as discussed in Chapter 2. Although its location is not firmly established, recent cytological studies strongly imply that it may be located with the hexosamine peptide-rich material of the cortex. The DPA and the cortex structure disappear as α-ε-diaminopimelic acid hexosamine peptides (mucopeptides) are extracted from spore coats by lysozyme digestion (Warth et al., 1962) and in cortexless mutants of *B. cereus* (Fitz-James, 1962) DAP and DPA synthesis are normal, but these components are not incorporated into the immature spore. These findings support the indirect studies of Rode et al. (1962) with germinated spores of *B. megaterium* showing that the cortex is the site of DPA. A particularly interesting observation was made by Young (1959) who observed that DPA could form a DPA-calcium-amino acid-chelate complex with a variety of amino acids and peptides. If similar complexes may exist between DPA-calcium and the polypeptides or proteins of the spore (such as the hexosamine peptides) then such complexes may render the proteins heat-resistant in a manner analogous to the increased thermostability of various enzymes in the presence of calcium. Powell (1957) reported that DPA fails to protect adenosine deaminase against heat-inactivation. However, such stabilization might be restricted to those enzymes requiring divalent metals in the tertiary structure. In fact, Doi (1960) has demonstrated that the soluble, reduced nicotinamide adenine dinucleotide ($NADH_2$) oxidase of spores is protected against heat-inactivation by DPA.

The DPA-calcium structures may play prominent roles in some other process which indirectly influences heat-resistance. In *B. megaterium*, heat-resistance is lost before DPA is released (Rode and Foster, 1960*a*) and in *B. coagulans* calcium is released faster by heat than DPA (Hunnell, 1961). On the other hand, Lund (1961) found that during heat-shock treatment of spores of *B. subtilis* at 85°C, DPA was lost before viability. From the work which has been described, studies on the stability of the cortical structure under various conditions will be required before an unequivocal answer to the role of DPA in heat-resistance is available.

PROTECTION BY LIPIDS. Lipids also have been thought to play a prominent role in the resistance of microbial cells. Sugiyama (1951) was able to increase the heat-resistance of spores of *Clostridium botulinum* by adding long-chain fatty acids to the medium. Cultural conditions have been known to influence the lipid content of spores. Sporulation in the presence of glycerol (Church et al., 1956) led to increases in size, lipid content, changes in electrophoretic mobility, and to increased resistance to ethylene oxide. Long and Williams (1960) observed that sporulation of *Bacillus stearothermophilus* at elevated temperature led to changes in the distribution of lipid and to increases in the degree of unsaturation of lipids in the spores.

The presence of lipids in cell membranes renders their participation in the regulation of permeability and intracellular partitioning likely. Therefore, it is reasonable to ask whether the observations noted can be explained in terms of membrane function. Unfortunately, little direct data exist for spores, but work by Morita and Burton (1963) on a marine psychrophilic bacterium may be pertinent. Thus, heating of the cell may disrupt a permeability barrier which regulates the activity of malic dehydrogenase *in vivo*. Although the extracted enzyme is very sensitive to elevated temperatures, its activity is maintained at such temperatures *in vivo*, so the cell, presumably through regulation of uptake, may be able to protect enzyme activity.

PROTECTION BY OTHER SUBSTANCES. Enhanced thermoresistance has been imparted to a mesophilic bacterium (*Bacillus sphaericus*) by a factor obtained from extracts of *B. stearothermophilus* (Sie et al., 1961*a, b*). Thermophily is retained by the mesophile for several transfers, but the factor is destroyed by deoxyribonuclease, ribonuclease, pepsin and papain, but not by trypsin, chymotrypsin, and carboxypeptidase. Furthermore, it is nondialyzable and unstable in dilute solution. Autolysates of *Saccharomyces cerevisiae* also increase the thermoresistance of *Bacillus sphaericus* but, in this case, thermophily is not retained without continual replenishment of the factor. A diffusible factor which increases thermoresistance also has been reported by Oates et al. (1961) but its chemical nature is unknown, as is the contribution of these factors to the thermoresistance of spores.

Thermostability of DNA from calf thymus has been reported to be enhanced by a factor, or factors, from mammalian cells and plasma (Savitsky, 1964). The active substance from cells was nondialyzable, heat-labile, and removed by deproteinization. An instantaneous physical event is suggested in which no molecular rearrangement is involved. Information of this sort about microbial DNA has not been acquired and could be of significance in helping to explain heat-resistance.

2. *Intrinsic Heat-Resistance.* It is assumed in this category of mechanism that there are genes which uniquely determine heat-resistant enzymes which are characteristic of spores and thermophiles. Also, it is possible that the genetic material itself, including DNA and RNA, may exist in forms which have differing degrees of thermostability. However, because of the paucity of information on this subject, little will be said about this possibility.

THERMOSTABLE ENZYMES. Numerous heat-resistant enzymes have been reported from bacterial spores. These include the particulate, heat-resistant alanine racemase (Stewart and Halvorson, 1953) and catalase (Murrell, 1952; Lawrence and Halvorson, 1954). Upon rupture of the spore, a second heat-labile catalase was found. Sadoff (1961) has purified the heat-stable and heat-labile enzymes and demonstrated the presence of a higher content of hydrogen bonds in the latter. A heat-resistant, hydrolytic nucleoside ribosidase has been reported in intact spores of several bacilli (Powell and Hunter, 1956; Lawrence, 1955). The heat stability of the enzyme was attributed by Powell and Hunter (1956) to the fact that it was associated with the spore coat. In this connection, Berger and Marr (1960) have recently provided evidence that alanine racemase is located on or near the exosporium.

Enzymes from thermophiles also have been studied, as in the work of Militzer and co-workers listed in Koffler (1957), but most of the systems have been relatively impure. A thermostable amylase which requires calcium for stability has been isolated from *B. stearothermophilus* var. *amylolyticus* (Endo, 1959). Campbell (1961) has recently studied the physicochemical properties of this enzyme and concluded that calcium is not the basis for heat-resistance. Both the thermostable amylase and a heat-sensitive one from *B. subtilis* (Stein and Fisher, 1958) have 2 moles of calcium per mole of enzyme. The thermostable enzyme (Manning et al., 1961) is composed of two subunits, which are sufficiently rich in proline to prevent helical structure. Heat-resistance is not lost when the enzyme is heated under conditions (guanidine) which break hydrogen bonds. Therefore, the enzyme would seem to gain its thermostability by existing in solution as hydrated random coils. The thermostable α-amylase differs from the enzyme from *B. subtilis* in containing much more proline, aspartate, and glutamate, and in having cystine as part of the molecule (Campbell and Manning, 1961).

Catalase from *Aphanocapsis thermalis*, a thermophilic blue-green alga, has been shown to be much more resistant to agents which rupture hydrogen bonds than the equivalent enzyme from a mesophilic *Anabaena* (Marré et al., 1958). However, there was much less difference in the response of the cytochrome-*c* reductases of these organisms, so the effect is not general in these organisms. A difference in the affinity of the latter enzyme for FMN was demonstrated by Marré and Servettaz (1957) but the significance of this observation in relation to thermoresistance is not clear.

Another system that has been used is flagellin, a protein purified from flagella. According to Koffler et al. (1957) and Kobayashi et al. (1959), the heat-resistance of flagellin is due to more "effective" hydrogen bonding, because of their greater numbers, strength or location, or all three.

That heat-resistant enzymes are found elsewhere than in spores and thermophiles has been well documented through studies like those of Horowitz and Fling (1953) and Fling et al. (1963) in which two forms of tyrosinase have been described in *Neurospora crassa*. The half life at 59°C for the stable enzyme is 65 minutes and that for the labile form is 5 minutes. No significant difference between these in enzymatic properties has been found (Sussman, 1961) but there appears to be a significantly higher amount of serine in the stable form of the enzyme (Horowitz, 1964, personal communication) although the inherent uncertainties in serine determinations render this conclusion a tentative one. An altered pantothenate synthetase has been found which is much more sensitive to heat than is the parental type in *Escherichia coli* so genetic effects of a similar type are known in bacteria as well as fungi (Maas and Davis, 1952). Thus, it is clear that the possession of thermoresistant enzymes alone does not guarantee that a cell will be durable under heat-stress.

Conclusions

There is general agreement that the Q_{10} for killing by heat is very high and is of the order found for the denaturation of proteins (Rahn, 1932). Amaha (1952) has recently shown that the energies (ΔE) and entropies (ΔS) of activation for the killing of several bacilli are of a similar order to those for the thermal denaturation of hemoglobin, trypsin, and pancreatic lipase. Furthermore, Amaha (1952) and others have shown that development of organisms at temperatures above the optimum results in increased requirements for vitamins, amino acids, and other metabolites. This is reflected in the effects of the medium upon survivors of heat-treatment. Such induced auxotrophy could be related to the progressive destruction of enzymes, genes or both, especially in view of evidence that mutation rates in conidia of *Neurospora crassa* (Mitchell, 1957) and spores of bacteria (Zamenhof, 1960) are increased by heat.

Whereas it seems likely that enzymes and genes are sensitive loci where thermal destruction is concerned, the reasons for the differing sensitivities of spores and vegetative structures, and of mesophiles and thermophiles, are still controversial. On the one hand, it is clear that environmental factors can influence heat-resistance markedly, on the other, there are heat-resistant enzymes which occur in spores and in thermophilic organisms. That heat-resistant enzymes are not restricted to spores and thermophiles suggests that the selective advantage of these enzymes in nature may derive not only from their heat-resistance but from associated changes in their properties. Moreover, it has not yet been shown that the entire complement of the enzymes which function in spores or in thermophiles is heat-resistant. Although Koffler (1957) has compared the coagulability of cytoplasmic proteins of *Proteus vulgaris* and *Bacillus stearothermophilus* and found that those of the latter are more heat-resistant, the extracts were not purified, nor were enzymatic activities measured.

But the native thermostability of enzymes must play only a small role in determining the resistance of the dormant spore, for when these are broken or germinated the majority of the enzymes liberated are heat-labile. Therefore it is probable that an important difference between the proteins of spores and the corresponding ones of vegetative cells is their stabilization by agents such as DPA, calcium, lipids, and so on. Moreover, diffusible factors that may be specific for spores (Oates et al., 1961) and thermophiles (Sie et al., 1961*a*, *b*) may play a role.

Other factors which may enter into heat-resistance, but about which data are scarce, include the melting characteristics of lipoprotein membranes and of DNA. Moreover, the rapid repair or resynthesis of damaged or destroyed cell constituents must be included among the factors which determine resistance (Gaughran, 1947). Therefore, it must be concluded that all the mechanisms which have been described may play a part in determining the heat-resistance of the spore. Which factor is most important probably is a function of the genome of the organism and of the complex of factors which have interacted in its formation, heat-treatment and recovery.

LOW TEMPERATURES

Effects of Low Temperatures

The spectacular resistance of spores of certain bacteria and fungi to low temperatures is illustrated by the work of Pierre Becquerel (1910, 1931, 1950*a*). In his latest work, Becquerel used the facilities of the Cryogenic Laboratory at Leyden in order to subject the spores of *Bacillus subtilis*, *B. mesentericus*, *Mucor mucedo*, *Rhizopus niger*, *Aspergillus niger*, and *Penicillium glaucum* to temperatures between 0.0075°K and 0.047°K, at very high vacuums (10^{-6} mm of mercury). Not only were these spores found to survive this drastic treatment, but seeds of clover, alfalfa, tobacco, and petunia, as well as the cysts of certain animals, developed immediately after such treatment. Other experiments by Becquerel (1931) demonstrated that spores of *Mucor mucedo*, *M. racemosus*, *Aspergillus niger* and *A. glaucus* germinated 2 years after having been exposed to liquid air for 492 hours (– 190°C), followed by 77 hours at the temperature of liquid hydrogen

(–253°C). Even the nonspore-formers, *Streptococcus lactis* and *Photobacterium phosphoreum*, survived exposure to liquid air for 11 days, or 45 minutes in liquid hydrogen (Beijerinck and Jacobson, 1908). On the other hand, the blue-green algae *Nostoc* and *Anabaena* were killed after 15 minutes' immersion in liquid air. Ascospores of yeasts were more resistant to such treatment than were the vegetative cells. Other examples in which spores have proved to be the more resistant stage include the conidia and ascospores of *Neurospora* (Faull, 1930), oospores of *Phytophthora infestans* (de Bruyn, 1916), aeciospores and uredospores of *Coleosporium solidaginis*, spores of *Clostridium perfringens* (Canada et al., 1964) and the several cases reviewed by Levitt (1956).

Several reviews and books are available in which the effects of low temperature upon microorganisms are discussed, including the report of the "Symposium on the Survival of Bacteria" (*J. Appl. Bacteriol.* vol. 26, 1963) and the "Proceedings of the Low Temperature Microbiology Symposium" (1962). In addition, Elliott and Michener (1961) have summarized the microorganisms that grow at low temperatures in foods. That spores survive extremely cold temperatures better than vegetative cells is generally accepted for bacteria and fungi and has recently been demonstrated experimentally under the exceptionally rigorous conditions of a simulated Martian atmosphere with *Bacillus subtilis* var. *globigii* (Hagen et al., 1964). Other studies of this kind are reviewed in a recent book by Mamikunian and Briggs (1965).

On the other hand, antarctic species of the blue-green algae that are cold-hardy probably survive in the vegetative state, according to Holm-Hansen (1963). This conclusion is dictated by the fact that several of the genera concerned are not known to form special reproductive bodies and by the kinetics of the decrease in the viability of these cells during storage at low temperatures.

Means of Preserving Microorganisms at Low Temperatures

A large variety of techniques are available for preserving cultures of bacteria and fungi, many of which are reviewed by Clark (1962) and Rey (1961). Other data are assembled in Table 3.1, which lists survival records and storage conditions.

Protection Against Cold-Injury

Cold-injury to microorganisms can be mitigated by the use of certain suspending media and by controlling the rate at which the cells are warmed after being frozen. Thus, Harrison (1956) found that *Escherichia coli* was killed at –22°C if suspended in NaCl, but that the presence of glycerol prevented this effect. Cells suspended in distilled water survived better at this temperature than those in broth, suggesting that high concentrations of electrolytes enhance cold-injury in bacteria. Harrison was able to duplicate the result of repeated freezing and thawing by cycling suspensions of bacteria between concentrated solute and diluent without freezing. Moreover, glycerol reduced the rate of killing in such experiments, as well as when freezing temperatures were used. Similar results were obtained with *Pasteurella tularensis* by Mazur et al. (1957) and with erythrocytes, sperm, and other animal cells (Smith et al., 1954). In plant cells, and others with rigid cell walls, plasmolysis results in protection against frost-injury so that nonpenetrating solutes protect (Levitt, 1956). Therefore it is of interest that a number of nonpenetrating polymeric solutes protect *Aerobacter aerogenes* during freezing and thawing (Nash et al., 1963).

Mechanisms of Cold-Injury

Several theories to account for cold-injury have been proposed and discussed in detail in a recent book (Smith, 1961) and in reviews (Luyet, 1962; Mazur, 1963*a*). However, only two of these are currently favored: one assigns the cause of damage to the concentration of solutes as ice forms during the freezing of a solution; the other relates such damage to the formation of intracellular ice crystals.

Until recently, the evidence supporting both hypotheses was primarily circumstantial, being based upon the effect of the temperature, cooling and warming rates, and suspending medium upon survival. However, Mazur (1963*b*) has applied differential thermal analysis and conductometry to the study of rapidly frozen yeast and concludes that about 90 percent of the intracellular water freezes. The fact that he, and others, have found that slow cooling increases the survival of cells suggests that the probability of intracellular freezing is decreased by the removal of water from the cell rapidly enough to keep protoplasm at its freezing point (Mazur, 1963*c*).

But it is likely that ice formation is not the only cause of cold-injury. Thus, even though ice formation is prevented by slow cooling rates, lethality in *Escherichia coli* and human red blood cells is increased, possibly because of the gradual concentration of solutes (Smith, 1961).

Mazur (1963*c*) has derived a relation between the amount of water in a cell and temperature which involves rate of cooling, surface-volume ratio, permeability to water, and the Q_{10} of the permeability constant. Whereas some of these parameters are equivalent for vegetative cells and spores, some differ so that the greater cold-resistance of the latter might be sought through this means. For example, the equation predicts that no intracellular ice can form in cells in which the water content is reduced to the equilibrium value or *to below 10 percent*. Therefore, the relatively lower water content of spores would provide a considerable advantage. Other parameters such as permeability to water and the Q_{10} for the permeability constant may play a role but have not been investigated in enough detail to permit a comparison to be drawn between spores and vegetative cells.

Properties of Cells at Very Low Temperatures

Organisms kept at very low temperatures, that is, between – 190 and – 272°C, display properties other than those shown at temperatures closer to freezing. These have been enumerated by Keilin (1959) and include the following:

1. The cell constituents solidify.
2. All gases, including nitrogen, oxygen, and carbon dioxide are liquefied or solidified.
3. Dissociation and ionization of molecules are completely suppressed.
4. Chemical reactions occur at about one-millionth the rate at 20°C.
5. The molecular states of substances like the cytochrome pigments are changed.

In addition, extreme desiccation, anoxia, and an increase in salt concentration occur, leading to the suspension of all reactions and, therefore, to a state of cryptobiosis. Under these conditions, according to Becquerel (1950*a*, *b*), the viability of some organisms can be maintained for long periods of time. Recognition of this fact has prompted speculation as to the possibility of the dissemination of spores through space. This will be discussed later in Chapter 4.

MOISTURE

A statement of the conditions of humidity, as well as of temperature, is necessary in any specification of thermal death points or other measures of the effect of environmental variables. Effects attributed to one variable are sometimes not clearly distinguishable from those induced by another. This is well illustrated by Levitt (1956) who points out that the effect of high temperature upon some organisms may be the result of drought-injury as well. Furthermore, frost-injury and the effect of desiccation may be relatable to similar mechanisms in that freezing leads to dehydration and to a rise in salt concentration. Another example is the imposition of anoxia during the maintenance of high vacuums which desiccate the organism as well. The response of microorganisms to radiation also may be markedly affected by humidity, according to Webb (1963) and Webb et al. (1964). Accordingly, many of the phenomena to be discussed here may often be the result of the interaction of two or more environmental variables.

Effects of Dehydration Upon Survival

There is little doubt that lowering the water content of organisms mitigates the lethal effects of temperature extremes. This fact is illustrated by the well-established superiority of wet sterilization over dry, discussed earlier, and by the data in Table 3.4 which reveal that organisms with low water content survive for very long times. An example from bacteria is found in the studies of Rode and Foster (1960*b*) with *Bacillus megaterium*, for they observed that lyophilizing vegetative cells dramatically enhanced their viability at 75°C, as compared with that of undried cells (Figure 3.8). In addition, the increased longevity of spores

Table 3.4 Comparison of the Water Content and Longevity of Spores

Organism	Stage	Water content (percent dry wt.)	Reference	Longevity	Reference
Erysiphe graminis	Conidia	75	Yarwood, 1950	78 days (−2°C)	Metzger, 1942
E. cichoracearum	Conidia	52	Yarwood, 1950	25 days (7°C)	Yarwood, 1954
E. polygoni	Conidia	52–74	Yarwood, 1950	12 days (7°C)	Yarwood, 1954
Claviceps purpurea	Conidia	71	Glaz, 1955	3 months	Glaz, 1955
Neurospora tetrasperma	Ascospores	5	Lingappa and Sussman, 1959	> 3 years	Sussman, 1960
Tilletia levis	Basidiospores	7.9	Zellner, 1911	> 3 years	Hahne, 1925
T. tritici	Basidiospores	8.0	Zellner, 1911	> 3 years	Hahne, 1925
Aspergillus oryzae	Conidia	17.4	Sumi, 1928	> 22 years	McCrea, 1923
A. fumigatus	Conidia	7	Zöbl, 1950	> 15 years	Roberg, 1948

stored in glycerol and certain alcohols may be attributable to the reduced stress placed upon protoplasm by plasmolysis (Levitt, 1956) although other interpretations are possible (cf. pp. 73–74). Finally, the lyophil method of preserving organisms argues for the effectiveness of dehydration as a means of extending the viability of organisms as diverse as bacteria, fungi, animals, and plants (Hesseltine et al., 1960; Rey, 1961; Meryman, 1960).

On the other hand, the spores of some organisms are sensitive to dehydration.

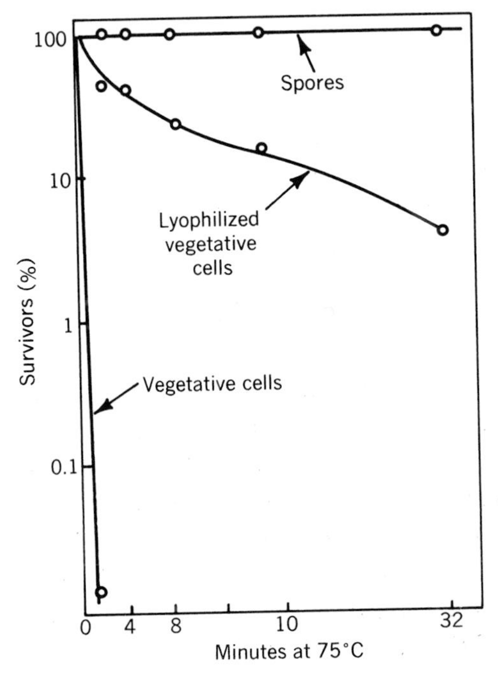

Figure 3.8 Survival curves of lyophilized vegetative cells of *Bacillus megaterium* when heated at 75°C compared with corresponding curves for nonlyophilized vegetative cells and for spores. (From Rode and Foster, 1960*b*.)

Such is the case with uredospores of *Puccinia glumarum* which survive best at 0–5°C and 40 percent relative humidity (Manners, 1951). Relative humidities in this range (20–40 percent) are optimal also for sclerotia of *Phymatotrichum omnivorum* (Taubenhaus and Ezekiel, 1936), uredospores of *Puccinia coronata* (Rosen and Weetman, 1940), conidia of *Helminthosporium oryzae* (Page et al., 1947) and spores of *Uromyces setariae* (Ramakrishnan, 1949). Moreover, storage under wet conditions is required to preserve the viability of some spores, including conidia of *Erysiphe graminis* (Metzger, 1942), *E. polygoni* (Yarwood et al., 1954), and *Oidium heveae* (Corner, 1935), basidiospores of *Tilletia tritici* (Buller, 1933), and gemmae of *Omphalia flavida* (Buller, 1934). Bimodal survival curves also have been reported which suggest a definite minimum at about 70 percent relative humidity (Hart, 1926; Page et al., 1947; Teitell, 1958). In this connection, the work of Murrell and Scott (1957) with several bacterial spores is relevant. They found that the survival of *Bacillus megaterium B. stearothermophilus*, and *Clostridium botulinum* was not optimal when drying was most vigorous (over P_2O_5); instead maximal heat-resistance was acquired at intermediate humidities.

Therefore, whereas it is still generally true that dehydration is effective in extending the life of spores, there are some instances known in which such treatment is injurious, if not immediately lethal (Buller, 1933; Glaz, 1955). Even more perplexing, perhaps, is the observation that intermediate relative humidities may be more damaging to survival than either extreme (Teitell, 1958).

Mechanisms of Dehydration Injury

Death of cells due to dehydration could take place due to the disruption or disorganization of vital structural components or by the denaturation or destruction of one or a few key molecules involved in metabolism or replication.

Among the former possibilities, disruption of permeability barriers often has been considered to be influential in the death of cells by dehydration. Although it has been shown that altered rates of entrance and exit of substances sometimes do accompany dehydration of microbial cells, Webb (1961) has found that parallel changes occur in dehydrated cells of *Escherichia coli* that are protected against injury. Therefore, it would appear in the detailed experiments of Webb on bacteria that increased permeability is not the direct cause of death.

Evidence for a "physical change in the structure of an essential macromolecule when the water, bound to this molecule, is removed" has been presented by Webb (1964). His studies with air-dried bacteria and yeasts have shown that the interaction of temperature, relative humidity, and chemical additives (Webb, 1960, 1964) determines the response of cells to drying in air. Because protein synthesis was the only function preserved when inositol protected cells during drying, it was suggested that this substance stabilized RNA in some way (Webb, 1961).

A dramatic change in the stability of cells occurs at relative humidities below 60 percent, at about the same point at which the structural water that is bound to macromolecules like DNA (Falk et al., 1963) is removed. Presumably inositol can prevent the effect of dehydration by replacing water in maintaining the structural integrity of macromolecules. It is interesting to note that Webb has found that inositol protects several bacteria below 70 percent relative humidity from ultraviolet radiation damage and he postulates that macromolecules are protected by a means similar to that postulated above for desiccation damage.

That the great resistance to environmental stress of spores, seeds, and other propagules may be related to their relatively low concentration of water often has been suggested. In fact, Table 3.4 shows a correlation between longevity of spores and reduced water content. However, desiccation of vegetative structures often is lethal, and lowered water content increases ultraviolet radiation damage in come microorganisms (Webb, 1964). Therefore, spores with lowered water content must have evolved some means of ameliorating these detrimental effects of drying, perhaps by substituting materials like inositol, or sugars for water as stabilizers of macromolecules. In this connection, it is worth suggesting that substances that appear in high concentrations in spores, such as DPA in bacteria, and trehalose and mannitol in fungi, may play such a role. Also, desiccation-resistant staphylococci (Webb, 1960) may use unusual conjugate molecules consisting of sugars, proteins, and nucleic acids for this purpose.

The surprising sensitivity of some spores to humidities in the range of 70 percent relative humidity (Page et al., 1947; Teitell, 1958) may be related to the fact that water bound to macromolecules is lost at this point, as discussed. Thus, it is possible that substances that can replace water as a stabilizer accumulate only at lower humidities. This is a reasonable possibility in view of the fact that respiration can increase upon dehydration of plants (Levitt, 1956), or decrease in conidia of *Aspergillus niger* (Terui and Mochizuki, 1955) and in lichens (Smyth, 1934, Fraymouth, 1928), so that metabolic effects of dehydration are known.

RADIATIONS

Resistance of Spores and Vegetative Cells Compared

Spores are more resistant to radiations of various kinds than are vegetative cells (Table 3.5). This is particularly true for bacterial spores for which detailed comparisons of the radiation-sensitivity of stages in the germination process are available. Thus, Stuy (1956*b*) exposed spores of *Bacillus cereus* to ultraviolet light and x-rays at various times after they had been incubated in a germination medium. Even after as little as 1 minute in the activating medium, resistance to x-rays diminished perceptibly, and after 90 minutes, the resistance of the spores was only about one-ninth that of dormant cells. Similar results were observed

Table 3.5 Comparison of the Sensitivity of Spores and Vegetative Stages of Microorganisms to Radiations

Organism	Stage	Dose	Reference
Ultraviolet light: (incident energies at 2537 Å needed to inhibit colony formation (ergs/cm$^2 \times 10^2$) in 90 percent of the organisms; from Zelle and Hollaender, 1955)			
Bacillus anthracis	Spores	452	Sharp, 1939
B. megaterium	Spores	273	Herčik, 1937
	Vegetative	113	
B. subtilis	Vegetative	520	Duggar and Hollaender, 1934
	Spores	900	Duggar and Hollaender, 1934
Neurospora crassa	Microconidia	1360	Norman, 1951
N. crassa	Macroconidia	2800	Norman, 1951
Aspergillus niger	Conidia	23,000	Zahl et al., 1930
Ustilago zeae	Chlamydospores	35,000	Landen, 1939
γ-rays in rad$\times 10^{-6}$ (dose required to prevent growth in all colonies):			
Clostridium tetani	Spores	1.4–2.1	Pepper et al., 1956
Bacillus pumilus	Spores	2.1	Pepper et al., 1956
Micrococcus pyogenes	Vegetative	0.05	Koh et al., 1956
Diplococcus pneumoniae	Vegetative	0.5	Koh et al., 1956
Escherichia coli	Vegetative	0.075–0.15	Koh et al., 1956
Aspergillus niger	Conidia	0.32	Bridges et al., 1956
Saccharomyces cerevisiae	Vegetative	0.9	Bridges et al., 1956
x-rays in r$\times 10^{-3}$ (dose required to kill 90 percent of cells; values may be inexact because interpolation from graphical data was necessary and conversion to roentgen units was performed)			
Bacillus megaterium	Spores, dormant	291.4	Woese, 1959
	Spores, germinating 35 minutes	29.6	Woese, 1959
B. brevis	Spores, dormant	47.0	Woese, 1959
	Spores, germinating 25 minutes	2.8	Woese, 1959
B. cereus	Spores, dormant	330.0	Stuy, 1956*b*
	Vegetative	27.0	Stuy, 1956*b*
Neurospora crassa	Microconidia	48.0	Giles, 1951
N. tetrasperma	Ascospores	40.0	Uber and Goddard, 1933

with ultraviolet light except that a transitory increase in resistance was found in cells activated for 30 seconds to 1 minute. Woese (1959) observed that the resistance of the spores of *B. megaterium* is tenfold greater than that of cells incubated for 35 minutes in a germination medium (Figure 3.9). This difference is even more exaggerated in the case of *B. brevis*. Moreover, cysts of *Azotobacter* have been shown to be much more resistant to ultraviolet light and γ-rays (Socolofsky and Wyss, 1962).

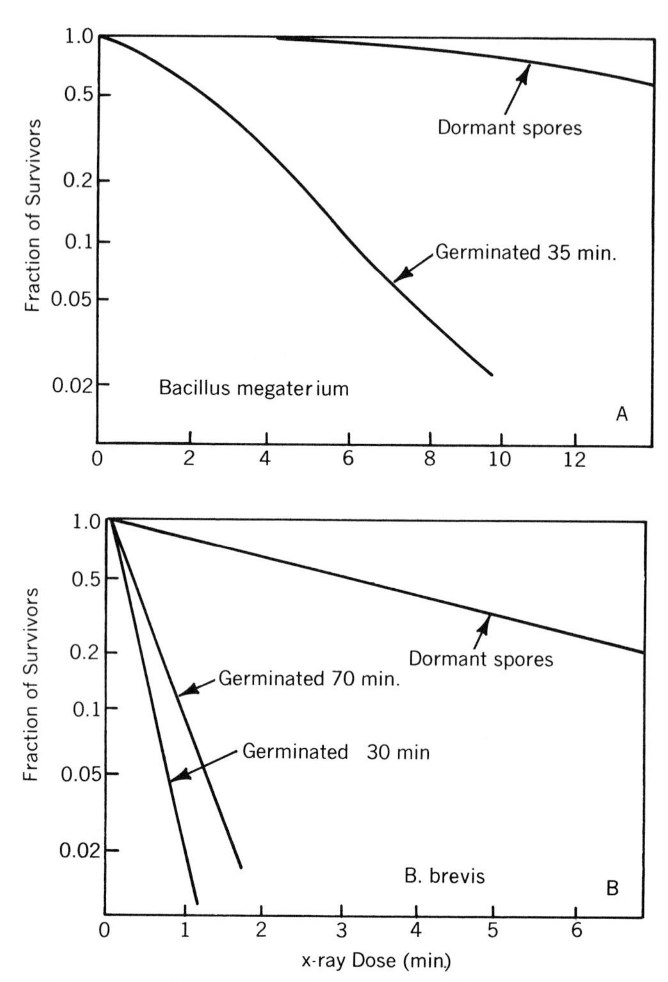

Figure 3.9 Inactivation of germinating bacterial spores as a function of x-ray dose. Dormancy of spores was broken by heating at 70°C for 5 minutes, followed by incubation in a medium containing yeast extract and L-alanine. x-Ray dose plotted in minutes of irradiation at 4700 r per minute. (From Woese, 1959.)

Unfortunately, the comparative data on fungus spores and vegetative cells are more meager, but it is clear from the work of Reissig (1960) that conidia of *Neurospora crassa* became more sensitive to ultraviolet light during the germination process. Similar results have been obtained by Maruyama and Hayashi (1963) with conidia of *Aspergillus niger* and it is likely that other fungus spores will be found to react in this way.

Cases in which radiation-resistance is greater in vegetative cells than in spores have been reported. In the yeast *Schizosaccharomyces pombe* it has been found that after irradiation with 16,000 r. of x-rays, the viable count of spores was 5–6 percent, whereas that of young vegetative cells was 45–50 percent (Ditlevsen and Hartelius, 1963*a*). However, as in the case of conidia of *Neurospora*, the resistance of the spores of *Schizosaccharomyces* decreased during the early part of the germination period but soon rose to higher levels than found in the spores. Anomalous results have been reported with anaerobic spore-former PA No. 3679 (Kan et al., 1958). These workers discovered that the resistance to γ-rays was enhanced during germination, but the uptake of protective substances from the medium (such as thioglycollate) by the germinating cells explained this effect satisfactorily.

An interesting difference between spores and vegetative cells has been reported for their responses to different types of irradiation. According to Spear (1944), the efficiency of densely ionizing radiations, such as alpha rays and neutrons, was greater in killing spores of *Bacillus mesentericus* than that of beta, γ- and x-rays. In *Escherichia coli*, however, γ-rays were five times more effective than neutrons. Similar effects with spores of *B. mesentericus* had been reported by Lea et al. (1941). Spores of *B. subtilis* (Donnellan and Morowitz, 1957), *Aspergillus niger* (Zirkle, 1940), *A. terreus* (Stapleton and Hollaender, 1952; Zirkle et al., 1952), *Neurospora crassa* (Atwood and Mukai, 1954), and ferns (Zirkle, 1954), as well as vegetative cells of yeast and other organisms (Zirkle, 1954) are more sensitive to the more densely ionizing radiations. However, the opposite response, that is, an increase in MLD with increasing ion density has been claimed for conidia of *Aspergillus niger* and *Glomerella cingulata* (Stapleton and Hollaender, 1952; Markert, 1956). Unfortunately, experiments have not been published on the effectiveness of different radiations on spores and vegetative cells of the same organism so that the significance of the observation by Spear cannot be assessed at this time. It is known (Zirkle, 1954), however, that the relative effectiveness of different radiations is modified by the stage of development at which the organism is irradiated (*Drosophila* eggs), strain of organism (wheat), oxygen tension (broad bean), as well as by the criterion of injury (mutation, lethality, and so on). In addition, sensitivity to different types of irradiation may have different causes. For example, the sensitivity of vegetative cells of *Bacillus megaterium* to x-rays is almost ten times that of spores of the same species, whereas there is only a twofold difference in sensitivity to ultraviolet light (Table 3.6).

Species differ markedly in their radiation-sensitivity (Table 3.5; Bacq and Alexander, 1961). For example, a sixfold difference is found when the resistance to x-rays of spores of *Bacillus megaterium* and *B. brevis* are compared (Figure 3.9). The differences between bacterial species can be very great, as shown in the work

Table 3.6 Comparative Effect of X-Irradiation upon Various Organisms

Organism	Stage	Dose ($r \times 10^{-3}$)	Reference
Bacillus megaterium	Spores	200	Woese, 1959
B. mesentericus	Spores	77.6	Woese, 1959
Escherichia coli	Vegetative	5.6	Bacq and Alexander, 1955
Yeast	Vegetative	30.0	Bacq and Alexander, 1955
Glomerella cingulata	Conidia	15	Markert, 1956
Aspergillus terreus	Conidia	30	Zirkle et al., 1952
A. terreus	Conidia (wet)	30	Stapleton and Hollaender, 1952
A. terreus	Conidia (dry)	82	Stapleton and Hollaender, 1952
Potato	Tubers	4	Sparrow et al., 1952
Bean	Roots	0.4	Gray and Read, 1943
Tradescantia	Pollen	0.1	Koller, 1943
Guinea pig	—	0.17–0.41	Remainder taken from Bacq and Alexander, 1955, 1961
Man	—	0.4 –0.5	
Rat	—	0.6 –0.97	
Fowl	—	1.0	
Newt	—	3.0	
Snail	—	8–20	
Amoeba	—	100	
Several infusoria (*Paramecium*, and so on)	—	300–350	
Drosophilia melanogaster	3-hour egg	0.2	
	pupae	2.8	

Data are presented as amount of irradiation necessary to kill 50 percent of the treated cells or individuals. Values may be inexact because of interpolation.

of Erdman et al. (1961*a*) and the review of Thornley (1963). The differences between unrelated organisms are even larger (Table 3.6). The MLD_{50} for x-rays varies from about 400 r for guinea pigs, dogs, and man, to over 300,000 for some infusoria. Bacteria and fungi rank high in the degree of resistance but there are exceptions such as *Phycomyces blakesleeanus* whose growth is affected by doses as low as 0.01 r of x-irradiation (Forssberg, 1941).

Factors Which Alter Radiation Sensitivity

Influences on the effect of irradiation on spores include structural barriers, such as a wall, pigments, environmental variables, and genetics.

Decreasing the water content of microbial cells has been found to both decrease and increase radiation sensitivity (Tallentire and Powers, 1963; Webb, 1963; Webb et al., 1964). Tallentire and Powers reported that spores of *Bacillus megaterium* became more sensitive to x-rays with decreasing water content. By contrast, Webb showed the opposite effect of desiccation on the response to x-rays of cells of *Serratia marcescens.* This effect upon vegetative bacterial cells has been confirmed by Matsuyama et al. (1964*a, b*). Tallentire and Powers suggest that unless protective materials are washed from the cells, they may be concentrated during drying and reverse the deleterious effects. The fact that Webb has shown that desiccation *increases* the sensitivity of *Escherichia coli* and *Pseudomonas aeruginosa* to ultraviolet light suggests that protective compounds are not involved unless one accumulates which influences only x-rayed cells or, alternately, cells of *Serratia* alone. Therefore, the contradiction in the results of these two groups has not been resolved. Because spores of *Bacillus megaterium* were used in one set of experiments and cells of *Serratia marcescens* in the other, simultaneous experiments with both types of cells are indicated. In fact, Matsuyama et al. (1964*a, b*) have shown less effect of freezing and dehydration on spores than on vegetative cells.

One of the best characterized of the modifying effects is that of oxygen tension which usually enhances sensitivity to irradiation. This has been demonstrated in the case of *Escherichia coli* in which fully ten times more energy in x-rays is required to inactivate the same number of bacteria maintained anaerobically, as compared to those kept in air (Hollaender et al., 1951). An "oxygen-effect" has also been demonstrated for conidia of *Aspergillus terreus* (Stapleton and Hollaender, 1952) and for dry spores of *Bacillus megaterium* (Powers et al., 1959). An example of this from the studies of Tallentire and Davies (1961) is shown in Figure 3.10.

Much of the early work on the effect of the temperature on irradiation damage showed that the MLD was independent of the temperature. This was the case when spores of *Bacillus mesentericus* were irradiated by β-rays at 4, 20, or $-20°$C (Lea et al., 1936) and when *Escherichia coli* was exposed to x-rays or ultraviolet light (Lea, 1947). Edwards et al. (1954) also observed no significant differences when spores of *Bacillus subtilis* were irradiated at 0, 44, and $-60°$C with 34,000 rep of 3 Mev electrons from a Van de Graaf accelerator. However, when spores were treated with 120,000 rad, the percentage of survivors varied from 3.92 percent at $-60°$ to 15.71 percent at 44°C. Similar results were obtained by Houtermans (1956) with spores of *B. subtilis*, for sensitivity to hard x-rays decreased from $-184°$ to $-40°$C. A break in the survivor curve occurred at $-40°$ and no further change in sensitivity was noted between this temperature and 20°C. The peak sensitivity to alpha particles occurred with dry spores irradiated at $-184°$ but no difference in the percentage of survivors was noted for hydrated cells maintained at $-184°$ to 20°C. Proctor et al. (1955) found that spores of this organism were more sensitive when irradiated at $-78°$ than at 4.4°C.

Opposing results have been reported by Webb et al. (1958, 1960) for the sensi-

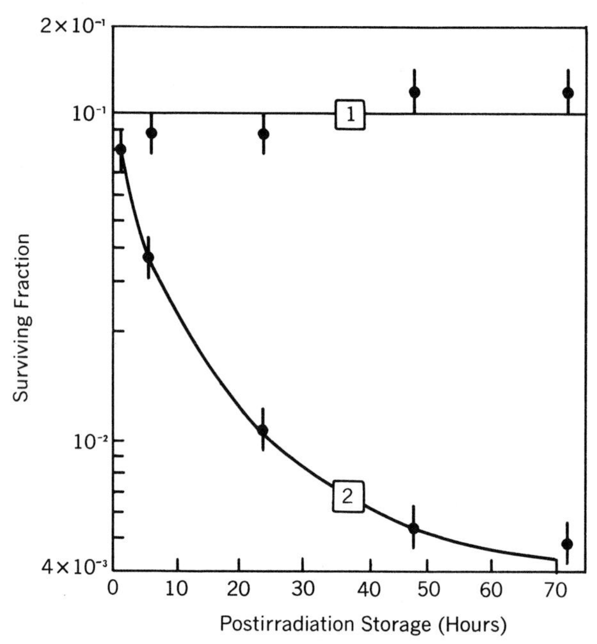

Figure 3.10 Postirradiation survival of spores of *Bacillus subtilis* in secondary dried kaolin powder at room temperature. Curve 1, irradiation in oxygen with 50 krads and stored under oxygen. Curve 2, irradiation under reduced pressure with 200 krads and stored under reduced pressure. (From Tallentire and Davies, 1961, courtesy Academic Press, Inc., Publishers.)

tivity of dry spores of *Bacillus megaterium* to 50 kv x-rays. No difference was noted in the range – 268° to – 145°C but sensitivity is temperature dependent between – 145° and 35°C. Over the latter range, sensitivity increased with increasing temperature during irradiation, but above 35°C, radiation-sensitivity dropped precipitously to a minimum at about 80°C. The data of Graikoski (1961) support those of Webb and co-workers in that the resistance of spores of anaerobes was found to be greater at – 70° than at 4°C. Maximum resistance occurs at temperatures just below that at which thermal inactivation of the spores occurs (about 80°C). The contradiction between these results and those of Edwards et al. (1954), which were discussed earlier, may be resolvable in part by the findings of Tallentire and Davies (1961) that very small differences in the water content of spores can affect postirradiation enhancement of damage to these cells, which is due to oxygen effects. Furthermore, the data of Houtermans (1956) and of Webb et al. (1960) suggest a considerable effect of hydration on the response of cells to irradiation at different temperatures so that the result of these two factors may help to explain the anomalies discussed previously.

Recently, heat-treatment of anaerobically irradiated dry spores of *Bacillus megaterium*, without intervening exposure to air, has been shown to decrease radiation sensitivity (Webb et al., 1960). This phenomenon, *thermorestoration*, was described for seeds of maize (Maxwell et al., 1942) and of barley (Caldecott et al., 1957) but differences in the techniques used render comparisons difficult. These results permit a distinction to be made between immediate and latent oxygen effects which influence radiation damage. As for the relation between thermorestoration and the dependence of radiation-sensitivity upon temperature, it appears that no interaction exists (Webb et al., 1960).

Visible light is known to reverse the effect of ultraviolet light upon many organisms (cf. Dulbecco, 1955 and Jagger, 1958 for reviews of this subject), an effect known as *photoreactivation*. Although this reaction has been demonstrated for a wide variety of organisms, including animals, plants, and microorganisms, it has not yet been shown for dormant bacterial spores (Stuy, 1956*a*,*c*). In these organisms, however, photoreactivation was possible only after dormancy had been broken and incubation carried to the point where considerable swelling and changes in refractive index had occurred (Stuy, 1956*c*). On the other hand, spores of actinomycetes (Kelner, 1949), *Penicillium chrysogenum* (Roegner, 1951), *P. notatum* (Kelner, 1952), *Neurospora crassa* (Goodgal, 1949; Norman, 1951; Brown, 1951), and *Ustilago zeae* (Brown, 1952) have been successfully photoreactivated, as have the vegetative stages of a number of bacteria and yeasts. Thus far, the effects of only ultraviolet have been proved to be reversed by visible light, although the sensitization of organisms to x-rays by infrared light has been reported (Zelle and Hollaender, 1955). It is likely that much of the photoreactivation effect can be attributed to light stimulation of an enzyme which splits thymine dimers (Wolff and Rupert, 1962).

Species and individual differences always must be considered as affecting survival (Table 3.6). As for individual variation, frequent notice of "tailing" in survival curves has been made. Markert (1953) analyzed this problem in *Glomerella cingulata* and concluded that occasional pigmented spores were responsible for the tailing in survival curves, by virtue of their increased resistance to radiation. Similarly, conidia of a dark-spored strain of *Cochliobolus sativus* were found to be much more resistant to high doses of ultraviolet light than were those of a white-spored strain (Tinline et al., 1960). That this mechanism probably exists in nature is suggested by the investigations of Johnson and Osborne (1964) on the survival of fungi in soil exposed to gamma radiation. They found that whereas most of the members of the Moniliaceae, which comprised a large portion of the soil population, were killed at intensities ranging from 250–1000 kr, a much greater proportion of the Dematiaceae, a group with dark walls, survived. Parallel finding have been reported by Durrell and Shields (1960) for fungi isolated from soils of the Nevada atomic bomb test site, so that the effect may be widespread.

Also, it has been possible to isolate strains of organisms that are more resistant to radiation than the original strain. Microconidia of *Neurospora crassa* were selected by Goodman (1958) with an LD_{90} for ultraviolet light of 184,000 ergs/cm^2 as compared with 115,000 for the parent organism. Macroconidia of the same strain were shown to have an LD_{90} of 506,000, confirming the observation by Norman (1951) that these multinucleate spores are more resistant than are the microconidia. Resistant strains of bacteria, including *Clostridium botulinum* Type A, as well as several nonspore-forming species, have been isolated by Erdman et al. (1961*b*) and others.

In addition, the criteria used in deriving survival curves are of considerable importance in determining its shape, as well as the MLD. A striking example of this is provided by the work of Uber and Goddard (1933) who treated ascospores of *Neurospora tetrasperma* with x-rays and obtained a bimodal curve when the percentage of germination was used as an index of viability. However, sigmoidal curves were obtained when growth, or the ability to produce mature ascospores, were used as criteria. The LD_{50} for growth was 30,000 r, production of ascospores 20,000 r, and germination over 500,000 r. Another instance of this kind is that of spores of *Schizosaccharomyces pombe* in which x-irradiation blocked cell division whereas cytoplasmic growth continued until cells were ten times their normal length (Ditlevsen and Hartelius, 1963*b*).

Finally, various substances have been reported to affect the radiation-sensitivity of organisms and several reviews of this subject are available, including those of Lea (1947), Bacq and Alexander (1955), Zelle and Hollaender (1955), Pomper and Atwood (1955), and Stapleton (1960). Cultural conditions, as they influence radiation-sensitivity, are discussed in the work of Stapleton and Engel (1960) but the basis of cultural variation is not always well understood. An interesting example with particular commercial interest is the radioresistance of Putrifactive Anaerobe (PA) 3679, the conventional indicator organism for thermal processing. Anellis and Koch (1962) reported that the S-2 strain of PA 3679 was capable of surviving 8.0 Mrad in cured ham and 12 Mrad in fresh raw pork.

Relation Between Heat- and Radiation-resistance

Germination leads to a decrease in resistance to both radiation and heat-treatment. Should resistance to both environmental factors be attributable to a common mechanism, and do they affect common loci?

In *Bacillus megaterium* and *B. cereus*, thermo- and radiation-resistance are reversed. Thus, spores of *B. megaterium* will not survive more than 10 minutes at 80°C, whereas spores of *B. cereus* survive even 15 minutes at 100°C (Duggar and Hollaender, 1934). However, as the data in Table 3.6 disclose, *B. megaterium* is about four times as resistant to ultraviolet light. Ascospores of *Neurospora* survive more than 4 hours at 60°C and conidia of this organism survive only 5 minutes at this temperature (Lingappa and Sussman, 1959); yet, conidia are as resistant to x-rays, or even more so. *Glomerella* conidia survive only 10 minutes at 50°C and are much less resistant than the ascospores of *Neurospora* (Hemmi, 1920); on the other hand, the conidia of the former are more resistant to x-irradiation than are the latter's ascospores.

Another line of evidence bearing on this question concerns the effect of sequential treatment with these two forms of energy. Sensitization of cells to heat has been reported with ultraviolet light for the spores of several species of bacteria (Curran and Evans, 1938), yeast cells (Anderson and Duggar, 1941), and *Paramecium* (Giese and Crossman, 1945). Exposure to light at 254 mμ, or between 35–160 mμ, rendered spores of *Bacillus albolactis, B. cohaerens,* and *B. mesentericus* more susceptible to heating at 98°C (Curran and Evans, 1938). The shorter wavelengths were the most efficient and the most heat-resistant organism tested, *B. cohaerens,* was the most susceptible to sensitization.

Ionizing radiation by x-rays was first shown to induce sensitization (Giese and Heath, 1948). More recently, spores of the thermophilic anaerobe NCA strain 3814 were sensitized to treatment at 115°C after exposures to doses of 250,000, 600,000 and 1,000,000 rep from cobalt-60 (Morgan and Reed, 1954). The studies of Kempe (1955) and Graikoski (1961) with spores of *Clostridium botulinum,* and those of Kan et al. (1957) with some bacilli, have confirmed the effectiveness of gamma rays as a sensitizer. In none of the cases mentioned was it possible to sensitize organisms to irradiation by a preliminary heat-treatment. If the mechanisms of resistance were identical, or the loci affected the same, it would be expected that the results of the reciprocal experiments we have described would be similar. Furthermore, as Graikoski (1961) and others have demonstrated, the thermal lethal temperature is not lowered by photosensitization so it is unlikely that similar sites are affected by the two environmental factors. The mechanisms responsible for the thermo- and radiation-resistance of spores, which will be discussed later, further differentiate these two.

Mechanisms of Killing by Irradiation

Two principal theories to explain the effects of radiation upon organisms have been advanced, including the *target theory* and the *indirect action* theory. The target theory postulates that the energy from irradiation is absorbed primarily within, or contiguous to, the key molecules of the cell. On the other hand, the indirect action theory assumes that the energy is absorbed by molecules inside, or near the cell, followed by the production of lethal substances that affect vital elements of the cell.

1. *Target Theory.* One of the arguments in support of this theory has been the lack of influence of temperature on radiation damage. A second is the fact that

plots of the amount of irradiation, against the logarithm of the fraction of survivors, imply that a defined number of sites within the cell are being affected. For this reason, the order of killing by irradiation has been the subject of intensive investigation and, as in the case of the lethal effects of high temperatures, disagreement has been recorded. Lea (1947, page 319) has stated that, for bacteria, "It is probable that exponential survival is the typical result," and several cases for which these kinetics were found are cited. On the other hand, the curves illustrated in Figure 3.9 for *Bacillus megaterium*, and for several other species (Table 3.7) show plainly that sigmoidal curves are obtained for dormant spores,

Table 3.7 Comparison of the Type of Survival Curve Obtained after X-Irradiation, the Radiation-Sensitive Volume for Inactivation, and the Amount of DNA per Spore

Organism	Type of Survival Curve[a]	Radiation-Sensitive Volume for Inactivation[b]	DNA/Spore (gm × 10^{-16})[c]
Bacillus subtilis	Exponential	7.7	5
B. cereus	Sigmoidal	13	10–11.5
B. megaterium	Sigmoidal	9.4–13	10–11.5
B. anthracis	Sigmoidal	—	11.5
B. cereus var. *mycoides*	Sigmoidal	20	14

[a] Woese (1958, 1959).
[b] Woese (1958).
[c] Fitz-James and Young (1959*a*).

as well as for other stages of these species. By contrast, Stuy (1956*b*) has obtained an exponential curve for dormant spores of *B. cereus*, and Herčik (1937) showed that exponential curves best described the survival of *B. megaterium* when spores were exposed to ultraviolet light. Recently, Bott and Lundgren (1964) reported that they confirmed the results of Stuy (1956*b*) but that at low doses of x-rays the inactivation curve reflected "a complex type of inactivation" which they ascribed to heterogeneity in the cell population. Similar differences have developed in the literature on the survival of fungus spores; Dimond and Duggar (1941) showed that a plot of surviving spores of *Aspergillus melleus* gave an exponential curve as a function of the dose of ultraviolet light, whereas *Rhizopus suinus* and *Mucor dispersus* gave sigmoidal ones.

The type of radiation may determine the shape of the survival curve. Zirkle et al. (1952), working with conidia of *Aspergillus terreus*, demonstrated that the use of α-rays resulted in an exponential survival curve whereas that obtained after x-irradiation was sigmoidal. The more densely ionizing radiations used by Markert (1953) on conidia of *Glomerella cingulata* also gave exponential curves as compared to the sigmoidal ones observed with ultraviolet light. The opposite effect was found in the experiments of Giles (1951) with microconidia of *Neurospora crassa* and of Stuy (1956*a*, *b*) with spores of *Bacillus subtilis*. Not all such experiments result in changed survival curves, for Atwood and Mukai (1954) have used γ-rays, x-rays, neutrons, and mixtures of these from bomb detonations to irradiate macroconidia of *Neurospora crassa* but obtained exponential kinetics in all cases.

The stage at which the irradiation is carried out can influence the shape of the survival curve. This was claimed by Duggar and Hollaender (1934) for spores and vegetative cells of *Bacillus subtilis* exposed to ultraviolet light, and by Stuy (1956*b*) with dormant and activated spores of *B. cereus*. However, when the spores of several species of *Bacillus* were exposed to x-rays by Woese (1959), before and after germination, no difference in the shape of the curves could be detected.

The number of nuclei may also have an important influence upon the order of killing by irradiation. Norman (1951) obtained exponential curves after ultraviolet-irradiation of microconidia of *Neurospora crassa*, but multihit curves with macroconidia. These data were correlated with the number of nuclei in the irradiated organism. Until recently, it has not been possible to test this relationship in bacterial spores. Fitz-James and Young (1959*a*) compared the nucleic acid content of several bacterial spores and the type of survival curve obtained after x-irradiation. The results (Table 3.7) suggest that those spores with the least amount of nucleic acid (haploid amount?) show single-hit survival curves, whereas those in which DNA occurs as a multiple of the lowest value give multihit curves. The change in the shape of the survival curve with the stage of development, and with the type of irradiation, cannot be explained by the nucleic acid content, nor can the fact that Stuy (1956*b*) has obtained an exponential curve with *Bacillus cereus* spores after x-irradiation. If the number of nuclei are the sole determinant of the shape of the survival curve, it would be expected that the irradiation of the uninucleate conidia of Glomerella would yield an exponential curve; however, a multihit curve was obtained with ultraviolet light by Markert (1953, 1956). In *Neurospora* the frequency of viable nuclei among conidia surviving a given dose was found to be greater than that expected if nuclear inactivation alone was responsible for lethality (Atwood, 1950). Other evidence against the hypothesis that killing of microorganisms by radiations is due solely to nuclear inactivation is discussed by Goodman (1958).

Several models have been proposed to resolve these discrepancies, including those of Atwood and Norman (1949), Tobias (1952), Woese (1958), Donellan and Morowitz (1960), and others. In general, the following independent processes may interact to inactivate microorganisms: (a) a nonheritable inactivation of the nucleus (Norman, 1951), (b) destruction of cytoplasmic elements (Kimball, 1957), and (c) induction of recessive lethal mutations (Atwood, 1954). Attempts to relate the DNA content, or a portion thereof, to the mean lethal dose of organisms have recently been made by Kaplan and Moses (1964) and Terzi (1965).

2. *"Indirect" Action Theory.* In the last 20 years a second theory to explain the effects of ionizing irradiation on biological systems has received considerable attention. This was first proposed by Risse (1929), who postulated that ionizing irradiation acted primarily on the solvent, producing atomic hydrogen and hydroxyl radicals, which in turn reacted with the materials in solution. Studies on the irradiation of solutions of inorganic chemicals (Bacq and Alexander, 1961), the protective effect of inorganic chemicals when added to biologically active materials (Dale, 1940, 1943; Dale et al., 1949; Stein and Weiss, 1948), and the identification of the intermediate products found in water after ionizing radiations have been applied (Allen, 1948; Hart, 1954) have supported this hypothesis.

Inasmuch as ionizing radiations produce oxidizing radicals in the medium, it would be expected that similar radicals are produced within the cytoplasm. The finding that sulfhydryl compounds, alcohols, sodium hydrosulfite, and metabolic intermediates provide protection against radiation damage in bacteria (Burnett et al., 1951; Hollaender et al., 1951; Thompson et al., 1951 and others) confirmed this view. Protective agents have also been described for bacterial spores (Kempe, 1955; Kempe et al., 1954; Williams and Kempe, 1957; Powers et al., 1959). Presumably hydrogen peroxide is one of the inactivating agents produced during irradiation inasmuch as the addition of catalase significantly reduces the lethal action of γ-rays on spores of *Clostridium botulinum* (Williams and Kempe, 1957).

Indirect effects of x-rays can be recognized in dry spores. Employing dry spores of *Bacillus megaterium*, Webb et al. (1960) recognized three classes of x-ray damage: (a) direct effects, (b) an indirect effect which is observed in the presence of oxygen or nitric oxide during the time of irradiation, and (c) an indirect effect due to the formation of free radicals of long lifetimes. In the latter case, exposure to oxygen converts these radicals into lethal substances, whereas exposure to nitric oxide or to heat renders them harmless. The thermorestoration of spores irradiated under anaerobic conditions renders them insensitive to subsequent exposure to oxygen (Webb et al., 1960; Murrell and Scott, 1960). An increased rate of inactivation of dry spores of *B. subtilis* in the presence of oxygen during γ-irradiation has been observed by Tallentire (1958). Latent oxygen effects on x-ray sensitivity have been observed in dry dormant barley seeds (Caldecott et al., 1957) and reduced sensitivity to x-rays in dry seeds of *Zea mays* (Kempton and Maxwell, 1941) when higher temperatures were employed.

The ability to reverse x-ray damage of spores with heat (Webb et al., 1960) or nitric oxide (Powers et al., 1959) decreases with time, indicating that the free radicals slowly lead to the formation of lethal agents. The formation of long-lived intermediate radicals in the presence of oxygen was confirmed by measurements of electron spin resonance of irradiated spores (Powers et al., 1959).

Although no generally acceptable model can be proposed to explain radiation effects, the observations which have been discussed make it likely that elements of both the target and indirect-action theories must be included. Thus the close fit of certain data to the target theory (Lea, 1947) must be reconciled with instances in which such conformity does not exist. Furthermore, the relatively recent discovery of effects of the temperature of radiation upon sensitivity, and thermorestoration, as well as oxygen effects and related chemical mitigations, make more reasonable the application of some form of the indirect-action theory in which the classes of lethal damage described by Powers (1961) and Tallentire and Powers (1963) are taken into account.

Mechanisms of Resistance

1. *Disulfide Bonds.* A possible basis for the resistance of spores to irradiation has emerged from studies of their sulfur content. Spores and vegetative cells differ dramatically in their content of sulfur-containing amino acids. Pfennig (1957) observed that hydrolysates of spores of *B. subtilis* and *B. mycoides* contain high levels of cyst(e)ine and low levels of methionine, whereas the reverse was true of vegetative cells. Vinter (1956) has recently extended these studies in *B. megaterium.* A significant increase in incorporation of cysteine-S^{35} but not of methionine-S^{35} was observed during spore formation. Moreover, the free spores of a number of bacilli were found to contain three to five times more cystine than the homologous vegetative cells (Vinter, 1959*a*, 1960).

The earlier results did not distinguish between cysteine or cystine as the major sulfur-containing component. From several observations, however, it appears that most of it is in the form of cystine. Mortenson and Beinert (1953) observed that the spores of *B. globigii* (since renamed *B. subtilis* var. *niger*) contained only 20 percent of the —SH groups present in vegetative cells, in spite of an apparently higher cyst(e)ine content in the former. In fact, germination was characterized by a rise in free —SH groups. Also, Widra (1956), on the basis of cytological methods, concluded that the concentration of free —SH groups decreased to negligible values during the latter stages of sporulation. During the final stages of spore development, only the spore wall contained any appreciable amount of protein-bound sulfhydryl. According to the experiments of Vinter (1960), only cystine is present in spores.

Although the identity of the cystine-rich component is as yet unknown, its formation is apparently essential for the development of mature spores. When vegetative cells of *B. megaterium* are incubated in the presence of hydrogen sulfide, added directly, or produced endogenously in the presence of high concentrations of cystine (10^{-4} *M*) by the action of a desulfhydrase, normal sporulation (Vinter, 1957) and the incorporation of cysteine S^{35} into the protein fraction (Vinter,

1959*b*) is inhibited with the formation of defective spores containing lowered amounts of calcium.

The relationship of these cystine-rich structures to irradiation resistance followed the recognition of stages in the sporulation process (for reviews see Hashimoto et al., 1960; Halvorson, 1961). Employing a synchronous culture technique, Halvorson (1957) followed growth, DPA content, and heat-resistance during sporulation of *Clostridium roseum*. Accumulation of DPA followed by several hours the appearance of refractile bodies (prespores). The heat-resistant cells (mature spores) appeared an hour or more after the maximum amount of DPA produced. Vinter (1960) has shown that the cystine-rich structures are developed during the first period of sporulation, and precede by several hours the formation of DPA and of thermoresistance. Romig and Wyss (1957) have shown that resistance to ultraviolet light develops prior to the appearance of DPA in sporulating cultures of *Bacillus cereus*. This same period is characterized by an increase in the frequency of postirradiation mutants (McDonald and Wyss, 1959). Moreover Vinter (1961, 1962) has shown that radiation-resistance is acquired during sporulation at the time of formation of cystine-rich structures, and prior to the development of heat-resistance (Figure 3.11). He also has shown (1962)

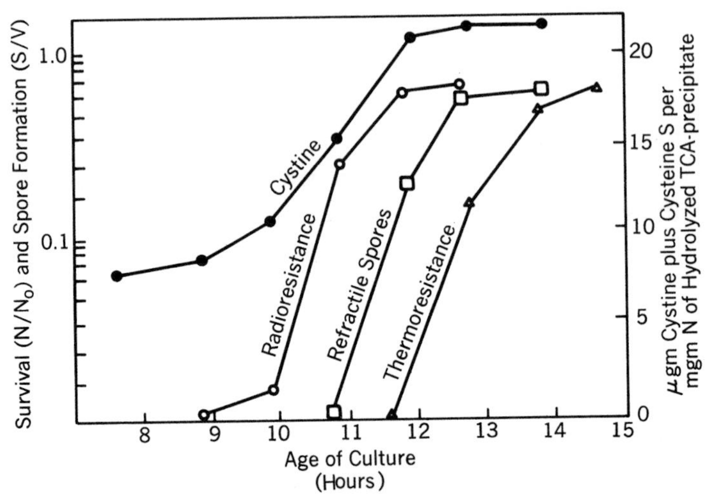

Figure 3.11 Changes in radioresistance, cystine content, and thermosensitivity of sporulating cells of *Bacillus cereus*. Legend: N, number of surviving pairs of cells; N_0, number of all pairs present; S, number of cells with spores; V, number of all cells present. (From Vinter, 1961.)

that the changes in radiation resistance and cystine content are distinct from changes in calcium and DPA content.

Recent work by Bott and Lundgren (1964) confirms many of Viner's observations. Thus, radiation-resistance increases as the spores of *B. subtilis* mature and seems to accompany the reduction in sulfhydryl level, and increases in disulfide groups. Furthermore, vegetative cells of a mutant that requires organic sulfur, when grown on certain levels of cystine, were the most resistant of any of the cells tested. However, spores of this mutant were shown to be *more* radiation-resistant when grown on cysteine than on cystine and those formed on the latter had even less resistance than some cells grown on methionine or cysteine. When mutant spores were compared, it was found that those with the fewest disulfide groups were most resistant to radiation. Therefore, the predictions based on Vinter's hypothesis are not borne out in the work on mutant spores. Perhaps, as the authors suggest, cyst(e)ine plays a morphogenetic role in spore formation in addition to affecting radiation-resistance, so that these separate effects must be distinguished before conclusions can be drawn. Although Csagoly (1962) found the SH/SS ratio of serum to be significant in the radiation-resistance of certain mammalian species, its increase was correlated with a *decline* in disulfide content.

Cysteine has been known to protect animals (Patt et al., 1949) and microorganisms (Hollaender et al., 1951) against damage caused by irradiation. A possible explanation for the radiation protection afforded by the disulfide-rich structures of spores arises from the studies of Gordy et al. (1955) who observed the formation of unpaired electrons in disulfide compounds after the irradiation of proteins. Presumably the disulfide can serve as a a donor source of electrons for repairing the damage caused by ionizing irradiation. The presence of such unpaired electrons has been detected in spores by the experiments of Powers et al. (1960) who measured the electron spin resonance induced by x-rays in dry spores of *B. megaterium*. The protective effects of free radical scavengers against irradiation damage in spores, discussed earlier, support the view that the cysteine-rich structure may act as a system for neutralizing secondary damage from irradiation.

2. *Other Mechanisms.* Other mechanisms of resistance to radiation have been proposed, including protective compounds like that which may account for the enhanced radiation-resistance of *Micrococcus radiodurans*, although its chemical nature is unknown (Bruce, 1964).

As was mentioned earlier (Webb et al., 1964), it has been proposed that that inositol and carbohydrates may protect microbial cells against radiation damage by replacing bound water. In fact, Woodside and Kocholaty (1964) have reported that radiation-resistant mutants of *Escherichia coli* contain the highest concentrations of intracellular sugars and radiation-sensitive ones the lowest. Furthermore, environmental conditions which favor increased concentrations of such sugars also increase radiation-resistance.

A structural feature of *Micrococcus radiodurans* that is unique except for one other tetrad-forming coccus, has been found (Thornley, 1963). It consists of a cell

wall constructed of a regular array of subunits, hexagonally arranged. But the connection between the multilayered wall structure and the great radiation-resistance of *M. radiodurans* is not yet known.

When the base composition of eight species of bacteria and their resistance to x-radiation was studied, Kaplan and Zavarine (1962) found that resistance and the guanine-cytosine (GC) content were inversely related. By contrast, they claimed that a *direct* relationship between resistance to ultraviolet light and the GC content exists. Therefore, it follows that the same organisms cannot be resistant to both types of radiation. However, it is known that *Micrococcus radiodurans* is very resistant to both x-rays and ultraviolet light, as are spores of *Bacillus megaterium* (Table 3.5). In fact, Mosely and Schein (1964) have discovered that there is a high GC content in *M. radiodurans* DNA so that the relationship discussed above is not general. This organism's DNA is not exceptionally resistant to ultraviolet radiation, but it seems to have a much more rapid and efficient repair mechanism than is found in *Escherichia coli*, and so this may explain some of its radiation-resistance (Setlow and Duggan, 1964).

The genetic differences between strains that confer radiation resistance upon spores probably operate in a parallel way in vegetative cells of *Bacillus subtilis*, according to Zamenhof, Bursztyn, Reddy, and Zamenhof (1965). As was found with *Micrococcus radiodurans*, the DNA of the several strains studied was similar enough to rule out resistant types of this macromolecule. Furthermore, in the case of a single gene mutant of *B. subtilis* the DNA repair mechanism was probably not involved. Finally, it was concluded that in the cases studied, ". . . the differences in radiation resistance of spores of different strains are not just a result of a superimposition of a common spore resistance mechanism(s) but rather are an amplification of genetically determined resistance differences in vegetative cells of these strains."

MISCELLANEOUS INFLUENCES UPON SURVIVAL OF SPORES

That heritable factors influence the longevity of spores has been inferred as a result of experiments in which the resistance of species could be increased by the selection and propagation of survivors after exposure to extreme environmental pressure. Goodman (1958) isolated a strain of *Neurospora crassa* with microconidia that were about 60 percent more resistant to ultraviolet light than were those of the wild type. Moreover, the thermoresistance of several aerobic bacteria can be increased by propagation of resistant survivors (Davis et al., 1948; Williams, 1929). Cytoplasmic influences upon the viability of conidia of *Aspergillus glaucus* have been described by Jinks (1959). Conidia derived from cell lineages displaying "vegetative death," a condition in which an irreversible cessation of growth occurs, were largely inviable, although a small percentage were capable of germination and development. In the imperfect fungi studied by Jinks, "vegetative death" was a regular feature of aging clones and was suppressive to wild-type phenotypes when heterokaryons were formed. Also, Good and Spanis (1958) collected 25 conks of *Fomes igniarus* containing spores from six different trees. The percentage germination after 7 days ranged from 1–47 percent and the variation within collections from one tree was less than that between those from different trees. Storage tests revealed that the germination of spores from one conk decreased from 94 percent at the start to 60 percent in 80 days; the equivalent figures for another conk were 92 percent and 0 percent in 10 days. Although a genetic basis is suggested for this variability, environmental causes have not yet been ruled out. Variability in longevity between strains has also been reported for conidia of *Penicillium chrysogenum* (Groom and Panisset, 1933), and *Colletotrichum nicotinae* (Lee and Yu, 1941).

Age is known to influence the resistance of spores to a marked extent. Spores of *Clostridum botulinum* (Esty and Meyer, 1922) are most resistant to heat when freshly harvested. Maximum resistance is not attained until after a period of maturation (Curran, 1952). For example, the spores of *Bacillus mycoides* were found by Magoon (1926) to increase in thermoresistance up to 60 days after their formation, following which a slow decline was noted. Furthermore, ripe ascospores of a wine yeast studied by Hansen (1908) could survive in 50 percent ethanol for at least 2 days, but immature ones, as well as vegetative cells, were destroyed in less than 1 minute. Radiation-sensitivity is also affected by the age of conidia in *Aspergillus melleus* (Dimond and Duggar, 1941). Three times more ultraviolet light was required to kill 34-day-old spores than 4-day-old ones.

The conditions under which spores are formed often influence their longevity. A direct correlation between the temperature at which spores of *Bacillus subtilis* and *B. stearothermophilus* were produced and their thermoresistance was noted by Williams (1929) and Williams and Robertson (1954), as well as for conidia of *Colletotrichum nicotinae* by Lee and Yu (1941). A similar effect on spores of *Clostridium botulinum* was observed by Sugiyama (1951) except that the resistance reached a maximum when incubation was at 37°C and fell when cultures were kept at 41°C. On the other hand, the claim has been made by Theophilus and Hammer (1938) that the thermoresistance of spores of several mesophilic bacteria was greatest at the optimum temperature for growth, and Yarwood et al. (1954) have reported the same effect on the viability of conidia of *Erysiphe polygoni* and *E. cichoracearum*. Slow or rapid drying, and alternate wetting and drying, result in greater thermoresistance in spores of *Clostridium welchii* and of several aerobes (Curran, 1952). Exceptionally dry as well as exceptionally wet conditions during the formation of aeciospores of *Cronartium fusiformis* depress their viability (Siggers, 1947). The conidia of the powdery mildews were longest lived when formed under dry conditions (Yarwood et al., 1954). Even light has been implicated as a factor in determining heat-resistance in zygospores of *Phycomyces* (Robbins et al., 1942).

The importance of the medium in which spores are formed upon their longevity is strikingly illustrated in the work of Darby and Mandels (1955) with conidia of *Myrothecium verrucaria* (Table 3.8). When this cellulolytic species

Table 3.8 The Effect of the Growth Medium In Which the Spores Have Been Produced Upon Some Physiological Properties of Conidia of *Myrothecium verrucaria*

	Medium			
Physiological Property	Filter Paper	Peptone	Succinate	Potato-Dextrose
Viability: number of days in which viability is decreased 50 percent	72	18	19	28
Dry weight at harvest: mg/10^9 spores	22	17.5	22	40
Loss in dry weight: days to decrease starting weight by 50 percent	78	65	23	20
Endogenous Q_{O_2} at:				
time of harvest	2	1.5	2	16
20 days	2	1	1	1.5
Maximum Q_{O_2} in presence of:				
peptone	54 at 30 days	47 at 1 day	47 at 12 days	31 at 1 day
sucrose	35 at 30 days	26 at 1 day	50 at 12 days	16 at 1 day
azide	27 at 10 days	22 at 1 day	21 at 1 day	16 at 1 day
Q_{O_2} after 40 days in:				
peptone	54	8	<1	<1
sucrose	35	4	2	<1
azide	9	1	<1	<1

The table summarizes the work of Darby and Mandels (1955) and in some cases the interpolations from graphical data may be inexact.

forms spores on filter paper, they can be stored for about 40 days with no loss in viability. However, when they are formed on peptone, or on a succinic acid, fewer than 1 percent of these conidia remain viable after 12–26 days. Those formed in potato-dextrose agar were intermediate in longevity between these extremes. Similar effects were demonstrated for conidia of *Aspergillus luchuensis*. An increase of 4° in the thermal death point (TDP) of conidia of *Colletotrichum nicotinae* was noted when they were formed on Richard's medium instead of on potato-dextrose agar (Lee and Yu, 1941).

Antibiotics are released in soils and aquatic environments by actinomycetes, fungi, and other organisms. Spores of bacteria (Phillips, 1952; Wynne, 1952;

Schmidt, 1955) and fungi (Lowry and Sussman, 1956; Sussman et al., 1958) are more resistant to these antibiotics than are vegetative cells. Penicillin (Wynne and Harrell, 1951) and streptomycin (Wynn et al., 1952) only slightly affect spores of *Clostridium* at high concentrations. Similarly, the respiration of dormant ascospores of *Neurospora tetrasperma* is not influenced by polymyxin B (Lowry and Sussman, 1956), or by a number of toxic cations and anions (Sussman et al., 1958); however, germination was repressed by these agents. Other antibiotics have been described, such as amidomycin (Taber and Vining, 1957), which affect a broad sprectrum of fungi, including uredospores of *Puccinia graminis* var. *tritici*. In these cases, however, it remains to be established whether sufficient amounts of the antibiotic are produced in nature to be of significance in the survival of spores. It is also known that a fungistasis of widespread distribution exists in soils to such an extent that conidia of many fungi cannot germinate freely unless the toxic principle is removed or otherwise rendered innocuous (Dobbs and Hinson, 1953). Factors affecting the lysis of fungal colonies on agar plates have been described by Carter and Lockwood (1957*a*, *b*) but, as in the case of antibiotics, their significance in nature is yet to be assessed. An extended discussion of the role of spores in the survival of microorganisms is provided in Chapter 11.

REFERENCES

ABE, T. 1933. *Ann. Phytopathol. Soc. Japan* 2:505–512.

AINSWORTH, G. C. 1965. *Nature.* (In press.)

ALDERTON, G. A., P. A. THOMPSON, and NEVA SNELL. 1964. *Science* 143:141–143.

ALLEN, A. O. 1948. *J. Phys. Coll. Chem.* 52:479–490.

ALLSOPP, A. 1952. *Nature* 169:79–80.

AMAHA, M. 1952. *J. Ag. Chem. Soc. Japan* 26:420–427.

AMAHA, M., and Z. J. ORDAL. 1957. *J. Bacteriol.* 74:596–604.

AMAHA, M., and K. SAKAGUCHI. 1954. *J. Bacteriol* 68:338–345.

AMAHA, M., and K. SAKAGUCHI. 1957. *J. Gen. Appl. Microbiol.* 3:163–192.

ANDERSEN, A. A., and H. D. MICHENER. 1950. *Food Technol.* 4:188–189.

ANDERSON, P. J., and W. H. RANKIN. 1914. *Cornell Univ. Agr. Exp. Sta. Bull.* 347:661–668.

ANDERSON, T. F., and B. M. DUGGAR, 1941. *Proc. Am. Phil. Soc.* 84:661–668.

ANELLIS, A., and R. B. Koch. 1962. *Appl. Microbiol.* 10:326–330.

ATWOOD, K. C. 1950. *Genetics* 35:95–96.

ATWOOD, K. C. 1954. *Proc. Internat. Photobiol. Congr. Amsterdam*, pp. 143–145.

ATWOOD, K. C., and A. NORMAN. 1949. *Proc. Nat. Acad. Sci. (U.S.)* 35:696–701.

ATWOOD, K. C., and F. MUKAI. 1954. *Am. Naturalist* 88:295–314.

BACQ, Z. M., and P. ALEXANDER. 1955. *Principes de Radiobiologie.* Masson et Cie., Paris, 478 pp.

BACQ, Z. M., and P. ALEXANDER. 1961. *Fundamentals of Radiobiology.* 2nd ed. Pergamon Press, N.Y., 555 pp.

BECQUEREL, P. 1910. *Compts. Rend. Acad. Sci. Francaise* 150:1437–1439.

BECQUEREL, P. 1931. "La Vie Latente des Spores des Bactéries et des Moissures." in *Travaux Cryptogramique*, Dedie's a'Louis Mangin., Paris, Muséum National d'Histoire Naturelle. Laboratoire de cryptogamie. 335 pp.

BECQUEREL, P. 1950*a*. *Compt. Rend. Acad. Sci.* 231:1392–1394.

BECQUEREL, P. 1950*b*. *Compt. Rend. Acad. Sci.* 231:1274–1277.

BEERS, C. D. 1937. *Am. Naturalist* 71:521–524.
BEIJERINCK, M. W., and M. G. JACOBSON. 1908. *Proc. 1 er Congr. Int. ou Froid Paris*, 9 pp.
BERESTNEFF, N. M. 1907. *Zentr. Bakteriol. Parasitenik, Abt. I.* 40:298.
BERGER, J. A., and A. G. MARR. 1960. *J. Gen. Microbiol.* 22:147–157.
BIGELOW, W. D. 1922. *J. Infect. Diseases* 29:528–536.
BISBY, G. R. 1945. *Nature* 155:732–733.
BLACK, S. H., T. HASHIMOTO, and P. GERHARDT. 1960. *Can. J. Microbiol.* 6:213–224.
BOSCO, G. 1960*a*. *Nuovi Ann. Igiene Microbiol.* 11:335–338.
BOSCO, G. 1960*b*. *Nuovi Ann. Igiene Microbiol.* 11:227–240.
BOTT, K. F., and D. C. LUNDGREN. 1964. *Radiation Res.* 21:195–211.
BRADLEY, D. E., and D. J. WILLIAMS. 1957. *J. Gen. Microbiol.* 17:75–79.
BRADLEY, D. E., and J. G. FRANKLIN. 1958. *J. Bacteriol.* 76:618–630.
BRIDGES, A. E., J. P. OLIVO, and VELNA L. CHANDLER. 1956. *Appl. Microbiol.* 4:147–149.
BROWN, J. S. 1951. *J. Bacteriol.* 62:163–167.
BROWN, J. S. 1952. Ph.D Thesis, Stanford Univ.
BRUCE, A. K. 1964. *Radiation Res.* 22:155–164.
BULLER, A. H. R. 1933. *Researches on Fungi.* vol. 5. Reprint, 1958, Hafner, N.Y.
BULLER, A. H. R. 1934. *Researches on Fungi.* vol. 6. Reprint, 1958, Hafner, N.Y.
BULLOCH, W. 1928. *Zentr. Bakteriol* 106:21–29.
BURNETT, W. T., JR., M. L. MORSE, A. W. BURKE, JR., and A. HOLLAENDER. 1951. *J. Bacteriol.* 63:595.
CALDECOTT, R. S., E. B. JOHNSON, D. T. NORTH, and C. F. KONZAK. 1957. *Proc. Nat. Acad. Sci. U.S.* 43:975—983.
CALESNICK, ELEANOR J., and J. W. WHITE, JR. 1952. *J. Bacteriol.* 64:9–15.
CAMPBELL, L. L. 1961. in *Spores II.* H. O. Halvorson, Ed. Burgess Pub. Co., Minneapolis, pp. 195–197.
CAMPBELL, L. L., and G. B. MANNING. 1961. *J. Biol. Chem.* 236:2962–2965.
CANADA, J. C., DOROTHY H. STRONG, and LELIA G. SCOTT. 1964. *Appl. Microbiol.* 12:273–276.
CARTER, P. H., and J. L. LOCKWOOD. 1957*a*. *Phytopathology* 47:169–173.
CARTER, P. H., and J. L. LOCKWOOD. 1957*b*. *Phytopathology* 47:151–154.
CHALAUD, G. 1932. *Ann. Bryologic.* 5:1–16.
CHAMBERLAIN, D. W., and J. L. ALLISON. 1945. *Phytopathology* 35:241–248.
CHANEY, R. W. 1951. *The Garden J., N.Y. Botan. Gard.* 1:137–139.
CHEREWICK, W. J. 1944. *Canad. J. Res.* C22:52–86.
CHINN, S. H. F., and R. J. LEDINGHAM. 1958. *Can. J. Botany* 36:289–295.
CHURCH, B. D., and H. HALVORSON. 1959. *Nature* 183:124–125.
CHURCH, B. D., and H. HALVORSON, D. S. RAMSEY, and R. S. HARTMAN. 1956. *J. Bacteriol.* 72:242–247.
CLARK, W. A. 1962. *Proc. Symp. Low Temp. Microbiol.* Campbell Soup Co., Camden, N.J., pp. 285–298.
COHN, F. 1876. *Beitr. Biol. Pflanz.* 2:249–276.
COHEN, S. P., and D. A. Wiener. 1954. *Appl. Spectroscopy* 8:23.
CORNER, E. J. H. 1935. *New Phytol.* 34:180–200.
CSAGOLY, E. 1959. *Advan. Polarog. Proc. 2nd Int. Congr.* 3:1048–1056. Cited in *Chem. Abstr.* 57:10154, 1962.
CURRAN, H. R. 1952. *Bacteriol Rev.* 16:111–117.
CURRAN, H. R., and F. R. EVANS. 1938. *J. Bacteriol.* 36:455–465.
CURRAN, H. R., and F. R. EVANS. 1945. *J. Bacteriol.* 49:335–346.
CURRAN, H. R., B. C. BRUNSTETTER, and A. T MYERS. 1943. *J. Bacteriol.* 45:485–494.
DALE, W. 1940. *Biochem. J.* 34:1367–1373.
DALE, W. 1943. *Brit. J. Radiol.* 16:171–173.
DALE, W. M., J. V. DAVIES and C. W. GILBERT 1949. *Biochem. J.* 45:93–99.
DARBY, R. T., and G. R. MANDELS. 1955. *Plant Physiol.* 30:360–366.
DARLINGTON, H. J., and G. P. STEINBAUER. 1961. *Am. J. Botany* 48:321–325.
DAVIS, F. L., O. WYSS, and O. B. WILLIAMS. 1948. *J. Bacteriol.* 56:561–567.
DE BRUYN, HELENA L. G. 1926. *Phytopathology* 16:121–140.
DEWEY, W. G., and L. J. TYLER. 1958. *Phytopathology* 48:579–580.
DICKSON, H. 1936. *J. Botany* 74:13–17.
DIMOND, A., and B. M. DUGGAR. 1941. *Proc. Nat. Acad. Sci. U.S.* 27:459–468.
DITLEVSEN, E., and V. HARTELIUS. 1963*a*. *Compt. Rend. Trav. Lab. Carlsberg* 33:319–346.
DITLEVSEN, E., and V. HARTELIUS. 1963*b*. *Compt. Rend. Trav. Lab. Carlsberg* 33:347–359.
DOBBS, C. A., and W. H. HINSON. 1953. *Nature* 172:197–199.

DOI, P. 1960. Ph.D. Thesis, Univ. of Wisconsin.

DOFLEIN, F., and E. REICHENOW. 1953. *Lehrbuch der Protozoenkunde.* 6th ed. Gustav Fischer, Jena.

DOMBROWSKI, H. J. 1960. *Zentr. Bakteriol. Parasitenk.* Abt. I. 178:83–90.

DOMBROWSKI, H. J. 1961. *Zentr. Bakteriol. Parasitenk.* Abt. I. 183:173–179.

DONNELLAN, J. E., and H. J. MOROWITZ. 1957. *Radiation Res.* 7:71–78.

DONNELLAN, J. E., and H. J. MOROWITZ. 1960. *Radiation Res.* 12:67–78.

DUGGAR, B. M., and A. HOLLAENDER. 1934. *J. Bacteriol.* 27:219–256.

DULBECCO, R. 1955. *Radiation Biology,* A. Hollaender, Ed., vol. 2. McGraw-Hill, N.Y. pp. 455–486.

DURRELL, L. W., and LORA M. SHIELDS. 1960. *Mycologia* 52:636–641.

EDWARDS, R. B., L. J. PETERSON, and D. G. CUMMINGS. 1954. *Food Technol.* 8:284–290.

ELLIOTT, R. P., and H. D. MICHENER. 1961. *Appl. Microbiol.* 9:452–468.

ELSER, W. J., R. A. THOMAS, and G. I. STEFFEN. 1935. *J. Immunol.* 28:433–473.

ENDO, S. 1959. *J. Ferment. Technol. (Hakko Kogaku Zasshi)* 37:356–360.

ERBISCH, F. 1961. Personal communication.

ERDMAN, I. E., F. S. THATCHER, and K. F. MACQUEEN. 1961*a*. *Can. J. Microbiol.* 7:199–205.

ERDMAN, I. E., F. S. THATCHER, and K. F. MACQUEEN. 1961*b*. *Can J. Microbiol.* 7:207–215.

ERIKSON, D. 1955. *J. Gen. Microbiol.* 13:119–126.

ESTY, J. R., and K. F. MEYER. 1922. *J. Infect. Diseases* 31:650–663.

FALK, M., K. A. HARTMAN, and R. C. LORD. 1963. *J. Am. Chem. Soc.* 86:337.

FARRELL, M. A., and H. G. TURNER. 1932. *J. Bacteriol.* 23:155–162.

FAULL, ANNA F. 1930. *Mycologia* 22:288–303.

FENNELL, D. 1960. *Botan. Rev.* 26:79–141.

FISCHER, B. 1911. cit. in *Bitter.* p. 6.

FISCHER, G. W. 1936. *Phytopathology* 26:1118–1127.

FITCH, F. W., and E. ANDERS. 1963. *Ann. N.Y. Acad. Sci.* 108:495–513.

FITZ-JAMES, P. C. 1962. *8th Intern. Congr. Microbiol.* p. 16.

FITZ-JAMES, P. C., and I. E. YOUNG. 1959*a*. *J. Bacteriol.* 78:743–754.

FITZ-JAMES, P. C., and I. E. YOUNG. 1959*b*. *J. Bacteriol.* 78:755–757.

FLING, M., N. H. HOROWITZ, and S. F. HEINEMANN. 1963. *J. Biol. Chem.* 238:2045–2053.

FORSSBERG, A. 1941. *Acta Radiol. (Stockholm)* 22:252–259.

FOSTER, J. W., and E. S. WYNNE. 1948. *J. Bacteriol.* 55:495–501.

FRANKLIN, J. G., and D. E. BRADLEY. 1957. *J. Appl. Bacteriol.* 20:467–472.

FRAYMOUTH, JOAN. 1928. *Ann. Botany* 42:74-100.

FROSSARD, P. 1962. *Fruits (Paris)* 17:382–385.

FUNK, A. 1963. *Can. J. Botany* 41:503–543.

GAUGHRAN, E. R. L. 1947. *Bacteriol Rev.* 11:189–225.

GIESE, A. C., and E. B. CROSSMAN. 1945. *J. Gen. Physiol.* 29:79–87.

GIESE, A. C., and H. E. HEATH. 1948. *J. Gen. Physiol.* 31:249–257.

GILES, N. H. 1951. *Cold Spr. Harb. Symp. Quant. Biol.* 16:283–313.

GLAZ, E. T. 1955. *Acta Mikrobiol. (Hungaria)* 2:315–325.

GLYNNE, M. D. 1926. *Ann. Appl. Biol.* 13:19–36.

GOOD, H. M., and W. SPANIS. 1958. *Can. J. Botany* 36:421–437.

GOODGAL, S. H. 1949. *Anat. Rec.* 105:496.

GOODEY, T. 1923. *J. Helminth.* 1:47–52.

GOODMAN, F. 1958. *Z. Vererbungslehre* 89:675–691.

GORDY, W., W. B. ARD, and H. SHIELDS. 1955. *Proc. Nat. Acad. Sci. U.S.* 41:983–996.

GRAIKOSKI, J. T. 1961. Ph.D. Thesis, Univ. of Michigan.

GRAY, L. H., and J. READ. 1943. *Nature* 152:53–54.

GRELET, N. 1952. *Ann. Inst. Pasteur* 83:71–79.

GROOM, P., and T. PANISSET. 1933. *Ann. Appl. Biol.* 20:633–660.

HAGEN, C. A., E. J. HAWRYLEWICZ, and R. EHRLICH. 1964. *Appl. Microbiol.* 12:215–218.

HAHNE, J. 1925. *Kühn. Arch. Arb. Land. Inst. Univ. Halle.* 9:224—226.

HALVORSON, H. 1961. in *Spores II.* H. O. Halvorson, Ed. Burgess Pub. Co., Minneapolis, pp. 149–164.

HALVORSON, H. O. 1957. *J. Appl. Bacteriol.* 20:305–314.

HALVORSON, H. O. 1958. *The Physiology of the the Bacterial Spore.* Tech. Univ., Trondheim, Norway.

HALVORSON, H. O. 1961. in *Cryptobiotic Stages in Biological Systems.* N. Grossowicz, S. Hestrin, and A. Keynan, Eds. Elsevier, Amsterdam, N.Y., London, pp. 32–63.

HAMPIL, B. 1932. *Quart. Rev. Biol.* 7:172–196.

Hansen, E. C. 1908. *Zentr. Bakteriol. Parasitenk.* 45:466–480.
Hansen, N. H., and H. Riemann. 1963. *J. Appl. Bacteriol.* 26:314–333.
Harrison, A. P., Jr. 1956. *Antonie van Leeuwenhoek, J. Microbiol. Serol.* 22:407–418.
Hart, H. 1926. *Phytopathology* 16:185–205.
Hart, H. 1954. in *Annual Review of Physical Chemistry.* G. J. Rollefson and R. E. Powell, Eds., vol. 5. Ann. Rev., Stanford, Calif.
Hashimoto, T., S. H. Black, and P. Gerhardt. 1960. *Can. J. Microbiol.* 6:203–212.
Hawker, Lilian E. 1957. in *Microbial Ecology, 7th Symp. Soc. Gen. Microbiol.,* Cambridge Univ. Press, London, pp. 238–258.
Hemmi, T. 1920. *J. Coll. Ag. Hokkaido Imp. Univ.* 9:(#1).
Herčik, F. 1937. *J. Gen. Physiol.* 20:589–594.
Hesseltine, C. W. 1947. *Mycologia* 39:126–128.
Hesseltine, C. W., J. Bradle, and C. R. Benjamin. 1960. *Mycologia* 52:762–774.
Hickman, C. J. 1958. *Trans. Brit. Mycol. Soc.* 41:1–13.
Hinton, H. E. 1951. *Proc. Zool. Soc. London* 121:371–380.
Hinton, H. E. 1953. *Trans. Soc. Brit. Entomol.* 11:209–227.
Hollaender, A., G. E. Stapleton, and F. L. Martin. 1951. *Nature* 167:103–104.
Holm-Hansen, O. 1963. *Physiol. Plantarum* 16:530–540.
Horowitz, N. H. 1964. Personal communication.
Horowitz, N. H., and M. Fling. 1953. *Genetics* 38:360–374.
Houtermans, Thea. 1956. *Z. Naturforsch.* 11б:636–643.
Hull, R. 1939. *Ann. Appl. Biol.* 86:800–811.
Hunnell, J. W. 1961. in *Spores II.* H. O. Halvorson, Ed. Burgess Pub. Co., Minneapolis, pp. 101–112.
Jacotot, H., and B. Virat. 1954. *Ann. Inst. Pasteur* 87:215–217.
Jagger, J. 1958. *Bacteriol. Rev.* 22:99–142.
Jensen, H. 1948. *Physiol. Plant.* 1:255–264.
Jensen, H. L. 1961. *Nature* 192:682–683.
Jinks, J. L. 1959. *J. Gen. Microbiol.* 21:397–409.
Johnson, L. F., and T. S. Osborne. 1964. *Can. J. Botany* 42:195–113.
Kan, B., S. A. Goldblith, and B. E. Proctor. 1957. *Food Res.* 22:509–518.
Kan, B., S. A. Goldblith, and B. E. Proctor. 1958. *Food Res.* 23:11–50.
Kaplan, H. S., and L. E. Moses. 1964. *Science* 145:21–25.
Kaplan, H. S., and R. Zavarine. 1962. *Biochem. Biophys. Res. Commun.* 8:432.
Kapterev, P. 1936. *Invest. Akad. Nauk S.S.S.R.* (Ser. Biol.) 6:1073–1088.
Kapterev, P. 1938. *Doklady Akad. Nauk S.S.S.R.* 20:315–317.
Katznelson, H. 1940. *Soil Sci.* 49:283–293.
Keilin, D. 1959. *Proc. Roy. Soc. (London) Ser. B* 150:149–192.
Kelner, A. 1949. *Proc. Nat. Acad. Sci. U.S.* 35:73–79.
Kelner, A. 1952. *J. Cell. Comp. Physiol.* Suppl. 1, 39:115–117.
Kempe, L. L. 1955. *Appl. Microbiol.* 3:346–352.
Kempe, L. L., J. T. Graikoski, and R. A. Gillies. 1954. *Appl. Microbiol.* 2:330–332.
Kempton, J. H., and L. R. Maxwell. 1941. *J. Agr. Res.* 62:603–618.
Kimball, R. F. 1957. *Ann. Rev. Microbiol.* 11:199–220.
Kitasima, K. 1916. *Ringyô Siken Hôkoku* 14:43–62.
Kobayshi, T., J. N. Rinker, and H. Koffler. 1959. *Arch. Biochem. Biophys.* 84:342–362.
Koffler, H. 1957. *Bacteriol. Rev.* 21:227–240.
Koffler, H., G. E. Mallett, and J. Adye. 1957. *Proc. Nat. Acad. Sci. U.S.* 43:464–477.
Koh, Won Young, Catherine T. Morehouse, and Velma L. Chandler. 1956. *Appl. Microbiol.* 4:143–146.
Koller, P. C. 1943. *Proc. Roy. Soc. Edinburgh* 61B:398–429.
Landen, E. W. 1939. *J. Cell. Comp. Physiol.* 14:217–226.
Lawrence, N. L. 1955. *J. Bacteriol.* 70:577–582.
Lawrence, N. L., and H. O. Halvorson. 1954. *J. Bacteriol.* 68:334–337.
Lea, D. E. 1947. *Actions of Radiations on Living Cells.* Macmillan, N.Y., 402 pp.
Lea, D. E., R. B. Haines, and C. A. Coulson. 1936. *Proc. Roy. Soc. (London) Ser. B* 120:47–76.
Lea, D. E., R. B. Haines, and E. Bretscher. 1941. *J. Hyg.* 41:1–16.
LeBlanc, M. F. R., K. A. Devlin, and C. R. Stumbo. 1953. *Food Technol.* 7:181–185.
Lechowich, R. L. 1959. Ph.D. Thesis, Univ. of Illinois.
Lee, L., and E. H. Yu. 1941. *Phytopathology* 31:264–270.
Levinson, H. S., and A. S. Wrigley. 1960. *Science* 131:1382.

LEVINSON, H. S., and MILDRED T. HYATT. 1964. *J. Bacteriol.* 87:876–886.
LEVITT, J. 1956. *The Hardiness of Plants.* Academic Press, N.Y., 278 pp.
LEWITH, S. 1890. *Arch. Exp. Pathol. Pharmakol.* 26:341–354.
LIBBY, W. F., and J. R. ARNOLD. 1951. *Science* 113:111–120.
LINGAPPA, Y., and A. S. SUSSMAN. 1959. *Am. J. Botany* 46:671–678.
LIPMAN, C. B. 1928. *Science* 68:272–273.
LIPMAN, C. B. 1931. *J. Bacteriol.* 22:183–198.
LIPMAN, C. B. 1932. *Am. Museum Novitates.* 588:1–19.
LONG, S. K., and O. B. WILLIAMS. 1960. *J. Bacteriol.* 79:629–637.
LOWRY, R. J., and A. S. SUSSMAN. 1956. *Arch. Biochem. Biophys.* 62:113–124.
LUND, A. in *Spores II.* H. O. Halvorson, Ed. Burgess Pub. Co., Minneapolis, pp. 49–58.
LUYET, B. 1962. *Proc. Symp. Low Temp. Microbiol.* pp. 63–87.
MAAS, W. K., and B. D. DAVIS. 1952. *Proc. Nat. Acad. Sci. U.S.* 38:785–797.
MAGOON, C. A. 1926. *J. Bacteriol.* 11:253–283.
MAKS, V. 1933. *Prirodoslovne Razprave* 2:125–164.
MAMIKUNIAN, G., and M. H. BRIGGS. 1965. *Current Aspects of Exobiology,* Pergamon, New York. 420 pp.
MANNERS, J. G. 1951. *Indian Phytopathol.* 4:21–24.
MANNING, G. B., L. L. CAMPBELL, and R. J. FOSTER. 1961. *J. Biol. Chem.* 236:2958–2961.
MARKERT, C. L. 1953. *Exptl. Cell. Res.* 5:427–435.
MARKERT, C. L. 1956. *Papers Mich. Acad. Sci., Arts, Letters* 41:27–41.
MARRÉ, E., and O. SERVETTAZ. 1957. *Rend. Accad. Nazl. Lincei, Ser. VIII,* 22:91–98.
MARRÉ, E., MARIA ALBERTARIO, and E. VACCARI. 1958. *Rend. Accad. Nazl. Lincei, Ser VIII,* 24:349–353.
MARUYAMA, Y., and K. HAYASHI. 1963. *J. Gen. Appl. Microbiol.* 9:425–431.
MATSUYAMA, A., MARGARET J. THORNLEY, and M. INGRAM. 1964*a*. *J. Appl. Bacteriol.* 27:110–124.
MATSUYAMA, A., MARGARET J. THORNLEY, and M. INGRAM. 1964*b*. *J. Appl. Bacteriol.* 27:125–133.
MAXWELL, L. R., J. H. KEMPTON, and V. MOSLEY. 1942. *J. Wash. Acad. Sci.* 32:18–24.
MAZUR, P. 1963*a*. in *Culture Collections: Perspectives and Problems.* Univ. of Toronto Press, Toronto, 303 pp.
MAZUR, P. 1963*b*. *Biophys. J.* 3:323–353.
MAZUR, P. 1963*c*. *J. Gen. Physiol.* 47:347–369.
MAZUR, P., M. A. RHIAN, and B. G. MAHLANDT. 1957. *Arch. Biochem. Biophys.* 71:31–51.
MCCREA, A. 1923. *Science* 58: 426.
MCCREA, A. 1931. *Mich. Acad. Sci. Arts and Letters* 13:165–166.
MCDONALD, W. C., and O. WYSS. 1959. *Radiation Res.* 11:409–417.
MCKAY, R. 1935. *Nature* 135:306–307.
MCKEEN, R. N., and C. D. WENSLEY. 1961. *Science* 134:1528–1529.
MCKNIGHT, K. 1960. Personal communication.
MENZIES, J. D. 1963. *Botan. Rev.* 29:79–122.
MEREK, E. L., and C. L. FERGUS. 1954. *Phytopathology* 44:61–64.
MERYMAN, H. T. (Ed.) 1960. *Freezing and Drying of Biological Materials.* Ann. N.Y. Acad. Sci. 85:501–734.
METZGER, ILSE. 1942. *Kuchn-Arch.* 56:163–172.
MICHENER, H. D. 1955. *J. Bacteriol.* 70:192–200.
MICHENER, H. D., P. A. THOMPSON, and J. C. LEWIS. 1959. *Appl. Microbiol.* 7:166–173.
MILLER, R. E., and L. A. SIMONS. 1962. *J. Bacteriol.* 84:1111–1114.
MITCHELL, H. K. 1957. in *Chemical Basis of Heredity.* W. D. McElroy, and B. Glass, Eds. Johns Hopkins Press, Baltimore, pp. 94-113.
MITCHELL, M. 1960. Personal communication.
MORGAN, B. H., and J. M. REED. 1954. *Food Res.* 19:357–366.
MORITA, R. Y., and SHERIL D. BURTON. 1963. *J. Bacteriol.* 86:1025–1029.
MORTENSON, L. E., and H. BEINERT. 1953. *J. Bacteriol.* 66:101–104.
MOSELEY, B. E. B., and A. H. SCHEIN. 1964. *Nature* 203:1298–1299.
MÜLLER, A., and W. SCHWARTZ. 1953. *Z. Deut. Geol. Ges.* 105:789–802.
MURRELL, W. G. 1952. Ph.D. Thesis, Univ. of Oxford.
MURRELL, W. G., and W. J. SCOTT. 1960. Unpublished results.
MURRELL, W. G., and W. J. SCOTT. 1957. *Nature* 179:481–482.
NASH, T., J. R. POSTGATE, and J. R. HUNTER. 1963. *Nature* 199:113.
NELSON, P. E., and S. WILHELM. 1958. *Phytopathology* 48:613–616.
NORMAN, A. 1951. *Exptl. Cell Res.* 2:454–473.
OATES, R. P., T. S. BEERS, and L. Y. QUINN. 1961. *Bacteriol. Proc.* p. 58.

O'Brien, R. T., D. S. Titus, K. A. Devlin, C. R. Stumbo, and J. C. Lewis. 1956. *Food Technol.* 10:352–355.

Ohga, I. 1923. *Botan. Mag. Tokyo* 37:87–95.

Omelyanskii, V. L. 1911. *Arch. Sci. Biol., St. Petersburg* 16:355–356.

Oparin, A. I. 1957. *The Origin of Life on the Earth.* Academic Press, N.Y., 495 pp.

Ordal, Z. J. 1964. *Spore Newsletter* #7 (Feb.), p. 8.

Page, R. M., A. F. Sherf, and T. L. Morgan. 1947. *Mycologia* 39:158–164.

Patt, H. M., E. B. Tyree, R. L. Straube, and D. E. Smith. 1949. *Science* 110:213–214.

Pepper, R. E., N. T. Buffa, and V. L. Chandler. 1956. *Appl. Microbiol.* 4:149–152.

Pfennig, N. 1957. *Arch. Mikrobiol.* 26:345–352.

Phillips, C. R. 1952. *Bacteriol. Rev.* 16:135–143.

Pomper, S., and K. C. Atwood. 1955. in *Radiation Biology.* vol. 2. McGraw-Hill, N.Y. pp. 431–453.

Porter, R. H. 1955. *Phytopathology* 45:637–638.

Powell, J. F. 1957. *J. Appl. Bacteriol.* 20:349–358.

Powell, J. F., and J. R. Hunter. 1956. *Biochem. J.* 62:381–387.

Powell, J. F., and R. E. Strange. 1953. *Biochem. J.* 54:205–209.

Powers, E. L. 1961. *J. Cell. Comp. Physiol.*, Suppl. 1, 58:13–25.

Powers, E. L., R. B. Webb, and C. F. Ehret. 1959. *Exptl. Cell. Res.* 17:550–554.

Powers, E. L., R. B. Webb, and C. F. Ehret. 1960. *Radiation Res.* 2:94–121.

Prasada, R. 1948. *Indian Phytopathol.* 1:119–126.

Proctor, B. E., S. A. Goldblith, E. M. Oberle, and W. C. Miller, Jr. 1955. *Radiation Res.* 3:295–303.

Prucha, M. J., and J. M. Brannon. *J. Bacteriol.* 11:27–29.

Rahn, O. 1932. *J. Gen. Physiol.* 15:257–277.

Ramakrishnan, K. 1949. *Indian Phytopathol.* 2:31–34.

Raper, K. 1951. *Quart. Rev. Biol.* 26:169–190.

Reissig, J. L. 1960. *Microb. Gen. Bull.* 17:18–19.

Rey, L. 1961. *Traité de Lyophilisation.* Hermann et Cie., Paris.

Reynolds, H., and H. Lichtenstein. 1952. *Bacteriol. Rev.* 16:126–135.

Rhodes, Mabel. 1950. *J. Gen. Microbiol.* 4:450–456.

Rippel, A. 1935. *Arch. Mikrobiol.* 6:350–359.

Risse, O. 1929. *Z. Phys. Chem. A.* 140:133–152.

Robbins, W. J., Virginia W. Kavanagh, and F. Kavanagh. 1942. *Botan. Gaz.* 104:224–242.

Roberg, M. 1948. *Arch. Mikrobiol.* 14:1–11.

Rode, L. J., and J. W. Foster. 1960*a*. *J. Bacteriol.* 79:650–656.

Rode, L. J., and J. W. Foster. 1960*b*. *Proc. Nat. Acad. Sci. U.S.* 46:118–128.

Rode, L. J., C. W. Lewis, and J. W. Foster. 1962. *J. Cell. Biol.* 13:423–435.

Roegner, F. R. 1951. *Bacteriol. Proc.* pp. 62–63.

Romig, W. R., and O. Wyss. 1957. *J. Bacteriol.* 74:386–391.

Rosen, H. R., and L. M. Weetman. 1940. *Ark. Univ. (Fayetteville) Agr. Exp. Sta. Bull.* 391:3–20.

Roth, N. G., and H. O. Halvorson. 1952. *J. Bacteriol.* 63:429–435.

Roy, S. K. 1935. *Geol. Ser., Field Museum of Nat. Hist.* 6:179–198.

Sadoff, H. 1961. in *Spores II.* H. O. Halvorson, Ed. Burgess Pub. Co., Minneapolis, pp. 180–194.

Sall, T. 1964. *Trans. N.Y. Acad. Sci.* 26:553–563.

Savitsky, J. P. 1964. *Biochem. Biophys. Acta* 80:183–192.

Schmidt, C. F. 1955. *Ann. Rev. Microbiol.* 9:387–400.

Schweizer, G. 1947. *Planta* 35:132–176.

Setlow, J. K., and D. E. Duggan. 1964. *Biochem. Biophys. Acta* 87:664–668.

Sharp, D. G. 1939. *J. Bacteriol.* 37:447–460.

Shull, J. J., and R. R. Ernst. 1962. *Appl. Microbiol.* 10:452–457.

Shull, J. J., G. T. Cargo, and R. R. Ernst. 1963. *Appl. Microbiol.* 11:485–487.

Sie, E. H., H. Sobotka, and H. Baker. 1961*a*. *Nature* 192:86–87.

Sie, E. H., H. Sobotka, and H. Baker. 1961*b*. *Biochem. Biophys. Res. Comm.* 6:205–209.

Siggers, P. V. 1947. *Phytopathology* 37:855–864.

Simidu, W., and S. Veno. 1954. *Bull. Res. Inst. Food Sci., Kyoto Univ.* 14:14–17.

Simidu, W., and S. Veno. 1955. *Bull. Japanese Soc. Scientific Fisheries* 20:930–933.

Simidu, W., and S. Veno. 1956. *Memoirs Res. Inst. Food Sci., Kyoto Univ.* 10:30–33.

Slepecky, R., and J. W. Foster. 1959. *J. Bacteriol.* 78:117–123.

Smith, A. U. 1961. *Biological Effects of Freezing and Supercooling.* Williams and Wilkins, Baltimore, 462 pp.

Smith, A. U., Polge, C., and J. Smiles. 1954. *Proc. Med. Soc. London* 47:57–60.

SMITH, E. C. 1929. *Mycologia* 21:321–323.
SMYTH, H. F., JR. 1934. *J. Bacteriol.* 28:333–341.
SNEATH, P. H. A. 1962. *Nature* 195:643–646.
SNELL, W. H. 1923. *Am. J. Botany* 10:399–411.
SOCOLOFSKY, M. D., and O. WYSS. 1962. *J. Bacteriol.* 84:119–124.
SPARROW, A. H., M. J. MOSES, and R. STEELE. 1952. *Brit. J. Radiol.* 25:182–188.
SPAULDING, P. 1922. *Bull. U.S. Dept. Agr.* 957, 87 pp.
SPAULDING, P., and P. RATHBUN-GRAVATT. 1926. *J. Agr. Res.* 33:397–433.
SPEAR, F. G. 1944. *Brit. J. Radiol.* 17:348–351.
SPECTOR, W. S. (Ed.) 1956. *Handbook of Biological Data.* W. B. Saunders, Philadelphia, 584 pp.
STAPLETON, G. E. 1960. in *Radiation Protection and Recovery.* A. Hollaender, Ed. Pergamon Press, N.Y., pp. 87–116.
STAPLETON, G. E., and M. S. ENGEL. 1960. *J. Bacteriol.* 80:544–551.
STAPLETON, G. E., and A. HOLLAENDER. 1952. *J. Cell. Physiol.* 39:101–133.
STEIN, E. A., and E. H. FISHER. 1958. *J. Biol. Chem.* 232:867–879.
STEIN, G., and J. WEISS. 1948. *Nature* 161:650.
STEINER, G., and F. E. ALBIN. 1946. *J. Wash. Acad. Sci.* 36:97–99.
STEINHAUS, A. J. 1960. *Insect Pathol.* 2:225–229.
STEWART, B. T., and H. O. HALVORSON. 1953. *J. Bacteriol.* 65:160–166.
STUY, J. H. 1956*a*. *Biochim. Biophys. Acta.* 22:238–240.
STUY, J. H. 1956*b*. *Biochim. Biophys. Acta.* 22:241–246.
STUY, J. H. 1956*c*. *Antonie van Leeuwenhoek, J. Microbiol Serol.* 22:337–349.
SUGIYAMA, H. 1951. *J. Bacteriol.* 62:81–95.
SUMI, M. 1928. *Biochem. Z.* 195:161–174.
SUSSMAN, A. S. 1960. *Anat. Rec.* 137:396–397.
SUSSMAN, A. S. 1961. *Arch. Biochem. Biophys.* 95:407–415.
SUSSMAN, A. S., R. HOLTON, and B. VON BÖVENTER-HEIDENHAIN. 1958. *Arch. Mikrobiol.* 29:38–50.
TABER, W. A., and L. C. VINING. 1957. *Can. J. Microbiol.* 3:953–965.
TALLENTIRE, S. 1958. *Nature* 182:1024–1025.
TALLENTIRE, A., and D. J. G. DAVIES. 1961. *Exptl. Cell Res.* 24:148–150.
TALLENTIRE, A., and E. L. POWERS. 1963. *Radiation Res.* 20:270–287.
TAUBENHAUS, J. J., and W. N. EZEKIEL. 1936. *Am. J. Botany* 23:10–12.
TAYLOR, C. F., J. J. SMOOT, D. O. QUINN, R. A. ROHDE, and E. S. ELLIOT. 1955. *Phytopathology* 45:673–675.
TEITELL, L. 1958. *Am. J. Botany* 45:748–753.
TERZI, M. 1965. *J. Theroet. Biol.* 8:233–243.
TERUI, G., and T. MOCHIZUKI. 1955. *Technol. Repts. Osaka Univ.* 5:219–227.
THEOPHILUS, D. R., and B. W. HAMMER. 1938. *Iowa Agr. Exp. Sta. Res. Bull.* 244:112.
THOMPSON, T. L., R. B. MEFFORD, and O. WYSS. 1951. *J. Bacteriol.* 62:39–44.
THORNLEY, MARGARET J. 1963. *J. Appl. Bacteriol.* 26:3334–345.
TINLINE, R. D., J. F. STAUFFER, and J. G. DICKSON. 1960. *Can. J. Botany* 38:275–282.
TOBIAS, C. A. 1952. in *Symposium on Radiobiology.* J. J. Nickson, Ed. Wiley, N.Y., pp. 357–392.
TOCHINAI, Y. 1926. *J. Coll. Agr. Hokkaido Swp. Univ. (Japan)* 14:171–236.
TOKUGAWA, Y., and Y. EMOTO. 1924. *Japan. J. Botany* 2:175–185.
TOMCSIK, J. 1955. *Proc. Soc. Biol. Med.* 89:459–463.
TSAUGI, H. 1933. *J. Imp. Agr. Exp. Sta.* 2:225–252.
TURNER, J. H. 1933. *Kew Bull.* 6:257–269.
UBER, F. M., and D. R. GODDARD. 1933. *J. Gen. Physiol.* 17:577–590.
VAN WAGTENDONK, W. J. 1955. in *Biochemistry and Physiol. of Protozoa.* S. H. Hutner and A. Lwoff, Eds., vol. 1. Academic Press, N.Y., pp. 57–90.
VAS, K., and G. PROSZT. 1955. *Acta Microbiol. Acad. Sci. Hung.* 3:235–248.
VAS, K., and G. PROSZT. 1957. *J. Appl. Bacteriol.* 20:413–424.
VINTER, V. 1956. *Folia Biol. (Prague)* 4:216–226.
VINTER, V. 1957. *J. Appl. Bacteriol.* 20:325–332.
VINTER, V. 1959*a*. *Folia Microbiol. (Prague)* 4:1–6.
VINTER, V. 1959*b*. *Nature* 183:998–999.
VINTER. V. 1960. *Folia Microbiol. (Prague)* 5:217–232.
VINTER, V. 1961. *Nature* 189:589–590.
VINTER, V. 1962. *Folia Microbiol.* 7:115–120.
WALKER, H. W., J. R. MATCHES, and J. C. AYRES. 1961. *J. Bacteriol.* 82:960–966.
WANG, D. I-C., J. SCHARER, and A. E. HUMPHREY. 1964. *Appl. Microbiol.* 12:451–454.
WARTH, A. D., D. F. OHYE, and W. S. MURRELL. 1962. *8th Internat. Congr. Microbiol.*, p. 16.
WEBB, R. B., C. F. EHRET, and E. L. POWERS. 1958. *Experientia* 14:324–326.
WEBB, R. B., E. L. POWERS, and C. F. EHRET. 1960. *Radiation Res.* 12:682–693.
WEBB, S. J. 1960. *Can. J. Microbiol.* 6:89–105.
WEBB, S. J. 1961. *Can. J. Microbiol.* 7:621–632.

Webb, S. J. 1963. *J. Appl. Bacteriol.* 26:307–313.
Webb, S. J., D. V. Cormack, and H. G. Morrison. 1964. *Nature* 201:1103–1105.
Widra, A. 1956. *J. Bacteriol.* 71:689–702.
Wilhelm, S. 1955. *Phytopathology* 45:180–181.
Williams, C. C., E. J. Cameron, and O. B. Williams. 1961. *Food Res.* 6:69–73.
Williams, N. J., and L. L. Kempe. 1957. *Appl. Microbiol.* 5:366–368.
Williams, O. B. 1929. *J. Infect. Diseases* 44: 421–265.
Williams, O. B., and W. J. Robertson. 1954. *J. Bacteriol.* 67:337–378.
Wilson, G. S., and H. L. Shipp. 1938. *Chem. Ind.* 57:834–836.
Wilson, J. B., and K. E. Russell. 1964. *J. Bacteriol.* 87:237–238.
Witenberg, G. 1961. in *Cryptobiotic Stages in Biological Systems.* N. Grossowicz, S. Hestrin, and A. Keynan, Eds. Elsevier, Amsterdam, N.Y., London, pp. 97–106.
Woese, C. R. 1958. *J. Bacteriol.* 75:5–8.
Woese, C. R. 1959. *J. Bacteriol.* 77:38–42.
Woodside, E. E., and W. Kocholaty. 1964. *J. Bacteriol.* 87:1140–1146.
Wulff, D. L., and C. S. Rupert. 1962. *Biochem. Biophys. Res. Comm.* 7:237–240.
Wynne, E. S. 1952. *Bacteriol. Rev.* 16:101–110.
Wynne, E. S., and J. W. Foster. 1948. *J. Bacteriol.* 55:61–68.
Wynne, E. S., and K. Harrell. 1951. *Antibiot. Chemotherapy* 1:198–202.
Wynne, E. S., R. E. Collier, and D. A. Mehl. 1952. *J. Bacteriol.* 64:883–886.
Yarwood, C. E. 1950. *Am. J. Botany* 37:636–639.
Yarwood, C. E. 1954. *Proc. Nat. Acad. Sci. U.S.* 40:374–377.
Yarwood, C. E., S. Sidky, M. Cohen, and V. Stantilli. 1954. *Hilgardia* 22:603–622.
Zahl, P. A., L. R. Koller, and C. P. Haskins. 1939. *J. Gen. Physiol* 22:689–698.
Zamenhof, S. 1960. *Proc. Nat. Acad. Sci. U.S.* 46:101–105.
Zamenhof, S., H. Bursztyn, T. K. R. Reddy, and P. Zamenhof. 1965. *J. Bacteriol.* 90: 108–115.
Zelle, M. R., and A. Hollaender. 1955. in *Radiation Biology.* A. Hollaender, Ed., vol. 2. McGraw-Hill, N.Y., pp. 365–430.
Zellner, J. 1911. *Mh. Chem.* 32:1065–1074.
Zimmerman, A. 1925. *Zentr. Bacteriol. Parasitenk. Abt. II* 65:311–418.
Zirkle, R. E. 1940. *J. Cell. Comp. Physiol.* 16:221–235.
Zirkle, R. E. 1954. in *Radiation Biology.* A. Hollaender, Ed., vol. 1. McGraw-Hill, N.Y., pp. 315–350.
Zirkle, R. E., and C. A. Tobias. 1952. *Arch. Biochem. Biophys.* 47:282–306.
Zirkle, R. E., Dorothy F. Marchbank, and Kathryn D. Kuck. 1952. *J. Cell. Comp. Physiol.* 39:75–85.
Zöbl, K. 1950. *Sydowia* 4:175–184.

CHAPTER 4

Spores in Space

Panspermia

THE ACCEPTED plausibility of the "de novo" origin of life has tended to diminish interest in theories which propose a universe-wide origin and dissemination of organisms. As far back as 1821, Sales-Guyon de Montlivault suggested that life on earth originated by transfer of "seeds" from the moon. The more detailed hypothesis of Richter (1865) stated that life has existed as long as matter and that living particles are distributed throughout space. He combined this idea with that of evolution by proposing that when such a particle, or spore, alights in a suitable planetary environment, the planet would ultimately be covered by forms which have become adapted to their habitats. That space is an eternal repository of life was also proposed by Wagner (1874) who is quoted earlier in this book (page 1). Similar ideas have intrigued well-known scientists such as Lord Kelvin, Ferdinand Cohn, and H. v. Helmholtz (1884). The most extensive treatment of the subject was provided by the chemist Svante Arrhenius (1908, 1910) who used the name *panspermia* to describe the migration of spores from one planet to another. Arrhenius (Figure 4.1) made quantitative estimates of the time required for the traverse of spores through space when impelled by radiation pressure, and he discussed the probability of their survival in space. A recent addition to the theory is that of Lederberg and Cowie (1958) who suggest that a distinction be made between *natural* and *artificial* panspermia on the basis of the motive force used in transport. Natural means would include light pressure, force fields, convection,

Figure. 4.1 Svante Arrhenius. (From Benjamin Harrow, *Eminent Chemists of Our Time.* Van Nostrand Company, 1920, facing page 111.)

impacts with other heliocentric bodies, and so forth, whereas artificial means include spacecraft of various kinds.

Although the hypothesis was granted a place in speculation on the origin of life, only sporadic attempts, such as that of Lipman's, were made to put it to test. Several reasons can be given to explain the skepticism with which scientists viewed the theory. First of all, the search for the origin of life was not aided by the theory, for the locus of this event was merely transferred to another planet. Therefore, the question was evaded and rendered far less accessible to scientific investigation. Furthermore, technical difficulties such as the lack of reasonable impulsive forces and the vulnerability of known forms of life to conditions in space discouraged serious scientific attention. However, recent developments have enhanced the status of the theory of *panspermia* to the point where a reexamination is indicated.

The Current Status of Panspermia

In defense of *panspermia* it must be admitted that the technical difficulties which militated against the theory's acceptance are not conclusive. The argument based upon the implausibility of natural impulsive forces is a negative one and, in any event, requires amplification. Although the escape of spores from planets with an atmosphere like ours is unlikely, impacts with other bodies, electrokinetic forces, force fields, convection, the Poynting-Robertson effect, and ionospheric turbulence increase the probability of such an event. Once the particle is expelled from the atmosphere, less force would be required for its migration.

Furthermore, for the theory to be substantiated, only a single spore need arrive on earth. Calculations of the exact degree of probability of this event's occurring may not be feasible, but experimental work in the field of the automigration in space of particles like spores may define the separate probabilities upon which the over-all estimate can be based.

One of the major difficulties in the panspermia hypothesis is the vulnerability of living things to the hazards of existence in space. Such hazards are outlined in Table 4.1 in which certain characteristics of the strato-, iono-, and exospheres are provided. The durability of spores at extremes of temperature is well documented, as discussed in Chapter 3. For example, Becquerel's studies at the Cryogenic Laboratory in Holland have shown that several organisms will survive temperatures as low as 0.0075K. Such cells, when dry, are rapidly destroyed

Table 4.1 Environmental Factors of Biological Interest Encountered at Different Altitudes

Altitude (approx. miles)	Temperature (°C)	Pressure (mm Hg)	Other Characteristics	Sphere
0–1.2	−50 to 80	600 to 760	—	Bottom layer
1.2–7.5	−80 to 20	600 to 140	—	Troposphere
7.5–50	−80 to 80	140 to 2×10^{-2}	—	Stratosphere
10	−62	—	Limit of oxygen	Stratosphere
12	—	—	Protoplasmic water boils	Stratosphere
13–26	—	—	Ozone filters ultraviolet light	Stratosphere
20–50	—	—	Intense ultraviolet; corrosive monatomic chemicals	Stratosphere (chemo-)
50–500	60 to 1200?	10^{-8} at 325 miles	Gases ionized by ultraviolet	Ionosphere
120–140 (and beyond)	—	—	Aerodynamic support ends; heat transfer by radiation only	Ionosphere (hetero-)
95–250	60 to 1000?	—	Seasonal sunspots and flares	Ionosphere (F-layer)
Above 500				Exosphere (outer space)
600	—	10^{-12} to 10^{-16}[a]	Molecules can escape earth's gravity	Exosphere
1400–40,000	—	—	Layers of intense radiation	Exosphere (Van Allen belts)

SOURCE: Table taken in part from Sells and Berry, 1961.
[a] Report of Simons, 1959.

only at temperatures above 100°C and it is unlikely, in the rarified conditions found in space, that temperature by itself will limit survival of spores.

The ionosphere, as will be noted in Table 4.1, is characterized by pressures below 10^{-8} mm Hg at its upper limit, and the exosphere by pressures lower than 10^{-12} mm Hg. It is often assumed (Lederberg, 1960) that spores will resist high vacuums but thus far it has not been possible to achieve in the laboratory the vacuums found in outer space. Becquerel (1950) observed that several spores and seeds survived 1×10^{-6} mm Hg and −190°C (see page 68). Later Bakanauskas (1959) found that spores of *Bacillus subtilis* (var. *niger*), *B. mycoides*, *Aspergillus flavus*, and *A. niger*, but not *Bacillus cereus*, survived vacuums as high as 5×10^{-7} mm Hg for extended periods. By contrast, Brueschke et al. (1961) report that spores of *B. subtilis*, *Aspergillus niger*, and *A. terreus* cannot survive pressures of 1.2×10^{-8} mm Hg for 30 days. Spores of *Penicillium citrinum* succumbed in less than 10 days. On the other hand, Portner et al. (1961) observed that at 2×10^{-10} mm Hg at ambient temperatures, spores of *Bacillus subtilis* (var. *niger*) and *Aspergillus fumigatus*, and vegetative cells of *Mycobacterium smegmatis* survived for 5 days. In fact, the recovery of these organisms was not significantly different from that of the controls, from pressures of 4×10^{-2} mm Hg, or from storage under nitrogen. Since several days are required before the pressures are reduced to the minimum of the experiment, the rate of pumping may be a factor which contributes to the differences noted. In addition, the temperature of preparation and treatment of spores (see Chapters 2 and 3) also can influence survival of spores. A fuller review of this subject can be found in Siegel et al. (1965).

The first successful direct exposure of unprotected terrestrial microorganisms to space environments, and their recovery, was made by Hotchin, Lorenz, and Hemenway (1965). Until then, as the data discussed above indicate, data on survivability in space had been derived by extrapolation from terrestrial laboratory data (Hagen, Hawrylewicz, and Ehrlich, 1964; Degens, 1964). When viruses were exposed on the outside of a rocket that was fired up to 150 km, the viability of unshielded T-1 bacteriophage was reduced by a factor of 10^4, leaving about 100 particles as survivors; viable poliovirus decreased by a factor of at least 10^3 to a level below the threshold of the assay system. Another experiment was performed with a balloon whose altitude varied between 33.5 to 35 km (20.7 to 21.7 miles) during the exposure of microorganisms. The sample temperature was between −75° C and −45° C for about an hour, and 24° C for the rest of the flight; the samples were in sunlight for about four hours of the six-hour exposure. Although drying (of controls) did not reduce the viable count of spores of *Penicillium roqueforti*, flight exposure reduced it by 10^2. Therefore, there were surviving viruses and mold spores in these experiments in space, but with a considerable loss in viability. Further experiments of this kind will be very important in assessing the probability of the occurrence of panspermia, as well as of contamination during rocket travel (Committee on Contamination by Extraterrestrial Exploration, 1959; Sneath, 1961; Geiger et al. 1965).

The times that would be required for automigration of spores are much longer than those used in the low-vacuum experiments which have been described. The calculations of Arrhenius (1911) suggest that spores having a diameter of 0.15 to 0.2 μ could travel through space impelled by light pressure and convection currents but would require 9000 years to reach Alpha Centauri, the nearest star! On the other hand, he calculated that only 20 days would be needed for a spore of this size to reach Mars, 80 days to reach Jupiter, and 15 months to get to Neptune. If life exists in our galaxy, and Arrhenius' calculations are correct, then the times necessary for migration may not be outside the realm of experimentation. However, the effect of the high vacuums encountered for prolonged periods in space are untested. In the experiments discussed previously (page 104), the conditions under which evacuation is carried out can influence survival, so it is important that this work be extended to include higher vacuums as well as different rates of evacuation. Moreover, rocket flights which expose spores to the exosphere are a direct way of investigating some of these effects (see above).

Radiations have long been recognized as being one of the prime hazards to life that is traveling in space. Three sources of ionizing radiation appear to be of significant danger: (a) the primary cosmic radiation, (b) the protons and electrons of the Van Allen belts, and (b) the time-variational part of the cosmic rays, of which the solar flare protons are the most important. The dose rate due to primary cosmic rays probably is negligible compared with that due to the protons in the Van Allen belts and those of solar flares (Ganguly and Lence, 1961) but their relative biological effectiveness (RBE), may be very high. However, Curtis (1961) has concluded that "the heavy cosmic ray primaries do not constitute as serious a hazard as was once feared."

The existence of the Van Allen belts was first indicated by the Geiger counter readings of the Explorer I satellite; more detailed knowledge was obtained through Explorers III and IV, Pioneer and Luniks. These belts are two separate zones (Figure 4.2) extending into space from 1400 to 40,000 miles above the earth. Particles with energies from 20 kev to several million electron volts or greater are to be found in these zones in which electrons and protons predominate (Newell, 1960). Although the maximum density of these particles is only about one per cubic centimeter, the extent of the Van Allen belts makes them a serious hazard to living organisms. As pointed out by Van Allen (1961), similar belts of radiation may extend around all other magnetized celestial bodies of the solar system, and possibly even of other systems as well, so that additional hazards of this kind will undoubtedly be encountered in space.

Important time variations (several percent) in protons have been found at 27-day intervals, corresponding to the solar rotational period. Also, variations of

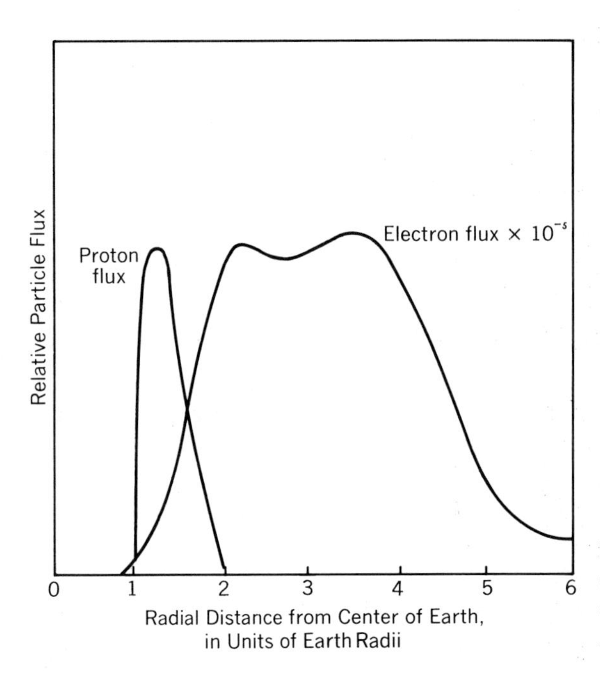

Figure 4.2 Radiation in the earth's outer atmosphere. (From N. K. Ganguly and J. T. Lence, *J. British Interplanetary Society* 18 : 110, 1961.)

up to 15 percent have been recorded during magnetic storms and smaller variations are recognized which correspond to sunspot cycles of 11 years (Ganguly and Lence, 1961). However, solar flare protons probably present the greatest danger to spores because increases in the primary flux of several thousand times the quiescent values have been recorded (Winckler and Freier, 1960). Heavy fluxes of 100 million volt protons, at relatively low altitudes, represent a danger which is difficult to control and to evaluate at present.

Ultraviolet radiation probably offers another great hazard to spores in space. Above the earth's atmosphere, about 1 percent of the total energy from the sun is in the ultraviolet range. The average intensity at about 2600 Å is over 200 ergs/cm^2 sec, so that continuous exposure would result in lethality (see Table 3.5) in relatively little time. But,as pointed out by Lederberg (1960), a thin layer of overlaying material would shield a spore from both ultraviolet and proton irradiation.

Possibilities of Survival in Space

As discussed in Chapter 3, temperature may either enhance or decrease the sensitivity of spores to irradiation, depending upon the degree of hydration. Although the data are too meager to permit definitive conclusions to be drawn, the amount of protection afforded appears to be too small to be of significant help to unshielded cells in space. This is probably true in view of the great length of time spores would be required to exist in space if propelled only by the means suggested by Arrhenius. For example, when Becquerel exposed spores to ultraviolet light under a high vacuum at $-190°C$, no survivors were recovered after only 6 hours of irradiation. Experiments have been conducted on the survival of bacteria in a simulated Martian environment, in which pressures of 85 mm Hg, and diurnally varying temperatures from 26–30°C to $-60°C$ were used. Although vegetative cells of *Clostridium tetani* did not survive 14 days in this environment, spores of this organism survived for 10 months and cells of *Klebsiella pneumoniae* for 8 months (Hawrylewicz et al., 1962). That other spore-formers survive the simulated Martian environment has been shown for *Bacillus cereus* (Roberts et al., 1963) and *B. subtilis* (Hagen et al., 1964). Nevertheless, no data exist on the effect of the high vacuums to be encountered in space on radiation sensitivity, so that there can be no finality in these conclusions either. A more complete review of this subject can be found in Siegel et al. (1965).

Far better protection might be afforded by attachment of spores to cosmic dust. For this mechanism to be effective, the spore must be protected on all sides, that is, it must be inside a granule or meteoritic fragment. In fact, as will be seen later, some claims have been made that organisms have survived in meteorites and increased attention undoubtedly will be paid to this possibility in the future.

Man-made protection and motive power are now available through the use of spacecraft. Therefore, the introduction of microbial life to other planets can be predicted in the foreseeable future. Interstellar space may even now be contaminated with terrestrial organisms that have survived in sheltered areas of orbiting vehicles. Because of the rapid generation time of many microbes and their easy disseminability, vast areas could be covered in a short time if the conditions for growth were extant. Lederberg (1960) has outlined the arguments for the rigorous exclusion of terrestrial contaminants from spacecraft. The opportunity of discovering whether life exists on other planets, as well as how it compares with our own, might be irretrievably lost by carelessness at this tentative point in our probing of space. In addition, Lederberg argues, the exhaustion or alteration of planetary resources by terrestrial organisms may deny us the use of these resources, thereby inadvertently depriving us of potentially precious materials. Moreover, inasmuch as round-trip interplanetary flights can be anticipated, the possibility must be considered that disease organisms and weeds against which we have no defense might be introduced to earth.

An opposing point of view is held by Abelson (1961) who claims that contamination of our moon, or of certain planets in our solar system, is not possible through organisms carried along with space devices. These conclusions are based upon the present inferences of physical and chemical characteristics of the space and planetary environments. Anders (1961) has calculated that it would be impossible to detect on the moon microorganisms of origin outside the solar system because they would occur in numbers far below the threshold for detection. Besides, they would be so far outnumbered (> 8×10^{11}) by creatures of terrestrial origin as to make their discovery even less likely. However, as Anders himself points out, these calculations do not refute the panspermia hypothesis. Although the deposition of the large numbers of extrasolar system microbes needed for detection (3.8×10^{13}) is highly improbable, only a single such spore arriving on earth is needed to prove the hypothesis. Also, Abelson is careful to point out that it is not possible to be certain at this time that no life exists on Venus or Mars, and his inferences do not extend beyond our solar system. Again, given extraterrestrial life, a finite probability exists that one or a small number of spores can survive. In the absence of data which can establish this probability with exactness, and recognizing the risks of contamination, it would seem prudent to exercise every caution to sterilize space vehicles as far as possible.

Evidences of Extraterrestrial Life

Some authors believe that natural panspermia is "in the limbo of irrefutable, untestable scientific hypotheses" (Lederberg, 1960). Since data of a kind have been accumulated, it is well to state some criteria for their evaluation. A basis for such criteria lies in the requirements set out previously (Chapter 3) for investigations of ancient terrestrial creatures, for there are many elements in common between studies of the latter type and those involving extraterrestrial materials. However, different emphases may be expected and many authors have stressed the possibility that life on other planets may be very different from that on earth. Such creatures might be based upon a similar chemistry but might have evolved in response to very different selective pressures, thereby requiring different kinds of adaptations in order to insure survival. To an extent, the same problem is faced on earth but the range of such possibilities is much more restricted than in the case of the many thousands of potential sites for extraterrestrial evolution. Furthermore, there is also the possibility that organisms exist which are based upon chemical systems different from our own. These possibilities are discussed by Haldane (1954), Spencer-Jones (1949), and others and are based in part upon differences in the relative abundance of chemical elements on certain planets. Criteria for the identification of life forms in extraterrestrial materials are set forth by Fitch and Anders (1963*a*), Sall (1964), and Lederberg (1965), and are discussed in Chapter 3, and in a recent book (Mamikunian and Briggs, 1965).

Chemical analyses of carbonaceous meteorites have revealed that materials of biological origin may be present. In the first half of the nineteenth century, Berzelius and Wohler both extracted organic compounds from chondrites.

Berthelot was able to isolate saturated hydrocarbons from a sample of the Orgueil meteorite. With more modern techniques, including mass spectrometry, this same material yielded mixtures of even-numbered hydrocarbons whose origin appears to be biological (Nagy et al., 1961). Acidic organic compounds and hydrocarbons were found in the Cold Bokkeveld meteorite, which fell in South Africa in 1838, and in the Orgueil meteorite (Nagy and Birz, 1963). Detailed studies of nitrogen-containing organic compounds have been performed by Calvin and Vaughn (1960) who found material with a long hydrocarbon chain, a carbonyl function, and an aromatic moiety. After fractionation on anionic resins, a sharp peak in the ultraviolet was found which, in combination with data on the change in absorption with *p*H, suggested the presence of cytosine. Purine-like substances appear to exist in the Orgueil chondrites (Briggs, 1961) and porphyrins as well (Hodgson and Baker, 1964).

But in the final analysis, the proof of the existence of extraterrestrial organisms will lie in their isolation. Such attempts have been made, including that of Lipman (1932) who claimed to have succeeded in culturing bacteria obtained from the interior of several stony meteorites. The organisms that were isolated were, as far as could be determined, identical to present-day terrestrial species. However, Roy (1935) painstakingly duplicated Lipman's techniques and sought to isolate organisms from similar materials. All his attempts failed, despite the use of the same media and the cooperation of Lipman, which permitted the development of precautional techniques not available in the previous experiments.

Fossil microorganisms have been stated to occur in carbonaceous meteorites (Claus and Nagy, 1961). Five samples of chondrites, including two from Orgueil (France, 1864), and one each from Ivuna (Central Africa, 1938), Mighei (Russia, 1889), and Murray (Arizona, 1950) were used, as well as two stony meteorites from Holbrook and Bruderheim. Numerous examples of microscopic particles resembling fossil algae (Figure 4.3) were found in the Orgueil and Ivuna materials but none were found in the stony meteorites. The Mighei and Murray meteorites yielded poorly defined elements which were, however, somewhat similar to those found in the other chondrites. The particles stained with a variety of familiar stains including zinc chloriodide, Janus green B, Feulgen, periodate-Schiff (PAS), hematoxylin, and ninhydrin. Furthermore, a diffusely staining material which the authors suggest could be a nucleus appeared in the cells. The large number of organisms found argue for the presence of considerable water during their formation. Yet the meteorites were kept dry for years and were out-of-doors only a few hours after reaching the earth. That the particles resemble aquatic algae argues against their having been introduced as contaminants from the soil in which the meteorites were embedded, but identifications of this kind can be misleading. Another significant fact is that similar types of particles were found in the Orgueil meteorite, which fell in the temper-

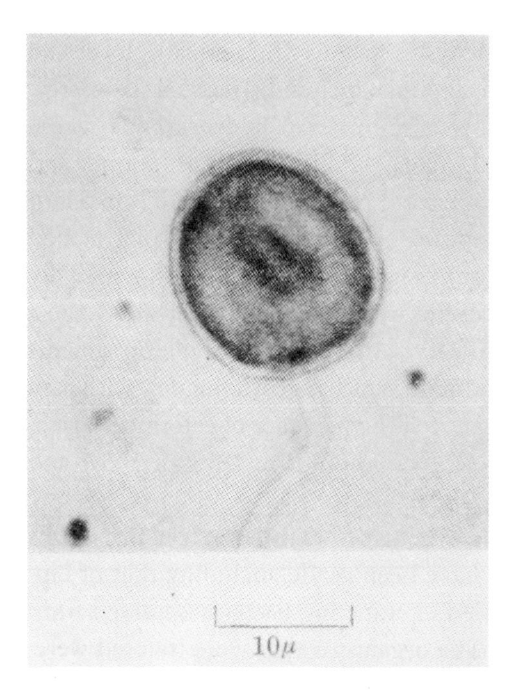

Figure 4.3 Organized element of Type 2 in Orgueil meteorite. (Taken from Claus and Nagy, 1961.)

ate region of southern France, and in the Ivuna meteorite, which fell 74 years later in the tropics of Central Africa. Subsequently, Nagy et al. (1962) reported that the Jonk and Alais meteorites contained particles similar to those in the Orgueil and Ivuna ones. These particles were found in meteorites that fell over a span of 132 years and thousands of miles apart. Such a coincidence in the types of elements contained in the chondrites would hardly be expected if they were terrestrial contaminants, so Claus and Nagy suggest extraterrestrial origin.

Additional recent evidence supporting the extraterrestrial origin of the particles from the Orgueil meteorite derives from the finding of porphyrins in this material (Hodgson and Baker, 1964). Thus, the virtual absence of chlorins in the meteorite extracts, and their marked excess over porphyrins in dusts, soils, and recent sediments argues against contamination by terrestrial materials. Furthermore, Nagy et al. (1963*a*) have shown that acid-leaching of minerals within the "organized elements" is necessary before absorption peaks between 2600–2800 Å are obtained, suggesting again that the materials are not terrestrial contaminants. Also electron-probe analyses of the organized elements reveal that they consist of the same chemical elements as those that are in the body of the meteorite and are in exact conformity with the texture of the meteorite (Nagy et al., 1963*b*). Corroboration of some of these findings has come from several sources which are cited by Claus et al. (1963).

However, this evidence is still not conclusive. The meaning of the staining reactions obtained by Nagy and co-workers is not clear, nor are the evidences of a "nuclear" region to which they allude. Thus, Fitch and Anders (1963*a*, *b*) claim that some of the particles they found in the Orgueil and Ivuna meteorites stained the brilliant magenta expected of the Feulgen and PAS stains without prior acid hydrolysis, thereby rendering the stains nonspecific. Because the methyl green-pyronin stain acts by complexing with phosphoric acid groups, as opposed to the affinity of Schiff's reagent for aldehydes, the presence of DNA was sought by the use of this stain. However, as in the case of the Feulgen and PAS stains, methyl green-pyronin reacted nonspecifically so that the presence of DNA was not confirmed by these means. The highly structured particles reported by Claus and Nagy were absent in the preparations of Fitch and Anders, although the same materials were used. Moreover, the latter authors claim (Fitch and Anders, 1963*a*, *b*) that some of these particles resemble common airborne contaminants like ragweed and juniper pollen. Although both groups report the presence of irregular, roughly spherical grains of smaller size, Fitch and Anders claim not to find as many as were first reported. They claim that these do not fluoresce or take biological stains in a manner that will distinguish them from mineral fragments. Others have pointed out that minerals may precipitate into patterns which are highly organized and bear striking resemblances to living creatures (Oparin, 1957).

Moreover, Mueller (1964) suggests that foreign bodies can penetrate to considerable depth in the course of the impact of a meteorite, especially in the case of porous and soft carbonaceous stones. Besides physical penetration of this kind, he argues that distillates of plant remains, which are contiguous to hot stones, could be absorbed ". . . as a result of vacuum forming through the cooling down of the meteorite. . ." Furthermore, Mueller could find no optically rotating molecules in the Cold Bokkeveldt meteorite and he asks whether the occurrence of such compounds is within the range of terrestrial impact and storage contamination. Nor could Hayatsu (1965) confirm the report of Nagy et al. (1964) regarding optical activity in the Orgueil meteorite, and he suggests that instrumental artifacts may have led to the latter group's results. Finally, Degens (1964) points out that the final fossil organic remains will be the same whether the molecules were of biogenic or abiogenic origin, and so the genetic nature of the precursor materials may not be derivable by chemical analyses alone.

In conclusion, there are three separate but related questions concerning the nature of organized elements in meteorites:

Are they of biogenic origin?
Did they originate indigenously to the meteorite?
Are they of terrestrial or of extraterrestrial origin?

As for the first question, it appears to be established that at least some of these elements contain substances which are characteristic of terrestrial organisms, including optically active fatty acids, porphyrins, materials which absorb between 2600–2800 Å and those that respond positively to a number of stains which are specific for substances found in present-day organisms. Some of these stains may react nonspecifically with the contents of some of the particles, but there are others for which the reaction seems specific. Moreover, the morphology of some of the organized elements is suggestive of that of certain algae and other organisms. However, full proof has not yet been provided that these are of biogenic origin.

The recent data of Claus and his co-workers, as well as of others, argues in favor of the suggestion that some of the organized elements are indigenous to the meteorites. Although contaminants like pollen have been found, the conformity of the particles to the structure of the meteorite, the small pore size (1 μ) of the rock, and the detailed chemical studies which have been mentioned support the conclusion that some of the organized elements may not be terrestrial contaminants.

Finally, the question of the place of origin of these elements must be answered. It is the most difficult question of all to answer because of the uncertainty surrounding the origin of the chondritic meteorites themselves. Thus, there are grounds for the belief that these are of terrestrial origin, so that the origin of the organized elements ultimately may be traced back to the earth. On the other hand, if the meteorites are proved to be of extraterrestrial origin, the origin of the organized elements must be sought in space. In any event, in view of new technical advances, as well as freshly exposed areas of ignorance, Oparin's (1957) conclusion that we must "reject the hypothesis that the germs of life reached the earth from somewhere else . . ." appears to be premature.

Life on Other Planets in the Solar System?

Speculations on the chemical theory of evolution have generally concluded that this process will occur anywhere in the universe where favorable conditions of atmosphere, temperature, and chemical environment exist (Oparin, 1960; Fox, 1960; Calvin, 1962). At the present time our information is inadequate to decide whether life as we know it can exist on other planets in our solar system or whether independent evolution has given rise to other forms of life unknown on Earth. On the basis of present information from direct observations, one can conclude unequivocally that the Moon, lacking an atmosphere, cannot support life. The Moon may, as has been frequently pointed out (Anders, 1961), serve as a repository of intracellular dormant forms of life from Earth or other planets. Our two nearest neighbors, Venus and Mars, are the most similar to Earth and provide the best prospects for supporting life (Table 4.2). A detailed examination of this subject is provided in the book by Mamikunian and Briggs (1965).

Table 4.2. Environments of the Planets

Planet	Relative Surface Gravity	Period: Rotation	Period: Revolution	Inclination of Axis to Ecliptic (deg)	Approx. Temp. (°C)	Mean Relative Energy from Sun (per unit area)	Radiation Striking Surface	Atmosphere[a] Water Vapor percent	Atmosphere[a] Oxygen percent	Atmosphere[a] Carbon dioxide percent	Atmosphere[a] Other	Relative atmospheric pressure
rcury	0.38	88 day	88 day		−234[b] +277[c]	6.60	Complete solar spectrum	0	0	0	0	0
us	0.88	10–30 day(?)	224.7 day		77[d]	1.90	?	< 2	< 2	> 10,000	?	0
th	1.00	23 hrs.– 56 mins.	365.3 day	23	−71 to +57	1.00	Most ultraviolet light filtered out	100	100	100	N, Ar, other	1.00
rs	0.39	24 hrs.– 37 mins.	687.0 day	25	−101 to +30	0.43	Ultraviolet sometimes penetrates	< 1	< 1	200	N, Ar[e]	~0.10
ter lanets[b]												
Uranus	1.05			98								
Jupiter	2.65	~10[b]		3								
Neptune		~16[b]										
All			12–165 yr		−134 and below	0.04 and less					Methane, NH_4, H_2, He	

RCE: Data from Salisbury, 1962.
xpressed as a percentage of that occurring above the Earth's surface.
ark side.
ght side.
obably too slow as a result of data from recent probes.
and Ar inferred.
uto excluded.

VENUS

Our nearest neighbor is Venus which has a smaller orbit near the Sun and is consequently warmer. Venus is about the same size as the Earth and has an atmosphere containing large amounts of carbon dioxide and possibly some water. The cloud cover has obscured vision of the planet, although information from the recent Venus probe may provide an insight into the nature of the surface of Venus. The fragmentary data available at this time from the Venus probe confirm the earlier conclusion that the temperature on Venus is very high (c. 500°C). This high temperature, if correct, would therefore eliminate Venus as a source of life.

MARS

Considerably greater interest has been generated in the possibility that life exists on Mars (Salisbury, 1962; Lederberg and Sagan, 1962). As shown in Table 4.2, Mars is smaller than the Earth, has a day length approximately that of Earth, and receives approximately 43 percent of the light that the Earth does. Estimates of the temperature of Mars and its daily variation are shown in Figure 4.4. The daily temperature on Mars fluctuates about 40°C cooler than that on the Gobi Desert, ranging from a high of about 5°C to a low of −70°C or −100°C.

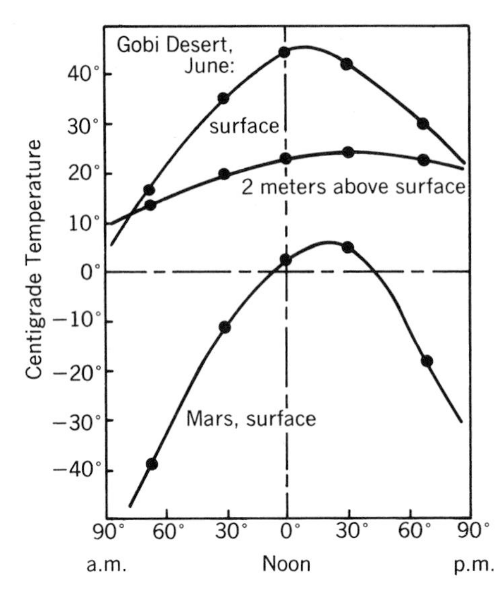

Figure 4.4 Average temperatures on Mars (at the equator) compared with temperatures on the Gobi Desert. The abscissa represents degrees of longitude east or west of the noon meridian. The curve may be thought of as an average lower limit. (From Salisbury, 1962.)

At present, only estimates can be made of the atmosphere of Mars (Table 4.1). The pressure is about 0.1 atm, which is made up largely of carbon dioxide and some nitrogen and argon. The extreme dryness of Mars has led Abelson (1961) to argue that life cannot exist. However, as pointed out by Lederberg and Sagan (1962) and Salisbury (1962), local variations, for example, frozen subsoil and geothermal warm spots, must be taken into consideration. In addition, some terrestrial microorganisms survive in a simulated Martian environment (Hawrylewicz et al., 1962), and forms of life might well have developed to withstand low relative humidities. As suggested by Horowitz (1962), "Such a flora might spend most of its metabolic energy in concentrating water from the atmosphere." It must therefore be concluded that at least microbial life on Mars is a possibility.

REFERENCES

Abelson, P. H. 1961. *Proc. Nat. Acad. Sci., U.S.* 47:575–581.

Anders, E. 1961. *Science* 133:1115–1116.

Arrhenius, S. 1908. *Vorstellung vom Weltgebäude im Wandel der Zeiten.* Trans. by Lily Bamberger. Akademische Verlags gesellschaft. Leipzig.

Arrhenius, S. 1910. *L'evolution des mondes. La Vie dans l'Univers.* Paris, 236 pp.

Arrhenius, S. 1911. *Das Weltall.* Akademische Verlagsgesellschaft. Leipzig.

Bakanauskas, S. 1959. *WADC.* TN 59–142. Sept.

Becquerel, P. 1950. *Compt. Rend. Acad. Sci.* 231:1392–1394.

Briggs, M. H. 1961. *Nature* 191:1137–1140.

Brueschke, E. E., R. G. Suess, and M. Willard. 1961. TM–679, Res. and Dev. Div., Hughes Aircraft Co., Culver City, Calif.

CALVIN, M. 1962. *Am. Inst. Biol. Sci. Bull.* 12:29.

CALVIN, M., and SUSAN K. VAUGHN. 1959. *Univ. Calif. Lawrence Radiation Lab. Rept.* UCRL–8993.

CLAUS, G., and B. NAGY. 1961 *Nature* 192: 594–596.

CLAUS, G., B. NAGY, and D. L. EUROPA. 1963. *Ann. N.Y. Acad. Sci.* 108:580–605.

Committee on Contamination by Extraterrestrial Exploration. 1959. *Nature* 183:925–928.

CURTIS, H. J. 1961. *Science* 133:312–316.

DEGENS, E. T. 1964. *Nature* 202:1092–1093.

FITCH, F. W., and E. ANDERS. 1963*a*. *Ann. N.Y. Acad. Sci.* 108:495–513.

FITCH, F. W., and E. ANDERS. 1963*b*. *Science* 140:1097–1100.

FOX, S. W. 1960. *Science* 132:200–208.

GANGULY, N. K., and J. T. LENCE. 1961. *J. Brit. Interplanet. Soc.* 18:110–114.

GEIGER, P. J., L. D. JAFFE and G. MAMIKUNIAN. 1965. *In* G. Mamikunian and M. Briggs, Ed. *Current Aspects of Exobiology*. Pergamon, New York. pp. 283–322.

HAGEN, C. A., E. J. HAWRYLEWICZ, and R. EHRLICH. 1964. *Appl. Microbiol.* 12:215–218.

HALDANE, J. B. S. 1954. in *New Biology*. M. L. Johnson, M. Abercrombie, and G. E. Fogg, eds. vol. 16. Penguin, London, pp. 12–27.

HAWRYLEWICZ, E., B. GOWDY, and R. EHRLICH. 1962. *Nature* 193:497.

HAYATSU, R. 1965. *Science* 149:443–447

HELMHOLTZ, H. VON. 1893. *Popular Lectures on Scientific Subjects*. Transl. by E. Atkinson. Longmans, Green & Co., London., 293 pp.

HODGSON, G. W., and B. L. BAKER. 1964. *Nature* 202:125–131.

HOROWITZ, N. H. 1962. *Federation Proc.* 21:687–691.

HOTCHIN, J., P. LORENZ, and C. HEMENWAY. 1965. *Nature* 206:442–445.

LEDERBERG, J. 1960. *Science* 132:393–400.

LEDERBERG, J. 1965. *Nature* 207:9–13.

LEDERBERG, J., and D. B. COWIE. 1958. *Science* 127:1473–1475.

LEDERBERG, J., and C. SAGAN. 1962. *Proc. Nat. Acad. Sci.*, U.S. 48:1473–1475.

LIPMAN, C. B. 1932. *Am. Museum Novitates* 588:1–19.

MAMIKUNIAN, G. and M. H. BRIGGS, 1965. *Current Aspects of Exobiology*. Pergamon, New York. 420 pp.

MUELLER, G. 1964. *Nature* 204:567.

NAGY, B., and SISTER MARY CAROL BITZ. 1963. *Arch. Biochem. Biophys.* 101:240–248.

NAGY, B., W. G. MEINSCHEIN, and D. J. HENNESSY. 1961. *Ann. N.Y. Acad. Sci.* 93:25–35.

NAGY, B., G. CLAUS, and D. J. HENNESSY. 1962. *Nature* 193:1129–1133.

NAGY, B., K. FREDRIKSSON, J. KUDYNOWSKI, and L. CARLSON. 1963*a*. *Nature* 200:565–566.

NAGY, B., K. FREDRIKSSON, H. UREY, G. CLAUS, C. A. ANDERSEN, and JOAN PERRY. 1963*b*. *Nature* 198:121–125.

NAGY, B., M. T. J. MURPHY, V. E. MODZELESKI, G. ROUSER, G. CLAUS, D. J. HENNESSEY, U. COLUMBO, and F. GAZZARRANI. 1964. *Nature* 202:228–233.

NEWELL, H. E. JR. 1960. *Science* 131:385–390.

OPARIN, A. I. 1957. *The Origin of Life on the Earth*. Academic Press, N.Y., 495 pp.

OPARIN, A. I. 1959–1960. *International Symposium on the Origin of Life on the Earth, Moscow*, Pergamon Press, London, 691 pp.

PORTNER, DOROTHY M., D. R. SPINER, R. K. HOFFMAN, and C. R. PHILLIPS. 1961. *Science* 134:2047.

RICHTER, H. E. 1865. *Schmidts Jahrb. Ges. Med.* p. 126.

ROBERTS, T. L., R. J. BALL, and E. S. WYNNE. 1963. *U.S. Air Force School of Aerospace Medicine, Tech. Doc. Rept.* No. SAM-TDR-62-151.

ROY, SHARAT KUMAR. 1935. *Geological Ser., Field Museum Nat. Hist.* 6:179–198.

SALISBURY, F. B. 1962. *Science* 136:17–26.

SALL, T. 1964. *Trans. N.Y. Acad. Sci.* 26:553–563.

SELLS, S. B., and C. A. BERRY. 1961. *Human Factors in Jet and Space Travel.* Ronald Press, N.Y., 386 pp.

SIEGEL, S. M., G. RENWICK, O. DALY, G. GIUMARRO, G. DAVIS and L. HALPERN. 1965. *In* G. Mamikunian and M. H. Briggs, Ed. *Current Aspects of Exobiology*. Pergamon. New York, pp. 119–178.

SIMONS, J. C. 1959. Paper 14th Annual Meeting and Astronautical Exposition, Am. Rocket Soc., Wash., D.C., Nov.

SNEATH, P. H. A. 1961. *In* N. W. PIRIE, Ed., *Biology of Space Travel.* Hafner. New York. pp. 95–106.

SPENCER-JONES, H. 1949. *Life on Other Worlds*. New American Library, N.Y., 157 pp.

VAN ALLEN, J. A. 1961. *Radiation Res.* 14:540–550.

WAGNER, M. 1874. *Augsburger Allgem. Z., Beilage*. Oct. 6, 7, and 8.

WINCKLER, J. R., and P. S. FREIER. 1960. *Phys. Rev. Letters* 3:19.

CHAPTER 5

Description of the Germination Process

Criteria for Measuring Germination

THE PROTRUSION of the epicotyl from a seed, or a germ tube from spores of actinomycetes and fungi, is considered an indication that germination has occurred. Germination in some other organisms results in the release of amoeboid or flagellate swarmers from cysts and spores, as in the case of some protozoans and fungi. In these organisms, the end point of germination is recognized through a gross morphological alteration, accompanied by the appearance of another stage in the life cycle. As will be seen later, the wall of the spore or cyst may be ruptured upon germination, as it is in many protozoans, algae, and fungi, or it may remain continuous with the wall of the following stage, as in other fungi and actinomycetes. In the latter instance, the morphological alteration consists of the formation of a unilateral swelling instead of the rupture of, and release from, the spore wall.

In conformity with the usage in other organisms, De Bary (1887) considered that germination of bacterial spores "consists chiefly in the development of the spore into a cell which assumes all the characters of the parent-cell as regards conformation and vegetation." More recently, Thimann (1955), Fitz-James (1956), and Knaysi (1957), among others, have continued this usage. However, many recent investigators have applied physiological criteria to judge the end of germination (Chapter 9). Among the physiological changes that occur after activation of the bacterial spore are the following:

1. Loss of resistance to environmental stresses such as extremes of temperature, desiccation, radiation, and chemicals (Williams, 1952).

2. Loss of refractility and darkening of the spore when examined by phase-contrast microscopy (Pulvertaft and Haynes, 1951).
3. Increased stainability with basic dyes (Powell, 1950; Levinson and Sevag, 1953).
4. Reduction in the optical density of spores in water, usually at 610 mμ (Powell, 1950; Hachisuka et al., 1954). Other wavelengths have been used, but all techniques of this kind rely upon the changes in refractive index mentioned in (2) above.
5. Decrease in dry weight of spores (Powell and Strange, 1953).
6. The release into the suspending medium of dipicolinic acid, calcium, and peptides containing muramic acid (Powell and Strange, 1953; Strange, 1959; Strange and Powell, 1954).
7. Swelling of the spore (Lamanna, 1940).
8. Enhanced respiratory activity (Mandels et al., 1956).
9. Hydration of the spore (Rode and Foster, 1960).
10. Appearance of nutritional differences (Amaha and Sakaguchi, 1954; Demain and Newkirk, 1960).
11. Increase in sensitivity to lysozyme (Demain and Newkirk, 1960).

Most of the changes listed above have been used as indexes of germination but most recent studies are based upon the definition provided by Campbell (1957): "spore germination in bacteria may be regarded as the change from a heat-resistant spore to a heat-labile entity which may not necessarily be a true vegetative cell." The advantages in the adoption of this criterion of germination lie in the convenience and accuracy of measurement, the fact that the degree of heat-resistance is an important and seemingly universal difference between spores and vegetative cells of bacteria, and in the good correlation of the change in heat-resistance with other changes that ensue upon activation. This criterion was applied first by Fischroeder (1909). Recently, Wynne and Foster (1948) drew attention to the advantages and feasibility of the technique.

The use of physiological criteria to judge the end point of germination has been criticized by Knaysi (1957), who prefers to use the appearance of the vegetative cell as the criterion. It can be argued that the classical biological definition of germination employed morphological markers (for example, the appearance of the germ tube and vegetative cell) so that other definitions violate established priority. However, the vegetative stage is frequently difficult to recognize or to use quantitatively. Bacteria as well as certain fungi may produce two or more stages sequentially after the spore case is broken. Furthermore, physiological and morphological states intervene between the activation of the spore and the time when a recognizable vegetative cell is liberated (page 125).

In view of these difficulties, the following guide lines are useful in the evaluation of criteria for germination:

1. The criterion employed should represent a stage in the development of the spore that is correlative with other markers.
2. The technique evolved should be accurate and convenient to use.
3. Different criteria will probably have to be evolved for different organisms. For example, heat-sensitivity cannot be used with spores that are not heat-resistant in the dormant state.

4. The marker used should be a stable and ubiquitous one that commits the spore to further development; the stage reached should, therefore, be irreversible.

The following definition of germination is presented in an attempt to apply these guide lines generally: *Germination occurs when the first irreversible stage that is recognizably different from the dormant organism is reached, as judged by physiological or morphological criteria.*

When bacterial germination is considered, the application of a physiological criterion, heat-sensitivity, will be accepted as outlined by Campbell. In the case of fungi, the protrusion of a germ tube, or the rupturing of the spore coat and exit of the next stage, will represent the end of the germination process. These differing criteria of germination have resulted in terminological divergences that are summarized in Figure 5.1.

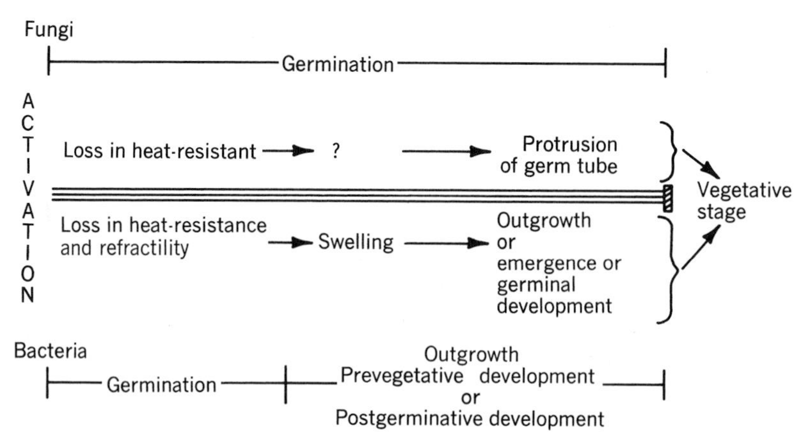

Figure 5.1 Terminology used in describing the germination process in bacterial and fungus spores.

The conversion of a bacterial spore to a vegetative cell occurs in two phases, germination and outgrowth (postgermination or prevegetative development). As will be discussed in Chapter 6, this process includes increase in respiratory capacity, loss of brilliance under dark-contrast phase-microscopy, and loss of DPA and heat-resistance. At this time the spores become stainable and may increase somewhat in size. During their postgerminative development they swell markedly, the vegetative cell emerges, elongates, and undergoes cell division concomitantly with other changes in respiratory rate (Levinson and Hyatt, 1956).

However, in certain bacteria, such as the cysts of *Azotobacter* (Socolofsky and Wyss, 1961; Tchan et al., 1962), and the spores of actinomycetes, difficulties arise in the application of the criteria of germination which has been described. These forms are heat-sensitive, lack DPA, but resist desiccation and, therefore, are functionally analogous to endospores. In the final analysis, the question that remains is, "Does the convenience inherent in the use of heat-resistance as a criterion of germination in bacterial spores justify the abandonment of a morphological criterion whose use is general wherever resistant structures are found in nature?"

Morphology of the Germination Process

The complexity of the events accompanying the breaking of the dormant state are well illustrated by inspection of the morphological changes involved. Although there are many common features in the germination of diverse types of spores, no one criterion can be applied to all germination systems. In order to illustrate the similarities and differences, the morphological changes accompanying the germination of three types of spores (bacteria, actinomycetes, and fungi) are summarized below.

BACTERIA

There is enough regularity in the germination of aerobic spore-formers to be of taxonomic use. Lamanna (1940) was able to distinguish between those spores that germinate by shedding the spore coat (*Bacillus subtilis, B. vulgatus* and *B. mesentericus*) and those that appear to absorb the spore coat (*B. cereus, B. megaterium*, and *B. mycoides*). Spores in the former group do not expand more than two-fold in volume previous to the protrusion of the vegetative cell, whereas the latter spores expanded three-fold or more. In addition, these organisms differ on the basis of the position at which the vegetative cell breaks through the coat.

Some of the changes that the spores of *B. megaterium* undergo upon germination are shown in Figure 5.2. In dormant spores the cortex is indistinguishable from the cytoplasmic core and spore coat. Early in germination the cortex becomes visible, and subsequently diminishes in visibility and disappears. Parallel studies with the electron microscope suggest the disintegration of the cortex during this period.

When dormant spores are viewed with a phase microscope in dark-contrast, they appear brilliant (Figure 5.2). During germination, the spore becomes more rounded, larger, heat-labile and stainable. At the same time, the spores lose their brilliance under dark-contrast phase microscopy and become dark, while under the ultraviolet microscope they no longer absorb, due to the loss of dipicolinic acid (see Chapter 9). The kinetics of these changes during germination are summarized in Chapter 6.

Electron microscopy of spores during germination and emergence has provided more detail for these observations. An example of this is shown in Figures

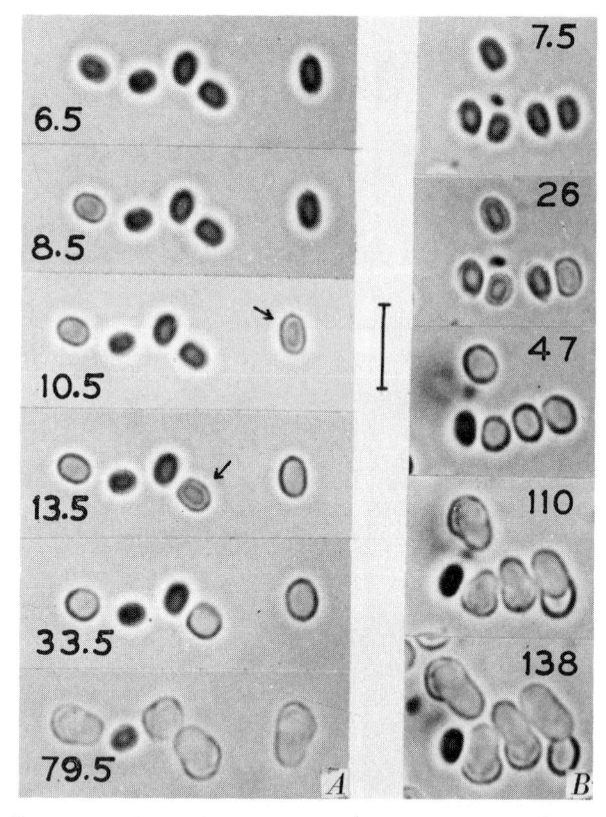

Figure 5.2 Successive stages in the germination of two groups of living spores of *Bacillus megaterium*. Arrows point to spores in which the cortex is visible as a white band within the dark spore coat. After becoming visible the cortex becomes indistinct as in the fourth and fifth pictures in series A. Numbers refer to minutes after the start of the experiments. × 3600. (Taken from Robinow, 1960, courtesy Academic Press, Inc., Publishers.)

5.3–5.10 for the germination of spores of *Clostridium tetani*. The structure of the mature spores (Figure 5.3) is similar to that described for other bacterial spores. When spores of *C. tetani* are activated and incubated for 2.5 hours, the "intermediate space" (IM) accumulates coarse reticulate material, and the inner spore coat (IC) and cortex (CX) swells (Figure 5.4). In addition, the new cell wall of the germinating spore becomes visible (Figure 5.5), the nuclear elements decrease in density, and their contours become distinct and confluent (Figure 5.6). The horseshoe shape of the nucleus is seen at this time and slightly later the nuclear material moves into the center of the spore and the cytoplasm becomes of low electron density and of rough texture like that of the vegetative cell. Some swelling has already taken place, as can be seen by comparing the magnification of Figure 5.7 with that of Figures 5.5. and 5.6.

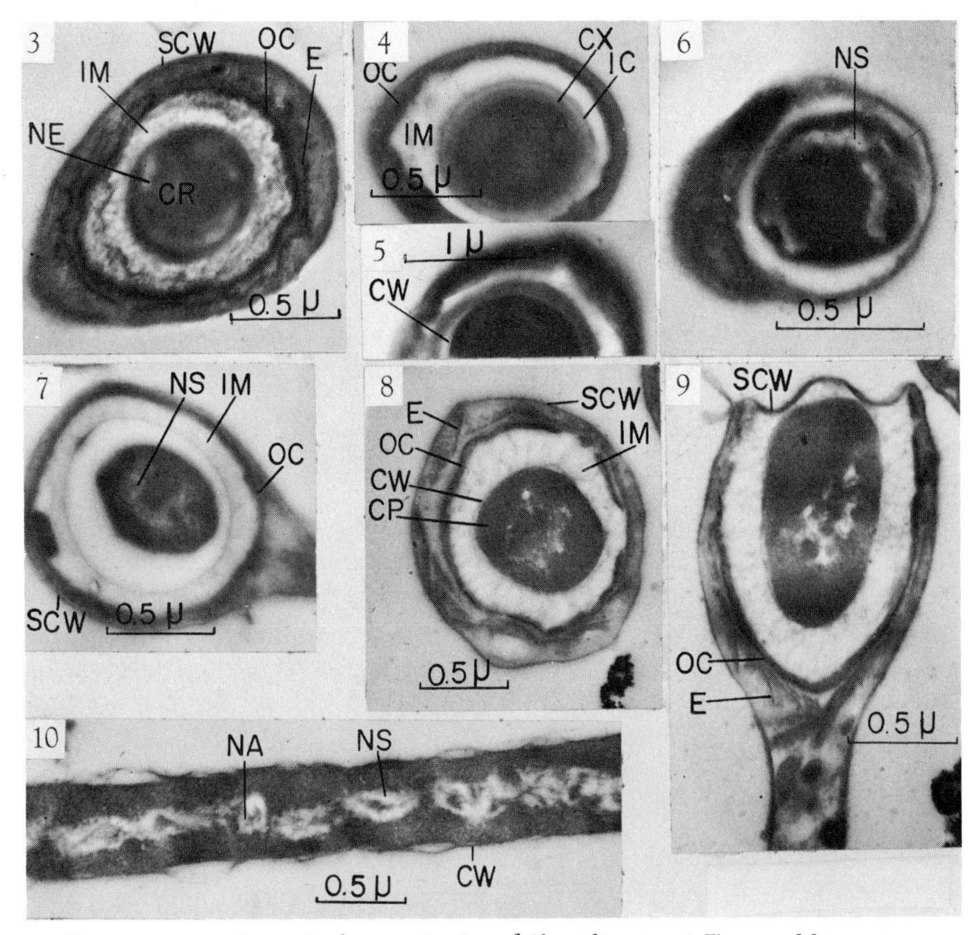

Figures 5.3–5.10 Stages in the germination of *Clostridium tetani*. Fig. 5.3 Mature spore from 48-hour culture. Figures 5.4–5.10 Sectioned spores, during germination. Fig. 5.4 The thick inner spore coat and the cortex are swollen and the intermediate space appears coarsely reticulate. Fig. 5.5 A delicate membrane can be seen to have formed around the core and probably is the cell wall of the newly germinated cell. Fig. 5.6 Inner coat and cortex disppear while the nuclear sites become more distinct. Fig. 5.7 Nuclear apparatus is visible and cytoplasm of spore becomes of low electron density. Fig. 5.8 Germinated cell, 3.5 hours after activation. Outer spore coat and exosporium visible, as is radial arrangement of cytoplasm in intermediate space. Fig. 5.9 Rupture of outer spore coat and exosporium, 3.5 hours after activation. Fig. 5.10 A young vegetative cell grown for 9 hours showing catenary arrangement of nuclear sites. Legend: CP, cytoplasm; CR, core; CW, cell wall; CX, cortex; E, exosporium; IC, inner spore coat; IM, intermediate space; NA, nuclear apparatus; NE, nuclear element; NS, nuclear site; OC, outer spore coat; SCW, sporangium cell wall. (All figures taken from Takagi et al., 1960.)

A germinated cell after 3.5 hours is shown in Figure 5.8, in which the radial arrangement of the remains of the cytoplasm surrounding the germinating spore is visible in the intermediate space. The outer spore coat and exosporium are still present but are ruptured upon the emergence of the vegetative cell (Figure 5.9). Rupture has occurred at the distal end of the spore and the sporangium cell wall (SCW) covers the new vegetative cell which enlarges as it emerges. A picture of a vegetative cell of *C. tetani* is presented in Figure 5.10 for comparison and the characteristic arrangement of the nuclear sites in a chain can be seen.

A point at issue in the sequence of morphological changes accompanying germination and outgrowth concerns the origin of the new cell wall. One suggestion has been that the inner spore coat of resting mature spores of *Bacillus cereus* becomes the cell wall of the new vegetative cell (Chapman and Zworykin, 1957). However, the innermost layer of the cortex becomes the cell wall, according to Mayall and Robinow (1957), and Takagi et al. (1960) claim that in the clostridia they studied the inner spore coat is separate from the cell wall.

ACTINOMYCETES

Glauert and Hopwood (1961) have studied the germination of spores of *Streptomyces violaceoruber*. The end point of germination in the Actinomycetes is usually taken as the appearance of the germ tube (see Figure 5.11). During germination, the double-layered spore wall seems continuous with that of the germ tube (Figure 5.12). The germ tube wall adjacent to the spore is thicker than the substrate hypha but thins out to reach its usual thickness as development proceeds. Vacuoles, which are present upon the formation of the spores (Figure 5.11), persist for a while after germination, then disappear. Possibly these represent "granulose," or other storage material like that found in the cytoplasm of some anaerobic bacilli during spore formation (Robinow, 1960).

Granules 15 mμ in diameter are found in the cytoplasm of germinating spores and young hyphae, but finer ones may be seen in more mature hyphae. Larger, and very dense granules (Figure 5.12) are more frequent in germ tubes than in the rest of the mycelium and may represent the metachromatic polyphosphate granules found in other bacteria.

Cross-wall formation begins with a triangular ingrowth of wall material (Figure 5.12) at the periphery of the hypha. The plasma membrane is continuous around this ingrowth. It is likely that an annulus of wall material extends around the inside of the hypha and gradually grows inwards until the cross-wall is complete.

FUNGI

The morphological description of the germination of yeast ascospores has been complicated by disagreement as to whether the nucleus is located in the vacuole (Lindegren et al., 1956) or in the cytoplasm (Widra and De Lamater, 1955, and others). However, the concensus of recent work would favor the latter point of view inasmuch as Feulgen-positive material of relatively light electron density,

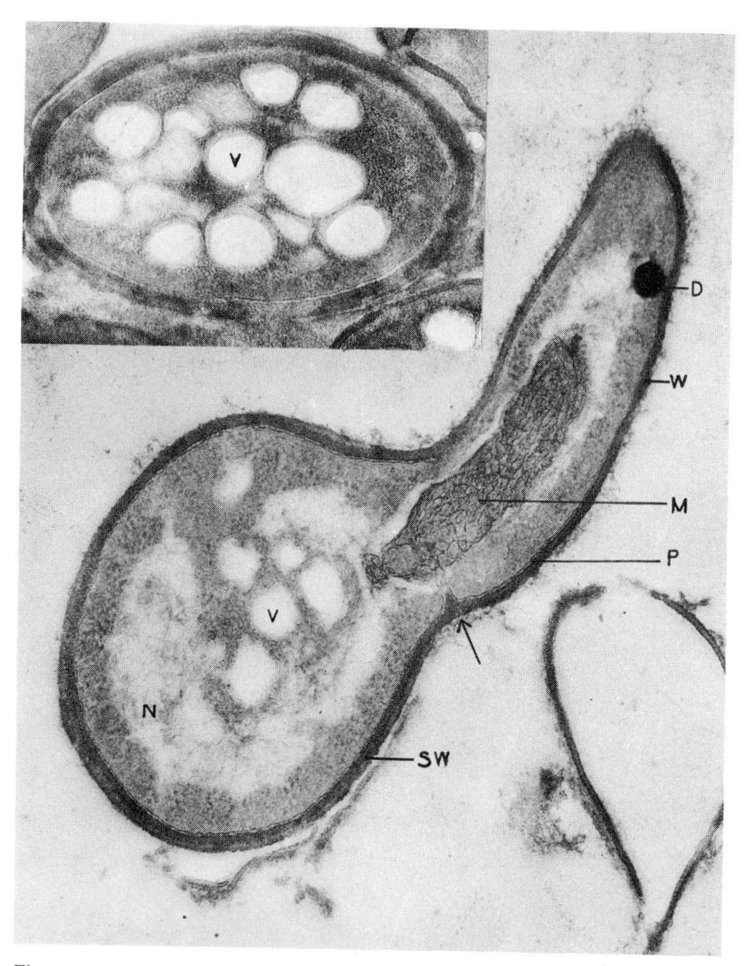

Figure 5.11 (*top left*) Mature spores of *Streptomyces violaceoruber*. Note the thick wall and vacuoles (V) in the nuclear region. Section stained with uranyl acetate. × 80,000. (Taken from A. M. Glauert and D. A. Hopwood, 1961.)

Figure 5.12 A germinating spore of *Actinomyces violaceoruber*. At an early stage in cross-wall formation a triangular ingrowth of wall material is seen at the periphery of the hypha (see arrow). The plasma membrane (P) extends inward around this ingrowth and is continuous with a large membranous body (M). Vacuoles (V) in the nuclear region (N) may represent the site of storage material and the very dense granule (D) a volutin granule. Wall material of hypha (W) end of spore (SW) are separated at incipient cross wall. × 80,000. (Taken from A. M. Glauert and D. A. Hopwood, 1961.)

surrounded by a double membrane, has been found in the cytoplasm of different yeasts (Agar and Douglas, 1957; Conti and Naylor, 1960) as well as in fungi as diverse as *Histoplasma* (Edwards et al., 1960), *Dictyostelium* (Gezelius, 1961), and *Neurospora* (Shatkin and Tatum, 1959; Zalokar, 1960). A consistent pattern of nuclear behavior in several of these organisms can be demonstrated in that chromosomes appear not to be formed during vegetative divisions; the nuclear membrane persists and duplication of the nucleus occurs by constriction.

There is one nucleus per ascospore in *Saccharomyces cerevisiae* whose structure seems similar to those in the vegetative cell (Hashimoto et al., 1958). During germination, the ascospores swell and vacuoles form near the nucleus. No alteration in the structure of the nucleus occurs during germination and the nuclear membrane appears to persist throughout the process. As swelling progresses, the outer spore coat breaks, usually at more than one point, whereas the inner coat resists disruption and forms the new vegetative cell wall. No mitochondria are found in resting ascospores, although small granules of various size can be found scattered through the periphery of the ascospore. As soon as swelling commences, mitochondria are formed and can be seen even prior to the breaking of the outer coat. The shapes of the mitochondria are varied, stain with neotetrazolium salts, and possess "cristae mitochondriales" of the usual kind (Hashimoto et al., 1958). However, poor fixation may have accounted for some of the observations on mitochondria discussed above.

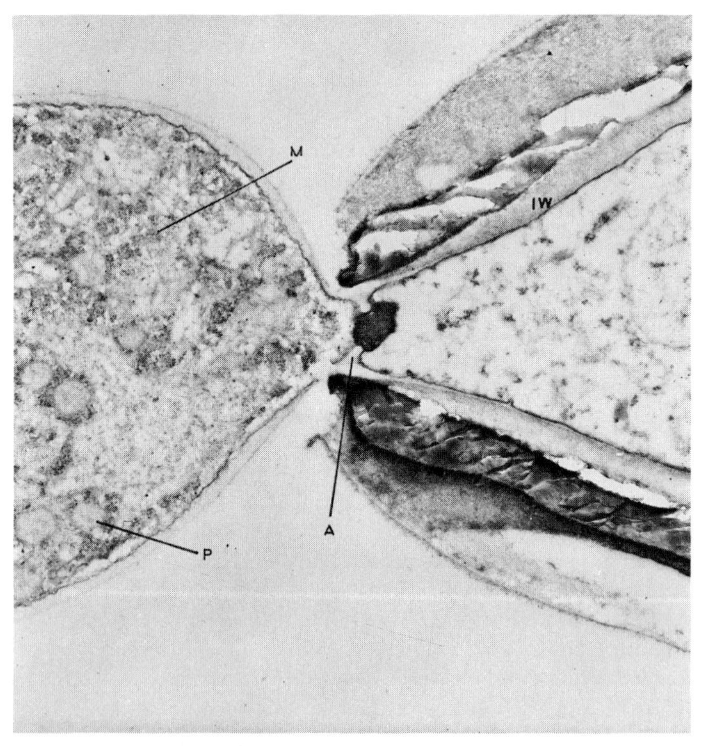

Figure 5.13 Section of germinating ascospore of *Neurospora tetrasperma* showing protrusion of germ tube. Note that there is a single wall of the germ tube as compared with the multiple one that is characteristic of the ascospore wall. Legend: A, annulus surrounding germ pore; IW, inner wall; M, microsomes; P, a protein-containing body. × 10,000. (Courtesy of T. Beals, unpublished photograph.)

Another fungal spore in which the morphology of germination has been studied in detail is that of *Neurospora* ascospores. Comparison of the structure of dormant ascospores (Figure 2.27) with that of the germinating one shown in Figure 5.13 reveals that the wall of the vegetative hypha is formed from the innermost wall (endospore) of the ascospore. The germ tube is formed at either end of the cell and appears to force its way through plugs at either end of the cell. The plugs close orifices which are surrounded by an annulus of wall material.

The cytoplasm of the germinating spore contains ribosomes as well as vesicles (protein-containing bodies?) whose function is unknown. Mitochondria are found at the tips of the germ buds but are not visible in the illustration. Several questions remain unanswered about the germination process in mycelial fungi, including the fate of the nuclei of the ascospore, as well as the behavior of formed elements of the cytoplasm, such as the mitochondria. Spore germination in other fungi was discussed previously (pp. 28–29).

Stages in Germination

One of the characteristic features of the germination process is that numerous stages are involved. Some of these are outlined in Figure 5.1 and discussed in greater detail in Chapters 6 and 9. No one sequence of stages can be applied to the germination of all dormant systems. For example, the loss in heat-resistance is used as a criterion for the germination of bacterial spores but not for fungus spores. One reason for this is that not all fungus spores are more heat-resistant than their vegetative stages, and secondly, observation of the protrusion of the germ tube (the first evidence of the vegetative condition) is not as difficult as in bacteria. Nevertheless, there is considerable evidence for the intervention of recognizable stages between the dormant cell and the time of germination.

When spores are placed in a germination medium, swelling often occurs before germ tube formation. Mandels and Darby (1953) used the increase in cell volume of conidia of *Myrothecium verrucaria*, *Curvularia brachyspora*, *Penicillium expansum*, *Aspergillus fumigatus*, and *Pullularia pullulans* as a measure of the progress of germination. Qualitative tests revealed that conidia of *Trichoderma viride* and *Alternaria tenuis* also germinated in this way. On the other hand, some members of the Fungi Imperfecti did not swell perceptibly.

Conidia of *Aspergillus niger* have been studied in detail by Yanagita (1957) who distinguished between "endogenous" and "exogenous" swelling. The former stage occurred in the absence of carbon dioxide whereas the latter required this gas for its completion. The endogenous phase was temperature-insensitive while the exogenous phase was temperature-sensitive and lost heat-resistance. A similar suggestion has been made by Wood-Baker (1955) as a result of her work with *Mucor rouxiana* and *M. hiemalis*, except that oxygen instead of carbon dioxide was required during the second phase and not in the first.

Nutritional differences may appear during germination. In *Myrothecium verrucaria*, yeast extract is needed for the swelling of conidia but does not support the development of later stages (Mandels and Darby, 1953). Light-sensitive periods occur during the incubation of spores of various smuts (Gassner and Niemann, 1955), as well as in the germination of *Physoderma maydis* (Herbert and Kelman, 1958), providing additional evidence that germination involves complex physiological and biochemical changes. Finally, in aerobic bacilli the nutritional requirements for outgrowth are more demanding than those for initiating germination (Hyatt and Levinson, 1957; Demain and Newkirk, 1960; O'Brien and Campbell, 1957).

Table 5.1 Summary of the Stages Between Activation and Germination and the Physiological Markers Which Characterize Them in *Neurospora tetrasperma*

Condition of Spores	Minutes after Activation	Physiological Markers: Q_{O_2}	RQ	Thermo-resistance	Deactivability at 4°C
Dormant	—	0.5	0.6	+	—
Activated					
Stage					
1	0–20	0.5–4	1.2	+	+
2	30–60	4–10	1.0	—	+
3	60–150	15–30	1.0	—	—
Germinating	150	30	0.6	—	—

SOURCE: Data taken from Sussman, 1961.

Sensitivity to metabolic poisons and differences in respiratory rates were used by Goddard and Smith (1938) to distinguish between several stages in the germination of ascospores of *Neurospora tetrasperma*. A detailed analysis of the germination stages in this organism is shown in Table 5.1. Stage 2 in the activated ascospore is the last one that can be reversibly deactivated by the means described by Sun and Sussman (1960). Despite the irreversibility of this stage, it is unlikely that it will be adopted as an end point for germination, due to the long tradition of use of morphological criteria in the germination of fungus spores.

REFERENCES

AGAR, HILDA D., and H. C. DOUGLAS. 1957. *J. Bacteriol.* 73:365–375.

AMAHA, M., and K. SAKAGUCHI. 1954. *J. Bacteriol.* 68:338–345.

CAMPBELL, L. L. 1957. in *Spores*. H. O. Halvorson, ed. Am. Inst. Biol. Sci., Wash., D.C., pp. 33–37.

CHAPMAN, G. B., and K. A. ZWORYKIN. 1957. *J. Bacteriol.* 74:126–132.

CONTI, S. F., and H. B. NAYLOR. 1960. *J. Bacteriol.* 79:417–425.

DEBARY, A. 1887. *Comparative Morphology and Biology of the Fungi, Mycetozoa and Bacteria*. Clarendon Press, Oxford, 525 pp.

DEMAIN, A., and JOANNE NEWKIRK. 1960. *J. Bacteriol.* 79:783–788.

EDWARDS, M. R., E. L. HAZEN, and G. A. EDWARDS. 1960. *Can. J. Microbiol.* 6:65–70.

FISCHROEDER, F. 1909. *Zentr. Bakteriol. Parasitenk. Abt. I Orig.* 51:320–417.

FITZ-JAMES, P. C. 1956. *Can. J. Microbiol.* 1:525–548.

GASSNER, G., and E. NIEMANN. 1955. *Phytopathol. Z.* 23:121–140.

GEZELIUS, KERSTIN. 1961. *Exptl. Cell Res.* 23:300–301.

GLAUERT, AUDREY M., and D. A. HOPWOOD. 1961. *J. Biophys. Biochem. Cytol.* 10:505–516.

GODDARD, D. R., and P. E. SMITH. 1938. *Plant Physiol.* 24:241–264.

HACHISUKA, Y., N. ASANO, N. KATO, and T. KUNO. 1954. *Nagoya J. Med. Sci.* 17:403–410.

HASHIMOTO, T., S. F. CONTI, and H. B. NAYLOR. 1958. *J. Bacteriol.* 76:406–416.

HEBERT, T. T., and A. KELMAN. 1958. *Phytopatholgy* 48:102–106.

HYATT, MILDRED, and H. S. LEVINSON. 1957. *J. Bacteriol.* 74:87–93.

KNAYSI, G. 1957. *J. Bacteriol.* 20:425–430.

LAMANNA, C. 1940. *J. Bacteriol.* 40:347–367.

LEVINSON, H. S., and M. T. HYATT. 1956. *J. Bacteriol.* 72:176–183.

LEVINSON, H. S., and M. G. SEVAG. 1953. *J. Gen. Physiol.* 36:583–590.

LINDEGREN, C. C., M. A. WILLIAMS, and D. O. MCCLARY. 1956. *Antonie van Leeuwenhoek J. Microbiol. Serol.* 22:1–20.

MANDELS, G. R., and R. DARBY. 1953. *J. Bacteriol.* 65:16–26.

MANDELS, G. R., H. S. LEVINSON, and M. T. HYATT. 1956. *J. Gen. Physiol.* 39:301–309.

MAYALL, B. H., and C. F. ROBINOW. 1957. *J. Appl. Bacteriol.* 20:333–341.

O'BRIEN, R. T., and L. L. CAMPBELL. 1957. *J. Bacteriol.* 73:522–525.

POWELL, J. F. 1950. *J. Gen. Microbiol.* 4:330–338.

POWELL, J. F., and R. E. STRANGE. 1953. *Biochem. J.* 54:205–209.

PULVERTAFT, R. J. V., and J. A. HAYNES. 1951. *J. Gen. Microbiol.* 5:657–663.

ROBINOW, C. F. 1960. in *The Bacteria*. I. C. Gunsalus and R. Y. Stanier, eds. vol. 1. Academic Press, N.Y., pp. 207–248.

RODE, L. J., and J. W. FOSTER. 1960. *Proc. Nat. Acad. Sci. U.S.* 46:118–128.

SHATKIN, A. J., and E. L. TATUM. 1959. *J. Biophys. Biochem. Cytol.* 6:423–426.

SOCOLOFSKY, M. D., and O. WYSS. 1961. *J. Bacteriol.* 81:946–954.

STRANGE, R. E. 1959. *Bacteriol. Rev.* 23:1–7.

STRANGE, R. E., and J. F. POWELL. 1954. *Biochem. J.* 58:80–85.

SUN, C. Y., and A. S. SUSSMAN. 1960. *Am. J. Botany* 47:589–793.

SUSSMAN, A. S. 1961. *Quart. Rev. Biol.* 36:109–116.

TAKAGI, A., T. KAWATA, S. YAMAMOTO, T. KUBO, and S. OKITA. 1960. *Japan. J. Microbiol.* 4:137–155.

TCHAN, Y. T., A. BIRCH-ANDERSEN, and H. L. JENSEN. 1962. *Arch. Mikrobiol.* 43:50–66.

THIMANN, K. V. 1955. *The Life of Bacteria*. Macmillan, N.Y., 775 pp.

WIDRA, A., and E. D. DELAMATER. 1955. *Am. J. Botany* 42:423–435.

WILLIAMS, O. B. 1952. *Bacteriol. Rev.* 16:89–90.

WOOD-BAKER, A. 1955. *Trans. Brit. Mycol. Soc.* 38:291–297.

WYNNE, E. S., and J. W. FOSTER. 1948. *J. Bacteriol.* 55:331–339.

YANAGITA, T. 1957. *Arch. Mikrobiol.* 26:329–344.

ZALOKAR, M. 1960. *Exptl. Cell Res.* 19:114–132.

CHAPTER 6

Kinetics of Germination

"If arithmetic, mensuration, and weighing be taken away from any art, that which remains will not be much."
Plato.

General Considerations

THE CYTOLOGICAL examination of germination, as outlined in Chapter 5, has led to the following picture of germination. The dormant state is associated with a rigid structure. During germination this structure is breached in a series of discrete degradative steps culminating in the emergence of a germ tube (especially in the case of fungi) and a return to vegetative growth. In later chapters (9 and 10) the linking of this process to the metabolic reactions of the cell will be discussed. From these and other considerations it is clear that germination is irreversible and is an integrated process.

In this chapter we shall concern ourselves with a kinetic description of germination. Although definitive decisions on mechanism cannot be based solely upon kinetic studies, they can provide a useful description of the sequence and timing of the individual stages involved. In addition, as more discrete models of the germination process are available, kinetic considerations can serve to test the adequacy of their predictions. However, before kinetic studies can be applied to measurements of the various parameters in germination (activation, loss of structure, swelling, metabolic activity, and so on), it is well to recall that these involve large populations of cells.

Ideally, the kinetic description of germination in a single spore would provide the most useful information of the stages involved. There are only limited studies available on the changes of individuals from microbial dormant systems with respect to time. Some of the earliest of these with bacterial spores were performed by Powell (1950) and Pulvertaft and Haynes (1951), and illustrate the importance of the lag period in determining the kinetics of germination. In a film taken of the germination of spores of *Bacillus cereus*, it was clear that, compared to the over-all time required for the population to germinate, the time required for an individual spore to change from a highly refractile (dormant) to a dark translucent body (germinated) was essentially instantaneous. However, following addition of a germinating agent, the lag period before such a transition occurred differed considerably in various spores in the population. A few spores germinated almost immediately, whereas others remained unchanged for a relatively long period of time and then rapidly germinated. The confirmation of these observations will be discussed later in this chapter.

A second method of analyzing the behavior of individuals is to determine the time required for two different events to occur. An example of this is shown by the studies of Powell (1957), who constructed an apparatus which could be mounted on a microscope stage and permitted the heating of selected spores on the surface of a thin agar layer on a slide. If a jet of boiling methyl alcohol was employed, the temperature could be raised to 60–64°C within a few seconds, cooled as quickly by the evaporation of residual alcohol, and the preparation reexamined microscopically. As shown in Table 6.1, 38 percent of the light spores which changed after heat was applied were nonviable, and thus, since they were in contact for a few minutes before heat was applied, heat-resistance was lost in the earlier stages of refractive index change.

Table 6.1 The Relationship Between Optical Density Change on Heating at 60–64°C for 5 Minutes and Viability of *B. subtilis* Spores

Optical Change[a] on Heating	Observed Number	Number Developing to Vegetative Form
L→L	34	33
L→I	2	0
L→D	22	0
I→I	1	0
I→D	2	0
D→D	19	0

[a] L, light spores; D, dark spores; I, intermediate (from Powell, 1957, courtesy Academic Press, Inc., Publishers).

Numerous measurements have been made on the kinetics of germination of populations of dormant cells. The kinetics often differ and depend to a large extent on the property (resistance, refractility, metabolic activity, and so on) which is being followed. In addition to the inherent differences between dormant systems, a number of factors, including heat-activation, age, and environmental factors all influence the rate and nature of the germination curve, making comparisons difficult between one set of germination experiments and another. In some cases, as will be illustrated later in this chapter for bacterial spores, alternative routes of germination can lead to variations in the kinetics of germination.

Methods for Measuring Spore Germination

Several methods have been employed to follow the kinetics of germination of dormant forms. These include the loss of resistance to heat and chemical agents, the loss of refractility, the gain of stainability, the gain in metabolic activity, and the loss of spore components and morphological markers. It has generally been considered in bacterial spores that the loss of heat-resistance is the critical change which delineates germination. In general, all of these phenomena seem to occur at approximately the same time.

DIRECT MICROSCOPIC EXAMINATION

In principle, the kinetics of germination of dormant forms could be followed by direct microscopic counts. Some of the transitions between dormant and germinated spores of *Bacillus cereus* strain T are shown in Figure 6.1. Under a dark phase-contrast microscope, dormant spores appear as refractile bodies, whereas germinated spores are dark. Under ultraviolet light microscopy, germination leads to a decrease in light absorption and when examined with an electron microscope, changes in the structure of both the exosporium and spore body are apparent. However, kinetic studies by direct microscopic examination are laborious, often lack precision, and obscure some of the biochemical changes accompanying germination.

LOSS OF RESISTANCE TO HEAT AND CHEMICAL AGENTS

The loss of viability can be used as a criterion of germination when a method is employed which will distinguish between the resistant dormant form and the sensitive germinated form. A suspension of dormant cells is incubated in the presence of a germination stimulant and at intervals samples are removed and treated under conditions which kill the germinated form. Viable counts are then made on the suspension before and after this treatment; the difference between the counts will represent the number of cells that have germinated. This procedure, although accurate and simple, should be applied with caution since it depends upon the subsequent growth of vegetative cells. For example,

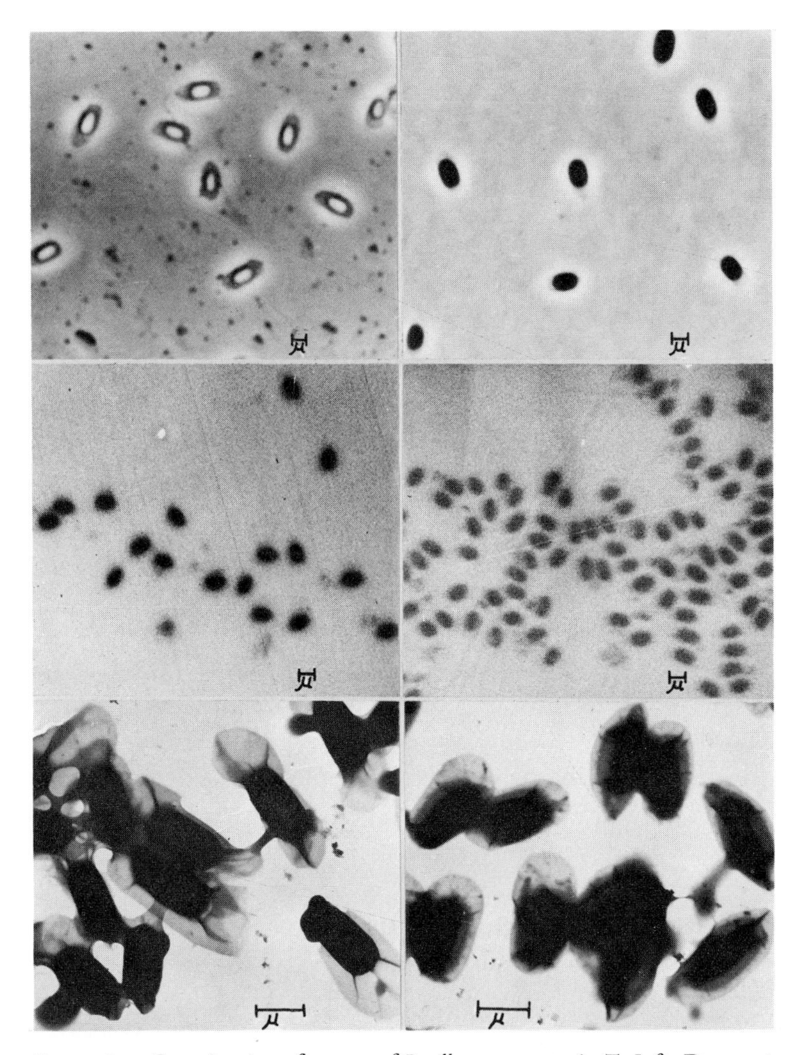

Figure 6.1 Germination of spores of *Bacillus cereus* strain T. *Left*: Dormant spores and *right* germinated spores. *Top*: Phase contrast microscope. Exosporium stained with Webb's (1954) cell wall stain. × 3000. *Middle*: Ultraviolet light microscope. 270 mμ. × 3000. *Bottom*: Electron microscope. × 13,000. (From P. Gerhardt, unpublished.)

dormancy can be broken under conditions in which the germinated form cannot survive or in which vegetative growth is inhibited (Campbell, 1957).

One of the most commonly used examples of this type of measurement of germination is the loss of heat-resistance accompanying the germination of bacterial spores. An example of this is shown in Figure 6.2 for the germination of spores of *B. subtilis* (Porton U strain) in alanine buffer at 33°C. At intervals during germination, samples were withdrawn, heated to 60°C for 15 minutes, and plated for viability. As is evident from Figure 6.2, the heat-resistance of the

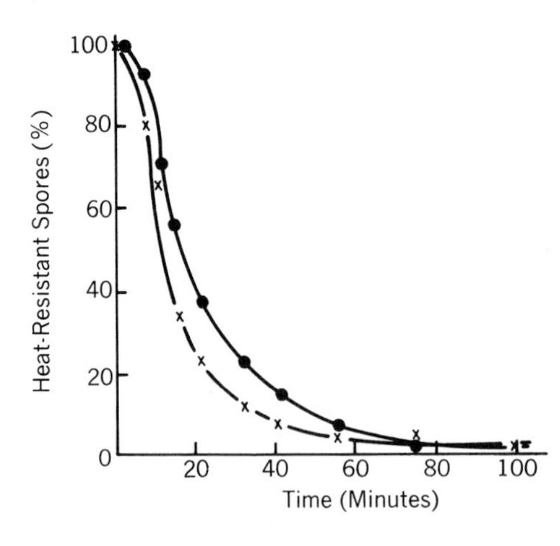

Figure 6.2 A comparison between the proportion of spores actually heat-resistant and the proportion inferred from the opacity in a germinating suspension. *B. subtilis* (Porton U strain) in alanine buffer at 33°C. Legend: Crosses, plate colony counts; full circles, values calculated from nephelometer readings. (From Powell, 1957, courtesy Academic Press, Inc., Publishers.)

population is lost slightly in advance of the decrease in optical density, supporting the findings reported for the properties of individual spores. The form of the germination curve by both procedures is, however, very similar.

The kinetics of germination measured by loss in resistance can be misleading since they depend to a large extent on the conditions employed for inactivation of the germinated form. For example, Fernelius (1960) observed that the time of germination of spores of *B. anthracis* by alanine, tyrosine, and adenosine depends upon the method used for determining germination. When the loss in heat-resistance was followed in thick spore suspensions, germination was complete within 2 minutes. However, when spores were heated in dilute solution or inactivated by exposure to phenol, the loss of heat-resistance was complete at 4 minutes. The faster germination in the thick suspension was attributed to the period required to raise the incubation temperature to that of heat-shock for a thick cell suspension. This period was eliminated when spores were diluted into media at the higher temperature, or when they were diluted into 1 percent phenol. If the measurement of germination in dilute suspension reflects the true kinetics of inactivation, the inactivation both by phenol and by heat occurred simultaneously.

The loss of heat-resistance is one of the most common methods for analyzing the extent of germination. The actual measurement of residual spores may be misleading. Although the thermal death of microorganisms usually obeys first-order kinetics, numerous nonlogarithmic thermal death curves for some bacterial spores have been reported. Spore populations either show a lag followed by a logarithmic decline in the number of viable spores or else behave as a bimodal population regarding heat-resistance. In this case the survival curve appears as a sum of two exponential functions.

The heterogeneity in heat-inactivation curves could be understood if (a) heat-activation preceded thermal death or (b) inactivation involved a multihit inactivation process (Halvorson, 1958). Shull et al. (1963) have recently investigated the role of heat-activation in the thermal death curves of spores of *B. stearothermophilus*. To evaluate the role of heat-activation, they have derived the equations relating heat-activation and thermal death.

If the number of nonactivated spores at time zero and time t is N_0 and N_t, and α is the activation rate constant, they assumed that

$$N_t = N_0 e^{-\alpha t}$$

The number of activated spores remaining at time t is $A_0 e^{-kt}$ where k is the heat-inactivation constant. Thus if heat-inactivation precedes thermal death of nonactivated spores, then the following relationship should exist:

$$A_t = A_0 e^{-kt} + \frac{\alpha N_0}{k - \alpha} (e^{-\alpha t} - e^{-kt})$$

In one test of this, Shull et al. (1963) observed a difference between the observed thermal death curve and that predicted from the equation given. Either the death of the spores does not necessarily require prior heat-activation, or heat-activation does not follow first-order kinetics. The relationship between thermal death and heat-activation will require further examination.

MEASUREMENTS OF CHANGES IN FORM AND STRUCTURE

The over-all structural changes accompanying germination provide an excellent basis for measurements of the germination process. Only a limited number of physical tools have been applied thus far which are based upon changes in size, shape, or density of the cell. One of the most direct methods is to directly measure the changes in the weight of spores. Thus, for example, Powell and Strange (1953) observed a 30 percent decrease in dry weight following the germination of spores of *B. megaterium* by glucose. In an organism in which germination is characterized by swelling and sprouting, such as the conidiospores of *Aspergillus niger*, the initial decrease is absent or minimal. As shown in Figure 6.3, the dry weight and packed volume of the spores increased almost exponentially with time. The sprouting of the spores followed the exogenous swelling, commencing after 5 hours, and was complete after 9 hours.

Changes in the concentration of cellular material also lend themselves to turbidimetric measurements which have the advantage of simplicity and accuracy. The principle involved can be seen in Figure 6.1, in which the conversion of a dormant spore into a vegetative cell is accompanied by striking changes in appearance under phase-contrast illumination. This transition can be observed either by a difference in light refractility as observed with a phase-contrast microscope, or by the change in optical density measured with a colorimeter or a

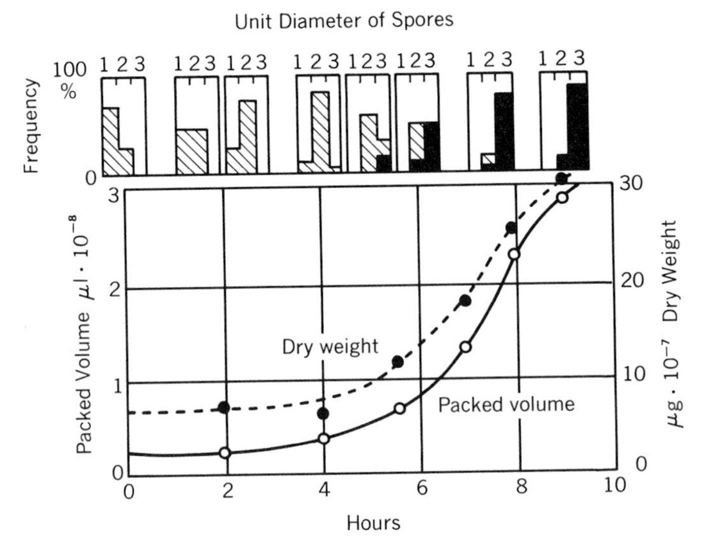

Figure 6.3 Changes in the diameter, weight, and volume per germinating spore of *Aspergillus niger*. (Data from Yanagita, 1957.)

nephelometer. Dormant forms are noted for their high density (McIntosh and Selbie, 1937). In addition, bacterial spores have an unusually high refractive index, about 1.52 (Ross and Billing, 1957). When germination occurs, much of the spore matter is lost to the medium (Powell and Strange, 1953), which is accompanied by a replacement of water and a corresponding decrease in both the density and the refractive index of the spore. In some mold spores, the swelling of the conidia as a result of water imbibition and assimilation leads to a decrease in the transmission of light during germination (Figure 6.4).

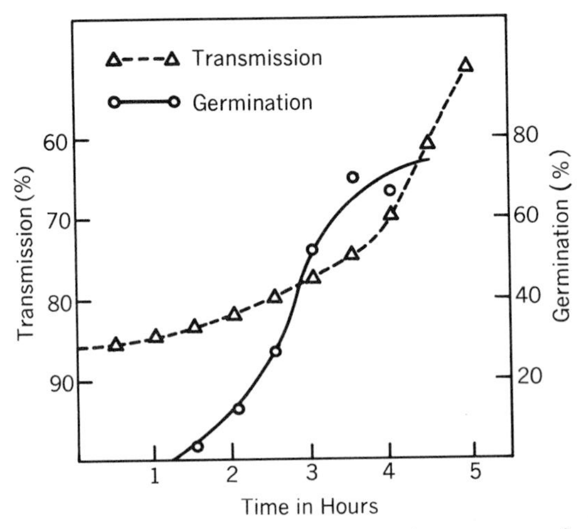

Figure 6.4 Light transmittancy and percentage of germination of conidial suspensions of *Aspergillus oryzae*. (From Terui and Mochizuki, 1955.)

Hachisuka et al. (1954) were the first to employ the changes in optical density to quantitatively measure the kinetics of germination. Their procedure was later confirmed by Woese and Morowitz (1958). These workers found that the changes in optical density could be related to the number of germinated spores by determining the ratio,

$$\frac{OD - OD_f}{OD_I - OD_f}$$

for each time interval where OD is the optical density at time t, and OD_I and OD_f are the initial and final (limiting) optical densities, respectively. The rate of germination was approximately determined by plotting the optical density decrease as an exponential decay in the following manner:

$$\log \frac{OD - OD_f}{OD_I - OD_F} \quad \text{versus time}$$

The log of this plot shows a linear relationship to time over a large portion of the germination curve (Woese and Morowitz, 1958), frequently preceded by a lag period (O'Connor and Halvorson, 1961).

It soon became clear that the relationship shown would not account for the later stages of germination. The kinetics of germination were found to be more accurately described by the equation

$$G = G_0{}^{t-k}$$

(McCormick, 1964), where G, the fraction germinated, is

$$\frac{OD_i - OD}{OD_i - OD_f}$$

t is time, and k is the germination rate. The log log plot of $1/G$ as a function of time gives a linear relationship (Figure 6.5), with the exception of the first several minutes of lag preceding germination.

The log log relationship of germination (Figure 6.5) can best be understood by a multiple probability function. Two probability functions which could influence the kinetics of germination are the lag preceding the germination of a given spore and the time required for a single spore to carry out the reactions involved in germination (see Chapter 9). Evidence that at least two probability functions are involved is seen by measurements of the lag and germination time of single spores in the population (Figure 6.6). Both of these show a skewed distribution which is accurately described by a Weibul distribution (Vary and Steinberg, 1964). The average lag period was approximately 200 seconds and the average germination time (loss of refractility) 16 seconds. These are independent processes; only the lag period is influenced by heat-activation. An accumulative plot of spores which have completed the lag period only trails the decrease in

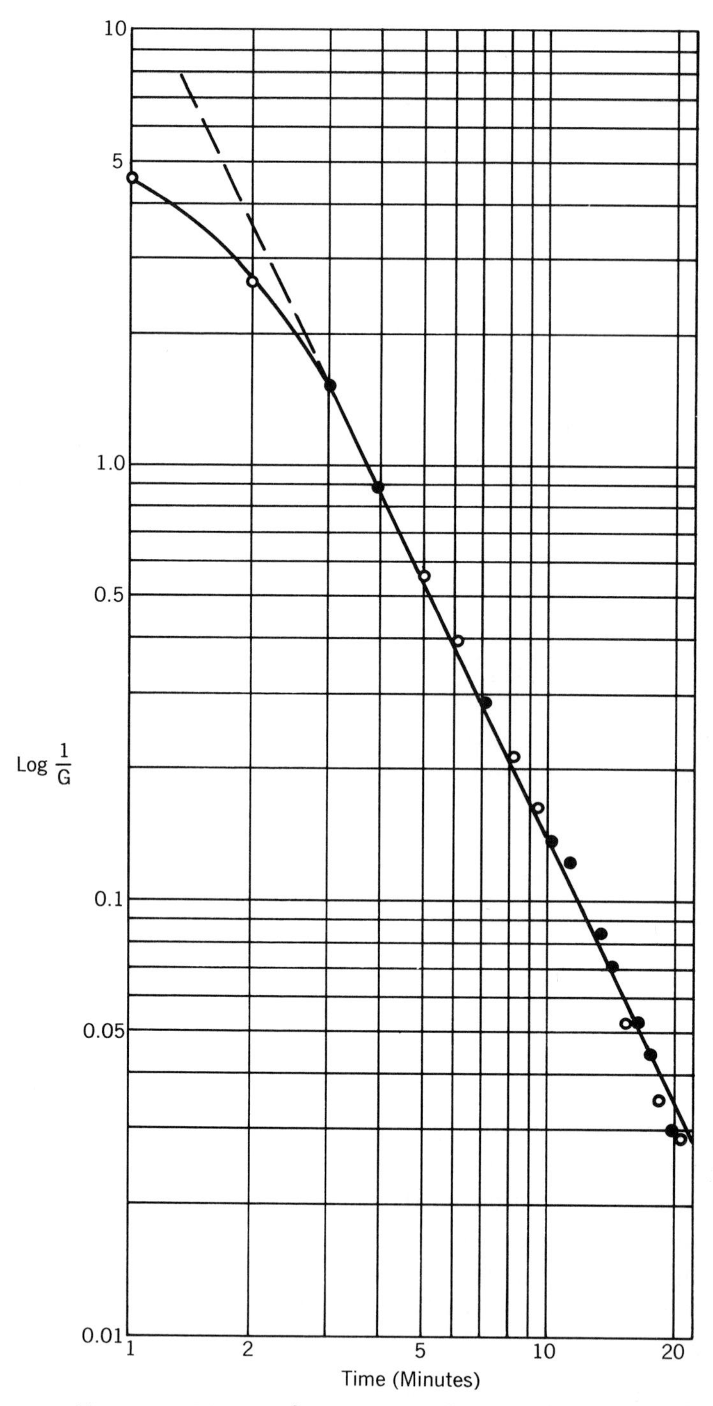

Figure 6.5 Kinetics of germination of spores of heat-activated spores of *Bacillus cereus* strain T. (Data from McCormick and Vary, unpublished.)

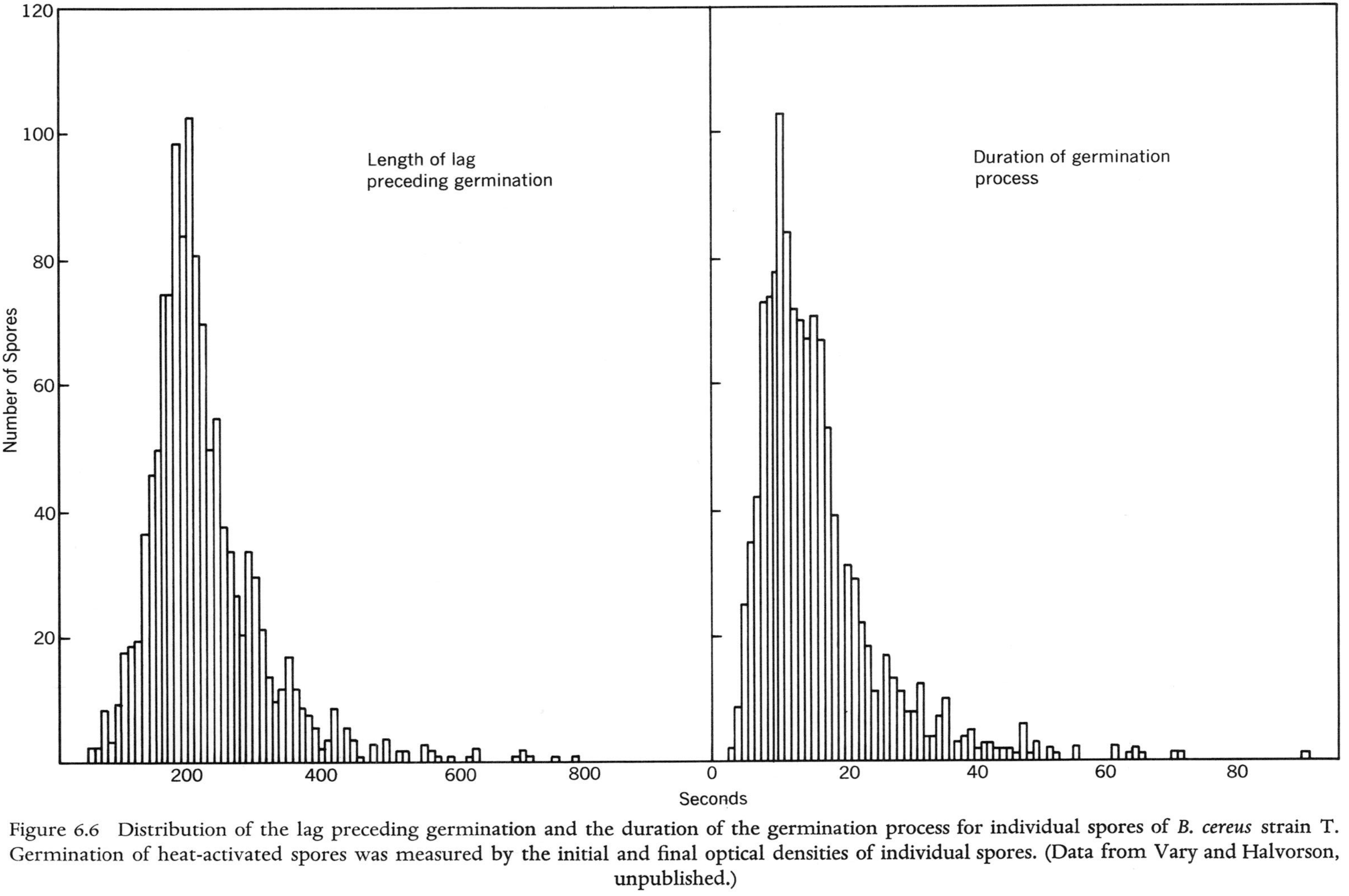

Figure 6.6 Distribution of the lag preceding germination and the duration of the germination process for individual spores of *B. cereus* strain T. Germination of heat-activated spores was measured by the initial and final optical densities of individual spores. (Data from Vary and Halvorson, unpublished.)

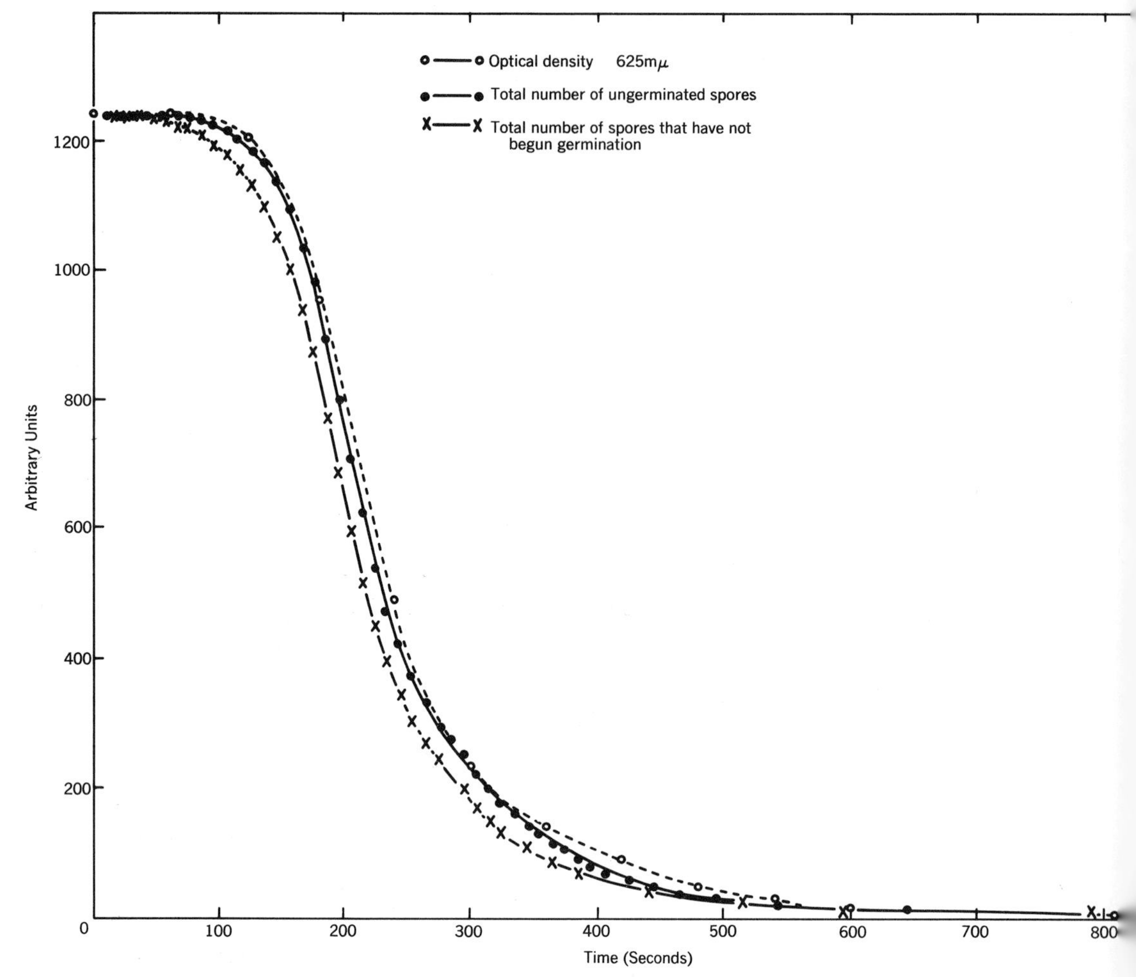

Figure 6.7 Comparison of the accumulative number of spores completing the lag period and loss of refractility during germination. Heat-activated spores of *B. cereus* strain T. (Data from Vary and Halvorson, unpublished.)

optical density plot by 15–20 seconds, as expected from the average germination time (Figure 6.7).

The ease of measurement of changes in optical density has lent itself to quantitating the kinetics of germination. It is clear that a number of stages are involved. This is evident from the preceding loss of heat-resistance and the appearance of translucent spores. For example, Hachisuka et al. (1954) found with spores of *Bacillus subtilis* that the rate of germination as determined by loss of thermostability was the most rapid and was followed by the appearance of translucent germinated spores. Germination as measured by the decrease in optical density occurred more slowly. From these considerations it is clear that kinetic studies employing optical density should contain several parameters which precede the change in refractive index. These will be discussed later in this chapter.

GAIN IN STAINABILITY

Germination can also be followed by measuring the ability of the germinated form to stain deeply while the ungerminated form will be unstained, except for a thin layer on the outer surface of the spore wall. It is difficult to measure the rate of germination by this procedure unless one removes samples frequently from the suspension and determines in each the percentage of cells that are stained. On occasion some spores are observed in which staining is intermediate between that of dormant and germinated spores. In general the kinetics of germination by staining follow those measured by the appearance of translucent spores.

THE LOSS OF SPORE COMPONENTS

Germination of dormant forms is frequently accompanied by a release of components of the spore. Therefore, germination could be followed by measuring the release of these materials. This method has been applied with bacterial spores to follow the release of two components which are enriched in the spore, calcium and dipicolinic acid.

Woese and Morowitz (1958) compared germination rate as measured by decrease in optical density and as indicated by the release of DPA in spores of *B. subtilis*. Dipicolinic acid was measured in the supernatant fluid by measurement of the optical density at 2700 Å, which is the maximum for DPA absorption. As can be seen in Figure 6.8 the time-course of release of DPA and the decrease in the optical density of the spore suspension agree very closely. During the first few minutes there is little decrease in turbidity or release of DPA, followed by a rapid decrease which followed the kinetics described above.

Although DPA release in *B. subtilis* spores follows after a lag and closely parallels germination as measured by decreases in optical density, this correlation was not observed for the release of calcium in spores of *B. cereus* strain T. As shown in Figure 6.8, the release of calcium during alanine-induced germination proceeded almost immediately following the addition of alanine, whereas a lag of 3 minutes was observed before the decrease in optical density of the suspension. In this case, presumably calcium release precedes the changes involved in refractility.

APPEARANCE OF METABOLIC ACTIVITY

Spores often are metabolically inert but contain a series of dormant enzymes (Chapters 9 and 10). Since these are released during germination, a number of

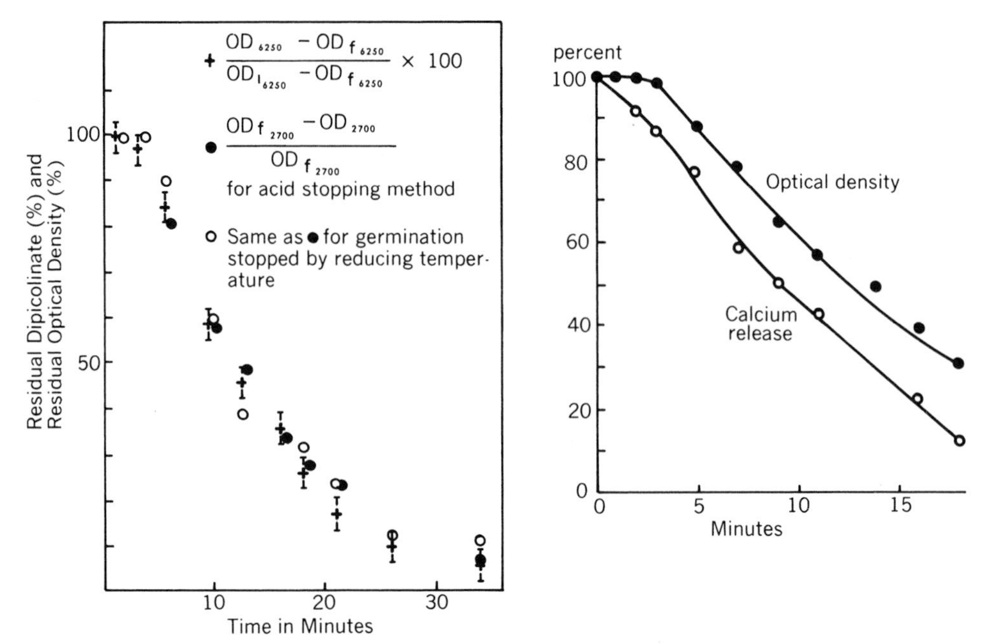

Figure 6.8 Kinetics of release of spore components during L-alanine-induced germination. *Left:* Release of dipicolinic acid during the germination of spores of *B. subtilis*. DPA was measured at 2700 Å and optical density at 6250 Å. (Data from Woese and Morowitz, 1958.) *Right:* Release of Ca^{45} during the germination of spores of *B. cereus* strain T. The decrease in optical density was plotted by the method of Woese and Morowitz (1958). (Data from Keynan and Halvorson, 1962.)

investigations have attempted to follow germination by monitoring the metabolic activity of the germination system. Unfortunately most of the relevant studies have failed to distinguish between activation and biosynthesis of new enzymes following germination. As will be discussed in Chapter 9, germination is characterized by a series of degradative reactions and is insensitive to inhibitors of protein synthesis, whereas outgrowth is blocked by inhibitors of protein and nucleic acid synthesis. Thus with the appropriate use of inhibitors such as chloramphenicol (Steinberg et al., 1965), germination and outgrowth can be separated.

One of the most frequently used systems is glucose oxidation. Dormant spores often have little or no metabolic activity against glucose. During the germination of spores of *B. megaterium* and of the fungus *Myrothecium verrucaria* (Mandels et al., 1956), increase in respiratory activity follows an increasing parabolic curve. Similar results have been observed in spores of *Bacillus subtilis* by Hachisuka and Sugai (1959).

When germination of spores of *B. cereus* is carried out in the presence of chloramphenicol to block protein synthesis, a single rapid rise in respiratory activity occurs which parallels the loss in refractility (Figure 6.9). In the absence of the inhibitor, protein synthesis is initiated at about 8 minutes after addition of the

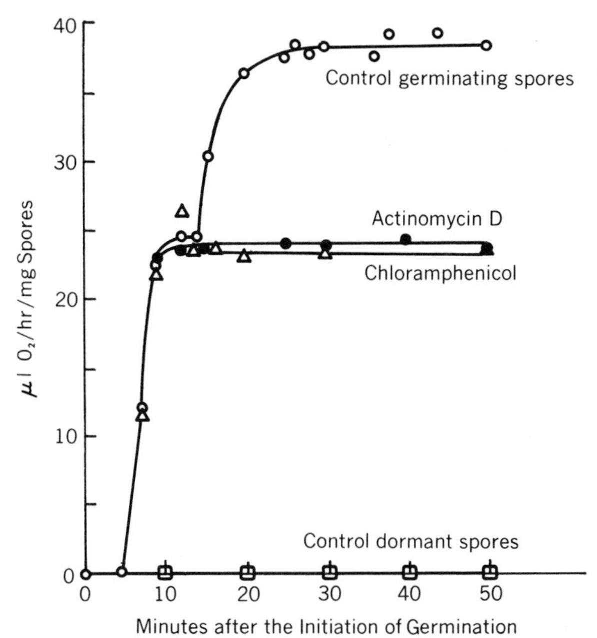

Figure 6.9 Effect of inhibitors of protein synthesis on the development of the respiratory activity in germinating spores of *B. cereus.* Respiratory activity was followed during germination by measuring the rate of O_2 uptake in the presence or absence of 30 μg/ml of actinomycin D or 40 μg/ml chloramphenicol. The glucose oxidation by dormant spores is included as a control. Germination of 2-hour heat-activated spores was initiated by the addition of 0.5 mg/ml adenosine, 2.5 mg/ml L-alanine, and 0.5 percent glucose at 30°C. (Data from Steinberg et al., 1965.)

germination agent and enables the further synthesis of components of the respiratory system, leading to a second rise in respiratory activity (Figure 6.9). Therefore during over-all germination and outgrowth, several stages in the development of respiration are evident. This is evident in Figure 6.10 which shows

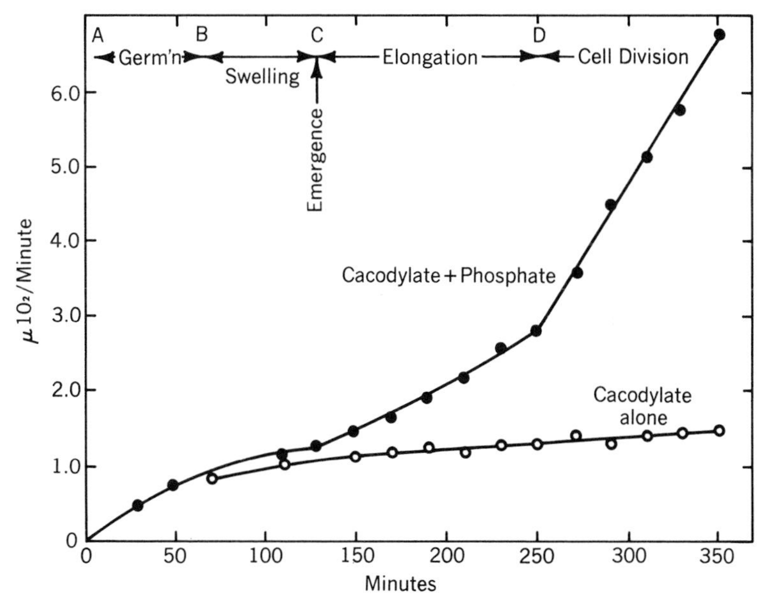

Figure 6.10 Effect of the addition of orthophosphate on the rate of oxygen consumption of spores of *Bacillus megaterium*. The reaction mixture contained glucose, K_2SO_4, cacodylate buffer, and orthophosphate where indicated. (Data from Hyatt and Levinson, 1959.)

that following germination of spores of *B. megaterium* in cacodylate buffer, glucose respiration rapidly rises during the first hour and then remains constant. In the presence of phosphate, the emergence of the germinated form, its elongation, and division signify increases in respiratory activity.

Similar changes are observed when conidiospores of *Aspergillus niger* are germinated in a medium supporting vegetative growth (Figure 6.11). After

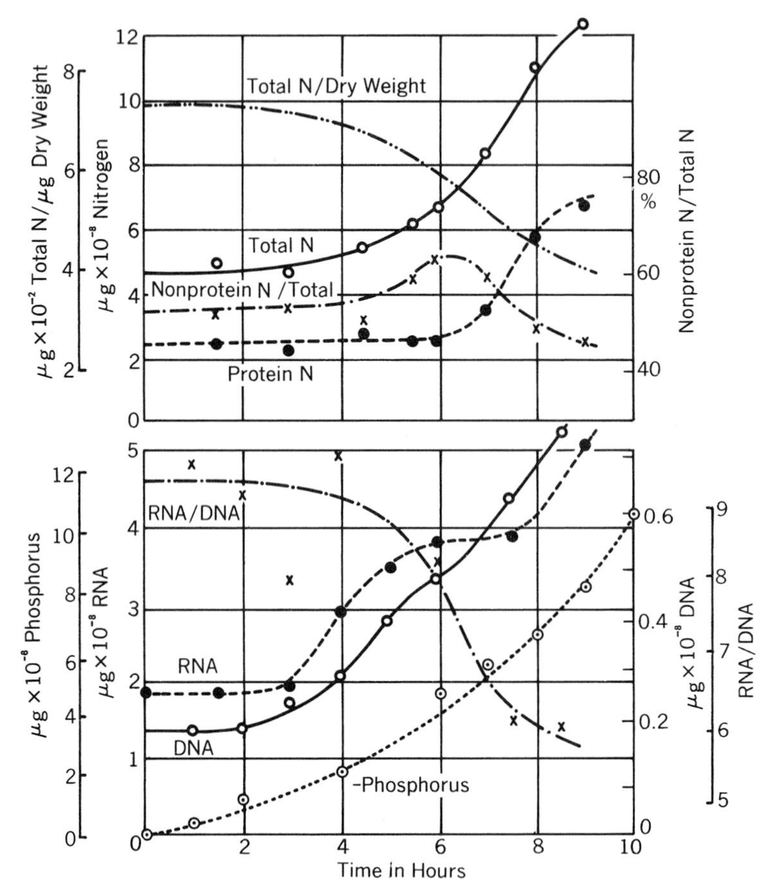

Figure 6.11 Changes in the cellular composition of conidiospores of *Aspergillus niger* during germination. (Data from T. Yanagita, 1957.)

several hours the total nitrogen increases almost exponentially; protein nitrogen dramatically rises after 6 hours, a period which coincides with the secondary rise in respiratory activity. During the initial endogenous swelling period, nucleic acid synthesis precedes protein synthesis, as has been observed during outgrowth of bacterial spores (Chapter 9). Outgrowth, and subsequent rises in respiratory activity, occur only under conditions permitting synthesis of macromolecules.

Factors Affecting the Rate of Germination

HEAT-ACTIVATION

Pretreatment of bacterial spores at elevated temperatures for various periods of time affects the kinetics of germination. As shown in Figure 6.12 both the rate of optical density change as well as the lag period preceding the decreases in

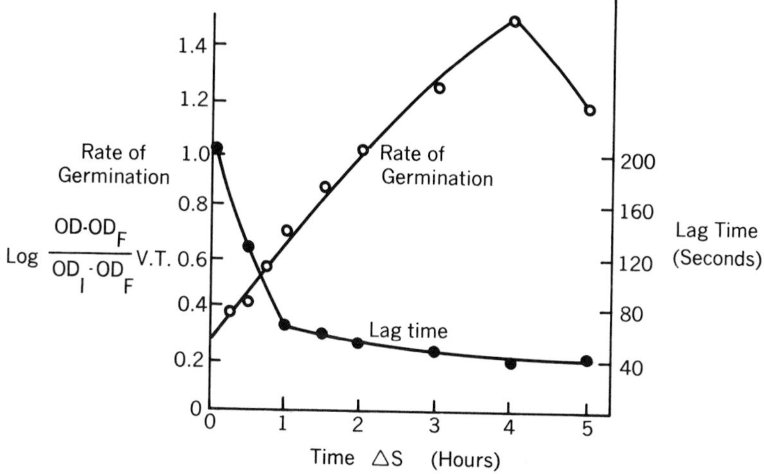

Figure 6.12 Effect of heat-activation on lag time and rate of L-alanine-induced germination. The germination medium consisted of 400 μmoles of L-alanine, 0.4 mg of spores (previously heat-shocked at 65°C for the time intervals indicated) in 4 ml of carbonate-bicarbonate buffer at *p*H 9.4. The incubation temperature was 30°C. Legend: V.T., versus time; S, heat-shock. (From O'Connor and Halvorson, 1961.)

optical density are affected by the time of heat-activation. The lag is decreased and the rate of germination is increased. In addition, the response of spores to different concentrations of germinating agent is also influenced by prior heat-activation treatment. The biochemical alterations underlying these changes are not well understood. Heat-activation could release endogenous stimulants, alter the properties of the initial binding site, modify the rate of linked reactions, alter the permeability, or remove an inhibitor of germination. Since ordinarily, heat-activation does not lead to spontaneous germination of bacterial spores, the release of endogenous stimulants would seem unlikely. On the other hand, with *Bacillus megaterium* (Powell and Strange, 1953), spontaneous germination follows extended heat-activation.

TEMPERATURE

The time-course and extent of germination of most dormant forms are influenced by environmental conditions such as temperature, *p*H, ionic conditions, and so on. The optimum conditions vary with the species involved, which will be discussed in Chapters 7 and 8. We shall illustrate the environmental effects of temperature with several types of dormant systems. Figure 6.13 shows the effects of various temperatures on the rate of germination of

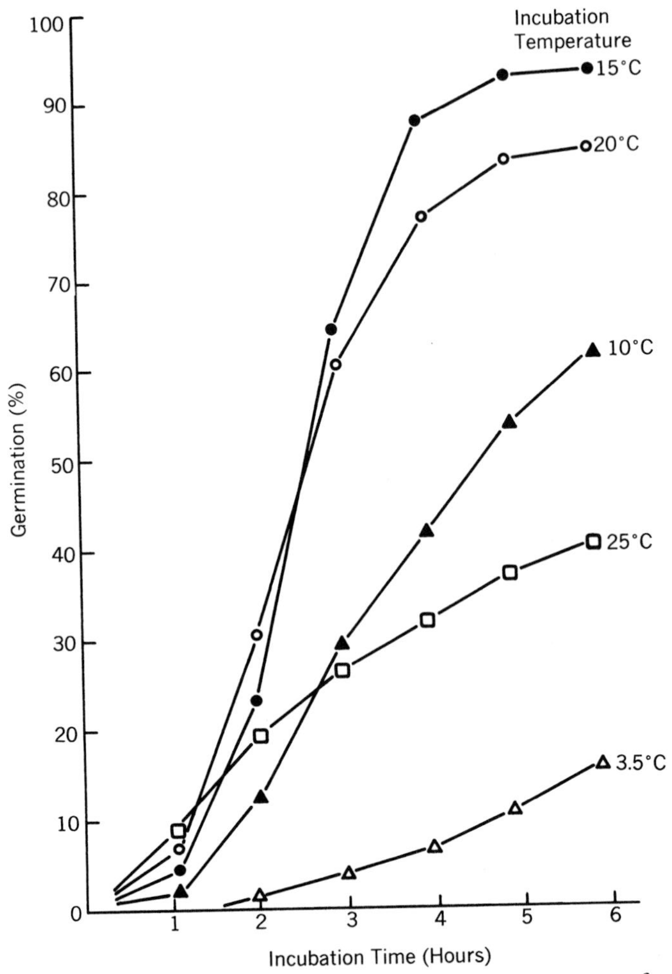

Figure 6.13 Effect of temperature on rate of germination of *Peronospora tabacina adam* on agar. (Data from Shepherd, 1962, courtesy *Australian J. Biol. Sci.*)

conidia of *Peronospora tabacina adam* on 2 percent Difco Bacto agar. The optimum rate of germination was observed in the range 15–20°C. At lower temperatures the rate of germination was slower and the latent period of germination was prolonged. The rate of germination was more sensitive to nonoptimal temperatures than was the latent period of germination (Shepherd, 1962). Similar differences have been observed for uredospore germination of *Phragmidium mucronatum* (Cochrane, 1945) and spores of *Peronospora parasitica* (Felton and Walker, 1946). These findings indicate that metabolic processes controlling the initiation of germination are different than those controlling the later stages.

The influence of temperature on the various stages of germination has been analyzed more thoroughly with bacterial spores. Here the effect of temperature depends upon the germination agent which is employed. As shown in Figure 6.14, the rate of germination of spores of *Bacillus cereus* strain T in L-alanine is

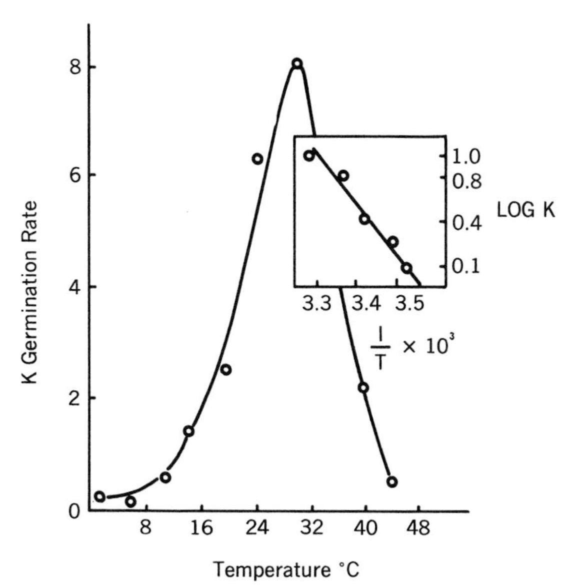

Figure 6.14 Effect of temperature on L-alanine-induced germination. The insert is an Arrhenius plot of the same data. The spores were previously heat-shocked at 65°C for 4 hours. (From O'Connor and Halvorson, 1961.)

strongly temperature-dependent, having a ΔH about 19,400 cal per mole. Similar values have been reported by Vas and Proszt (1957) for spores of *B. cereus* germinating in complex medium. In spores of *B. subtilis* strain 5230, Busta and Ordal (1964) observed slightly higher values (see Figure 7.2). For further discussion see Chapters 7 and 8.

On the other hand, when germination is induced by calcium DPA, the rate of change in optical density is relatively temperature-independent. But the lengths of the lag period show a temperature dependence characteristic of an enzymatic reaction (Figure 6.15). The ΔH for the shortening of the lag is similar to that for the rate of germination induced by L-alanine. These findings suggest that some metabolic reaction is taking place during the lag period of calcium DPA-induced spores.

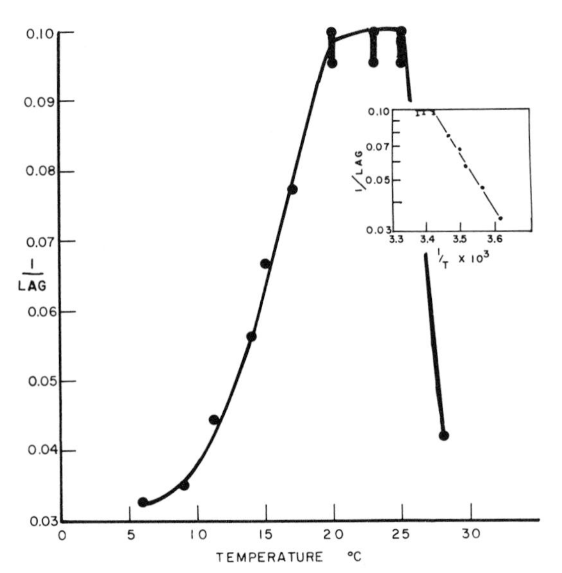

Figure 6.15 Effect of temperature on the lag period of calcium DPA-induced germination. The inverse lag time in minutes is plotted as a function of temperature. Lag time is the time from addition of calcium DPA to spore suspension until decrease in optical density can be detected photometrically. The insert is an Arrhenius plot of the same data, using time of lag as reaction rate. (From Keynan and Halvorson, 1962.)

EFFECT OF CONCENTRATION OF GERMINATING AGENT

The rate of germination in many systems has been reported to be influenced by the concentration of the germinating agent. This is discussed in Chapter 7. In the amino acid-induced germination of aerobic spores the rate of germination as measured by changes in optical density shows a first-order dependence on the alanine concentration. The response to alanine concentration can be described by the following equation:

$$k_0 = \frac{kC}{C + K}$$

where k_0 = the germination rate constant, k and K are constants characteristic of the initiator, and C is the concentration of the germinating agent. This response is characteristic of either an adsorption isotherm or Henri-Michaelis relationship for an enzyme reaction. The relationship described by this equation permits one to calculate an over-all constant which is characteristic of various germinating stimulants. As illustrated in Chapter 7, these constants differ for the various germinating stimulants employed, and permit an analysis by competitive inhibition of the specificity of the germination site.

EFFECT OF SPORE CONCENTRATION

The influence of spore concentration on both the rate and level of germination is shown in Figure 6.16 for the germination of spores of the cellular slime mold *Dictyostelium mucoroides*. When conditions of maximum moisture were main-

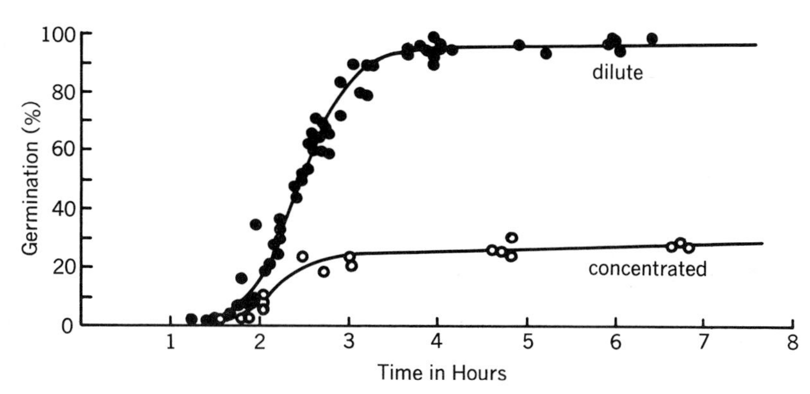

Figure 6.16 The percent germination of dilute and concentrated suspensions of *Dictyostelium mucoroides* on nutrient agar. (Data from Russell and Bonner, 1960.)

tained at spore densities of less than 33 spores/mm^2, complete germination was achieved in about 4 hours. However, at densities above 400 spores/mm^2, the rate of germination was slower and reached a maximum of about 20 percent. This phenomenon is commonly represented in germination experiments and must be considered in comparing the kinetics of germination of two different spore populations. Competition for limiting nutrients or the release of inhibitory substances by the spores themselves could explain results. Opposite effects have also been reported. Smart (1937) reported that in the true slime molds, the myxomycetes, high spore concentrations increased the percent germination.

Description of the Overall Process

Our understanding of the chemical structures or structures which must be breached during germination is as yet too incomplete to permit construction of models which could yield quantitative predictions of the kinetics of germination. Problems of population heterogenity and considerations of the parameters which are measured must be studied. The empirical mathematical description of the entire germination curve by McCormick (1965) and Vary and Halvorson (1965) provides for the first time a basis for quantitatively evaluating some of the variables in this process.

Several conclusions can be reached from the data described in this and later chapters (7 and 9), which serve as a basis for models of spore dormancy. These can be summarized as follows:

1. The dormant spore has a rigid structure which must be broken before germination can proceed.
2. Both the initial and later stages of germination are governed by enzymatic reactions.
3. A population of spores is heterogeneous and this heterogeneity is reflected in the kinetics of germination.
4. There are a number of stages in germination.

In the case of the germination of bacterial spores, where our information is more complete, the following tentative model is consistent with our available information. The dormant state is maintained by a series of structural links. There are a fixed number of these per spore. During activation and the early stages of germination these are enzymatically split. When the number of these sites per spore decreases to *Y*, a critical level, the rigid structure is lost, and swelling and metabolic activity occur. The conversion of —S—S— to —SH HS— (see Chapters 7 and 9) could be an example of this. To explain the kinetics, one need only assume that the breaking of any particular bond is random.

Whatever model is proposed, one of the main questions remaining is the number and interrelationships of the enzymatic reactions upon which germination depends. Although specific binding sites have been proposed for some germination systems, it should be recalled that alternate pathways of germination exist, as in the case of spores of aerobic bacteria. The lag period preceding the visible changes accompanying germination of an aerobic bacterial spore is undoubtedly a period in which the enzymatic reactions leading to germination actually take place. Investigation of the mechanism of germination, given the heterogeneity of spore populations, will unfortunately require the development of methods to follow the biochemical changes in single spores.

REFERENCES

Busta, F. F., and Z. J. Ordal. 1964. *J. Food Res.* 29:345–353.

Campbell, L. L. 1957. in *Spores.* H. O. Halvorson, ed. Am. Inst. Biol. Sci., Wash., D.C., pp. 33–37.

Cochrane, V. W. 1945. *Phytopathology* 35: 361–366.

Felton, N. W., and J. C. Walker. 1946. *J. Agr. Res.* 72:69–81.

Fernelius, A. L. 1960. *J. Bacteriol.* 79:755–756.

Hachisuka, Y., and K. Sugai. 1959. *Japan. J. Microbiol.* 3:211–222.

Hachisuka, Y., N. Asano, N. Kato, and T. Kuno. 1954. *Nagoya J. Med. Sci.* 17:403–411.

Halvorson, H. O. 1958. *The Physiology of the Bacterial Spore.* Tech. Univ. of Tronheim, Norway.

Hyatt, M. T., and H. S. Levinson. 1957. *J. Bacteriol.* 74:87–93.

Hyatt, M. T., and H. S. Levinson. 1959. *J. Bacteriol.* 77:487–496.

Keynan, A., and H. O. Halvorson. 1962. *J. Bacteriol.* 83:100–105.

MANDELS, G. R., H. S. LEVINSON, and M. T. HYATT. 1956. *J. Gen. Physiol.* 39:301–309.
MCCORMICK, N. G. 1964. *Biochem. Biophys. Res. Comm.* 14:443–446.
MCCORMICK, N. G. 1965. *J. Bacteriol.* 89:1180–1185.
MCINTOSH, J., and F. R. SELBIE. 1937. *Brit. J. Exp. Pathol.* 18:162–174.
O'CONNOR, R. J., and H. O. HALVORSON. 1961. *J. Bacteriol.* 82:706–713.
POWELL, E. O. 1957. *J. Appl. Bacteriol.* 20:342–348.
POWELL, J. F. 1950. *J. Gen. Microbiol.* 4:330–338.
POWELL, J. F., and R. E. STRANGE. 1953. *Biochem. J.* 54:205–209.
PULVERTAFT, R. J. V., and J. A. HAYNES. 1951. *J. Gen. Microbiol.* 5:657–663.
ROSS, K. F. A., and E. BILLING. 1957. *J. Gen. Microbiol.* 16:418–425.
RUSSELL, G. K., and J. T. BONNER. 1960. *Bull. Torrey Botan. Club* 87:187–191.
SHEPHERD, C. J. 1962. *Australian J. Biol. Sci.* 15:483–508.
SHULL, J. J., G. T. CARGO, and R. R. ERNST. 1963. *Appl. Microbiol.* 11:485–487.
SMART, R. F. 1937. *Am. J. Botany* 24:145–159.
STEINBERG, W., H. O. HALVORSON, A. KEYNAN, and E. WEINBERG. 1965. *Nature*. (In press.)
TERUI, G., and T. MOCHIZUKI. 1955. *Technol. Rept. Osaka Univ.* 5:219–227.
VARY, J. C., and H. O. HALVORSON. 1965. *J. Bacteriol.* 89: 1340–1347.
VARY, J. C., and W. STEINBERG. 1964. *Bacteriol. Proc.*, p. 36.
VAS, K., and G. PROSZT. 1957. *J. Appl. Bacteriol.* 20:413–596.
WOESE, C., and J. FORRO. 1960. *J. Bacteriol.* 80:811–817.
WOESE, C., and H. MOROWITZ. 1958. *J. Bacteriol.* 76:81–83.
YANAGITA, T. 1957. *Arch. Mikrobiol.* 26:329–344.

CHAPTER 7

"Triggers" and Chemical Germinating Agents— The Means of Activation

"Triggers"—The Means of Activation

RETURN TO the conditions which permit vegetative development is the only treatment required for the breaking of environmental dormancy. On the other hand, according to our definition, constitutive dormancy can be overcome only by a treatment that is *not* required by the organism during its vegetative development. To put it another way, organisms which are constitutively dormant will fail to develop even when provided with conditions under which vegetative development will proceed, unless an activation treatment (trigger) is applied. The kinds of activators and the organisms which require such treatment will be explored in this chapter.

Various physical and chemical factors which serve as activators include temperature, light, moisture, and the composition of the medium. Frequently, a combination of treatments is required in which more than one environmental variable must be manipulated before activation is accomplished. In any case, it is often possible to relate the treatment required to the distribution of the organism in nature, thereby defining the selective advantage which accrues to a particular trigger. However, this is not invariably the case and the biological role of some activators remains undefined.

High Temperature as a "Trigger"

BACTERIA

One of the frequently encountered phenomena in the germination of bacterial spores is the need for a pretreatment with heat. Incomplete or delayed germination was frequently observed in the early studies on bacterial spores until Weizmann (1919) observed that a treatment of 90° to 100°C for 1 to 2 minutes stimulated the germination of spores of *Clostridium acetobutylicum*. Evans and Curran (1943) and Curran and Evans (1947) first systematically demonstrated that spores which did not germinate or whose germination was delayed in the absence of heat, overcame this "dormancy" when heat-activated. For example, in *Bacillus coagulans* (Murrell, 1961), heat-activation increases the viable counts by 100-fold.

Evans and Curran (1943) observed that preheating of spores of *B. megaterium*, *B. subtilis*, *B. cereus*, and *B. coagulans* decreased the time required for germination in those species, and also the minimum temperature at which germination would take place. In more recent years, studies on the kinetics of germination have shown that, depending upon the germination stimulant employed, heat-activation can decrease the time for germination. The effect of heat-activation on the kinetics of germination has been discussed in Chapter 6. The main influence of heat-activation was a reduction in the lag period preceding germination.

Analysis of the effect of heat-activation on the properties of spores can provide useful insights into the mechanisms involved in germination (see Chapters 8 and 10). For example, the effect of heat-activation on the rate of L-alanine-induced germination (Chapter 6) strongly resembles the effect of heat-shock on L-alanine deamination (via the L-alanine dehydrogenase) by intact spores (O'Connor and Halvorson, 1959). In both cases, maximal rates were obtained after 4-hour heat-activation at 65°C. In *B. megaterium*, heat-activation enhances the rate of both L-alanine and glucose-induced germination (Levinson and Hyatt, 1955; Hyatt and Levinson, 1961).

Heat-activation does not enhance germination induced by all chemical agents. Riemann and Ordal (1961) observed that equimolar amounts of Ca^{++} and DPA are effective germinating agents for bacterial spores. The rate of germination of spores of *B. cereus* in the presence of calcium DPA however, is not influenced by prior heat-activation (Keynan et al., 1961). Even in systems in which heat-activation is *required* for breaking dormancy on nutrient medium, dormancy is completely broken by exposure of spores to calcium DPA (Ordal, 1964). Similarly, Black (1964) has observed that heat-activation does not influence the rate of nitrate-induced germination.

An important clue to the nature of heat-activation is its temperature dependence. The temperature and duration of optimal heating for this effect vary widely between different species and even between different spore preparations of the same strain. Two types of heat-dependencies have been reported. In the first (Figure 7.1), in spores of *B. cereus* strain T, for a given time of treatment there

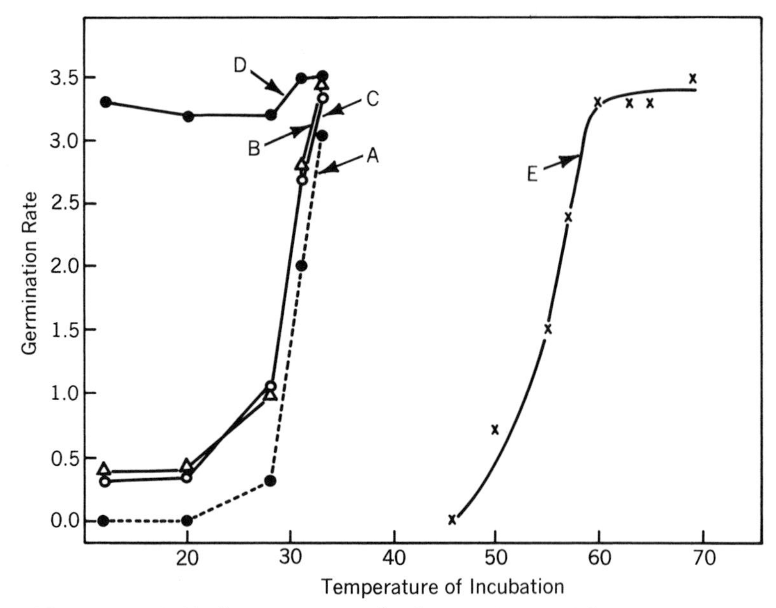

Figure 7.1 Critical temperatures for heat-activation. The experiments illustrated at the left of the figure (A, B, C, D) were carried out by incubating spore suspensions for 45 hours, whereas in curve E a 45-minute incubation time was used. The spores were suspended during incubation in 0.2 *M* succinate buffer, *p*H 5.5. They were then washed twice in distilled water, resuspended in phosphate buffer at *p*H 7.8, and rates of germination over the first 20 minutes were determined. Legend: A, Incubation for 48 hours followed by germination assay. B, As in A but with 0.02 *M* mercaptoethanol during incubation. C, As in A but with 0.2 *M* thioglycollic acid during incubation. D, As in A but with heat-activation (45°C for 45 minutes) after incubation. This illustrates potentiality of spores. E, Incubation for 45 minutes followed by germination assay. (Data from Keynan et al., 1964.)

is a critical temperature required, below which activation does not take place. At longer incubation periods the critical temperature required is lowered. In both cases the temperature range from inactive to complete activation is only a few degrees, suggesting that the apparent energy of activation is very high.

A second type of time-temperature dependence was reported by Ordal (1964) for a spore suspension (*B. subtilis* 5230) which has a mandatory activation requirement for germination. He observed a continuous activation over the temperature range of 5°C to 94°C. The Arrhenius plot (Figure 7.2) gives a $\Delta H^{\ddagger}$ of 27.9 kcal.

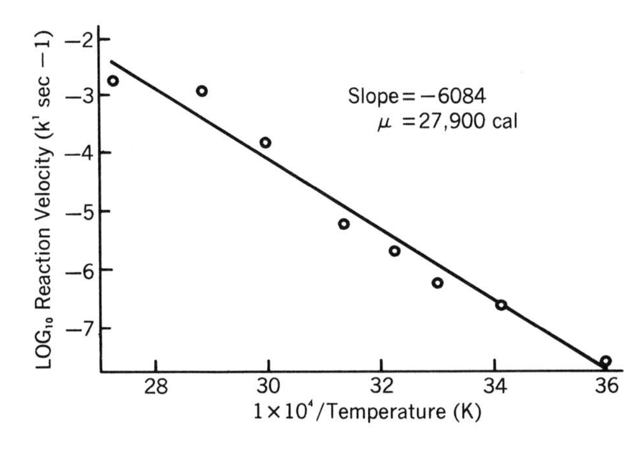

Figure 7.2 Effect of temperature on the rate of heat-activation. An Arrhenius plot of the reaction velocity versus the reciprocal of the absolute temperature. (Data from Ordal, 1964.)

Since the $\Delta F^{\ddagger}$ was between 25.1 to 26.4 kcal, Ordal estimated the $\Delta S^{\ddagger}$ for activation to be between 4.6 to 8.1 cal/degree. This value is also indicative of a strong bond being broken during activation. The possible nature of this bond is discussed in Chapters 8 and 10.

Factors Influencing Heat-Activation

The effect of heat-activation on germination varies with the organism and is influenced by a variety of factors (Curran and Evans, 1945). For example, the medium employed for sporulation influences the heat-activation of spores—which probably explains the findings that different spore preparations of the same strains differ in their temperature response. Undoubtedly, these differences reflect chemical changes in the spore in response to the sporulation medium. For example, the content of DPA can be varied by the conditions of growth and sporulation (Church and Halvorson, 1959). When the amount of heat-activation necessary to give optimal L-alanine-induced germination was determined, it was found that the extent of heat-treatment necessary was related to the DPA content (Keynan et al., 1962). As shown in Figure 7.3, the heat-activation requirements increase with increasing content of DPA, suggesting that DPA may be associated with the system responsible for the dormant state of the spore.

Heat-activation may also be influenced by the components of the medium. Splittstoesser and Steinkraus (1962) found that potassium ions interfered with the heat-activation of spores of *B. popillae*. The inhibition diminished with aging of the spore preparations, suggesting that during this process an activation of the potassium-sensitive systems had taken place. In spores of *B. cereus* strain T (Keynan et al., 1964) reducing agents such as mercaptoethanol or thioglycollic acid, or higher concentrations of H^+ (pH values below 5) accelerated activation. Both of these treatments would be expected to favor the rupture of protein-disulfide bonds. That these bonds may be involved in dormancy was suggested to Gould and Hitchins (1963) by the finding that exposure to reducing agents

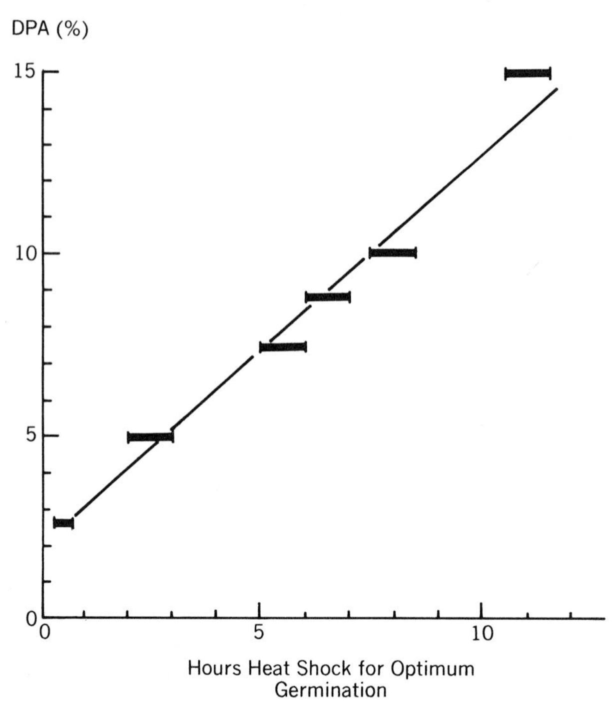

Figure 7.3 Dependence of the duration of heat-shock on intrasporal DPA concentration. Spores were heat-shocked for various periods at 65°C and germinated at 30°C in M/50 Tris buffer, *p*H 8, containing 15 mg/ml L-alanine. The bars indicate the approximate time of heat-shock to obtain maximum germination rates. (From Keynan et al., 1962.)

or to hydrogen peroxide at *p*H 10 in the presence of metal ions sensitized the spores to the action of lysozyme.

Reversibility of Activation

The conversion from a dormant to an activated state is a reversible process in most bacterial spores. This phenomenon was first recognized by Curran and Evans (1945) who found that spores which became deactivated during storage could be reactivated by a second heat-treatment. Two properties of activated spores, rapid germination and the newly acquired metabolic activity (Church Halvorson, 1957; Powell and Hunter, 1955) are lost when activated spores are stored for some period of time. After prolonged storage, the ability to be reactivated by heat is irreversibly lost and a decrease in viability occurs (Williams, 1929) which is influenced by the conditions of storage. Presumably solutes and endogenous reserves are lost during storage, and there is a limit to the number of cycles during which spores will continue to respond.

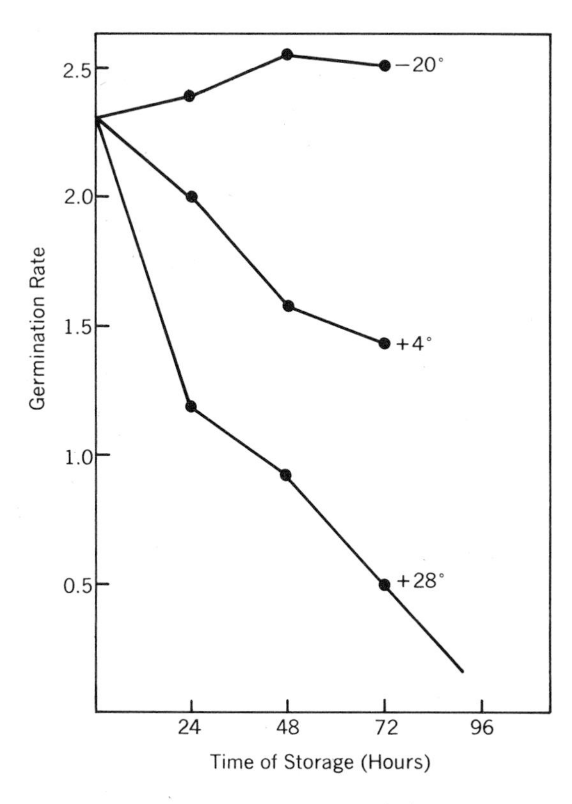

Figure 7.4 Influence of temperature on the rate of deactivation of heat-activated spores of *Bacillus cereus* strain T. Suspensions of freshly heat-activated spores were suspended in distilled water and stored at the temperature indicated. After 24 and 48 hours, the spores were centrifuged and resuspended in phosphate buffer (*p*H 7.8), and the rates of germination were estimated over the first 20 minutes. The rate at zero time was measured immediately after the heat-shock. (From Keynan et al., 1964.)

The reversal of heat-activation is temperature-dependent (Figure 7.4). After 72 hours at 28°C, the rate of germination decreased to nearly that of the dormant spore, whereas at 4° the rate of germination decreased only 40 percent over the same period. When spores stored at 28° or 4°C were re-exposed to a second heat-treatment, *all* the spores germinated normally in the presence of L-alanine and adenosine. Activation by reducing agents is also reversible (Keynan et al., 1964). Spores activated by mercaptoethanol lose their ability to germinate after 48 hours' storage in distilled water; reexposure to reducing agents or heat-treatment fully reactivates the population.

The reversibility of activation of metabolic activity has recently been questioned (Halvorson, 1958; Busta and Ordal, 1964*b*). These workers suggested that deactivation may be merely an inactivation process occurring during storage; reactivation may be the initial activation of a fraction of the population which escaped the initial activation process. It should be noted that Busta and Ordal (1964*a*, *b*) in indirectly measuring activation by the ability of spores to form colonies, failed to observe reactivation of endospores of *B. subtilis* strain 5230. Inactivation, however, cannot explain the observed reversibility of the activation phenomenon. In the case of activation of glucose oxidation (Church and Halvorson, 1957), the metabolism of activated and reactivated spores approaches that of germinating spores and presumably represents the behavior of the majority of the population. In the case of germination rates, in the experiments described, *all* of the spores in the population rapidly germinate after initial activation or upon reactivation. The reversibility of activation therefore applies to the entire population. Whether colony formation and initial germination respond differently to the reversibility of activation is yet to be determined.

Spores reduce their dependence on activation after storage for prolonged periods. Ball (1961) recently suggested that there may be a relationship between activation by aging and by heat-treatment. It might be assumed that "aging" might simply be a "temperature activation" at the lower temperature for longer periods of time. The one difference between these two phenomena is that aging is nonreversible. In this connection, it should be noted that in several experiments (Keynan et al., 1964), spores which were stored for 3 years, although still responsive to heat-activation, had lost the ability to become reactivated. If we assume that some kind of equilibrium exists between activation and its reversal in spores, then the aging phenomenon could also be viewed as loss of the ability to reverse activation.

FUNGI

The need for heat-treatment in activation of spores is not as characteristic of fungi as it is of bacteria. Although there are some fungal spores which can be activated by heat (Table 7.1), there are many others which utilize other triggers.

Table 7.1 Microorganisms Which Require High-Temperature Treatment for Activation or Breaking of Dormancy

Organism	Stage	Treatment (°C)	Duration	Reference
Bacteria				
Bacillus coagulans	Spore	100	6 minutes	Murrell, 1961
B. megaterium	Spore	80	10 minutes	Powell and Hunter, 1955
B. subtilis SJ2	Spore	100	30 minutes	Hermier, 1962
B. cereus	Spore	100	30–60 minutes	Powell, 1957
B. anthracis	Spore	100	30–60 minutes	Powell, 1957
B. polymyxa	Spore	100	30–60 minutes	Powell, 1957
Clostridium spp.	Spore	75	20 minutes	Wynne, 1957
Micromonospora vulgaris	Conidium	75–90	5 minutes	Erikson, 1952
Fungi				
Reticularia sp.	Spore	37	5 minutes	Jahn, 1905
Phytophthora infestans[a]	Sporangium	40	5 minutes	Taylor et al., 1955
Phycomyces blakesleeanus	Spore	50	4 minutes	Sommer and Halbsguth, 1957, Halbsguth and Rudolph, 1959

Table 7.1 (*Continued*)

Organism	Stage	Treatment (°C)	Duration	Reference
Byssochlamys fulva	Ascospore	70	2 hours	Hull, 1939
Ascophanus aurora	Ascospore	48	3 hours	Gwynne-Vaughan and Williamson, 1934
Dasyobolus immersus	Ascospore	48	3–4 hours	Gwynne-Vaughan and Williamson, 1933
Daldinia concentrica, D. vernicosa	Ascospore	70–80	5–15 minutes	Child, 1929
Ascobolus carbonarius	Ascospore	80–95	—	Betts, 1926
A. furfuraceus	Ascospore	38	—	Welsford, 1907
A. carbonarius	Ascospore	70–75	5 minutes	Dodge, 1912
A. furfuraceus, A. winteri, A. glaber, Saccobolus neglectus	Ascospore	60–70	15–30 minutes	Dodge, 1912
A. winteri, A. immersus	Ascospore	37	24 hours	Yu, 1954
Thecotheus pelletieri	Ascospore	70	20 minutes	Dodge, 1912
Thelebolus stercoreus	Ascospore	55–60	—	Dodge, 1912
Lasiobolus equinus	Ascospore	65–68	15–17 minutes	Dodge, 1912
Lachnea stercorea	Ascospore	37–38	50.5 hours	Fraser, 1907
Humaria granulata	Ascospore	48.5	2 hours	Gwynne-Vaughan and Williamson, 1930
Wawelia regia	Ascospore	40 55	4 hours 20 minutes	Doguet, 1961
Neurospora crassa, N. sitophila, N. tetrasperma	Ascospore	70 approx.	10–20 minutes	Shear and Dodge, 1927
N. tetrasperma	Ascospore	50–60	5–30 minutes	Goddard, 1935
N. tetrasperma[b]	Conidium	45–50	5 minutes	Lingappa and Sussman, 1959
N. sitophila[b]	Conidium	35–37	1–3 hours	Ishii and Miyamoto, 1954
Phragmidium mucronatum	Uredospore	27	8 hours	Cochrane, 1945*a*
Ustilago striiformis	Spore	32–35	32 days	Kreitlow, 1943

[a] Rate of germination only is affected.
[b] Slight stimulation only.

The requirement for a heat-shock appears to be most characteristic of the ascomycetes (Table 7.1). Many of these are coprophilous and it is possible that the requirement for heat is associated with their passage through the digestive tracts of animals and subsequent incubation in an enviroment in which high temperatures are known to be generated by microbial action. In fact, Janczewski (1871) and De Bary (1887) noticed that certain organisms appeared to germinate better after passage through animals. This finding led to the surmise that either exposure to body temperature or to the digestive enzymes was responsible for the improved ability to germinate. Welsford (1907), whose data are included in Table 7.1, was led to test these alternatives and concluded that incubation at 38°C in cow dung offered the most favorable conditions for the disruption of dormancy in *Ascobolus furfuraceus*. This work was followed soon after by that of Dodge (1912) who seems to have been the first investigator to have used temperatures in excess of body temperature.

It will also be noted that the highest temperatures are required among the spores of bacteria and ascomycetes. Thus, even though two basidiomycetous fungi (*Phragmidium* and *Ustilago*) are included in Table 7.1, the temperatures required for spore activation are only slightly above those needed for vegetative growth. The range of temperatures over which ascospores of *Neurospora* will be induced to germinate is provided in Figure 7.5.

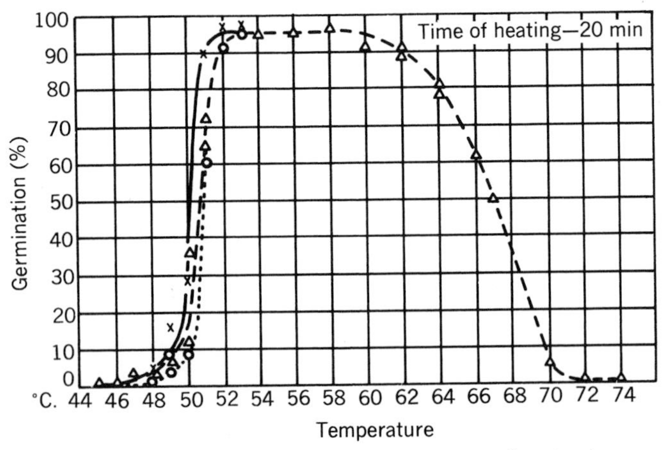

Figure 7.5 The effect of the temperature of activation on germination. Germination was at room temperature and counts were made 6–8 hours after activation. Three separate spore lots were used. Each point based on counts of 350–500 spores. (From Goddard, 1935.)

As would be expected, especially in heat-resistant spores, exposure to high temperatures may affect the rate as well as the extent of germination. This is true of the germination of spores of the slime mold, *Reticularia*, in which transfer to 21°C after treatment at 38°C reduced the germination time by one-third. Such is also the case in conidia of *Neurospora sitophila* (Ishii and Miyamoto, 1954) and *N. tetrasperma* (Lingappa and Sussman, 1959), in which small increases in germination were induced by heat-activation, whereas the time at which the germ tubes appeared was appreciably shortened.

Relatively few insects and other animals with dormant periods appear to require elevated temperatures for the breaking of dormancy (Table 7.2). Similarly, among plants, the propagules of certain algae and ferns, as well as of

Table 7.2 Organisms Which Require High-Temperature Treatment as a Means of Breaking Dormancy (Exclusive of Microorganisms)

Organism	Stage	Treatment (°C)	Duration	Reference
Insects				
Bombyx mori	Egg	56 or 60	—	Emme, 1949
Diparopis castanea	Diapausing pupa	28	24 weeks	Pearson (cited by Lees, 1955)
Leptinotarsa decimlineata	Diapausing beetle	25 30	2–3 months 3 weeks	De Wilde, 1949, 1953
Locustana pardalina	Egg	35	—	Matthé, 1951
Nematodes				
Ascaris lumbricoides	Egg	38–40	—	Spector, 1956
Algae				
Chlamydomonas chlamydogama	Zygospore	37	48–96 hours	Starr, 1949
Chlorococcum (s.11/c.6)	Zygospore	37	48–72 hours	Starr, 1949
Chlorogonium elongatum	Zygospore	40 60	48–91 days 6 days	Strehlow, 1929
Nostoc punctiforme	Akinete	30	—	Harder, 1918
Bryophytes				
Riella americana	Spore	40–75	1–2 hour	Studhalter, 1931
Ferns				
Aneimia phyllitidis, Aspidium filix-mas, Pteridium aquilinum	Spore	32 (dark)	—	Klebs, 1917
Platycerium alcicorne	Spore	32 (dark)	—	Hartt, 1925
Marsilea quadrifolia	Sporocarp	65	1 hour	Bloom, 1955
Phanerogams				
Crataegus mollis	Seed	21–27, then 5	60 days + 75–90 days	Spector, 1956
Juniperus scopularum	Seed	20–30, then 5	120 days + 120 days	Spector, 1956
Paspalum notatum	Seed	50–60	2–4 days	Hodgson, 1949
Poa (Kentucky blue-grass and Canada blue-grass)	Seed	40	8 days (dry)	Hite, 1923
Hordeum vulgare	Seed	40	8 days (dry)	Harrington, 1923
Avena sativa	Seed	40	8 days (dry)	Harrington, 1923
Cosmos (Orange Flare)	Seed	29	Several months	Carleton, 1936
Digitaria ischaemmum	Seed	3 + 20–40	4–8 weeks + 1 year	Toole and Toole, 1941

a few seed plants and a bryophyte, respond to heat-activation. On the other hand, cold-treatment is a common activator in most of these groups of organisms.

Low Temperature as a "Trigger"

"Overwintering" is of great significance in the life history of organisms as diverse as hibernating mammals, diapausing insects, and dormant seeds; it provides the natural mechanism in these organisms for the overcoming of dormancy. Thus, over a hundred species of phanerogams which require such treatment are listed by Crocker and Barton (1955) and Spector (1956). Many insects (Lees, 1955) and mammals (Lyman and Dawe, 1960) also require such treatment.

By contrast, bacterial spores are relatively unresponsive to activation by low temperature. The temperature coefficient for heat-activation is high (see Figures 7.1 and 7.2). Keynan et al. (1958) could not obtain activation of *B. subtilis* spores below 18°C, but if spores were activated above 18°C, germination continued even at 0°C. The aging of bacterial spores, which minimizes the need for subsequent heat-activation, also proceeds at temperatures of either 5°C or −20°C. Numerous investigators have observed decreases in the viability of spore preparations which have been stored at low temperatures. Wolf and Mahmoud (1957) have interpreted this decrease as germination and death of the germinated cells. However, examination of spores which had decreased in viability by 80 percent over a 4-year period of low-temperature storage (Halvorson, 1959), were cytologically indistinguishable from normal spores, and underwent normal germination when exposed to L-alanine and adenosine in a buffer solution. It is more likely that storage leads to an impairment of the ability of germinated spores to grow and divide.

Dormant stages of fungi are much more responsive to cold temperatures than are those of bacteria (Table 7.3). The dormant forms of basidiomycetes represent the majority of fungi which require cold-treatment for activation, whereas only a few of this group respond to high-temperature treatments. Although the reasons for the difference between the response to low temperature activation of the dormant forms listed in tables 7.1 and 7.3 can only be guessed at, one interesting correlation concerns the fact that the large majority of organisms which respond to low temperatures are plant parasites or mycorrhizal fungi. Perhaps the requirement for the cold-treatment assures synchronization of the fungus with the renewal of the activities of host plants in the spring. On the other hand, those fungi for which heat-shocks are needed to break dormancy are mainly saprophytes, although *Phytophthora infestans* is a parasite on potatoes.

Wide differences exist in the time needed to break dormancy at low temperatures. Thus, there is a range of 3 hours in the case of aeciospores of *Puccinia graminis* to 5 or 6 months in the resting spores of *Physoderma* and spores of *Tilletia tritici.* However, factors such as maturity and the source of the spores

Table 7.3 Fungi Which Require Low-Temperature Treatment to Break Dormancy

Organism	Stage	Treatment (°C)	Duration	Reference
Cystopus sp.	Oospore	1–5	24 hours	Melhus, 1911
Peronospora schleideni	Oospore	1–3	1 month	Blackwell, 1935
Physoderma pluriannulatum	Resting spore	8	96 hours	Sparrow, 1957
P. dulichii	Resting spore	8	6 months	Johns, 1958
Ustulina sp.	Ascospore	0	48 hours	Wilkins, 1938
Daldinia vernicosa	Ascospore	−5	3 months	Child, 1929
Taphrina coryli	Ascospore	10	12 hours	Martin, 1924
Nadsonia richteri	Ascospore	0–5	—	Ingram, 1955
Claviceps purpurea	Sclerotium	0–3	Several weeks	Kirchoff, 1929
Flammula conissans	Basidiospore	−7	11 weeks	Denyer, 1960
Agaricus subrufescens, *Amanitopsis parcivolvata*, *Lactarius luteolus*, *Marasmius* sp., *Paxillus involutus*, *Tricholoma equestre*	Basidiospore	−7	40–140 days	Kneebone, 1950
Puccinia glumarum	Teliospore	Freezing	—	Raeder and Bever, 1931
P. graminis	Aeciospore	3	3 hours	Eriksson and Henning, 1896
Tilletia tritici	Spore	3	16 days	Gassner and Niemann, 1954
T. tritici	Spore	4	5 months	Holton, 1943
T. asperifolioides, *T. bromi-tectorum*, *T. caries*, *T. contraversa*, *T. elymi*, *T. fusca*, *T. guyotiana*, *T. holci*, *T. scrobiculata*	Spore	5	—	Meiners and Waldher, 1959
T. cerebrina	Spore	5–10	—	Meiners and Waldher, 1959
T. asperifolia	Spore	10	—	Meiners and Waldher, 1959
T. pallida	Spore	15	—	Meiners and Waldher, 1959
T. caries	Spore	10–15	10 days	Purdy and Kendrick, 1957
T. caries	Spore	5–8	3 weeks	Siang, 1956
T. contraversa	Spore	8–25	3 weeks	Siang, 1956

influence the duration of the treatment, as in the case of *T. tritici*, which can germinate in 16 days at 3°C (Gassner and Niemann, 1954) but which are said by Holton (1943) to require 5 months at 4°C.

In some species, low temperature alone is not enough to ensure optimal germination. For example, when cold-treated uredospores of *Puccinia graminis* and *P. triticina* were transferred to room temperature after germination had stopped at the lower temperature, many of the remaining spores germinated. The reciprocal experiment in which uredospores were transferred to 9–10°C for 48 hours, after germination had ceased at 29–30°C resulted in an increase in germination (Raeder and Bever, 1931). Often a distinction has to be made between the temperature that is optimal for after-ripening and that which is optimal for germination. Thus, it is frequently necessary to transfer the organism from the low temperature at which it is after-ripened to its optimum for germination, which is usually between 15–30°C. The basidiomycetes listed by Kneebone (1950), as well as several of the other species in Table 7.3 fall in this category. On the other hand, certain of the smuts can be incubated at 3°C continually in order to obtain maximal germination (Holton, 1943).

Among other organisms, several algae have been reported to respond to cold-temperature activation but ferns and bryophytes appear not to respond in this way (Sussman, 1965). Moreover, as was discussed in the opening paragraph of this section, cold-treatment is probably the most widely used trigger in dormant stages of mammals, insects, and seed plants.

Light as a "Trigger"

MICROORGANISMS

As in the case of the organisms which respond to cold-treatment, those that are activated by light are mostly parasites and, of these, the basidiomycetes are the majority (Table 7.4). This generalization holds true except for *Aphanomyces stellatus, Protoachlya hypogyna, Achlya recurva, Thraustotheca primoachlya,* and *Oidium monilioides,* but it is clear that the rest of the organisms in Table 7.4 are pathogens. It is reasonable to suppose that, as in the case of the cold-temperature requirement, light is a means through which an environmental signal helps to synchronize the activities of a host and its pathogen.

Not all rusts and smuts are dependent upon light as a trigger because many species have been shown to germinate well in the dark. Included in this category are teliospores of *Cronartium ribicola*, aeciospores, and uredospores of *Melampsora lini*, uredospores of *Puccinia coronifera, P. dispersa,* and of *P. graminis-tritici*, sporidia of *P. malvacearum*, aeciospores of *P. poarum*, and chlamydospores of *Tilletia secalis* (cf. bibliography of Marsh et al., 1959), *T. bromi-tectorum, T. asperifolia,* and *T. caries* (Meiners and Waldher, 1959). When these species are compared with the ones in Table 7.4 it becomes apparent that the different spore types of a single organism may respond differently to light. Thus, whereas the teliospores of *Puccinia graminis* germinate better in blue light, according to

Table 7.4 Microorganisms Which Require Light for the Breaking of Dormancy

Organism	Stage	Conditions	Reference
Phytophthora infestans	Conidium	Daylight	Blackwell and Waterhouse, 1931
Aphanomyces stellatus	Oospore	North window	Sorokine, 1876
Physoderma maydis	Resting sporangium	North window	Voorhees, 1933
P. maydis	Resting sporangium	Blue light	Hebert and Kelman, 1958
Protoachlya hypogyna, Achlya recurva, Thraustotheca primoachlya	Zygote	North window	Ziegler, 1948
Erysiphe graminis hordei	Conidium	—	Jones, 1945
E. cichoracearum	Conidium	14°C	Morrison, 1964
Tilletia controversa	Spore	Infection outdoors	Böning et al., 1953
T. tritici	Spore	Diffuse light	Riehm, 1920
T. tritici, T. levis	Spore	Light plus citrate	Hahne, 1925
T. brevifaciens	Spore	5–6°C on loam	Baylis, 1955; Pichler, 1953
T. brevifaciens, T. secalis, T. tritici, (T. contraversa)	Spore	Light or certain chemicals; 3°C	Gassner and Niemann, 1954, 1955*b*
T. brevifaciens	Spore	Light at 5–14°	Gassner-Hoechst, 1953
T. contraversa	Spore	150–200 ft-c at 5°C	Baylis, 1958
T. contraversa, T. bornmulleri, T. panicii, T. guyotiana, T. decipiens, T. lolii, T. hordei, T. secalis	Spore	3°C on loam	Niemann, 1956*a*
T. horrida	Spore	Short wavelengths in visible range	Lin, 1936
T. horrida	Spore	Blue or white light	Kreitlow, 1938
T. fusca, T. guyotiana, T. holci	Spore	Sun or artificial light	Meiners and Waldher, 1959
Neovossia horrida	Spore	46 hours with 50 ft-c fluorescent light or 2 hours sunlight	Lin, 1955
Cronartium ribicola	Uredospore	Glass-filtered sunlight	Duff, 1918
Urocystis occulta	Uredospore	Light plus benzaldehyde	Ling, 1940
Hemileia vastatrix	Uredospore	Blue light	Butler and Jones, 1949
Puccinia graminis	Teliospore	Ultraviolet, infrared	Sibilia, 1930
P. emiliae, P. helianthi, P. xanthii	Teliospore	Alternate light and dark	Maneval, 1927
Alternaria oleracea	Conidium	—	Neergaard, 1941
Oidium monilioides	Conidium	550–400 mμ	Sempio and Castori, 1950

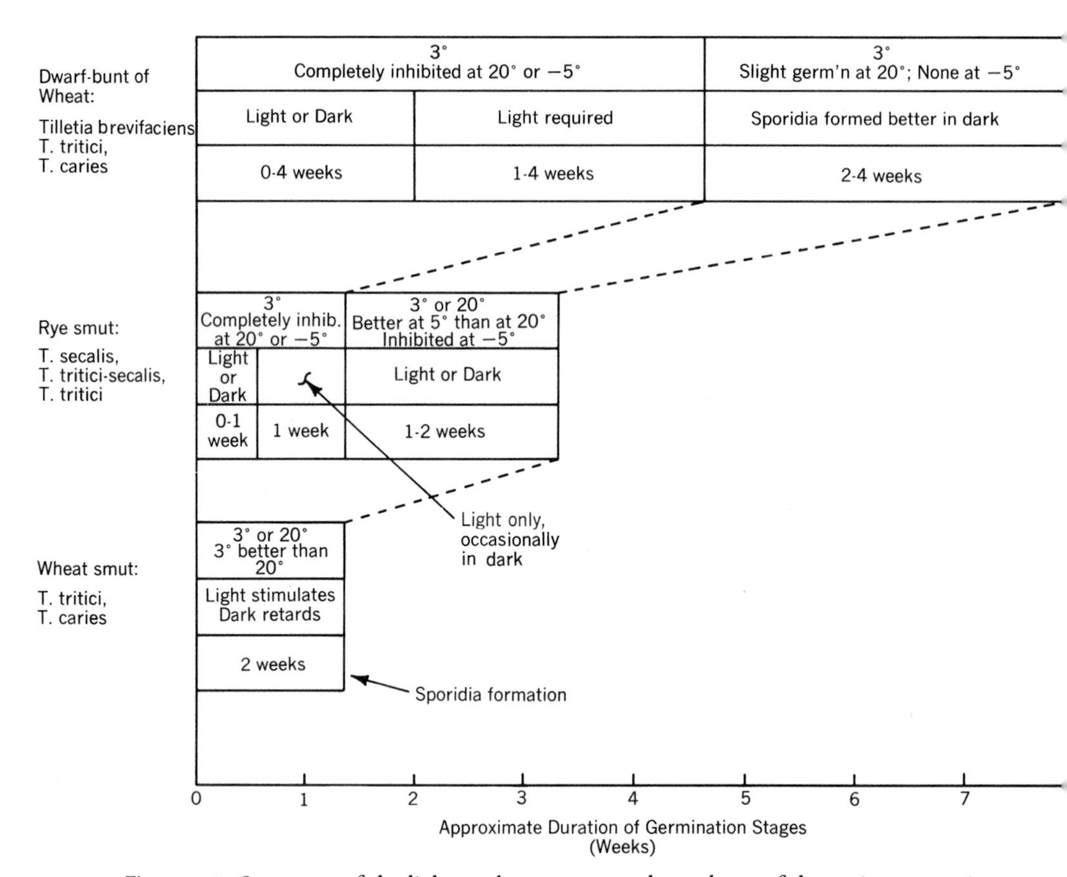

Figure 7.6 Summary of the light- and temperature-dependence of the various stages in the germination of smut spores. (Redrawn from Gassner and Niemann, 1954.)

Sibilia (1930), its uredospores do not require light to germinate; similarly, uredospores of *Cronartium ribicola* require light but teliospores do not.

A contradiction arises in the case of spores of *Tilletia secalis* which are reported by Gassner and Niemann (1954) and Niemann (1956) to require light, whereas Meiners and Waldher (1959) claim that they germinate in the dark. Data such as these led Fischer and Holton (1957) to express reservations concerning the necessity for light in smut spore germination. These anomalies may stem in part from changes in the responsiveness of the spores during the course of their development. Thus, Figure 7.6 reveals that if spores of the dwarf-bunt of wheat ("Zweigsteinbrand") and of rye smut ("Roggensteinbrand") are irradiated too soon after being collected, they are insensitive to light because they require 1 week in the latter case and from 1 to 4 weeks in the former to reach their peak in responsiveness. Moreover, once these fungi have been illuminated for the required time, the subsequent stages of after-ripening and germination can proceed in the dark.

Another variable that must be considered is the age of the spore, for Hahne (1925) refers to the fact that only older spores of *Tilletia tritici* and *T. levis* require light, whereas those that are younger than 2 years will germinate without such treatment. These facts might help to explain why light had only a negligible effect on the germination of *T. tritici glumarum* (Rabien, 1928) and why Hahne found that light was most effective at 20°C instead of at 3°C as in the case of Gassner and Niemann's (1954) work. Furthermore, inasmuch as the time of collection, strain, treatment before germination, and temperature of incubation must also be considered, it is not surprising that discrepant results should be obtained. A clear case where variation in collections is exhibited was described by Meiners and Waldher (1959) in which two collections of *T. cerebrina* were inhibited by light but the germination of a third was stimulated. Data like these may help to reconcile conflicting results which may also arise because of difficulties in nomenclature which have beset workers with the smuts.

Interaction between light and temperature is very well demonstrated in the work of Gassner and Niemann (1954) which is outlined in Figure 7.6. The proper combination of light and temperature is required by each group of rusts and, in fact, stages in the germination process are delimitable through progressive changes in the requirements. (See page 4 for a discussion of stages in the germination process.) Other cases in which cold temperatures must be used with the proper light regime are listed in Table 7.4.

Unfortunately, very little detailed information is available as to the action spectra and exact quantities of light needed to break dormancy in spores. Hebert and Kelman (1958) have shown that as little as 0.1–0.2 foot-candles of illumination for 8 hours daily effected a significant increase in the germination of resting sporangia of *Physoderma maydis*. In this case, blue light was most effective but no quantitative studies were performed from which action spectra could be derived. In the case of conidia of *Oidium monilioides* (Sempio and Castori, 1950), wavelengths between 400 and 550 mμ were shown to be most effective in stimulating germination. As in the case of the seeds of some higher plants, light of longer wavelengths (550–750 mμ) inhibited this process. Also, Meiners and Waldher (1959) have reported that the germination of spores of *Tilletia scrobiculata* and *T. cerebrina* is suppressed by visible light. However, in all the cases reported in Table 7.4, blue light is stimulatory, in contrast to the situation in higher plants in which the "red-far-red" system is of widespread importance.

Differentiation following germination may be influenced by light, as in the case of uredospores of *Puccinia graminis tritici* which form appressorium-like structures 2–3 hours after inoculation in the light, followed by penetration pegs and vesicles. However, the sequence of these events can be interrupted if the conditions of light and temperature are not in balance (Emge, 1958).

OTHER ORGANISMS

Certain algal spores are known to require light for germination to occur. Among these are zygospores of *Ulothrix* (Hygen, 1948; Grosse, 1931), zygotes of *Enteromorpha linza*, *Ulva lactuca* (Kylin, 1947), and *Acetabularia crenulata* (Hämmerling, 1944), as well as the akinetes of some blue-green algae (Harder, 1918). In addition, many bryophyte and vascular cryptogam spores require light for germination and, in the few instances which have been studied in detail, wavelengths in the red region of the visible spectrum are the most effective. However, there are indications in other cases that wavelengths in the blue are effective (cf. the review by Sussman, 1965). Those seeds of higher plants that require light for germination generally use red light and are inhibited by the near-infrared (735 mμ). Inhibition by visible light has been reported for cryptogamic spores as well and, in the case of the fern, *Dryopteris filix-mas*, the red-far-red interaction has been found to occur (Bünning and Mohr, 1955; Mohr, 1956).

Chemicals can replace light in the case of certain seeds, including lettuce (Kahn et al., 1957; Evenari et al., 1958), *Arabidopsis thaliana* (Kribben, 1957), *Sedum kamtschaticum* (Fujii et al., 1960) and *Bidens radiata* (Rollin, 1964). In these seeds gibberellins are the effective factor but, as will be shown later, many other chemicals can be substituted for the light requirements of other organisms.

The interaction of light and chemical inhibitors of germination is evident in certain seeds. For example, a light requirement for germination can be induced by naringenin (5,7,4′-trihydroxyflavanone) in certain lettuce seeds that usually germinate in the dark (Phillips, 1961). As in the cases discussed, this light requirement is removed by gibberellic acid.

Temperature and light interact to influence seed germination, as in *Panicum turgidum* (Koller and Roth, 1963) and the plants reviewed by Amen (1963).

Photoperiodic control of development has been reported in seeds of several species (Negbi and Koller, 1964; Amen, 1963; Rollin, 1964), and in insects (Beck and Alexander, 1964; Bell and Adkisson, 1964) where diapause is influenced by day length.

Several detailed chapters on the effect of various environmental factors on seed germination can be found in Volume 15, Part 2, of the *Encylopedia of Plant Physiology* (Lang, 1965).

Chemicals as "Triggers" and Germinating Agents

SUBSTANCES OF KNOWN COMPOSITION

It has long been recognized that specific chemical stimulants will rapidly initiate the germination of bacterial and fungal spores. Table 7.5 summarizes the more effective of these, which fall into 2 classes: (a) those which affect the metabolism of the spore and (b) those whose action appears to be physical in nature. The former generally includes metabolites whereas the latter are primarily surface-active agents (Chapter 10). The success of the first class of germination stimulants appears dependent upon the physiological competence of the activated spore and differences between various spores probably represent differences in the enzyme patterns of spores. The chemical activators that are metabolites suggest that germination has an enzymatic basis for the following reasons:

1. Germination agents are usually normal metabolites and in a number of cases disappear during germination.
2. Stereospecific binding sites can be recognized for germinating agents which are subject to competitive inhibition.
3. The temperature-dependence of germination is that expected of an enzymatic reaction (see Chapter 6).
4. Germination can be blocked by a number of metabolic poisons.

An understanding of the role of the germination agent requires a closer examination of the primary reaction (trigger) as well as the metabolic reactions essential to germination. These agents will be reviewed briefly in the following sections and the mechanisms of their action discussed in Chapter 10.

Chemical Activation of Bacterial Spores

Triggering agents will be defined as those chemicals that induce germination but whose continued presence is not necessary for germination. Following brief exposure of the spore to a triggering agent, the chemical can be removed before germination starts, and the germination process will continue after its removal. *Germination agents* are those chemicals whose continued presence is required for the germination process to continue. In the latter case, a triggering action may be operative, but the process is too rapid to isolate the triggering event or else it is followed by rapid metabolism of the germination agent. Only a few studies have been carried out in order to recognize triggers in the germination of bacterial spores and these are discussed in the following material. On the other hand, many germination stimulants are known for bacterial spores (Table 7.5) but these have, in large part, not been examined for a triggering stage.

Table 7.5 Chemicals Which Break the Dormancy of Microbial Spores

Organism	Stage	Treatment	Reference
Bacillus anthracis	Spore	Inosine, adenosine, tyrosine, L-alanine, DL-valine, DL-cystine, methionine, adenine, guanine	Hills, 1949*a*, *b*; Powell and Hunter, 1955
B. cereus	Spore	Inosine, adenosine, L-alanine, L-cysteine, glucose, lactate, pyruvate, xanthosine, guanosine, phosphate	Powell and Hunter, 1955; Church et al., 1954; Krask, 1961; O'Connor, and Halvorson, 1961; Fitz-James, 1955, Lawrence, 1955
B. megaterium	Spore	L-Alanine, glutamic acid, glucose, maltose, acetate, formate, propionate, adenosine, phosphate, manganese, mannose, cobalt, zinc, chloride, alkylamines, quaternary ammonium compounds	Powell, 1951; Levinson and Sevag, 1953; Powell and Hunter, 1955; Fitz-James, 1955; Hills, 1950; Rode and Foster, 1960*a*, *b*, *c*, *d*
B. subtilis	Spore	Glucose, L-alanine (18 other amino acids), lactose, sucrose, pyruvate, succinate, fumarate, malate, phosphate	Hills, 1950; Powell, 1950; Hachisuka et al., 1954; 1955
B. circulans	Spore	L-Alanine	Wolf and Mahmoud, 1957
B. polymyxa	Spore	L-Alanine, adenosine	Church et al., 1954
B. sphairicus	Spore	L-Alanine	Wolf and Mahmoud, 1957
B. stearothermophilus	Spore	Glucose	O'Brien and Campbell, 1957
Clostridium acetobutylicum	Spore	L-Alanine, L-arginine, L-phenylalanine, oxalacetate	Hitzman, 1955; Hitzman et al., 1957
C. botulinum	Spore	Glucose, L-alanine, L-arginine, L-phenylalanine, CO_2, oxalacetate	Wynne et al., 1954; Halvorson, 1957; Treadwell et al., 1958; Wynne et al., 1954
C. perfringens	Spore	Glucose	Wynne et al., 1954
C. sporogenes	Spore	Glucose	Wynne et al., 1954
C. roseum	Spore	L-Arginine, L-alanine, L-phenylalanine	Hitzman et al., 1957
58 Species of myxomycetes	Spore	Na glycocholate, Na taurocholate	Elliott, 1949
Enteridium rozeanum	Spore	trisodium PO_4, Dreft of Soilax	Elliott, 1949
Allomyces arbuscula	Resting sporangium	Indole butyrate, indole acetate, tryptophan	Machlis and Ossia, 1953*b*; Turian, 1956
Peronospora tabaci	Conidium	Riboflavin, PO_4, Ca^{--} Mg^{--}, amino acids	Shepherd, 1962
Phycomyces blakesleeanus	Conidiospore	Glyoxylate, acetate, acetaldehyde, propionate, butyrate	Brinckmann, 1960; Rudolph, 1961
Phycomyces blakesleeanus	Conidiospore	Heated glucose, propionate, pyruvate, acetate	Sommer and Halbsguth, 1957
Neurospora crassa	Ascospore	Furfural, furfuryl alcohol	Emerson, 1948
N. crassa	Ascospore	Benzaldehyde, 5-hydroxymethyl furfural	Emerson, 1954
N. tetrasperma	Ascospore	Various furans, pyrrole, thiophene chloride	Sussman, 1953
N. tetrasperma	Ascospore	Aliphatic esters, alcohols, ethers	Sussman et al., 1959
Gelasinospora calospora	Ascospore	Furfural	Tylutki, 1955
Sordaria fimicola	Ascospore	Acetic acid	Bretzloff, 1954

Table 7.5 (*Continued*)

Organism	Stage	Treatment	Reference
Ascobolus magnificus, A. stercorarius, A. viridulus	Ascospore	NaOH at 37°C; also KOH, $Ca(OH)_2$; bile salts	Yu, 1954
Saccharomyces cerevisiae	Ascospore	Glucose, fructose, mannose	Palleroni, 1961
Agaricus campestris	Basidiospore	2,3-Dimethyl-1-pentene	McTeague et al., 1959
Tilletia tritici	Spore	Rose bengal, eosin, methylene blue	Ettel and Halbsguth, 1963
Merulius silvester	Basidiospore	Malic acid	Falk, 1912
Puccinia graminis tritici	Uredospore	2, 4-Dinitrophenol, methyl naphthoquinone, coumarin	Allen, 1955
P. graminis tritici	Uredospore	Aldehydes and ethanol, *n*-nonanal (most active)	French and Weintraub, 1957
P. graminis tritici	Uredospore	Indole acetate, coumarin, protocatechuic acid, umbelliferone, daphnetin, coumaric acid	Van Sumere et al., 1957
P. graminis tritici	Uredospore	Ketones, aldehydes, terpenes	French, 1961
P. graminis	Uredospore	Organic or inorganic acids at *p*H 2.0	Sibilia, 1930
Melampsora occidentalis	Uredospore	Methyl *p*-hydroxybenzoate + Ni^{++} + chlortetracycline	Turel, 1955
Ustilago zeae	Spore	Indole acetate, L-alanine, glutamate, niacinamide	von Güttenberg and Strutz, 1952
U. maydis	Spore	Acetate, citrate, mineral acids, K^+	Leszcenko, 1928
Urocystis tritici	Spore	Benzaldehyde, Na stearate, salicylaldehyde, acetone, butyrate	Noble, 1924
U. occulta	Spore	Benzaldehyde	Stakman et al., 1934; Ling, 1940
Piricularia oryzae	Spore	Cholesterol, diosgenin, gitogenin, hecogenin, smilagenin	Weintraub et al., 1957
Botrytis cinerea	Conidium	Ethyl acetate, ethyl citrate, ethyl malate	Brown, 1922
Aspergillus niger	Conidium	L-Alanine	Yanagita, 1957
A. niger	Conidium	L-Alanine	Hoshino et al., 1962
Diplosporium sp.	Conidium	Oxidized sulfur	Kidder, 1964
Eremothecium ashbyii	Spore	H_2O_2	Minoura, 1955

Two examples of triggering action of L-alanine on the germination of aerobic spores have been reported. Harrell and Halvorson (1955) observed that the germination of spores of *Bacillus cereus* could be arrested by lowering the *p*H to about 2; raising the *p*H again to above 7 permitted germination to continue. When spores were exposed to L-alanine for 45 seconds, the *p*H lowered, and the L-alanine removed by washing, over 40 percent of the spores germinated after 20 minutes' incubation at *p*H 8.3. There was no detectable germination after 45 seconds and control spores in the absence of L-alanine failed to germinate under similar conditions. Anaerobic conditions during the activation period inhibited the trigger mechanism. In experiments with C^{14} labeled L-alanine, about 3–8 × 10^{-21} moles of L-alanine were fixed per spore.

Keynan and Halmann (1961) have investigated some of the properties of the

L-alanine trigger mechanism in the germination of spores of *B. licheniformis*. Spores of this organism can be triggered by L-alanine at temperatures above 20°C but not below. However, if spores were first exposed to L-alanine at 37°C for a few minutes and then transferred to 15°C, germination ensued. At 37°C a 4-minute lag period was observed preceding germination. In the transfer experiments, the degree of activation or triggering during the lag period was dependent upon the duration and temperature of preincubation. The triggering action was found to be inhibited by D-alanine, a number of salts (many of which did not inhibit the germination process), and octyl alcohol (see Chapter 10). L-Alanine failed to activate spores at *p*H below 6.5; however, activated spores were able to germinate in the *p*H range 5.0 to 6.5 when they had been previously triggered by L-alanine above *p*H 6.5.

Delays in the germination of spores after the addition of the germinating stimulants have been observed in a number of cases (Chapter 6). Woese et al. (1958) also observed a delay between L-alanine activation and the subsequent release of dipicolinic acid from spores of *B. subtilis*.

The triggering mechanism is understood in only a few cases. In Chapter 10 the proposed mechanism of action for a number of amino acids, carbohydrates, and inorganic ions will be discussed.

Miscellaneous Nonnitrogenous Compounds

A number of nonnitrogenous compounds have been reported to initiate or stimulate germination in a wide variety of strains. A number of these are summarized in Table 7.5. This list includes simple sugars, carbohydrates, and the normal metabolic products of hexose metabolism. For more comprehensive reviews see Stedman (1956), Heiligman et al. (1956) and Schmidt (1955).

The added stimulation has, in a number of cases, been examined in complex medium. For instance, a marked stimulation of the germination of spores of *Clostridium* by carbon dioxide in complex medium has been reported in the older literature. Wynne and Foster (1948) observed that this requirement was absolute in synthetic medium and that oxaloacetic acid would replace carbon dioxide. L-Malic acid, fumaric, and succinic acids accelerated germination in *C. botulinum* and in *Bacillus mesentericus* but not in four other aerobes and four other anaerobes. The effects of the organic acids are frequently as complementary germination stimulants. Lactate, pyruvate, acetate, formate, succinate, fumarate, and malate have been reported as stimulants for the germination of *B. subtilis* (Hachisuka et al., 1955), *B. megaterium* (Levinson and Sevag, 1953), and *B. cereus* (Lawrence, 1955; Halvorson and Church, 1957). Lactate and pyruvate can spare the requirements for germination of *B. cereus* for L-alanine (Lawrence, 1955). The stimulation by these compounds, however, is not a general phenomenon and a number of negative results have been reported (Hills, 1949*a*, 1950; Hachisuka et al., 1955; Powell, 1951). These differences are poorly understood but may reflect the state of activation of the spores. Although lactate is inactive and pyruvate is a poor germinating stimulant for spores of *B. subtilis* (Hachisuka et al., 1955), both compounds are stimulants if the spores are preheated with these substrates (Lawrence, 1955). The changes in the germination requirements following preheating are particularly pronounced for spores of *B. megaterium*. For example, Levinson and Hyatt (1962) found that in unheated spores the only nitrogenous germination stimulants were L-alanine, glucosamine, and *N*-acetylglucosamine, whereas heated spores germinated in response to nitrate, nitrite, and seven other amino acids. Rode and Foster (1961) have reported a similar spectrum of germination stimulants in heated spores of *B. megaterium*. As will be discussed further in Chapter 10, the metabolism of organic acids by intact spores requires prior activation.

Disaccharides such as maltose (Powell, 1951), lactose, and sucrose (Hachisuka et al., 1955) have been reported as stimulants of germination. It is not clear whether they are first converted to glucose. In aged spores of *B. cereus*, a number of products of glucose metabolism (gluconate, pyruvate, acetate, 6-phosphogluconate, ribose 5-phosphate, and to a lesser extent, 2-keto-gluconate) are germination stimulants (Halvorson and Church, 1957).

In some instances spores are produced which fail to germinate, due to either unrecognized germination requirements or defects in the trigger mechanism. A recent example of this was reported by Markova et al. (1962) for spores of *B. megaterium* var. *phosphaticum*. The production of nongerminating spores depends upon the strain and cultural conditions. They are maximally produced in submerged culture and their production is correlated with the failure of the culture to produce hydrogen sulfide in the early stages of growth.

Fungi and Other Microorganisms

In most cases, a variety of substances have been found to serve as triggers within the different groups of microorganisms (Table 7.5), except for the myxomycetes in which a single type of treatment is effective. Thus, the successful use of either sodium glycocholate or sodium taurocholate by Elliott (1949) with spores of more than fifty species of this group, and the success of Cayley (1929) in germinating *Didymium* spores with ethanol suggest a general requirement for a wetting agent. In this connection, even Gilbert's (1929) success in germinating the species with which he worked may have been attributable, in part, to his use of hexylresorcinol as a component of an antiseptic rinse in the preparation of the spores (Elliott, 1949).

On the other hand, the treatments which activate spores in other groups of fungi are much more heterogeneous than those required by the myxomycetes. Solvents such as alcohols and acetone, which also function as wetting agents, activate ascospores of *Neurospora tetrasperma* (Sussman et al., 1959), uredospores of *Puccinici graminis tritici* (French et al., 1957), of *Urocystis tritici* (Noble, 1924), and conidia of *Penicillium frequentans* (Dobbs and Hinson, 1953) and of *Aspergillus flavus* (Duggar, 1901). In addition, other solvents such as chloroform and ethyl ether have a similar effect upon *Neurospora* ascospores (Sussman, 1953), uredospores of *Puccinia graminis tritici* (Thiel and Weiss, 1920), spores of several smuts (Enomoto, 1934), and conidia of *Aspergillus niger* (Duggar, 1901). The furans, pyrroles, and thiophenes which activate ascospores of *Neurospora* (Emerson, 1948, 1954; Sussman, 1953) might also be placed in this category, along with the aldehydes that were found by French et al. (1957) to activate uredospores of *Puccinia graminis tritici*.

Reasoning from the fact that extracts of many plant materials, and the emanations from some, could activate conidia of *Botrytis cinerea*, Brown (1922) used the ethyl esters of acetate, malate and citrate and found that they were effective substitutes. More recently, these and other esters have been found to break the dormancy of ascospores of *Neurospora tetrasperma* (Sussman et al., 1959). Noble's (1924) observations on the germination of spores of *Urocystis tritici* followed a parallel course in that benzaldehyde, a major constituent of oil of almonds, could substitute for this natural material in very low concentrations. Since then, this substance has been used in the same way with other smut spores (Stakman et al., 1934; Ling, 1940) as well as on ascospores of *Neurospora crassa* (Emerson, 1954) and *N. tetrasperma* (Sussman et al., 1959). Indole acetic acid and related substances which affect the growth of higher plants have also been found to disrupt dormancy in the case of spores of *Ustilago zeae* (von Güttenberg and Strutz, 1952), uredospores of *Puccinia graminis tritici* (Van Sumere et al., 1957), and resting sporangia of *Allomyces arbuscula* (Machlis and Ossia, 1953*b*). In addition lactones and other materials of frequent occurrence in higher plants have been found to shorten after-ripening in uredospores of *Puccinia graminis tritici* (Allen, 1955; Van Sumere et al., 1957; and French, 1961).

A wide variety of other organic compounds have been shown to induce germination in fungus spores. These include organic acids such as oxalate (Duggar, 1901; Rabien, 1928; Gassner and Niemann, 1955*b*; Niemann, 1957), acetate (Lesczenko, 1928; Bretzloff, 1954), citrate (Thiel and Weiss, 1920; Lesczenko, 1928), butyrate, and stearate (Noble, 1924). Amino acids such as L-alanine or L-proline (Yanagita, 1955), glutamate (von Güttenberg and Strutz, 1952), and tryptophan (Machlis and Ossia, 1953*b*) may also be required by some organisms. That vitamins are also a specific requirement for germination has been shown by Schöpfer (1942) in the case of *Rhizopus suinus* which requires inositol, as well as in that of *Ustilago zeae* which needs niacinamide (von Güttenberg and Strutz, 1952). Miscellaneous requirements like those for chlortetracycline, methyl *p*-hydroxybenzoate and Ni^{++} (Turel, 1955), glucose (Uppal, 1924; Dobbs and

Hinson, 1953), and glycerine (Malychev, 1929) have also been reported. The work of Gassner (1951) and Niemann (1956*b*, 1957) is an interesting example since the vapors of certain organic mercurials, as well as the dissolved materials themselves, activated spores of *Tilletia contraversa*.

Alkalinity has been frequently invoked as a necessity for the germination of certain spores. For example, Welsford (1907) and Fraser (1907) claimed that Na_2CO_3 was an effective activator for this reason while Lesczenko (1928) with *Ustilago zeae*, and Yu (1954) with *Ascobolus magnificus*, found the same for several inorganic bases. The observation of Wilhelm (1931) that NH_4^+ activated urediospores of *Puccinia glumarum tritici* may also fit into this category.

Inorganic materials of various other kinds have been shown to be required for the germination of a number of different fungi. One of the most frequently used is $Ca(NO_3)_2$ which has been used with spores of some smuts (Riehm, 1923; Rabien, 1928; Lobik and Dahlstrom, 1936). Among the other inorganic materials used are acids, including HCl, HNO_3, H_3PO_4 and H_2SO_4 (Lesczenko, 1928; Sibilia, 1930) and various salts (Rabien, 1928; McKay, 1939; Yarwood, 1942; Gassner and Niemann, 1955*b*; Niemann, 1957). The role of these inorganic materials is subject to some question because it is not clear in some instances whether they are required specifically for the germination process, for after-ripening, or for subsequent development.

Further caution must be observed in the interpretation of some other data, especially from the older literature. It must be remembered that convenient methods of measuring and controlling *p*H were not evolved until after 1920 and work even after that date suffers from the inability to control *p*H. The fact that Sibilia (1930) found inorganic and organic acids equally effective for the germination of teliospores of *Puccinia graminis*, as long as the *p*H equaled 2.0, suggests that the specificity of some of the substances recorded in Table 7.5 is open to question. In addition, the purity of chemicals must always be of concern for there are instances in which contaminants have turned out to be the active principle (von Güttenberg and Strutz, 1952).

Higher Organisms

As can be seen in Table 7.6, a wide diversity of known chemicals is useful in breaking the dormancy of plant propagules. Growth regulators like indole acetic acid, gibberellin, and coumarin appear on the list but, as was mentioned before, soil extracts are more generally useful among the lower plants. Thiourea, ethylene chlorohydrin and certain of its derivatives, and nitrates are frequently useful in breaking seed dormancy (Crocker and Barton, 1953; Toole et al., 1956), as well as the dormancy which delays the development of certain buds and tubers. The requirement for vitamins like thiamine, as well as other nutrilites, for the germination of seeds of orchids (Crocker and Barton, 1953) probably explains earlier observations regarding the symbiotic relationship between fungi and these plants. On the other hand, there are some seeds, such as those of *Thesium humile* (Chabrolin, 1934) which germinate only when the walls of the achene are infiltrated with the hyphae of a fungus. Diffusates (secretions from the roots of host plants) have been shown to influence the germination of seeds of parasites, as in the case of *Orobanche* sp., *Alectra vogelii*, and *Pyrola* spp. (Crocker and Barton, 1953). Furthermore, an endogenous stimulator of the germination of seeds of *Striga lutea* has been described (Brown and Edwards, 1946; Brown *et al.*, 1949) which appears to be related to a factor produced by the roots of *Sorghum vulgare*. Based upon this case, and others found in a variety of plants, Brown (1946) has postulated that biological stimulation of germination is of considerable significance in nature. These and other aspects of seed germination are discussed in Volume 15, Part 2, of the *Encylopedia of Plant Physiology* (Lang, 1965).

Table 7.6 Chemicals Which Break Dormancy in Plants and Animals

Organism	Stage	Treatment	Reference
Insects			
Loxostege sticticalis	Larva	Vapors of xylol or CCl_4	Pepper, 1937
Melanoplus differentialis	Diapausing egg	Xylol	Slifer, 1946
Protozoans			
Colpoda steinii	Cyst	Animal and plant extracts	Barker and Taylor, 1933
C. steinii	Cyst	K^+ + Citrate, glutamate, malate, propionate, or ATP	Strickland and Haagen-Smit, 1947
Entamoeba histolytica	Cyst	Cysteine, thioglycollic acid	Snyder and Melleney, 1941
Didinium nasutum	Cyst	Living bacteria	Beers, 1946
Amoeba sp.	Cyst	Living bacteria	Crump, 1950
Nematodes			
Heterodera rostochiensis (potato eelworm)	Cyst	Potato, tomato, or *Solanum nigrum* leachate[a] of root	Winslow, 1955
H. rostochiensis (potato eelworm)	Cyst	Diffusate[b] of cyst from potato root	Widdowson and Wiltshire, 1958
H. carotae (carrot eelworm)	Cyst	Carrot, Veronica, potato, pea, oat, caraway, or other root leachate	Winslow, 1955, 1960
H. humuli (hop eelworm)	Cyst	Hop, pellitory, hemp, or nettle root leachate	Winslow, 1955, 1960
Mammals			
Hedgehogs	Hibernating	Thyroid extract	Uiberall, 1934

Table 7.6 (*Continued*)

Organism	Stage	Treatment	Reference
Algae			
Volvox carteri	Zygospore	Soil extract (cold)	Metzner, 1945
Hydrodictyon reticulatum	Zygospore	Soil ext. + KNO_3	Mainx, 1931
H. reticulatum	Zygospore	Indole acetate, arsenic, strychnine	Rowan, 1937
Bryophytes			
Riella affinis	Spore	Ext. of pond water and soil	Thompson, 1941
Funaria hygrometrica	Spore	Ext. of *Boletus*	Heitz, 1942
Marchantia polymorpha	Spore	Colchicine	Mader, 1952
Vascular Cryptogams			
Cystopteris fragilis	Spore	Soil ext. or $CaCl_2$	Musaack, 1933
Dryopteris erythrosora	Spore	Gibberellin	Kato, 1955
Ophioglossum moluccanum, O. intermedium	Spore	Soil water	Campbell, 1907
Lycopodium complanatum	Spore	95 percent ethanol	Barrows, 1935
Phanerogams			
Lactuca sativa (lettuce)	Seed	Gibberellin	Kahn et al., 1957; Evenari et al., 1958
L. sativa (lettuce)	Seed	Thiourea	Nutile, 1945
Arabidopsis thaliana	Seed	Gibberellin	Kribben, 1957
Sedum kamtschaticum	Seed	Gibberellin	Fujii et al., 1960
Kok- and Tau-Saghiz	Seed	Thiourea	Poptsov, 1952
Several species	Seed	Alkaloids	Dragone-Testi, 1931
Lepidium virginicum	Seed	Coumarin	Toole et al., 1955
Nicotiana sp.	Seed	Nitrates, hydroxylamine, organic and amino acids	Ogawara and Ono, 1955
Quercus sp.	Seed	Thiourea, ethylene chlorohydrin	Deuber, 1932
Several shrubs	Buds	Ethylene chlorohydrin, vinyl chloride, furfural, and so on	Crocker and Barton, 1953
Solanum tuberosum (potato)	Tuber	Ethylene chlorohydrin, vinyl chloride, furfural, and so on	Crocker and Barton, 1953

[a] Leachates are considered to be the water, with dissolved and suspended material, obtained from the vicinity of plants growing in soil, sand, and so on (Winslow, 1960).
[b] Diffusates are considered to be material which has diffused directly from the plant in question.

Dormant animals, however, respond very poorly to chemical treatment, except for a few insects and protozoans. The latter group, at least, responds to a variety of chemical treatments, many of which parallel the types discussed here which are useful with fungi and bacteria.

Specificity of Fungus Activators

A case which has been studied in detail is that of the ascospores of *Neurospora*

Table 7.7 Furans Which Are Active in Breaking the Dormancy of *Neurospora* Ascospores

Substance	Formula[a]	Relative Activity Percent[b]	Reference
Furfural	RCHO	100	Emerson, 1948
2-Furfuryl alcohol	RCH_2OH	77	Emerson, 1948
2-Methyl furan	RCH_3	76	Sussman, 1953
2-Furfuryl methyl ether	RCH_2OCH_3	9	Sussman, 1953
2-Furfural acrolein	RCNCHCHO	51	Sussman, 1953
2-Furfuryl diacetate	⁄$COOCH_3$ RCH \\$COOCH_3$	113	Sussman, 1953
5-Methyl furfural	CH_3RCHO	66	Emerson, 1954
3-Hydroxymethyl furfural	$CH_2OHRCHO$	9	Emerson, 1954
Methyl 2-furoate	$RCOOCH_3$	36	Sussman et al., 1959
n-Propyl furoate	$RCOOCH_3CH_2CH_3$	10	Sussman et al., 1959
2-Furfuryl isobutyrate	CH_3 | RCH_2OCOCH_3 | CH_3	53	Sussman et al., 1959
2-Furfuryl-*n*-butyrate	$RCH_2OCOC_3H_7$	114	Sussman et al., 1959

[a] 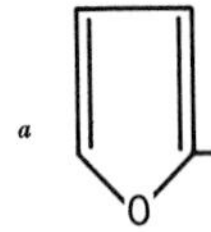

[b] Calculated as a percentage using furfural as 100 percent.

for which its was first shown by Emerson (1948), in *N. crassa* that chemical activation could substitute for heat. She discovered that a factor in autoclaved xylose activated these spores and that furfural and furfuryl alcohol in very low concentrations also were effective. These data were extended by Sussman (1953) to include *N. tetrasperma* which was shown to germinate in the presence of a number of furans, as well as other heterocyclics. Subsequent experiments by Emerson (1954) have confirmed these results and revealed that several other compounds, including benzaldehyde and salicylaldehyde, are active. As the data in Tables 7.7 and 7.8 disclose, the most active compounds are 2-furfuryl-*N*-butyrate and 2-furfuryl diacetate. Many related heterocyclics and other compounds were tested which showed no activity, including furan, several furoic acid derivatives, 2-furfuryl mercaptan, 2-nitrofuran, furil, furoin, 2-tetrahydrofurfuryl alcohol, 2-methyl tetrahydrofuran, pyrrolidine, 2,5-dihydropyrrole, pyridine, and others. Moreover, the following compounds, which have various physiological activities, were also ineffective in activating ascospores: adenine, adenosine, adenylic-5-acid, adenosine triphosphate (ATP), thiamine, coumarin, nicotinic acid, riboflavin, imidazole, folic acid, glutathione, cysteine, cystine,

Table 7.8 Heterocyclics, Other Than Furans, Which Are Active in Breaking the Dormancy of *Neurospora* Ascospores

Substance	Formula[a]	Relative Activity (percent)[b]	Reference
Thiophene	RH	4	Sussman, 1953
2-Thiophene chloride	RCl	86	Sussman, 1953
2-Thiophene aldehyde	RCHO	80	Sussman, 1953
2-Thiophene bromide	RBr	38	Sussman, 1953
Pyrrole	R′H	53	Sussman, 1953
2-Acetyl pyrrole	$R'COCH_3$	3	Emerson, 1954
Pyrrole 2-aldehyde	R′CHO	9	Sussman, 1953

[a] 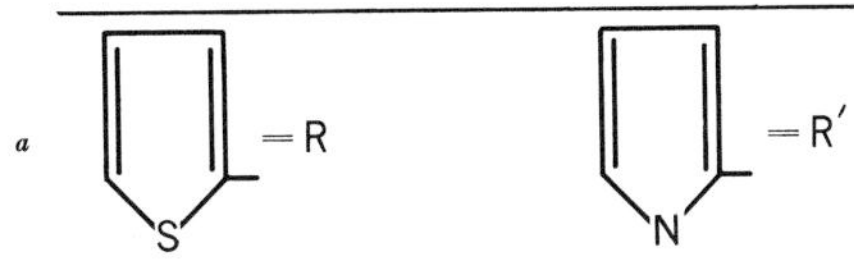

[b] Calculated as a percentage using furfural as 100 percent.

L-proline, L-hydroxyproline, indole-3-acetic acid, indole-3-propionic acid, nicotine, yeast extract, nucleic acid (yeast), casein hydrolysate (enzymatic), hemin, hemoglobin, ribose, glucose, thiazole, several organic acids, and others. In all, over 120 compounds have been tested and only the heterocyclics listed in Tables 7.7 and 7.8 were found to be active.

However, it was found in some of the earlier experiments (Sussman, 1953) that ethyl ether and benzene could activate in relatively high concentrations. This led to an investigation of the effect of organic solvents on *Neurospora* ascospores (Sussman et al., 1959), with the results outlined in Table 7.9. Therefore, aliphatic alcohols, ethers, and esters can activate these cells but are required in 100- to 1000-fold higher concentrations than the heterocyclics discussed previously. This difference is underlined by the data in Table 7.10 in which the furfural uptake per germinating spore was computed. These and other experiments reveal that significant activation occurs in concentrations as low as 1 part per million of furfural (Emerson, 1948).

On the basis of these experiments, certain generalizations can be made as to the relation between chemical structure and activity among the heterocyclic activators:

1. Of the furans and pyrroles tested, only the fully unsaturated compounds were active (tetrahydrofurfuryl alcohol, pyrrolidine, 2,5-dihydropyrrole, and 2-methyl tetrahydrofuran were inactive, in contrast to their completely unsaturated analogs).
2. Oxygen, nitrogen, or sulfur can serve as the heteroatom, and a —CH=CH— group may substitute for the heteroatom (furans, pyrrole, and thiophenes, as well as benzaldehyde and salicylaldehyde were active).

3. Conjugated derivatives are not active (hemoglobin, hemin, furoin, and furil failed to activate).

4. When side chains are present, a nonpolar chain in the 2-position is necessary for activity (furoic acid, 2-pyrrole carboxylic acid, and 2-furyl acrylic acid are toxic or inactive; 3-furfuryl acrolein is inactive).

This is all that can be stated positively about the relation between structure and activity of the chemicals which break dormancy in *Neurospora*. Although the

Table 7.9 Solvents Which Activate Ascospores of *Neurospora*

Substance	Duration of Treatment (hours)	Molar Concentration	Germination (percent)
Methanol	2	10	91
Ethanol	2	5	83
i-Propanol	3	10	74
n-Butanol	0.5	10	47
Acetone	3	2	76
Ethyl acetate	0.25	Anhydrous	22
Ethyl butyrate	0.5	Anhydrous	37
4-Heptanone	0.5 minutes	Anhydrous	12
4-Methyl 2-pentanone	0.5 minutes	Anhydrous	12

SOURCE: Data from Sussman et al., 1959.
A heat-treatment of 30 minutes at 46°C was applied to all spores.

Table 7.10 Uptake of Furfural by Ascospores of *Neurospora tetrasperma* and the Percentage Germination Induced by This Treatment

Spores per Vessel ($\times 10^6$)	Furfural Uptake: Total $\times 10^8$ Moles	Furfural Uptake: Molecules per Spore	Germination: Percent	Germination: No. of Spores	Furfural Uptake: Molecules per Germinating Spore
67	20.0	1.8×10^9	7.8	5.2×10^6	23.0×10^9
50	19.7	2.4×10^9	10.0	5.0×10^6	23.6×10^9
32	10.0	3.6×10^9	19.7	6.3×10^6	16.1×10^9
16	14.5	5.4×10^9	36	5.8×10^6	14.9×10^9
4.5	4.9	6.5×10^9	45	2.2×10^6	13.6×10^9
2.2	2.8	7.3×10^9	55	1.2×10^6	13.6×10^9
0.9	0.6	4.0×10^9	55	0.3×10^6	7.3×10^9

SOURCE: Unpublished experiments of Drs. Aristid Lindenmayer and A. Sussman.
The starting concentration of furfural was 20×10^{-8} moles per vessel, in a volume of 2 ml. Cells were incubated 2 hours at 6°C in furfural, filtered free of the activator, washed, and resuspended and incubated at 34°C in distilled water. The filtrate was used for the analyses of residual furfural.

active heterocyclic compounds comprise a somewhat diverse group of chemical structures, and aliphatic solvents also serve as activators, there are reasons for believing that they play specific roles in the activation process. First of all, the small amounts of heterocyclics required for activation, as compared with the aliphatic solvents, argue for specificity. Finally, the toxicity of compounds closely related to activators suggests that inhibition of a key reaction or reactions occurs. Thus, the data in Table 7.11 show that 2-furoic acid, 3-pyrrole carboxylic acid, 3-furfuryl acrolein, and certain nitro derivatives are extremely toxic to the ascospores.

SUBSTANCES OF UNKNOWN COMPOSITION

Microorganisms

That the ecological niche occupied by an organism often has served as a guide for the search for materials upon which germination and development will occur is illustrated by the data in Table 7.12. Thus, infection by the club-root of cabbage pathogen, *Plasmodiophora brassicae*, is encouraged by an extract of cabbage seedlings; other cases will be found in the table in which extracts of hosts stimulate the germination of pathogens. Also, saprophytes like the myxomycete *Fuligo septica* are helped to germinate by extracts of the wood and leaves which constitute the substratum upon which the plasmodium travels and feeds. The germination of spores of a large group of coprophilous organisms, which includes fungi from every group, is induced upon media containing dung or extracts therefrom. Soil extracts are effective in stimulating the germination of

Table 7.11 Heterocyclics Which are Toxic to the Germination of Heat-Activated Ascospores of *Neurospora tetrasperma*

Compound	LD_{50} [a]
2-Furoic acid	2×10^{-4}
3-Furfuryl acrylic acid	5×10^{-4}
2-Pyrrole carboxylic acid	c. 1×10^{-3}
3-Pyrrole carboxylic acid	4×10^{-4}
3-Furfuryl acrolein	8×10^{-4}
2-Nitrofuran	5×10^{-4}
5-Nitro-2-furfuraldoxime	5×10^{-4}
5-Nitro-2-furfurylmethyl ether	4×10^{-4}
5-Nitro-2-furfurylidine acetone	5×10^{-3}
5-Nitro-2-acetyl pyrrole	4×10^{-4}

SOURCE: Data from Sussman, 1953.
[a] Molarity of compound which reduces the ability of ascospores to germinate by 50 percent.

Table 7.12 Organisms Where Complex Media are Required for Germination

Medium	Organism	Stage	Reference
Plant Extracts			
Cabbage seedling extract	*Plasmodiophora brassica*	Infection	Chupp, 1917
Oak wood and hemp fibre extract	*Fuligo septica*	Spore	Cooke and Holt, 1928
Rotting oak wood or leaves; pine extract	*F. septica*	Spore	Smart, 1937
Exudate of turnip seedlings	*Pythium mamillatum*	Oospore	Barton, 1957
Platanus wood extract	*Daldinia concentrica*	Ascospore	Child, 1929
Bean, clover exudates (host plants)	*Erysiphe polygoni*	Conidium	Yarwood, 1936, 1939
Volatile products of oak, beech wood or bark	*Bulgaria polymorpha*	Ascospore	Neger, 1904
Bark of larch	*Dasyscypha willkommii*	Ascospore	Malychev, 1929
Mushroom extract	*Boletus luteus, B. variegatus*	Basidiospore	Fries, 1943
Agaricus campestris or *Amanita spissa* extract	*Agaricus campestris*	Basidiospore	Kneebone, 1950
Oils of rice, peanut or okra seed	*Puccinia graminis tritici*	Uredospore	Weintraub et al., 1957
Pieces of wheat seedlings	*Urocystis tritici*	Spore	Noble, 1924
Field peas or bean extract; oil of bitter almond	*U. tritici*	Spore	Noble, 1924
Maize extract	*Ustilago zeae*	Spore	von Güttenberg and Strutz, 1952
Oat pale extract	*U. avenae, U. levis*	Spore	Sampson, 1928
Oils of rice, peanut, or okra seed	*Piricularia oryzae*	Spore	Weintraub et al., 1958
Distillates from various leaves; volatile emanation from plants	*Botrytis cinerea*	Conidium	Brown, 1922
Lentil extract	*B. cinerea, Fusarium fructigenum*	Conidium	Singh, 1940
Yeast extract	*Myrothecium verrucaria*	Conidium	Mandels and Norton, 1948
Apple juice	*Penicillium expansum*	Conidium	Baker and Heald, 1932
Fresh bean tissue	*Colletotrichum lindemuthianum*	Conidium	Leach, 1923
Peptone	*Dictyostelium mucoroides*	Spore	Russell and Bonner, 1960

Table 7.12 (*Continued*)

Medium	Organism	Stage	Reference
Diffusates (Materials that have diffused directly from plants)			
Medium in which other spores had germinated	*Enteridium rozeanum*, *Reticularia lycoperdon*, *Dictydiaethalium plumbeum*	Spore	Smart, 1937
"Honey-dew" from infected rye	*Claviceps purpurea*	Conidium	Garay, 1956
Cultures of *Trichoderma lignorum*, *Alternaria tenuis*, or *Stemphylium* ilicis on agar	*Tilletia secalis*	Spore	Gassner and Niemann, 1955*a*
Cultures of *Alternaria tenuis* or *Stemphylium ilicis* on agar	*T. brevicaule*	Spore	Gassner and Niemann, 1955*a*
Incubation in the presence of one of following: *Torula singanii*, *Torulopsis sanguinea*, *Trichosporium heteromorphum*, *Cladosporium* sp., and two unidentified fungi	*Lycoperdon umbrinum*	Basidiospore	Fries, 1941
Incubation in presence of yeast "X"	*L. echinatum*, *L. nigrescens*, *L. pratense*, *L. pyriforme*, *Scleroderma aurantium*, *Tricholoma* sp., *Boletus* sp.	Basidiospore	Fries, 1941
Incubation with *Torulopsis sanguinea*	*Amanita mappa*, *Tricholoma* sp., *Boletus* sp.	Basidiospore	Fries, 1943
"Endogenous stimulator"	*Puccinia graminis tritici*	Uredospore	Ezekiel, 1930; French et al., 1957
Dung Media			
Dung extract at 38°C	*Lachnea stercorea*	Ascospore	Fraser, 1907
Horse dung	*Sordaria fimicola*	Ascospore	Greis, 1936
Cow dung extract at 38°C	*Ascobolus furfuraceus*	Ascospore	Welsford, 1907
Dung decoction	*Ascodesmis nigricans*	Ascospore	van Tieghem, 1876
Dung decoction	*Rhyparobius pachyascus*	Ascospore	Zukal, 1889

Table 7.12 (*Continued*)

Medium	Organism	Stage	Reference
Dung at 39°C	*Coprinus sterquilinus*	Basidiospore	Baden, 1915
Horse or cow dung	*Psilocybe mutans*	Basidiospore	McKnight, 1956
Cow dung	*Ustilago striiformis*	Spore	Cheo and Leach, 1950
Paraffins			
Paraffin oil, Vaseline	*Phytophthora infestans*	Oospore	Uppal, 1924
Paraffin or Vaseline	*Puccinia coronata*	Uredospore	Melhus and Durrell, 1919
Paraffin	*P. helianthi*	Teliospore	Bailey, 1923
Soil Extracts			
Lawn soil, humus extract; (rotting stump)	*Amanita glaericeps, A. rubescens, Hypheloma velutinum, Amanitopsis vaginata, Lepiota procera*	Basidiospore	Kneebone, 1950
Wet soil	*Tilletia tritici*	Spore	Volkart, 1906
Autoclaved soil	*T. secalis*	Spore	Gassner and Niemann, 1955*a*
Passage Through Animals, Digestion			
Mouse hairs egested by owls	*Onygena corvina*	Ascospore	De Bary, 1887
Pepsin + HCl	*O. equina*	Ascospore	Brierley, 1917
Gastric juices	*O. equina*	Ascospore	Ward, 1899
Digestive tract of rabbits; mucous membrane of stomach of living animals	*Ascobolus furfuraceus*	Ascospore	Janczewski, 1871
Digestive tract of slugs	*Hebeloma fastibile, Russula* sp., *Lactarius* sp.	Basidiospore	Voglino, 1895

dormant spores of a large number of different organisms. A few fungi which are so affected are listed in Table 7.12 and certain algae, bryophytes, and ferns are known to be similarly influenced (Table 7.6).

Interactions between microorganisms are illustrated in Table 7.12 under the heading of *Diffusates*. Certain fastidious organisms, such as puffballs and other fleshy basidiomycetes, worked on by Fries (1941), cannot germinate in the absence of living yeasts such as *Torula singanii* or *Torulopsis sanguinea*, or of the other fungi listed in the table. Although spores of certain smuts show enhanced germinability in the presence of cultures of fungi, light and cold-temperature treatments can be substituted (Gasner and Niemann, 1955*b*). Zygospores and azygospores of *Empusa muscae* and *Entomophthora* sp. are reported by Schweizer (1947) to require the activity of a chitinase of bacterial origin before germination will occur. Chitosan was detectable only after the spores were incubated with bacteria, but bacterial-free filtrates of the growth medium produced the same effect after 15–25 days of incubation. Only qualitative chemical tests were used and no direct connection between the activity of the chitinase and the breaking of dormancy was demonstrated, so that further experiments are necessary before Schweizer's conclusion can be accepted. Furthermore, a recent report by Hall and Halfhill (1959) discloses that of the small percentage of zygospores (2.5 percent) of *Entomophthora virulenta* which germinate under their conditions, none require the presence of chitin-splitting bacteria. However, the low germinability, and the fact that they used a species differing from that used by Schweizer, renders their criticism inconclusive at this time.

Endogenous stimulators of germination exist in a number of instances. For example, the enhancement of germination in the presence of media in which other spores had germinated has been demonstrated for myxomycete spores by Smart (1937). Better-defined cases include the material from *Puccinia graminis tritici* which stimulates the germination of uredospores (Ezekiel, 1930; French et al., 1957), the factor from *Agaricus campestris* which increases the germination of its own basidiospores (Kneebone, 1950), which has been shown to be 2:3-dimethyl-1-pentene (McTeague et al., 1959), and the "honey-dew" of ergot-infested rye plants which is reported to favor the germination of conidia of the pathogen *Claviceps purpurea* (Garay, 1956). In the case of the wheat rust organism *Puccinia graminis tritici*, considerable effort has gone into the analysis of the endogenous stimulator and French and Weintraub (1957) have suggested that it may be identical to *n*-nonanal (pelargonaldehyde). However, there is reason to believe that the naturally occurring factor may be very labile, so that pelargonaldehyde could be the product of its alteration. In any event, aliphatic aldehydes and ethanol have effects similar to those of the endogenous material (Table 7.5).

Passage through the intestinal tract of animals has been shown to break the dormancy of certain organisms. In this category are included the ascospores of *Onygena corvina* which appear to require egestion by owls to ensure germination (De Bary, 1887) and *O. equina* whose ascospores are activated by digestive juices (Ward, 1899; Brierley, 1917). The most detailed work on this subject is that of Janczewski (1871) who actually fed rabbits the spores of *Ascobolus furfuraceus* and observed that the violet exosporium was entirely dissolved by passage through the intestine. A large increase in the volume of the spore and the origin of vacuoles accompanied the removal of the exosporium. Inasmuch as his observations of fresh dung revealed spores in the first stages of germination, he concluded that this treatment was necessary before the spores could develop. Voglino (1895) has suggested that lower animals may also serve in this way, for he discovered that the spores of certain hymenomycetes (Table 7.12) did not germinate in ordinary media but did so readily in the fluid of the digestive tract of slugs. Although toads were found to contain germinating spores of *Russula* and *Lactarius* he did not perform experiments to establish the necessity for passage through the animal. Apart from the ecological implications which stem from these data, interesting questions arise as to the mechanism of dormancy in spores such as these. Is enzymatic treatment a necessity, and is the warmth of the animal a significant factor? If enzymes are necessary, which ones are effective? At the time the experiments of Ward (1899) and Brierley (1917) were performed, highly purified preparations of digestive enzymes were probably not available and it would be important to know the nature of the substrate affected by enzymatic treatment. Thus, it is possible that chitinases and other enzymes which hydrolyze polymeric polysaccharides coexist with proteinases in the gut of certain animals so that results like those of Schweizer's (1947) in which bacterial enzymes may influence the germination of certain of the Entomophthorales, may bear on the necessity for the passage through animals. Other questions present themselves—for instance, the site of action of the enzymes which have been discussed—but much remains to be done before it will be profitable to be more specific.

The last of the classes of treatment listed in Table 7.12 is that using paraffins and related materials. Very little is known about the mode of action of these substances but it is possible that self-inhibitors may be rendered innocuous by absorption into the hydrocarbons. This possibility will be discussed later when self-inhibition is considered (Chapter 10).

Higher Organisms

The chemical requirements of dormant stages of organisms other than fungi and bacteria are similar to those which have been reviewed to the extent that plants as diverse as algae, bryophytes, and ferns require soil extract for germination in some cases (Table 7.6). Moreover, examples can also be found in which extracts of various kinds of plants, and even animals, are useful in breaking dormancy. Excellent examples are furnished by the cyst-forming nematodes of the genus *Heterodera*, some of which are included in Table 7.6. In the species listed, the amount of larvae emerging from cysts in tap water is usually less than 5 percent of the amount in the presence of leachates. As in the case of several of the fungal parasites of plants discussed earlier, and listed, the source of the leachate usually serves as a host for the particular nematode whose cysts respond to the factor. Thus, the potato eelworm attacks potatoes and tomatoes, the carrot eelworm carrots, and the hop eelworm hops, nettle, and hemp. On the other hand, reference to Table 7.6 will reveal that there are plants from which the eelworm hatching factor may be obtained, which do not serve as hosts. Still, despite the exceptions, considerable selective advantage appears to accrue to the parasite whose inactivity and resistance during the cyst stage is prolonged until contiguity with its host is achieved. Most of the work that has been done with the chemical nature of the eelworm hatching factors has been concentrated on that of *Heterodera rostochiensis* in tomato and potato root leachates. Until now, the evidence suggests that the factors are organic acids of a complex structure which is yet to be defined (Marrian et al., 1949; Carroll, 1958).

Miscellaneous Methods of Shortening Dormancy

Rode and Foster (1960) found that when spores of *Bacillus megaterium* were crushed or abraded with glass beads approximately 90 percent of the viable spores were germinated. They were non-refractile, stainable, sensitive to a number of lethal agents, heat-sensitive, had lost peptides and dipicolinic acid, and oxidized glucose. Rode and Foster concluded that the mechanical treatment removed the permeability barrier and permitted the hydration of the spore. Similarly, sclerotia of *Sclerotium cepivorum* are activated after abrasion (Coley-Smith, 1959).

A number of surface-active agents such as quaternary ammonium compounds have been found to cause rapid germination of spores of *B. megaterium* under conditions of mild heat-treatment (Rode and Foster, 1960*a*; 1960*b*). The germinated forms, however, were rapidly killed by the surface-active agents. When *n*-dodecylamine was employed (Rode and Foster, 1960*c*), germination could be separated from inactivation. Within 2 minutes at 42°C after the addition of the alkylamine, the spores underwent the normal changes involved in germination, whereas viability was not lost until 4 minutes of exposure or longer. The conditions for alkylamine-induced germination were unphysiological, and resistant to a number of inhibitors, suggesting that the process does not have an enzymatic basis. The response of fungi to surface active agents is discussed on pp. 171–172.

Alternate wetting and drying has been suggested to be the equivalent of freezing (Arthur, 1929) and this treatment has been commonly used to break the dormancy of fungi, particularly the rusts (Maneval, 1922) and myxomycetes, as well as some phycomycetes (Table 7.13). A mechanism to explain the effectiveness of such a treatment has been proposed by French et al. (1957) who claim that a diffusible inhibitor within uredospores of *Puccinia graminis tritici* is dissipated by rehydration after drying. The presence of such an inhibitor is well documented in the case of uredospores of wheat rust (Allen, 1955) and it will be of interest to learn whether substances with similar effects can be found in the other spores listed in Table 7.13.

Table 7.13 Spores of Microorganisms Whose Dormancy is Broken by Alternate Wetting and Drying

Organism	Stage	Reference
Actinomyces violaceus	Conidium	Berestneff, 1907
Physarum flavicomum	Spore	Elliott, 1949
Enteridium rozeanum	Spore	Durand, 1894
Ceratium hydnoides, C. porioides	Spore	Famintzin and Woronin, 1873
Trichia and *Hemitrichia* sp.	Spore	Gilbert, 1929
Reticularia sp.	Spore	Jahn, 1905
Didymium difforme, Badhamia utricularis	Spore	Lister, 1901
Blastocladia pringsheimii	Resting spore	Blackwell, 1940
Allomyces arbuscula	Meiosporangium	Hatch and Jones, 1944
Cystopus candidus	Sporangium	Napper, 1933
Aphanomyces spp.	Oospore	Scott, 1958
Calvatia saccata, Lycoperdon pyriforme	Basidospore (low germination)	Swartz, 1929
Puccinia dispersa	Uredospore	Ward, 1903
P. graminis tritici	Teliospore	Prasada, 1948
P. graminis, P. magnusiana, P. phragmitis	Teliospore	Klebahn, 1914

High and low temperature fluctuations may also serve to disrupt dormancy in certain spores, including teliospores of *P. glumarum* (Raeder and Bever, 1931) and resistant sporangia of *Blastocladia pringsheimi* (Blackwell, 1940). This kind of fluctuating environment, along with wetting and drying, may describe the overwintering treatment received by many spores in nature.

Floating or soaking have been described as affecting the germination of certain dormant spores. Thus, Arthur (1929) lists several rusts which must be floated as part of their after-ripening period, while Noble (1924), Holton (1943), and Lowther (1948) specify that smut spores must be "pre-soaked" before maximal germination is possible. As was mentioned before, an endogenous inhibitor has been found in uredospores of the wheat rust and Allen (1955) has shown that this substance is dissipated after the spores are floated aerobically on water. Similar finding have been reported for *Erysiphe graminis* (Domsch, 1954), thereby advancing the possibility that endogenous inhibitors may be of wide distribution. Analogous results have been reported for the germination of conidia of *Peronospora tabacina* (Shepherd, 1962), in which a number of analogs of natural metabolites have been found to be inhibitory for germination. Washing of the conidia increases the percentage of conidia which germinate, suggesting the presence of endogenous inhibitors.

The transfer of spores to distilled water, or to a dilute medium, is sometimes a means of activation, as in the case of *Blastocladiella* (Cantino, 1951). Thus, the "cracking" of the pitted wall of the resting sporangium is inhibited by even trace amounts of anions such as NO_3^- and CO_3^-, so that the old medium must be replaced by one containing low levels of these substances.

Fresh medium is a useful means of breaking the dormancy of the spores of several algae (Sussman, 1965) and protozoa. For example, excystment of "unstable" cysts of *Woodruffia metabolica* (Johnson and Evans, 1941) is ensured by transfer to distilled water at 20°C.

It is clear from the survey of germinating agents in this chapter that a tremendous diversity of triggering mechanisms exists for breaking dormancy. This diversity is evident not only among different species but within a given dormant strain itself. The existence of alternative germination triggers in a dormant spore is undoubtedly of selective advantage in nature and ensures rapid germination and growth immediately following exposure to nutrients. (For further discussion, see Chapter 11.)

REFERENCES

Allen, P. J. 1955. *Phytopathology* 215:259–266.

Amen, R. D. 1963. *Am. Scientist* 51:408–424.

Arthur, J. C. 1929. *The Plant Rusts (Uredinales)*. Wiley, N.Y., 446 pp.

Baden, M. L. 1915. *Ann. Botany* 29:135–142.

Bailey, D. L. 1923. *Minn. Univ. Agr. Exp. Sta. Tech. Bull.* 16:1–31.

Baker, K. F., and F. D. Heald. 1932. *Phytopathology* 22:879–898.

Barker, H. A., and C. V. Taylor. 1933. *Physiol. Zool.* 6:127–136.

Barrows, F. L. 1935. *Contrib. Boyce Thompson Inst.* 7:267–294.

Barton, R. 1957. *Nature* 180:613–614.

Baylis, R. J. 1955. *Plant Disease Reptr.* 39:159–160.

Baylis, R. J. 1958. *Can. J. Botany* 36:17–32.

Beck, S. D., and Nancy Alexander. 1964. *Biol. Bull.* 126:175–184.

Beers, C. D. 1946. *J. Exp. Zool.* 103:201–231.

Bell, R. A., and P. L. Adkisson. 1964. *Science* 144:1149–1151.

Berestneff, N. M. 1907. *Zentr. Bakteriol. Parasitenk. Abt. I Ref.* 40:298.

Betts, E. M. 1926. *Am. J. Botany* 13:427–432.

Black, S. H. 1964. *Bacteriol. Proc.*, p. 36.

Blackwell, E. 1935. *Nature* 135:546.

Blackwell, E. 1940. *Trans. Brit. Mycol. Soc.* 24:68–86.

Blackwell, E., and G. M. Waterhouse. 1931. *Trans. Brit. Mycol. Soc.* 15:294–321.

Bloom, W. 1955. *Trans. Ill. Acad. Sci.* 47:72–76.

Böning, K., F. Wagner, and Astrid Mickwitz. 1953. *Pflanzenbau Pflanzenschutz.* 4:49–71.

Brachfeld, B. A. 1955. Ph.D. Thesis, Univ. of Illinois.

BRETZLOFF, C. W. 1954. *Am. J. Botany* 41:58–67.

BRIERLEY, W. B. 1917. *Ann. Botany* 31:127–132.

BRINCKMANN, MARIANNE. 1960. *Arch. Mikrobiol.* 37:161–187.

BROWN, R. 1946. *Nature* 157:64–69.

BROWN, R., and M. EDWARDS. 1946. *Ann. Botany* 10:133–142.

BROWN, R., A. W. JOHNSON, E. ROBINSON, and A. R. TODD. 1949. *Proc. Roy. Soc. Lond. Ser. B* 136:1–12.

BROWN, W. 1922. *Ann. Botany* 36:285–300.

BÜNNING, E., and H. MOHR. 1955. *Naturwiss.* 42:212–213.

BUSTA, F. F., and Z. J. ORDAL. 1964*a*. *J. Food Sci.* 29:345–353.

BUSTA, F. F., and Z. J. ORDAL. 1964*b*. *Appl. Microbiol.* 12:111–114.

BUTLER, E. J., and S. G. JONES. 1949. *Plant Pathology*. Macmillan, London, 979 pp.

CAMPBELL, D. H. 1907. *Ann. Jard. Botan. Buitenzorg.* 21:138–194.

CANTINO, E. C. 1951. *Antonie van Leeuwenhoek, J. Microbiol. Serol.* 17:59–96.

CARLETON, R. M. 1936. *Horticulture* 14:40.

CARROLL, K. K. 1958. *Nematologica* 3:197–204.

CAYLEY, D. M. 1929. *Trans. Brit. Mycol. Soc.* 14:227–248.

CHABROLIN, C. 1934. *Compt. Rendu Acad. Sci.* (Paris) 199:225–226.

CHEO, P. C., and J. G. LEACH. 1950. *Phytopathology* 40:584–589.

CHILD, M. 1929. *Ann. Missouri Botan. Gard.* 14:411–479.

CHUPP, C. 1917. *Cornell Univ. Agr. Exp. Sta. Bull.* 387:419–452.

CHURCH, B. D., and H. HALVORSON. 1957. *J. Bacteriol.* 73:470–476.

CHURCH, B. D., and H. HALVORSON. 1959. *Nature* 183:124–125.

CHURCH, B. D., H. HALVORSON, and H. O. HALVORSON. 1954. *J. Bacteriol.* 68:393–399.

COCHRANE, V. W. 1945. *Phytopathology* 35:361–366.

COLEY-SMITH, J. R. 1959. *Ann Appl. Biol.* 47:511–518.

COOKE, W. R., and E. M. HOLT. 1928. *Mycologia* 20:340–352.

CROCKER, W., and L. V. BARTON. 1953. *Physiology of Seeds*. Chronica Botanica, 267 pp.

CRUMP, L. M. 1950. *J. Gen. Microbiol.* 4:16–21.

CURRAN, H. R., and F. R. EVANS. 1945. *J. Bacteriol.* 49:335–346.

DEBARY, A. 1887. *Comparative Morphology of the Fungi, Mycetozoa and Bacteria.* Clarendon Press, Oxford, 525 pp.

DENYER, W. B. G. 1960. *Can. J. Botany* 38:909-924.

DESROSIER, N. W., and F. HEILIGMAN. 1956. *Food Res.* 21:54–62.

DEUBER, C. G. 1932. *J. Forestry* 30:674–679.

DEWILDE, J. 1949. *Bijdr. Dierk.* 28:543–544.

DEWILDE, J. 1953. *Acta Physiol Pharm. Néerl.* 3:141–143.

DOBBS, C. G., and W. H. HINSON. 1953. *Nature* 172:197–199.

DODGE, B. O. 1912. *Bull. Torrey Botan. Club* 39:139–197.

DOGUET, G. 1961. *Rev. Générale Botan.* 68:621–637.

DOMSCH, K. H. 1954. *Arch. Mikrobiol.* 20:163–175.

DRAGONE-TESTI, G. 1931. *Ann. Botan.* (*Toniro-Roma*) 19:1–8.

DUFF, G. H. 1918. *Phytopathology* 8:289–292.

DUGGAR, B. M. 1901. *Botan. Gaz.* 31:38–66.

DURAND, E. J. 1894. *Botan. Gaz.* 19:89–95.

ELLIOTT, E. W. 1949. *Mycologia* 41:141–170.

EMERSON, M. R. 1948. *J. Bacteriol.* 55:327–330.

EMERSON, M. R. 1954. *Plant Physiol.* 29:418–428.

EMGE, R. G. 1958. *Phytopathology* 48:649–652.

EMME, A. M. 1949. *Compt. Rendu Acad. Sci. SSSR (N.S.)* 67:747–750.

ENOMOTO, S. 1934. *Trans. Sapporo Nat. Hist. Soc.* 13:167–172.

ERIKSON, D. 1952. *J. Gen. Microbiol.* 6:286–294.

ERIKSSON, J., and E. J. HENNING. 1896. *Die Getreideroste, ihre Geschichte und Natur, sowie Massregeln gegen dieselben.* Norstedt and Söner, Stockholm, 463 pp.

ETTEL, G. E., and W. HALBSGUTH. 1963. *Beitr. Biol. Pflanzen* 39:451–488.

EVANS, F. R., and H. R. CURRAN. 1943. *J. Bacteriol.* 46:513–523.

EVANS, F. R., and H. R. CURRAN. 1960. *J. Bacteriol.* 79:361–368.

EVENARI, M., G. NEUMANN, S. BLUMENTHAL-GOLDSCHMIDT, A. M. MAYER, and A. POLJAKOFF-MAYBER. 1958. *Bull. Res. Council Israel*, 6 D:65–72.

EZEKIEL, W. N. 1930. *Minn. Univ. Agr. Exp. Sta. Tech. Bull.* 67:1–62.

FALK, R. 1912. *Hausschwammforschungen* 6:1–405.

FAMINTZIN, A., and M. WORONIN. 1873. *Mémoires de l' Acad. Impériale des Sci. de St. Petersbourg* Vii. Serie T. XX (3).

FISCHER, G. W., and C. S. HOLTON. 1957. *Biology and Control of the Smut Fungi.* Ronald Press, N.Y., 622 pp.
FITZ-JAMES, P. C. 1955. *Can. J. Microbiol.* 1:525–548.
FRASER, H. C. I. 1907. *Ann. Botany* 21:349–360.
FRENCH, R. C. 1961. *Botan. Gaz.* 122:194–198.
FRENCH, R. C., and R. L. WEINTRAUB. 1957. *Arch. Biochem. Biophys.* 72:235–237.
FRENCH, R. C., L. M. MASSEY, JR., and R. L. WEINTRAUB. 1957. *Plant Physiol.* 32:389–393.
FRIES, N. 1941. *Arch. Mikrobiol.* 12:266–284.
FRIES, N. 1943. *Symbolae Botan. Upsalienses* 6:1–81.
FUJII, T., S. ISIKAWA, and A. NAKAGAWA. 1960. *Botan. Mag. Tokyo* 73:404–411.
GARAY, A. ST. 1956. *Physiol. Plantarum* 9:344–349.
GASSNER, G. 1951. *Nachrbl. Deut. Pflanzenschutzdienst* 3:113–117.
GASSNER, G., and E. NIEMANN. 1954. *Phytopathol. Z.* 21:367–394.
GASSNER, G., and E. NIEMANN. 1955*a*. *Phytopathol. Z.* 23:395–418.
GASSNER, G., and E. NIEMANN. 1955*b*. *Phytopathol. Z.* 23:121–140.
GASSNER-HOECHST, G. G. 1953. *Phytopathol. Z.* 21: 53–62.
GILBERT, F. A. 1929. *Am. J. Botany* 16:280–286.
GODDARD, D. R. 1935. *J. Gen. Physiol.* 19:45–60.
GOULD, G. W., and A. D. HITCHINS. 1963. *Nature* 197:622.
GREIS, H. v. 1936. *Botan. Archiv.* 38:113–151.
GROSSE, I. 1931. *Arch. Protistenk.* 73:206–234.
GÜTTENBERG, H. VON, and I. STRUTZ. 1952. *Arch. Mikrobiol.* 17:189–198.
GWYNNE-VAUGHAN, H. C. I., and H. S. WILLIAMSON. 1930. *Ann. Botany* 44:127–145.
GWYNNE-VAUGHAN, H. C. I., and H. S. WILLIAMSON. 1933. *Trans. Brit. Mycol. Soc.* 18:127–134.
GWYNNE-VAUGHAN, H. C. I., and H. S. WILLIAMSON. 1934. *Ann. Botany* 48:261–272.
HACHISUKA, Y., N. ASANO, N. KATO, and T. KUNO. 1954. *Nagoya J. Med. Sci.* 17:403–411.
HACHISUKA, Y., N. ASANO, N. KATO, M. OKAJIMA, M. KITAORI, and T. KUNO. 1955. *J. Bacteriol.* 69:399–406.
HAHNE, J. 1925. *Kühn-Arch., Arb. Landwirtsch. Inst., Univ. Halle* 9:157–163.
HALBSGUTH, W., and H. RUDOLPH. 1959. *Arch. Mikrobiol.* 32:296–308.
HALL, I. M., and J. C. HALFHILL. 1959. *J. Econ. Entomol.* 52:30–35.
HALVORSON, H., and B. D. CHURCH. 1957. *Bacteriol. Rev.* 21:112–131.
HALVORSON, H. O. *The Physiology of the Bacterial Spore.* The Technical Univ. of Norway, Trondheim, 128 pp.
HALVORSON, H. O. 1957. *J. Appl. Bacteriol.* 20:305–314.
HALVORSON, H. O. 1959. *Bacteriol. Rev.* 23: 267–272.
HAMMERLING, J. 1944. *Arch. Protistenk.* 97:7–56.
HARDER, R. 1918. *Z. Botan.* 10:177–244.
HARRELL, W. K., and H. HALVORSON. 1955. *J. Bacteriol.* 69:275–279.
HARRINGTON, G. T. 1923. *J. Agr. Res.* 23:79–100.
HARTT, C. E. 1925. *Botan. Gaz.* 79:427–440.
HATCH, W. R., and R. C. JONES. 1944. *Mycologia* 36:369–381.
HEBERT, T. T., and A. KELMAN. 1958. *Phytopathology* 48:102–106.
HEILIGMAN, F., N. W. DESROSIER, and H. BROUMAND. 1956. *Food Res.* 21:63–69.
HEITZ, E. 1942. *Ber. Deut. Botan. Ges.* 60:17–27.
HERMIER, J. 1962. *Ann. Inst. Pasteur* 102:629–643.
HILLS, G. M. 1949*a*. *Biochem. J.* 45:353–362.
HILLS, G. M. 1949*b*. *Biochem. J.* 45:363–370.
HILLS, G. M. 1950. *J. Gen. Microbiol.* 4:38–47.
HITE, B. C. 1923. *Proc. Assoc. Seed Anat. N. Am.* 14/15:97.
HITZMAN, D. O. 1955. Ph.D. Thesis, Univ. of Illinois. 90 pp.
HITZMAN, D. O., H. O. HALVORSON, and T. UKITA. 1957. *J. Bacteriol.* 74:1–7.
HODGSON, H. J. 1949. *Agron. J.* 41:531–533.
HOLTON, C. S. 1943. *Phytopathology* 33:732–735.
HOSHINO, J., A NISHI, and T. YANAGITA. 1962. *J. Gen. Appl. Microbiol.* 8:233–245.
HULL, R. 1939. *Ann. Appl. Biol.* 26:800–822.
HYATT, M. T., and H. S. LEVINSON. 1961. *J. Bacteriol.* 81:204–211.
HYGEN, G. 1949. *Blyttia (Oslo)* 7:1–6.
INGRAM, M. 1955. *An Introduction to the Biology of Yeast.* Sir Isaac Pitman and Sons, London, 273 pp.
ISHII, R., and T. MIYAMOTO. 1954. *J. Ferment. Technol.* 22:276–278.
JAHN, E. 1905. *Ber. Deut. Botan. Ges.* 23:489–497.
JANCZEWSKI, E. v. G. 1871. *Botan. Zeitung* 29:257–262.
JOHNS, R. M. 1958. Ph.D. Thesis, Univ. of Michigan.

JOHNSON, W. H., and F. R. EVANS. 1941. *Physiol. Zool.* 14:227–237.

JONES, J. F. 1945. M.S. Thesis, Univ. of Manitoba.

KAHN, A., J. A. GOSS, and D. E. SMITH. 1957. *Science* 125:645–646.

KATO, Y. 1956. *Botan. Gaz.* 117:16–24.

KEYNAN, A., and M. HALMANN. 1961. in *Cryptobiotic Stages in Biological Systems*. N. Grossowicz, S. Hestrin, and A. Keynan, eds. Elsevier, Amsterdam, N.Y., London, pp. 64–70.

KEYNAN, A., M. HALMANN, and Y. AVI-DOR. 1958. *Proc. 7th Intern. Congr. Microbiol., Stockholm,* Almquist and Wiksells, Uppsala, p. 37.

KEYNAN, A., W. G. MURRELL, and H. O. HALVORSON. 1961. *Nature* 192:1211–1212.

KEYNAN, A., W. G. MURRELL, and H. O. HALVORSON. 1962. *J. Bacteriol.* 83:395–399.

KEYNAN, A., Z. EVENCHIK, H. O. HALVORSON, and J. W. HASTINGS. 1964. *J. Bacteriol.* 88:313–318.

KIDDER, G. W. 1964. *Allgem. Mikrobiol.* 4:137–142.

KIRCHOFF, H. 1929. *Zentr. Bakteriol, Parasitenk. Abt. II* 77:310–369.

KLEBAHN, H. 1914. *Z. Pflanzenkrank. Pflanzenschutz* 24:1–32.

KLEBS, B., S. B. HEIDELBERG. 1917. *Akad. Wiss. Math.-Nat. Kl.* 7 Abh.

KNEEBONE, L. R. 1950. Ph.D. Thesis, Pennsylvania State Univ.

KOLLER, D., and N. ROTH. 1963. *Israel J. Botany* 12:64–73.

KRASK, B. J. 1961. in *Spores II*, H. O. Halvorson, ed. Burgess Pub. Co., Minneapolis, pp. 89–100.

KREITLOW, K. W. 1938. Ph.D. Thesis. Louisiana State Univ.

KREITLOW, K. W. 1943. *Phytopathology* 33:1055–1063.

KRIBBEN, F. J. 1957. *Naturwiss.* 44:313.

KYLIN, H. 1947. *Kgl. Fysiograf. Sallskap. Lund, Forh.* 17:1–4.

LAWRENCE, N. L. 1955. *J. Bacteriol.* 70:577–582.

LEACH, J. G. 1923. *Minn. Univ. Agr. Exp. Sta. Tech. Bull.*, No. 14.

LEE, W. H., and Z. J. ORDAL. 1963. *Bacteriol.* 85:207–217.

LEES, A. D. 1955. *The Physiology of Diapause in Arthropods.* Cambridge Univ. Press, London, 115 pp.

LESCZENKO, P. 1928. *Trans. Phytopath. Sect., Bydgoszcz State Inst. Agr. Sci.* 6:1–37.

LEVINSON, H. S., and M. T. HYATT. 1955. *J. Bacteriol.* 70:368–374.

LEVINSON, H. S., and M. T. HYATT. 1962. *J. Bact.* 83:1224–1230.

LEVINSON, H. S., and M. G. SEVAG. 1953. *J. Gen. Physiol.* 36:617–629.

LIN, C. K. 1936. *Univ. Nanking Coll. Agr. For. Bull.* No. 45.

LIN, C. K. 1955. *Acta Phytopathol. Sinica* 1:183–190.

LING, L. 1940. *Phytopathology* 30:579–591.

LINGAPPA, Y., and A. S. SUSSMAN. 1959. *Plant Physiol.* 34:466–472.

LISTER, A. 1901. *J. Botany* 4:5–8.

LOBIK, V. I., and A. F. DAHLSTROM. 1936. *Summ. Sci. Res. Wk. Inst. Pl. Prot. Leninga.* pp. 177–178.

LYMAN, C. P., and A. R. DAWE. 1960. *Mammalian Hibernation.* Bull. Museum Comp. Zool., Harvard Coll. vol. 124, 549 pp.

MACHLIS, L., and ESTHER OSSIA. 1953*a*. *Am. J. Botany* 40:358–365.

MACHLIS, L., and ESTHER OSSIA. 1953*b*. *Am. J. Botany* 40:465–468.

MADER, W. 1952. *Phyton, Ann. Sci. Botan.* 4:109–120.

MAINX, F. 1931. *Mitt. Z. Botan.* 24:481–527.

MALYCHEV, M. N. 1929. *Rev. Gen. Botan.* 41:185–190.

MANDELS, G. R., and A. B. NORTON. 1948. *Quart. Gen. Labs. Res. Rept., Microbiol.* Ser. No. 11:1–50.

MANEVAL, W. E. 1922. *Phytopathology* 12:471–488.

MANEVAL, W. E. 1927. *Phytopathology* 17:491–498.

MARKOVA, Z. S., E. A. KRONGAUS, T. V. SHMIREVA, M. G. GANDMAN, and Z. S. BUDNITSKAJA. 1962. *Mikrobiol.* 31:103–110. (In Russian.)

MARRIAN, D. H., P. B. RUSSELL, A. R. TODD, and W. S. WARING. 1949. *Biochem. J.* 45: 524–528.

MARSH, P. B., E. E. TAYLOR, and L. M. BASSLER. 1959. *Plant Disease Reptr. Suppl.* 261:251–312.

MARTIN, E. M. 1924. *Trans. Wis. Acad. Sci., Arts and Letters* 21:345–354.

MATTHÉE, J. J. 1951. *Bull. Un. S. Afr. Dept Agr. Sci.* No. 316, 83 pp.

MCKAY, R. 1939. *J. Roy. Hort. Soc.* 64:272–285.

MCKNIGHT, K. 1956. *Proc. Utah Acad. Arts, Sci., and Letters* 33:177–178.

MCTEAGUE, D. M., S. A. HUTCHINSON, and R. I. REED. 1959. *Nature* 183:1736.

MEINERS, J. P., and J. T. WALDHER. 1959. *Phytopathology* 49:724–728.

MELHUS, I. E. 1911. *Wis. Univ. Agr. Exp. Sta. Res. Bull.* 15.

MELHUS, I. E., and L. W. DURRELL. 1919. *Iowa Agr. Exp. Sta. Res. Bull.* 49:114–144.

METZNER, J. A. 1945. *Bull. Torrey Botan. Club* 72:86–113; 121–136.

MINOURA, K. 1955. *J. Ferment. Technol.* 33:526-530.

MOHR, H. 1956. *Planta* 47:127–158.

MORRISON, R. M. 1964. *Mycologia* 56:232–236.

MURRELL, W. G. 1961. *Symposium Soc. Gen. Microbiol.* 11:100–150.

MUSSACK, A. 1932. *Ber. Deut. Botan. Ges.* 50: 391–392.

NAPPER, M. E. 1933. *J. Pomol.* 11:177–184.

NEERGAARD, P. 1941. *Gartnertidende* 27:1–4.

NEGBI, M., and D. KOLLER. 1964. *Plant Physiol.* 39:247–253.

NEGER, F. W. 1904. *Naturwiss. Z. Land.-Forstwirtsch.* 2:484–490.

NIEMANN, E. 1956*a*. *Phytopathol. Z.* 28:113–166.

NIEMANN, E. 1956*b*. *Angew. Botan.* 30:1–13.

NIEMANN, E. 1957. *Angew Botan.* 31:191–196.

NOBLE, R. J. 1924. *J. Agr. Res.* 27:451–489.

NUTILE, G. E. 1945. *Plant Physiol.* 20:433–442.

O'BRIEN, R. T., and L. L. CAMPBELL. 1957. *J. Bacteriol.* 73:522–525.

O'CONNOR, R., and H. HALVORSON. 1959. *J. Bacteriol.* 78:844–851.

O'CONNOR, R. J., and H. HALVORSON. 1961. *Biochim. Biophys. Acta* 48:47–55.

OGAWARA, K., and K. ONO. 1955. *Bull. School Educ. Okayama Univ.* No. 1, 97–104.

ORDAL, Z. J. 1965. *Symp. on Food Sci.*, U.S. Army Quartermaster Corps, Natick, Mass. (In press.)

PALLERONI, N. J. 1961. *Phyton, Ann. Sci. Botan.* 16:117–128.

PEPPER, B. B. 1937. *J. Econ. Entomol.* 30:332–336.

PHILLIPS, I. D. J. 1961. *Nature* 192:240–241.

PICHLER, F. 1953. *Pflanzenschutz Ber.* 11:12–17.

POPTSOV, A. V. 1952. *Akad. Nauk Doklady (U.S.S.R.)* 84:619–622.

POWELL, J. F. 1950. *J. Gen. Microbiol.* 4:330–338.

POWELL, J. F. 1951. *J. Gen. Microbiol.* 5:993–1000.

POWELL, J. F. 1957. *J. Appl. Bacteriol.* 20:349–358.

POWELL, J. F., and J. R. HUNTER. 1955. *J. Gen. Microbiol.* 13:59–67.

PRASADA, R. 1948. *Indian Phytopathol.* 1:119–126.

PURDY, L. H., and E. L. KENDRICK. 1957. *Phytopathology* 47:591–594.

RABIEN, H. 1928. *Arb. Biol. Reichsanst. Land.-Forstwirtsch.* 15:297–353.

RAEDER, J. M., and W. M. BEVER. 1931. *Phytopathology* 21:767–789.

RIEHM, E. 1920. *Mitt. Biol. Reichsanst.* 18:20–30.

RIEHM, E. 1923. *Z. Angew. Chem.* 36:3–4.

RIEMANN, H., and J. ORDAL. 1961. *Science* 133:1703–1704.

RODE, L. J., and J. W. FOSTER. 1960*a*. *J. Bacteriol.* 79:650–656.

RODE, L. J., and J. W. FOSTER. 1960*b*. *Proc. Nat. Acad. Sci. U.S.* 46:118–128.

RODE, L. J., and J. W FOSTER. 1960*c*. *J. Bacteriol.* 81:1132–1134.

RODE, L. J., and J. W. FOSTER. 1960*d*. *Arch. Mikrobiol.* 36:67–94.

RODE, L. J., and J. W. FOSTER. 1961. *J. Bacteriol.* 81:768–779.

ROLLIN, P. 1964. *Can. J. Botany* 42:463–471.

ROWAN, M. 1937. Ph.D. Thesis, Columbia Univ.

RUDOLPH, H. G. 1961. *Z. Naturforsch.* 16b: 611–614.

RUSSELL, G. K., and J. T. BONNER. 1960. *Bull. Torrey Botan. Club* 87:187–191.

SCHMIDT, C. F. 1955. *Ann. Rev. Microbiol.* 9:387–400.

SCHOPFER, W. H. 1942. *Actes Soc. Helv. Sci. Nat.* 122–123.

SCHWEIZER, G. 1947. *Planta* 35:132–176.

SCOTT, W. W. 1958. Ph. D. Thesis, Univ. of Michigan.

SEMPIO, C., and M. CASTORI. 1950. *Riv. Biol., N.S.* 42:287–293.

SHEAR, C. L., and B. O. DODGE. 1927. *J. Agr. Res.* 34:1019–1042.

SHEPHERD, C. J. 1962. *Australian J. Biol. Sci.* 15:483–508.

SIANG, W. N. 1956. *Res. Studies, State Univ. Wash.* 24:291–306.

SIBILIA, C. 1930. *Boll. R. Staz. Patol. Veg.* 10:164–190.

SINGH, B. 1940. Ph.D. Thesis, Univ. of London.

SLIFER, E. H. 1946. *J. Exp. Zool.* 102:333–356.

SMART, R. F. 1937. *Am. J. Botany* 24:145–159.

SNYDER, T. L., and H. E. MELLENEY. 1941. *Am. J. Trop. Med.* 21:63–74.

SOMMER, L., and W. HALBSGUTH. 1957. *Nordrhein-Westfalen* No. 411.

SOROKINE, N. 1876. *Ann. Sci. Natur.*, Ser. VI, 3:46–52.

SPARROW, F. K. 1957. *Mycologia* 49:426–429.

SPECTOR, W. S., ed. 1956. *Handbook of Biological Data.* W. B. Saunders, Philadelphia, 584 pp.

SPLITTSTOESSER, D. F., and K. H. STEINKRAUS. 1962. *J. Bacteriol.* 84:278–282.
STAKMAN, E. C., R. C. CASSELL, and M. B. MOORE. 1934. *Phytopathology* 24:874–889.
STARR, M. R. 1949. *J. Bacteriol.* 57:253–258.
STEDMAN, R. L. 1956. *Am. J. Pharm.* 128:84–97.
STREHLOW, K. 1929. *Botany* 21 (11/12) 625–692.
STRICKLAND, A. G. R., and A. J. HAAGEN-SMIT. 1947. *J. Cell. Comp. Physiol.* 30:381–390.
STUDHALTER, R. A. 1931. *Botan. Gaz.* 92:172–191.
SUSSMAN, A. S. 1953. *J. Gen. Microbiol.* 8:211–216.
SUSSMAN, A. S. 1961. *Quart. Rev. Biol.* 36:109–116.
SUSSMAN, A. S. 1965. In *Encyclopedia of Plant Physiology*. Vol. 15, Part 2. A. LANG, Ed. Springer-Verlag, Berlin. pp. 933–1025.
SUSSMAN, A. S., R. J. LOWRY, and E. Tyrrell. 1959. *Mycologia* 51:237–247.
SWARTZ, D. 1929. *Pap. Mich. Acad. Sci.* 9:299–204.
TAMARI, K., J. KANJI, N. OGASSAWARA, and M. SUGA. 1958. *Bull. Agr. Chem. Soc. Japan* 22:125–126.
TAYLOR, C. F., J. J. SMOOT, D. O. QUINN, R. A. ROHDE, and E. S. ELLIOTT. 1955. *Phytopathology* 45:673–675.
THIEL, A. F., and F. WEISS. 1920. *Phytopathology* 10:448–452.
THOMPSON, R. H. 1941. *Am. J. Botany* 28:845–855.
TOOLE, E. H., and V. K. TOOLE. 1941. *J. Agr. Res.* 63:65–90.
TOOLE, E. H., V. K. TOOLE, H. A. BORTHWICK, and J. R. HENDRICKS. 1955. *Plant Physiol.* 30:15–21.
TOOLE, E. H., S. B. HENDRICKS, H. A. BORTHWICK, and V. K. TOOLE. 1956. *Ann. Rev. Plant Physiol.* 7:299–324.
TREADWELL, P. E., G. J. JANN, and A. J. SALLE. *J. Bacteriol.* 76:549–556.
TUREL, F. L. M. 1955. *Can. J. Microbiol.* 1:293–298.
TURIAN, G. 1956. *Actes Soc. Helv. Sci. Nat.* 127–128.
TYLUTKI, E. E. 1955. Ph.D. Thesis, Michigan State Univ.
UIBERALL, H. 1934. *Pflügers Arch. Ges. Physiol.* 234:78–97.
UPPAL, B. N. 1924. *Phytopathology* 14:32–33.
VAN SUMERE, C. F., C. VAN SUMERE-DE PRETER, L. C. VINING, and G. A. LEDINGHAM. 1957. *Can. J. Microbiol.* 3:847–862.
VAN TIEGHEM, P. 1876. *Bull. Soc. Bot. France* 23:271–279.
VOGLINO, P. 1895. *Nuovo Giorn. Bot. Ital.* 27:181–185.
VOLKART, A. 1906. *Landwirtsch. Jahrb. Schweiz.* 20:445–490.
VOORHEES, R. K. 1933. *J. Agr. Res.* 47:609–615.
WARD, H. M. 1899. *Phil. Trans. Roy. Soc. London Ser. B* 191:269–291.
WARD, H. M. 1903. *Ann. Mycol.* 1:132–151.
WEINTRAUB, R. L., N. E. MILLER, and E. J. SCHANTZ. 1958. *Phytopathology* 48:7–10.
WEIZMANN, C. 1919. U. S. Patent No. 138978.
WELSFORD, E. 1907. *New Phytol.* 6:156–161.
WIDDOWSON, E., and G. H. WILTSHIRE. 1958. *Ann. Appl. Biol.* 46:95–101.
WILHELM, P. 1931. *Arb. Biol. Reichsanst. Land.-Forstwirtsch.* 19:1–23.
WILKINS, W. H. 1938. *Trans. Brit. Mycol. Soc.* 22:47–83.
WILLIAMS, O. B. 1929. *J. Infect. Disease* 44:421–465.
WINSLOW, R. D. 1955. *Ann. Appl. Biol.* 43:19–36.
WINSLOW, R. D. 1960. in *Nematology*. J. N. Sasser and W. R. Jenkins, eds. Univ. N. Carolina Press, Chapel Hill, pp. 341–415.
WOESE, C. R., H. J. MOROWITZ, and C. R. HUTCHINSON. 1958. *J. Bacteriol.* 76:578–588.
WOLF, J., and S. A. Z. MAHMOUD. 1957. *J. Appl. Bacteriol.* 20:373–383.
WYNNE, E. S. 1957. *Bacteriol. Rev.* 21:259–262.
WYNNE, E. S., and J. W. FOSTER. 1948. *J. Bacteriol.* 55:331–339.
WYNNE, E. S., D. A. MEHL, and W. R. SCHMEIDING. 1954. *J. Bacteriol.* 67:435–437.
YANAGITA, T. 1957. *Arch. Mikrobiol.* 26:329–344.
YARWOOD, C. 1936. *J. Agr. Res.* 52:645–657.
YARWOOD, C. 1939. *Phytopathology* 29:828–829.
YARWOOD, C. 1942. *Am. J. Botany* 29:132–135.
YU, C. C. C. 1954. *Am. J. Botany* 41:21–30.
ZIEGLER, A. W. 1948. *J. Elisha Mitchell Sci. Soc.* 64:13–40.
ZUKAL, H. 1889. *Denkschr. Kais. Akad. Wiss. Wien* 98:1–84.

CHAPTER 8

Environmental and Other Influences upon the Germination Process

The transition from the spore to the vegetative stage defines the period of germination (see Chapter 5). When a dormant period intervenes, as we have seen in the last chapter, a special set of conditions must be met for its interruption, thereby adding to the complexity of the requirements for the germination of such organisms. Thus, as was pointed out when the data in Table 7.3 were discussed (page 162), it is frequently necessary to transfer organisms from the low temperature at which they are activated to their optima for germination. This is the case for the basidiomycetes listed by Kneebone (1950), as well as several other organisms in Table 7.3. This chapter will be devoted to the factors which influence germination specifically, although it is recognized that there may be cases where these conditions are identical with those required for the development of other stages.

Environmental Influences

TEMPERATURE

That the temperatures required for germination may differ from those required at prior or subsequent stages in development is demonstrated by the

Table 8.1 Cardinal Temperatures for Spores and Vegetative Stages of Microorganisms in Which These Differ

Organism	Stage	Minimum (°C)	Optimum (°C)	Maximum (°C)	Reference
Bacillus cereus	Vegetative cell	12	—	49	Mol, 1957; Wolf and Mahmoud, 1957*a*; Casman and Rettger, 1933
	Spore	8	30–34	—	Mol, 1957; Wolf and Mahmoud, 1957*a*
B. cereus strain T	Spore	3	3, 25, 41	55	Wolf and Mahmoud, 1957*a*
	Spore	8	30	44	O'Connor and Halvorson, 1961
B. licheniformis	Spore	20	50	—	Keynan and Halmann, 1961; Thorley and Wolf, 1961
B. megaterium	Spore	—	41	—	Thorley and Wolf, 1961; Casman and Rettger, 1933; Edwards and Rettger, 1937
	Vegetative cell	—	—	44–54	
B. subtilis	Spore	> 18	41	55–60	Keynan et al., 1958; Thorley and Wolf, 1961; Casman and Rettger, 1933; Blau, 1906
	Vegetative cell	—	—	59	
B. simplex	Vegetative cell	—	—	40–45	Blau, 1906
	Spore	—	—	35–40	
B. sphericus	Vegetative cell	—	—	40–45	Blau, 1906
	Spore	—	—	45–50	
Clostridium sporogenes	Vegetative cell	> 10	—	—	Mundt et al., 1954
	Spore	4	—	—	
C. feseri	Vegetative cell	—	—	48	Wynne et al., 1955
	Spore	—	—	75	
C. perfringens	Vegetative cell	—	—	48	Wynne et al., 1955
	Spore	—	—	75	
C. botulinum	Vegetative cell	10	20–25	48	Wynne et al., 1955
	Spore	—	—	> 75	
C. roseum	Vegetative cell	8	37	62	Naghshi et al., 1945; Hitzman, 1955
Plasmodiophora brassicae	Oospore	—	27–30	—	Chupp, 1917
	Vegetative	—	16–21	—	Chupp, 1917
Peronospora schachtii	Conidium	—	4–7	—	Leach, 1931
	Vegetative	—	12	—	Leach, 1931
P. parasitica	Conidium	—	8–12	—	Gardner, 1920
	Vegetative	—	3–4	—	Thung, 1926
P. sinaciae	Conidium	—	9	—	Gardner, 1924
P. effusa	Vegetative	—	16	—	Gardner, 1924
P. tabacini	Conidium	> 10	15–20	25	Shepherd, 1962
Rhizopus delemar	Zygospore	—	26–38	—	Harter and Weimer, 1923

Table 8.1 (*Continued*)

Organism	Stage	Minimum (°C)	Optimum (°C)	Maximum (°C)	Reference
several strains	Vegetative	—	41–45	—	Harter and Weimer, 1923
Coccomyces hiemalis	Conidium	>4	16–28	32	Keitt et al., 1937
	Ascospore	<4	12–28	32	Keitt et al., 1937
	Vegetative	—	20–28	—	Keitt et al., 1937
Pyrenophora bromi	Conidium	—	28	—	Chamberlain and Allison, 1945
	Vegetative	—	20	—	Chamberlain and Allison, 1945
Valsa japonica	Ascospore	—	18–23	—	Togashi, 1930
	Vegetative	—	23–25	—	Togashi, 1931
Urnula craterium	Ascospore	5	27–30	35	Fergus and Schein,
	Vegetative	15	24–27	30	1960
Pseudopeziza ribis	Ascospore	—	12	—	Blodgett, 1935, 1936
	Vegetative	—	20–24	—	Blodgett, 1935, 1936
Cronartium ribicola	Aeciospore	4	16	24	Van Arsdel et al., 1956
	Uredospore	10	20	30	Van Arsdel et al., 1956
	Teliospore	c.0	—	24	Van Arsdel et al., 1956
	Basidiospore	—	—	20	Hirt, 1935
C. fusiforme	Aeciospore	10	21	29	Siggers, 1947
	Uredospore	c.8	18	29	Siggers, 1947
	Teliospore	15	c.21	26	Siggers, 1947
	Basidiospore	13	22	29	Siggers, 1947
Urocystis occulta	Spore	—	15	—	Stakman et al., 1934
	Vegetative	—	24	—	Stakman et al., 1934
Ustilago hordei	Spore	—	22–30	—	Herzberg, 1895
	Vegetative	—	16–20	—	Herzberg, 1895
Tilletia contraversa	Chlamydospore	5	—	8	Siang, 1956
	Basidiospore	2	15–20	28	Siang, 1956
T. caries	Chlamydospore	8	—	25	Siang, 1956
	Basidiospore	2	15–20	28	Siang, 1956
Lenzites sepiaria	Basidiospore	—	32–36	40	Snell, 1922
	Oidium	<5	36	>44	Snell, 1922
	Vegetative	8	30–34	44	Snell, 1922
L. trabea	Basidiospore	<3	30–32	<40	Snell, 1922
	Oidium	—	32	>44	Snell, 1922
	Vegetative	—	28	<34	Snell, 1922
Lentinus lepideus	Basidiospore	<5	25–28	—	Snell, 1922
	Vegetative	>8	28	40	Snell, 1922
Botrytis fabae	Conidium	—	15–20	—	Ikata, 1933
	Vegetative	—	20–25	—	Ikata, 1933
Ceratophorum setosum	Conidium	—	20–28	—	Pulselli, 1928
	Vegetative	—	10–15	—	Pulselli, 1928
Coniothyrium pirinum	Conidium	—	25	—	Crabill, 1915
	Vegetative	—	18–20	—	Crabill, 1915
Alternaria brassicae	Conidium	1.5	33–35	40–46	Weimer, 1924
	Vegetative	—	25–27	—	Weimer, 1924

data in Table 8.1 and Figure 7.3. Striking differences between the optima for germination and growth are revealed by the data in the table, as in the case of *Rhizopus delemar* (Harter and Weimer, 1923), *Urocystis occulta* (Stakman et al., 1934), and others. The optimum for growth may be higher or lower than that for the spores and might depend upon the ecological adaptations of the organism. Spores of the dwarf-bunt of wheat and of rye smut afford a graphic illustration of this phenomenon (Figure 7.3) for, as Gassner and Niemann have shown, the range of temperature at which they will germinate is extended after the first week or two of cold-treatment. Other types of data underline these differences as, for example, those from *Erysiphe graminis* in which temperatures of 5°–9°C are favorable for germination but fail to support much growth of the germ tube. Reciprocally, at 25°C, germination is repressed but growth progresses well (Graf-Marin, 1934). Another example is that of *Helminthosporium vagans* in which conidia germinate well at 35°C and at 3°C but in which growth is much retarded at these temperatures (Horsfall, 1930). Perhaps the most clear-cut example is that of *Clasteriosporium carpophilum* which is discussed by Gäumann (1950). Whereas there is little correlation between air temperature and the amount of germination in the range 9°–27°C, there is a pronounced optimum for growth at about 22°C. In view of these facts, it is essential to specify which stage cardinal temperatures describe and to be specific about the criteria used in judging the rate of germination.

The influence of temperature upon germination is manifested in several important ways, including its effect upon the amount, rate, and kind of germination. Effects of the first two kinds are reviewed for the bacteria Murrell (1961). The book by Togashi (1949) is a very complete one on the subject of temperature effects on fungal spore germination and additional data may be obtained from the reviews of Doran (1922), Gottlieb (1950), Cochrane (1958), and Sussman (1965).

INFLUENCES ON CARDINAL TEMPERATURES

That strain differences can be large is most strikingly illustrated by the data in Table 8.2 which provide temperature optima for spore germination in *Rhizopus nigricans*. Not only is the optimum different in these strains but the maxima and minima may differ as well. Other cases of this kind include uredospores of *Puccinia antirrhini* whose optimum ranges from 10°C in some strains to 19°C in others (Togashi, 1949), and conidia of *Colletotrichum lindemuthianum* and *Botrytis cinerea* in which the difference between the optima for certain strains is as wide as 11°.

In bacterial spores the optimum temperature for the germination of spores is also frequently different than that for vegetative growth (Table 8.1). This was

Table 8.2 Cardinal Temperatures for the Germination of Strains of *Rhizopus nigricans*

Strains	Minimum (°C)	Optimum (°C)	Maximum (°C)	Reference
Unnumbered strains	3–4	38–41	41	Ames, 1915
	10	19–20	—	Doran, 1922
	1.5	26–28	34	Harter and Weimer, 1923
18 strains	1.8	31	33.5–35.5	Harter and Weimer, 1923
Strain # 465	—	26.7	—	Harter and Weimer, 1923

first suggested by Holzmüller (1909) who found in a study of five strains of *Bacillus mycoides* and four of other *Bacillus* species that the temperature range for growth was 5° narrower than that for germination. In *Clostridium sporogenes*, germination was observed at 4°C, whereas vegetative growth was completely inhibited at the same temperature (Mundt et al., 1954). Lower minimum temperatures for germination than for vegetative growth have been observed in *Bacillus cereus* (Mol, 1957) and *B. subtilis* (Wolf and Mahmoud, 1957*a*). Ohye and Scott (1953, 1957) have reported that the temperature range for vegetative growth of *Clostridium botulinum* is broader than that for germination. However, Wynne et al. (1955) found that spores of this organism germinated at 75°C, whereas vegetative growth was arrested at 48°C.

The influence of temperature upon germination is manifested in several important ways, including its effect upon the amount (activation), rate, and kind of germination, some of which were discussed in Chapter 6. These effects are not necessarily related as evidenced by the observations of Vas and Proszt (1957). They found that both the yield and rate of germination of spores of *Bacillus cereus* in a complex medium were influenced by temperature (Table 8.3). The

Table 8.3 Effect of Temperature and *p*H on the Germination of Spores of *Bacillus cereus*

Temperature (°C)	Germination Rate: *p*H 5.1	Germination Rate: *p*H 7.0	Extent of Germination: *p*H 5.1	Extent of Germination: *p*H 7.0
15	0.84	1.26	80.5	76.5
20	2.70	4.03	92.9	96.8
25	2.90	6.26	71.7	93.2
30	3.51	12.36	68.1	100.0
35	4.58	19.58	53.4	94.9
40	0.88	39.77	19.1	98.0
45	0	15.88	0	88.9

SOURCE: Vas and Proszt, 1957.

differential response was *p*H-dependent; at *p*H 7 the rate of germination was strongly influenced by temperature, whereas the yield of germination was relatively unaffected. At *p*H 5.1. the converse was observed.

In contrast to the single-temperature optimum for germination frequently observed in *B. cereus* strain T (O'Connor and Halvorson, 1961), Wolf and Thorley (1961) reported three distinct optima (3°C, 25°C, and 43°C) for this same organism. The explanation for this difference is not clear at this time; however, the use of lower concentrations of L-alanine and different germination conditions may provide an explanation. Only one temperature optimum has been reported for the germination of spores of *Bacillus cereus* (Vas and Proszt, 1957; Thorley and Wolf, 1961), *B. licheniformis* (Keynan and Halmann, 1961; Thorley and Wolf, 1961), and *B. megaterium* and *B. subtilis* (Thorley and Wolf, 1961).

The effect of temperature on the rate of germination is also dependent upon the germinating agent employed. An example of this was found by Riemann and Ordal (1961). As shown in Table 8.4, aerobic spores have an unusually low optimum temperature for germination with calcium DPA. L-Alanine-induced germination is optimal under temperatures in which calcium DPA-induced germination is inhibited. A similar phenomenon was found by Keynan and Halvorson (1962) for the germination of spores of *B. cereus* strain T. In this case, however, the rate of calcium DPA-induced germination was relatively temperature-independent whereas the lag period preceding germination was temperature-sensitive.

Table 8.4 Germination of *Bacillus* Spores With Calcium DPA at Different Incubation Temperatures

Temperature °C	Percent Germination after 18 hours: *B. coagulans*	*B. mycoides*	*B. subtilis* A
10	32	100	38
20	32	19	95
30	15	1	73
37	11	0	0
45	11	0	0

SOURCE: Rieman, 1961.

When the temperature was lowered below 20°C, the germination lag in response to calcium DPA was greatly extended. From an Arrhenius plot of these data, a linear relationship between temperature and lag was observed between 8°–20°C. The $\Delta H^{\ddagger}$ calculated from these data was 14,500 cal/mole. By comparison, the temperature-dependence of L-alanine-induced germination has been systematically studied in this same organism by McCormick (1965) and Vary and Halvorson

(1965). Based both on optical density changes and on observations of the length of the lag period and on the rate of phase darkening of individual spores, the optimum temperature for germination was about 30°C.

In the anaerobic spore-formers, calcium DPA-induced germination takes place over a wider temperature range (Riemann and Ordal, 1961). The optimum temperature was about 45°C and the temperature range 3° to above 65°. The rate of germination in this case also showed a temperature response expected from an enzymatic reaction.

Among bacteria, strain differences have been observed. Holzmüller (1909) found that although the optimum temperature for the germination of S strains of *B. mycoides* was the same, the temperature ranges of the strains were different. Thorley and Wolf (1961) also observed that strains of *B. cereus* differed in their temperature optima (Table 8.5). For example, in *B. cereus* strain 634 the temperature optimum for adenosine-induced germination was 30°C whereas for strain 945 it was 37°C.

The medium in which germination is carried out has a decided influence, for it may determine whether the range of temperatures at which germination occurs is wide or narrow. In the case of the conidia of *Colletotrichum coffeanum*, a rather sharp optimum exists at 22° C when they are germinated in water but the optimum is broadened and raised to the range of 22°–26°C when potato-dextrose agar or coffee berry skins are used. Moreover, 50 percent of maximum germination occurs at 30°C, a temperature which is inhibitory in pure water (Nutman and Roberts, 1961). Also, it was shown by Gardner (1918) that conidia of *C. lagenarium* form appressoria in prune juice between 9°–27°C when exposed drops are observed, whereas this range is drastically reduced to 17°–20°C when hanging drops were used. Similar effects have been observed in the cases of spores of *Merulius silvester* (Falck, 1909), *Mycosphaerella brassicicola* (Weimer, 1926), and *Colletotrichum circinans* (Walker, 1921), so that it is desirable that the conditions of incubation be reported when data on cardinal temperatures are given.

As for bacteria, the influence of temperature on germination is strongly

Table 8.5 Temperature Optima for Various Germination Agents

Strain of *B. cereus*	Germinating agent: L-Alanine (°C)	Adenosine (°C)	Inosine (°C)
634	30	30	30–34
945	30	37	—
7464	30	—	30–34
var. *terminalis*	3, 25, 41–45	30	25

SOURCE: Thorley and Wolf, 1961.

dependent on the conditions for germination. Two cases of this have already been presented. Vas and Proszt (Table 8.3) demonstrated that the optimum temperature for germination was *p*H-dependent. Riemann and Ordal (1961) found that the temperature optimum for calcium DPA-induced germination was lower than that for L-alanine-induced germination (Table 8.4). The results of Table 8.5 illustrate similar effects. The temperature optimum for germination of *Bacillus cereus* strain 945 was 7° higher in adenosine than in L-alanine, whereas in *B. cereus* strain *terminalis* adenosine-induced germination had a temperature optimum 5° higher than in inosine.

Passage through different hosts and other aspects of the conditions under which spores are produced are reported to influence their response to temperature. In the fungi, Pichler (1950) reported that the optimal temperature for the germination of spores of *Tilletia tritici secalis* were altered after passage through different hosts. On the other hand, Niemann (1956) was not able to detect such changes in the several strains of smuts that he investigated. Growth conditions have been shown to have an effect by Robbins et al. (1942) who showed that zygospores of *Phycomyces* that had been produced in the light were much more sensitive to heat-killing. A similar effect upon uredospores of strains of *Puccinia graminis* was noted by Melander (1935), for spores formed under a light intensity of 300 ft-c were better able to withstand temperatures as low as − 40° C than those formed at either higher or lower intensities.

The reasons for the diverse influence upon the temperature relations of microbial spores are not yet delineated but certain possibilities are suggested. For one, the work of Sizer (1941) demonstrates that the temperature characteristics of the urease–urea system of *Proteus vulgaris* can be altered in response to the constituents of culture media. A shift in the optima of certain enzymes of spores, or the substitution of one for another, might explain the kinds of effects which have been discussed. Activation of certain enzymes by elevated temperatures is known to occur in several organisms (Kaplan, 1955) and provides another possible mechanism. Furthermore, the medium has important effects on inducible enzyme systems whose temperature optima may differ, thereby leading to changes in the response of organisms to temperature. That strains of a single species may possess a single enzyme with drastically different temperature maxima has been shown by Horowitz and Fling (1952, 1953) with the tyrosinase of *Neurospora crassa* for which the half life at 60°C may vary from 10 minutes to 70 minutes.

OXYGEN

Germination is markedly influenced by the presence or absence of oxygen, depending upon the type and species of organisms involved. This is illustrated in the classic case of anaerobic organisms in which growth and sporulation are sensitive to oxygen. Germination of *Clostridium botulinum* in glucose 1-phosphate (Wynne et al., 1954) and *C. roseum* and *C. botulinum* in L-alanine, arginine, and L-phenylalanine (Hitzman, 1955) occurs only under anaerobic conditions and can be stopped by the admission of oxygen: thioglycollate did not reverse the inhibition by oxygen. On the other hand, *C. perfringens*, *C. chauveri*, and a putrefactive anaerobe germinate slowly in either glucose phosphate (Wynne et al., 1954) or a complex medium (Wynne and Harrell, 1951) under aerobic conditions. Knight and Fildes (1930) established the upper limit for germination of spores of *C. tetani* at Eh + 0.11V.

That spores of aerobic organisms germinate under anaerobic conditions has been recognized for some time. This has been shown in spores of *Bacillus anthracis*, *B. subtilis* var. *niger*, *B. megaterium*, *B. mycoides*, and *B. cereus*, even in the presence of thioglycollate (Knaysi, 1945; Roth and Lively, 1956; Murty and Halvorson, 1957; Hyatt and Levinson, 1959). Based on the lack of resazurin reduction and the presence of thioglycollate, Roth and Lively (1956) estimated that aerobic spores germinate at Eh − 0.3V. Harrell and Halvorson (1955), however, reported that the triggering of spores of *B. cereus* strain T was inhibited by anaerobic conditions. The germination of aerobic spores under anaerobic conditions does not necessarily mean that the process is independent of oxidative metabolism (see Chapter 10) since there is some evidence that DPA may serve as an endogenous reservoir for electrons (Doi and Halvorson, 1961).

Most fungi are aerobic or at least microaerophilic, so it is not surprising that oxygen has been reported to be an absolute requirement for the germination of many fungus spores. These include spores of smuts (Schaffnit, 1926; Platz, 1928), conidia of *Botrytis cinerea* (Brown, 1922) and *Erysiphe graminis* (Domsch, 1954), ascospores of *Neurospora tetrasperma* (Goddard, 1935) and of *Coccomyces hiemalis* (Magie, 1935). The amount of oxygen required may be as low as 0.0003 percent, as in the case of certain mucors (Lopriore, 1895), or greater than 1 percent, as in conidia of *Botrytis cinerea* (Brown, 1922*a*) and spores of *Ustilago zeae* (Platz, 1928).

Some evidence suggests that concentrations of oxygen above that found in air stimulate germination. Such is the case for zygospores of *Rhizopus stolonifer* and *Phycomyces blakesleeanus* (Wood-Baker, 1955) and perhaps for ascospores of *Daldinia concentrica* (Child, 1929). The statistical significance of the latter work has been questioned by Wilkins (1938) and additional negative evidence is to be found in the work of Brown (1922) who could find no effect of high concentrations of oxygen on the germination of conidia of *Botrytis cinerea*.

Germination occurs anaerobically in spores of *Tilletia contraversa* (Böning et al., 1953), conidia of *Sclerotinia fructicola* (Lin, 1940) and oospores of *Phytophthora infestans* (Uppal, 1926). In the case of *Sclerotinia fructicola*, this effect was demonstrable when glucose was the substrate but oxygen was a definite requirement when ethanol was used. As for the oospores of *Phytophthora infestans*, germination by means of a germ tube was precluded anaerobically, but zoospores could be produced under these conditions. As was pointed out previously (Chapter 5), certain stages in the germination process can proceed anaerobically, even though oxygen is required for its completion. This is the case with spores of *Mucor rouxiana* and *M. hiemalis* in which the first stage can proceed anaerobically. Also, the work of Goddard (1935) with ascospores of *Neurospora tetrasperma* reveals that activation, as measured by anaerobic carbon dioxide production, can occur anaerobically but the spores are reversibly deactivated if oxygen is not admitted after about an hour. These findings were corroborated by Sussman et al. (1956) who used the production of acetaldehyde as a measure of germination, as in Figure 8.1.

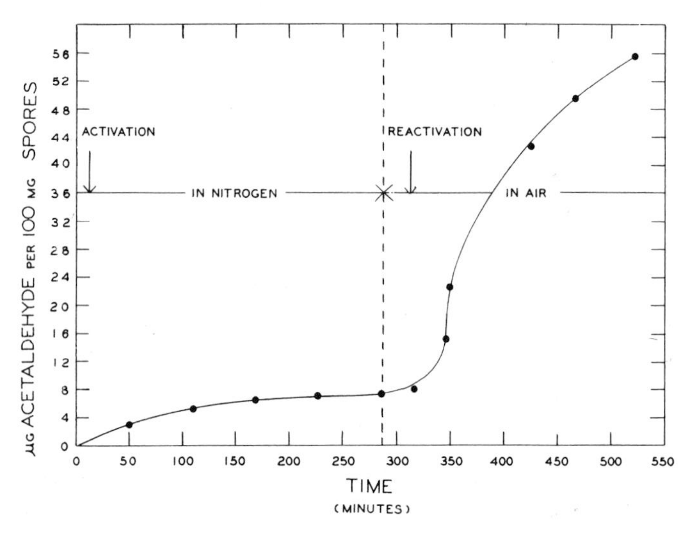

Figure 8.1 Effect of anaerobiosis and subsequent reactivation and return to air upon acetaldehyde production by ascospores of *Neurospora tetrasperma*. Activation and reactivation were accomplished by heating at 58°C for 15 minutes, and acetaldehyde analyses were of the suspending medium. (Taken from Sussman et al., 1954.)

The complete removal of oxygen from germination media presents technical difficulties that may not always have been circumvented in the work discussed. Thus, Wood-Baker (1955) has shown that it takes 10–30 minutes, depending on the rate of bubbling, to free a solution completely of oxygen when nitrogen is passed through it. Consequently, the early stages of such experiments are not completely anaerobic and erroneous results may be obtained, especially when only small amounts of oxygen are required.

CARBON DIOXIDE

The initiation of germination in *Clostridium botulinum* and other clostridia is delayed in complex medium by the absence of carbon dioxide (Wynne and Foster, 1948). In synthetic medium, no germination occurred unless 1 percent carbon dioxide was included. The carbon dioxide requirement could be eliminated in complex medium, but not in synthetic medium, by oxalacetate or a tricarboxylic acid cycle intermediate. The phenomenon is not general among the anaerobic spore formers since four other species of *Clostridium* and four species of bacilli showed no carbon dioxide effect. These findings were confirmed in *C. botulinum* by Andersen (1951) and Treadwell et al. (1958) and in PA 3679 by Reynolds et al. (1952).

Among the fungi, smut spores (Schaffnit, 1926; Platz, 1928), conidia of *Aspergillus niger* (Yanagita, 1957), and teliospores of *Puccinia graminis* (Sibilia, 1928) have been shown to require carbon dioxide for germination. Morphogenetic influences have been reported by Schaffnit (1925) who showed that when carbonic acid was provided in excess, spores of *Ustilago hordei* formed tubes instead of sporidia, thereby promoting the formation of infection hyphae.

Deleterious effects of carbon dioxide also have been observed, as in the case of spores of *Coccomyces hiemalis* (Magie, 1935) whose germination is inhibited by the small amount of this gas evolved by cherry fruits. The germination of certain rusts is inhibited by as little as 1 percent carbon dioxide (Stock, 1931) whereas higher concentrations are required to inhibit that of conidia of *Botrytis cinerea* (Brown, 1922*a*), *Erysiphe graminis* (Brodie and Neufeld, 1942; Domsch, 1954), conidia of *Aspergillus niger* (Yanagita, 1957), and others. In most of the cases listed, concentrations in excess of 10 percent are required although the exceptions noted are much more sensitive.

As in the case of oxygen, the complete removal of carbon dioxide is difficult, especially because it is a respiratory product. The importance of this consideration is pointed up by the data of Yanagita (1957) who showed that conidia of *Aspergillus niger* germinate in evacuated Thunberg tubes, presumably because of the recycling of carbon dioxide. On the other hand, they failed to do so in a medium through which carbon dioxide-free air was bubbled.

HYDROGEN ION CONCENTRATION

The germination of spores is markedly sensitive to *p*H, a relationship which is not only of considerable commercial importance but is important in the classification of spore-forming organisms. The optimum *p*H for germination varies not only with the strain but also with the germinating agent. For example, in *Bacillus subtilis* the optimum *p*H for germination initiated by glucose is 5.5 whereas for L-alanine-initiated germination it is 8.5 (Wolf and Thorley, 1957). An alkaline *p*H optimum for L-alanine-induced germination has been reported for *B. cereus* (Lawrence, 1955; Church et al., 1954; Thorley and Wolf, 1961), *B. subtilis* (Wolf and Mahmoud, 1957*b*), and *B. megaterium* and *B. licheniformis* (Thorley and Wolf, 1961). In a survey of *B. cereus* strains, Thorley and Wolf (1961) found that most had a *p*H optimum for L-alanine-induced germination of *p*H 7.8–8.3 with a few at *p*H 6–6.2. Powell (1951) has reported a broad *p*H range in *B. megaterium* and Church et al. (1954) found no difference in the rate of germination of *B. cereus* from *p*H 7–10.

Below *p*H values of 5, the germination of both aerobic and anaerobic spores is inhibited. The *p*H at which germination stops was found by Vas and Proszt (1957) to depend upon the organic acid used as a germinating agent.

A sample of cardinal *p*H values is presented in Table 8.6 and these data attest to the broad *p*H optimum for germination that is characteristic of many fungi. However, the optimum for most fungi appears to be on the acid side and the extremes extend farther into this region than into the alkaline. Exceptions to this rule include the spores of certain of the basidiomycetes studied by Kaufmann (1934) and the conidia of *Colletotrichum gossypii* which can develop well into the alkaline range (Webb, 1921).

As in the case of bacteria, growth conditions may strongly influence the

Table 8.6 Cardinal Points in the Effect of *p*H upon the Germination of Certain Spores

Organism	Stage	Minimum	Optimum	Maximum	Reference
Several *myxomycetes*	Spore	2.5–4.0	6.0–7.0	9.0–10.0	Smart, 1937
Sclerospora graminicola	Oospore		4.5–7.0		Evans and Harrar, 1930
Endoconidiophora fagarum	Ascospore		4.0–8.0		Cole and Fergus, 1956
Urnula craterium	Ascospore	2.5	5.3	9.3	Fergus and Schein, 1960
Byssochlamys fulva	Ascospore	1.8	3.5	8.0	Hull, 1939
Venturia inequalis	Ascospore	2.6	—	6.8	Palmiter, 1934
Neurospora tetrasperma	Ascospore	4.0	5.0–6.5	8.0	Sussman, 1954
Urocystis occulta	Spore	5.0	6.8	8.9	Ling, 1940
Puccinia triticina	Uredospore	3.0	4.6–7.5	9.0	Stock, 1931
Agaricaceae and *Nidulariaceae*	Spore	5.0	7.5	8.5	Kaufmann, 1934
Penicillium digitatum	Conidium	2.4	9.7–5.3	9.4	Marloth, 1931
Aspergillus niger	Conidium		6.2	7.4	Yanagita, 1957
Myrothecium verrucaria	Conidium		4.5–7.0		Mandels and Norton, 1948

cardinal *p*H values of germinating fungi. For example, when spores of *Botrytis cinerea* were germinated in water, the minimum was *p*H 2.2, the optimum 3.0, and the maximum *p*H 10 (Webb, 1921). The corresponding values for germination in various other media were as follows: mannitol-phosphate, 1.6, 3.0, and 6.9; Czapek's medium (sucrose-nitrate), 2.5, 3.0–3.6, and 9.6; peptone, 2.1, 4.0–5.3, and 8.7; and sugar beet decoction, 2.0, 4.0–7.0, and 9.8. Therefore, each of the cardinal points for the germination of these spores was affected by the growth medium. Other work has implicated the buffer system in the variations observed in different media for, according to Itzerott (1938), spores of *Ustilago zeae* germinate at *p*H 2.5 in lactic, citric, hydrochloric, or phosphoric acids but fail to do so even at *p*H 3.5 in acetic acid. A similar effect was shown with ascospores of *Neurospora tetrasperma* (Sussman, 1954) where acetate and phosphate were shown to be toxic in the acid and basic ranges respectively.

Age has been reported to affect the *p*H at which spores of *Ustilago zeae* will germinate, according to Itzerott (1938). Thus, freshly harvested spores will germinate at *p*H 8.5, in contrast to one-year-old ones that will not.

WATER

A higher relative humidity is required for the germination of bacterial spores than is required for the growth of vegetative cells. The lower limit of the initiation of germination varies with the species, ranging from 96.3 percent to 97.5 percent water. These figures can be compared for those obtained for vegetative growth which were between 93.7 percent to 94.7 percent (Beers, 1956, 1957). In addition, the lower limit for spores of *Bacillus cereus* was slightly less for freshly harvested spores than for aged ones.

Although fungus spores, as do those of bacteria, seem generally to require high humidities for germination, many can develop at humidities lower than 90 percent (Table 8.7). The most extreme instances of this kind occur among the powdery mildews which actually germinate better at low humidities than at high and will germinate throughout the range of 0–100 percent relative humidity. One explanation that has been proposed is that the high osmotic pressure of the spores accounts for their extreme resistance to low humidities (Brodie, 1945). However, Yarwood (1950) disagrees and argues that the slow release of water explains the facts. Resolution of these contradictions is difficult due to technical problems stemming from the need to measure intracellular osmotic tensions and the rapid loss of water after removal of the spores from the host. These questions are dealt with in more detail in the review by Sussman (1965). Other instances in which fungus spores can germinate in subsaturated atmospheres are listed in Table 8.7 but, except for the powdery mildews, these require at least 60 percent relative humidity.

Table 8.7 Minimum Relative Humidities at Which Spores Will Germinate

Organism	Stage	Relative Humidity (percent)	Reference
Rhizopus nigricans	Zygospore	93	Snow, 1949
Peronospora nicotianae	Oospore	100	Goldsworthy and Smith, 1931
Uncinula salicis, Erysiphe graminis, E. polygoni, Microsphaera alni	Conidium	0	Brodie, 1945; Yarwood, 1936
Venturia inequalis	Conidium and ascospore	99	Clayton, 1942
Ustilago nuda	Spore	95	Clayton, 1942
Puccinia graminis	Uredospore	99	Stock, 1931
Beauveria bassiana	Conidium	94	Hart and MacLeod, 1955
Cladosporium herbarum	Conidium	88	Snow, 1949
Penicillium rugulosum	Conidium	86	Snow, 1949
Aspergillus niger	Conidium	83	Snow, 1949
A. repens	Conidium	71	Snow, 1949
A. echinulatus	Conidium	62–66	Snow, 1949

At the other extreme to *Erysiphe* and its relatives are those organisms that have an absolute requirement for water in the liquid state. These include fungi in which reproduction by zoospores and myxamoebae is obligatory, as well as the conidia of *Sclerotinia fructicola* (Clayton, 1942), and *Endoconidiophora fagarum* (Cole and Fergus, 1956), and ascospores of *Ustulina vulgaris* (Wilkins, 1938). The explanation of this requirement may not be attributable solely to the need for water for the hydration of colloids, for several cases exist in which endogenous inhibitors must first be removed before germination can proceed (see Chapter 10). Under these circumstances, water might be required as a means through which the inhibitor can be dissipated.

On the other hand, water in liquid form, or completely saturated atmospheres, may inhibit the germination of the powdery mildews (Corner, 1935; Brodie, 1945). This may also be the case for spores of *Tilletia tritici* (Hawker, 1950) and *T. foetida* and *T. caries* (Rabien, 1928), but it is not clear whether lack of oxygen contributed to the effect in these cases.

Other environmental variables also influence the effect of humidity upon germination. Thus, Bonner (1948) found that the optimum conditions for germination of conidia of *Aspergillus niger* are at a relative humidity of 93 percent at 40°C but that 100 percent was required at 30°C.

Morphogenetic influences are exerted by humidity in the case of conidia of *Phytophthora infestans* which produce zoospores when liquid water is present and germ tubes otherwise. In addition, spores of *Ustilago hordei* produce sporidia when germinated in water but germ tubes when exposed to 95–100 percent humidity (Clayton, 1942).

As noted for bacterial spores, the water requirements for germination of fungus spores may differ from those for other stages. The effect is the reverse of that in bacteria, for the germ tube usually requires much moister conditions for its normal development than does the spore. Thus, Snow (1949) observed that misshapen structures were produced by the germ tubes of certain aspergilli at humidities that permitted abundant germination.

Pitfalls in experimentation exist in the study of the effect of water, as in the case of the other environmental variables mentioned. For one, condensation of liquid water may occur at high humidities so that reports of germination in water vapor may sometimes be attributable to the presence of water droplets (Clayton, 1942). Furthermore, as Snow (1949) points out, the "latent" period before germination may extend for almost 2 years at low humidities, and so negative results may be suspect if insufficient time was allowed. Instrumentation and techniques which overcome some of these difficulties have been devised by Snow (1949) and Hart and MacLeod (1955).

CONDITIONS OF SPORE FORMATION

Many aspects of the spore's physiology are influenced by the medium and, in the case of parasites, by the host. Such influences have been shown repeatedly upon the response of spores to irradiation, heating, and other environmental factors reviewed previously. That this is also the case for the ability to germinate has been shown by Darby and Mandels (1955) with conidia of *Myrothecium verrucaria*. Optimal viability was ensured by using spores grown on filter paper, even though the initial dry weight and endogenous Q_{O_2} were greater in the case of those grown in potato-dextrose medium. These data also disclosed that similar effects were demonstrable with conidia of *Memnoniella echinata* and *Aspergillus luchuensis*. In addition, Kent (1946) has shown that spores of *Diplodia zeae* from colonies grown on oatmeal agar were much more able to germinate than those from any other medium used. The presence of NH_4^+ ions induces the formation of colorless or light-colored spores of *Ascobolus* sp. (Gwynne-Vaughan and Williamson, 1933) which germinate without the heat shock required by the more normal ones. Some observations made by Brierley (1917) with uncolored ascospores of *Onygena equina* are reminiscent of the latter findings because such spores germinated without any treatment at all, in contrast to dark spores which required digestion by peptic enzymes. These factors are also treated on pp. 91 and 92.

That the temperature at which spores are formed may affect their ability to germinate was shown by Van Arsdel et al. (1956) with teliospores of *Cronartium ribicola*. When telia were formed at 16°C they yielded spores that germinated very well, but when these were formed at 20°C they germinated erratically.

An example of the influence of the host is that reported by Kolk (1943) who states that spores of *Ustilago hypodytes* differ in the time required for germination, depending upon whether they were produced on *Stipa* or *Elymus*. In addition, definite differences in the size range of these spores were also observed, although no attempt was made to correlate size and the duration of the germination period. Another case in which the host appears to affect the morphology of spores is that reported by Palmiter (1934), in which conidia formed on different varieties of apples varied in length even when the same culture was used as inoculum. What is even more striking, Palmiter reported that spores taken from the ventral side of a leaf were consistently longer than those from the dorsal side. An effect of the host upon the necessity for an after-ripening period was discussed by Cotter (1940), who showed that a collection of teliospores of *Puccinia graminis tritici* on Durum wheat germinated on *Berberis* in December, whereas those that were collected at the same time from Marquis wheat, Bond oats, *Agropyron repens*, and *Phleum pratense* were not viable. Similar observations in which several workers have shown that collections of the same smut on different hosts, or at different times, affected the duration of the after-ripening period were discussed by Fischer and Holton (1957).

The condition of the host at the time of sporulation is of importance, according to several authors (Ericksson, 1895; Spaulding, 1922; Mains, 1924) who observed that the ability of rust spores to germinate varied directly with the amount of spores produced. It is also possible that heavy infections, which result in enhanced sporulation, may strain the capacity of the host so that germination may be affected. This is corroborated by the work of Melhus and Durrell (1919) on *Puccinia coronata* because uredospores from young plants, when harvested 13 days after their appearance, showed 14 percent germination whereas there was none at the end of 17 days, when the plants died. By contrast, when more mature oat plants were used, 12 percent germination was obtained as long as 54 days after spore formulation.

Innate Factors

Occasional reference has been made to the influence of age on the after-ripening period, as in the response of smut spores to light during "light-sensitive" periods (Gassner and Niemann (1954)). Another instance of such an effect is the response of spores of *Tilletia levis* and *T. tritici* to light, for Hahne (1925) has shown that only spores that are more than 2 years old require such treatment to germinate.

Periods of sensitivity to chemical activators have been noted in ascospores of *Neurospora* by Emerson (1954) and Sussman (1953*a*, *b*), and Brown (1922*b*) demonstrated that young conidia of *Botrytis cinerea* are uniformly more responsive to the several chemical stimulators of germination that he used than are older ones. The reverse situation was described in *Allomyces* by Machlis and Ossia (1953) in that the younger resistant sporangia responded less well to indole acetic acid than did older ones. The requirement for an exogenous energy source for the germination of conidia of *Myrothecium verrucaria* was reported to be present only in older spores (Mandels and Norton, 1948). In addition, these workers showed that the maximum in germination was reached only with 30-day-old spores when liquid cultures were used. As far as heat-activation is concerned, Gwynne-Vaughan and Williamson (1933) found that ascospores of *Dasyobolus immersus* respond only after 5 months. However, this is not general, for in *Neurospora* the ascospores respond to such treatment immediately after being harvested and retain their responsiveness to heat-activation for years (Sussman, 1954).

Morphogenetic effects also are exerted by age in the case of *Phytophthora infestans* and certain downy mildews in which young conidia were shown to liberate zoospores, whereas older ones produced a germ tube (Blackwell and Waterhouse, 1931). Bond's (1936) work supports these data inasmuch as he reported interaction between age and temperature in determining which of the types of germination will occur in *P. infestans*. In another phycomycete, *Synchytrium endobioticum*, Curtis (1921) and Köhler (1956) have reported that gametes capable of fusion were produced in older sporangia instead of the planospores which are the usual product of these organs. In addition, spores of *Tilletia tritici* are less branched in the promycelial state when older spores are used (Holton, 1943).

Even the optimum temperature for germination is determined by the age of spores of *Ustilago avenae*, according to Jones (1923). Also, Itzerott (1938) has called attention to the fact that 1-year-old spores of *U. zeae* failed to germinate at *p*H 8.5 although younger ones did.

The time required for germination is a function of age in the case of oospores of *Plasmopara viticola* (Arens, 1929). In this instance it took 12 days for germination to occur when the spores were tested in December, but in June it took less than 2 days. These findings parallel those of Gilbert (1928) with spores of certain myxomycetes which required 2½ days to germinate when freshly harvested but only 12 hours when allowed to age. This phenomenon is, of course, the reciprocal of that noted by many workers in which the time required for germination increases and the viability decreases as the spores age (Gäumann, 1950). Maruyama et al. (1961) found that spores of *Aspergillus niger* germinated most rapidly when they were harvested from 15-day-old cultures whereas those from younger or older cultures took longer to germinate.

Maturation of spores on the parent, or within it, is often necessary if the spores are to germinate maximally. Thus, the age of teliospores of *Puccinia graminis tritici* at the time of harvest is of importance in their response to activation by citric acid and chloroform (Thiel and Weiss, 1920). These parallel the observations of Doran (1922) and others who have shown that the detachment of spores before they are mature results in their failure to germinate. For example, in the spore horns of *Gymnosporangium juniperi-virginianae* it has been observed that the teliospores at the apex, that is, those that are the most mature, germinate best (Weimer, 1917). Foreman (1910) showed that this was the case for conidia of *Sphaerotheca mors-uvae* of which only the large spores at the tips of the chains of spores germinated. The studies of Jinks (1956) on *Penicillium cyclopium* and two species of *Aspergillus* have suggested that aging of conidia is, at least, a secondary agent in the induction of variations in such asexual spores. By contrast, aging of the conidiophores or of the mycelium does not seem to be a factor in the introduction of such variations.

On the other hand, it is difficult to avoid the conclusion that the age of the parent mycelium is important in determining the ability to germinate in certain cases. Thus, Doran (1922) found that it became increasingly difficult to obtain good germination of conidia of *Venturia inequalis* as the season advanced in the autumn, even when they were obtained from fresh lesions. In addition, the data of Cotter (1940) disclose that teliospores of *Puccinia graminis tritici* formed later in the season germinated better than those formed earlier. At about the same time, Singh (1940) demonstrated the same effect with conidia of *Fusarium fructigenum* and *Botrytis cinerea* and also showed that, after reaching a maximum, the germination ability decreased. The observation by Young and Cooper (1917) may be related in that conidia from cultures of *Glomerella rufomaculans* that were grown for 8–15 days were more resistant to fungicides than were those from cultures grown only 4–8 days. A relation between aging and strain differences was shown to exist in certain smut spores by Lowther (1950) inasmuch as the viability of the spores was less markedly reduced in certain strains of the same organism than in others.

Some reports suggest that certain organisms can germinate even if removed from the parent mycelium before maturity. This is so for conidia of *Botrytis cinerea* (Doran, 1922) and ascospores of *Onygena equina* (Brierley, 1917). In fact, in the latter case, the after-ripening period was actually shortened when immature, uncolored spores were used instead of the dark mature ones.

The possibility that these aging effects are related to physiological changes is suggested by several lines of evidence. Brierley's work, mentioned earlier, indicates that changes in the cell wall which accompany maturation impose the requirement for treatment with activating chemicals inasmuch as immature spores can germinate without them. It was also shown by Mandels and Norton

(1948) that the dry weight of freshly harvested conidia of *Myrothecium verrucaria* increases immediately upon the induction of germination, but the dry weight of older spores begins to increase only after a lag period. Furthermore, there is a marked decrease in dry weight and total nitrogen as changes associated with senescence become observable (Darby and Mandels, 1955) and fewer spores will germinate on simple substrates such as glucose or sucrose (Mandels and Norton, 1948). Another sensitive indicator of aging is the rate of swelling of germinating conidia; Mandels and Darby (1953) have detected a decrease in this rate in spores of *M. verrucaria* that were harvested from cultures more than 16 days old. It should be noted that age and the conditions in which the spores were formed interact and effect the physiological changes which have been referred to. Although these effects will be discussed, it is pertinent to mention that the changes in respiratory rate and dry weight which accompany senescence in these spores, as well as their response to respiratory poisons and substrates, are dependent upon their age, as modified by their previous growth conditions (Darby and Mandels, 1955). Respiratory effects of other kinds have also been noted by Sussman (1953*b*) in ascospores of *Neurospora tetrasperma* (Figure 8.2) in

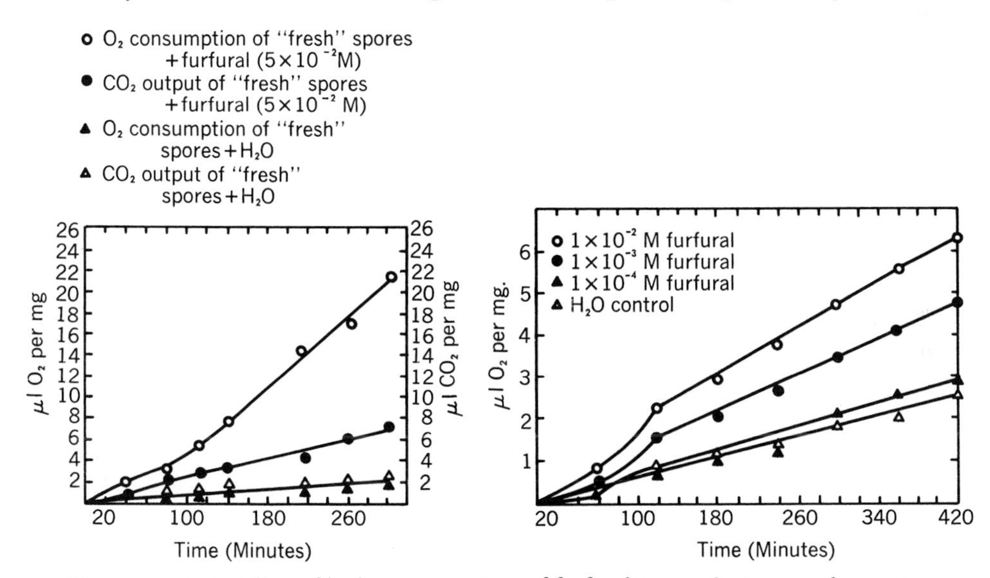

Figure 8.2 *Left:* Effect of high concentrations of furfural (5×10^{-2} *M*) upon the respiration of "fresh" ascospores of *Neurospora tetrasperma*. Ascospores were used 19 days after harvesting. *Right:* Effect of furfural upon the oxygen uptake of "old" ascospores of *Neurospora tetrasperma*. Ascospores were used approximately 9 months after harvesting. In all cases where the μlO_2 are calculated per milligram, the dry weights were used. Measurements were begun (zero time) from the instant of tipping of furfural. (Data from Sussman, 1953b.)

which it was shown that the increased Q_{O_2} attendant upon activation in the presence of furfural was greatly restricted when old spores were used. Goddard and Smith (1938), using the same organism, noted that the oxygen uptake of dormant ascospores that were 3 weeks old was only half that of spores that were 9 weeks old. More recently, Terui and Mochizuki (1955) have shown that the R.Q. of conidia of *Aspergillus niger*, *Penicillium chrysogenum*, *Rhizopus nigricans*, and *Mucor javanicus* increases in older spores, suggesting the possibility that the kind of substrate, as well as the amount, may change during aging. However, it should be pointed out that carbon dioxide fixation and other biochemical possibilities may provide false impressions when the R.Q. alone is used as evidence of a change.

Only scattered references to the effect of aging upon the chemical and enzymatic constitution of spores have appeared. Among these is the paper of Bajaj et al. (1954) in which it was shown by chemical means that the total phosphate content of the conidia of *Aspergillus niger* decreases with age, and that of Adams and Miller (1952) who report similar findings in this organism on the basis of radioautographic techniques. As for the presence of enzymes, Van Sumere et al. (1957) have demonstrated that uredospores of *Puccinia graminis tritici*, harvested in the fall of 1955, contained more than twice as much hemicellulose and "C_x" enzyme than did those harvested a year later. In this case, however, it is difficult to distinguish between an aging effect and one due to inherent differences between collections.

REFERENCES

Adams, A. M., and J. J. Miller. 1952. *Nature* 170:239.

Ames, A. 1915. *Phytopathology* 5:11–19.

Andersen, A. A. 1951. *J. Bacteriol.* 62:425–432.

Arens, K. 1929. *Jahr. Wiss. Botan.* 70:57–92.

Bajaj, Violet, S. P. Damle, and P. S. Krishnan. 1954. *Arch. Biochem. Biophys.* 50:451–460.

Beers, R. J. 1956. *Dissertation Abstr.* 16:1558.

Beers, R. J. 1957. in *Spores*. H. O. Halvorson, ed. Am. Inst. Biol. Sci., Wash., D.C., pp. 45–55.

Blackwell, E., and G. M. Waterhouse. 1931. *Trans. Brit. Mycol. Soc.* 15:294–321.

Blau, O. 1906. *Zentr. Bakteriol. Parasitenk. Abt. II* 15:97–143.

Blodgett, E. C. 1935. *Phytopathology* 25:6–7.

Blodgett, E. C. 1936. *Phytopathology* 26:115–152.

Bond, T. E. T. 1936. *Ann. Appl. Biol.* 23:11–29.

Böning, K., F. Wagner, and Astrid Mickwitz. 1953. *Z. Pflanzenbau Pflanzenschutz, Sonderh.* 4:49–71.

Bonner, J. T. 1948. *Mycologia* 40:728–738.

Brierley, W. B. 1917. *Ann. Botany* 31:127–132.

Brodie, H. J. 1945. *Can. J. Res. Sec. C* 33:198–224.

Brodie, H. J., and C. C. Neufeld. 1942. *Can. J. Res. Sec. C* 20:41–61.

Brown, W. 1922*a*. *Ann. Botany* 36:257–283.

Brown, W. 1922*b*. *Ann. Botany* 36:285–300.

Casman, E. P., and L. F. Rettger. 1933. *J Bacteriol.* 26:77–123.

Chamberlain, D. W., and J. L. Allison. 1945. *Phytopathology* 35:241–248.

Child, M. 1929. *Ann. Missouri Botan. Gard.* 14:411–479.

Chupp, C. 1917. *Cornell Univ. Agr. Exp. Sta. Bull.* 387:419–452.

Church, B. D., H. Halvorson, and H. O. Halvorson. 1954. *J. Bacteriol.* 68:393–399.

Clayton, C. N. 1942. *Phytopathology* 32:921–943.

Cochrane, V. W. 1958. *Physiology of Fungi*. Wiley, N.Y., 524 pp.

Cole, H. Jr., and C. L. Fergus. 1956. *Phytopathology* 46:159–163.
Corner, E. J. H. 1935. *New Phytol.* 34:180–200.
Cotter, R. V. 1940. *Phytopathology* 30:689–691.
Crabill, C. H. 1915. *Am. J. Botany* 2:449–467.
Curtis, K. M. 1921. *Phil. Trans. Roy. Soc. London Ser. B* 210:409–478.
Darby, R. T., and G. R. Mandels. 1955. *Plant Physiol.* 30:360–366.
Doi, R. H., and H. Halvorson. 1961. *J. Bacteriol.* 81:642–648.
Domsch, K. H. 1954. *Arch. Mikrobiol.* 20:163–175.
Doran, W. L. 1922. *Bull. Torrey Botan. Club* 49:313–340.
Edwards, O. F., and L. F. Rettger. 1937. *J. Bacteriol.* 34:489–515.
Emerson, M. R. 1954. *Plant Physiol.* 29:418–428.
Ericksson, J. 1895. *Zentr. Bakteriol Parasitenk. Aht. II* 1:557–565.
Evans, M. M., and G. Harrar. 1930. *Phytopathology* 20:993–997.
Falck, R. 1909. in *Hausschwammforschungen in amtlichen Auftrage.* A. Möller, Jena, Heft 3, pp. 9–32, 1–234.
Fergus, C. L., and R. D. Schein. 1960. *Mycologia* 52:719–725.
Fischer, G. W., and C. S. Holton. 1957. *Biology and Control of the Smut Fungi.* Ronald Press, N.Y., 622 pp.
Foreman, F. W. 1910. *J. Agr. Sci.* 3:400–416.
Gardner, M. W. 1918. *U.S. Dept. Agr. Bull.* 727:68.
Gardner, M. W. 1924. *Proc. Indiana Acad. Sci.* 33:163–201.
Gassner, G., and E. Niemann. 1954. *Phytopathol. Z.* 21:367–394.
Gäumann, E. A. 1946. *Pflanzliche Infektionslehre.* Verlag Birkhäuser, Basel, 611 pp. (*Principles of Plant Infection.* English edn., Crosby Lockwood, London, 1950.)
Gilbert, F. A. 1928. *Am. J. Botany* 15:345–352.
Goddard, D. R. 1935. *J. Gen. Physiol.* 19:45–60.
Goddard, D. R., and P. E. Smith. 1938. *Plant Physiol.* 24:241–264.
Goldsworthy, M. C., and R. E. Smith. 1931. *Phytopathology* 21:133–168.
Gottlieb, D. 1950. *Botan. Rev.* 16:229–257.
Graf-Marin, A. 1934. *Cornell Univ. Agr. Exp. Sta. Mem.* 157:1–48.
Gwynne-Vaughan, H. C. T., and H. S. Williamson. 1933. *Trans. Brit. Mycol. Soc.* 18:127–134.
Hahne, J. 1925. *Kühn Arch. Arb. Land. Inst. Univ. Halle* 9:157–163.
Harrell, W. K., and H. Halvorson. 1955. *J. Bacteriol.* 69:275–279.
Hart, M. P., and D. M. MacLeod. 1955. *Can. J. Botany* 33:289–292.
Harter, L. L., and J. L. Weimer. 1923. *J. Agr. Res.* 26:363–371.
Hawker, Lillian. 1950. *Physiology of Fungi.* Univ. of London Press, London, 360 pp.
Herzberg, P. 1895. Ph.D. Thesis, Friedrichs Univ.
Hirt, R. R. 1935. *N.Y. State Coll. Forestry, Bull.* 8, 3:1–25.
Hitzman, D. O. 1955. Ph.D. Thesis, Univ. of Illinois, 90 pp.
Holton, C. S. 1943. *Phytopathology* 33:732–735.
Holzmüller, K. 1909. *Zentr. Bakteriol. Parasitenk. Abt. II Orig.* 23:304–354.
Horowitz, N. H., and M. Fling. 1952. *Genetics* 37:591.
Horowitz, N. H., and M. Fling. 1953. *Genetics* 38:360–374.
Horsfall, J. G. 1930. *Cornell Univ. Agr. Exp. Sta. Mem.* 130:1–139.
Hull, R. 1939. *Ann. Appl. Biol.* 26:800–822.
Hyatt, M. T., and H. S. Levinson. 1959. *J. Bacteriol.* 77:487–496.
Ikata, S. 1933. *Okayama Agr. Exp. Sta. Spec. Rept.* 38:1–28.
Itzerott, Dorothea. 1938. *Arch. Mikrobiol.* 9:368–374.
Jinks, J. L. 1956. *Compt. Rend. Trav. Lab. Carlsberg Ser. Physiol.* 26:183–203.
Jones, Edith St. 1923. *J. Agr. Res.* 24:577–591.
Kaplan, J. G. 1955. *Exptl. Cell Res.* 8:305–328.
Kaufmann, F. H. O. 1934. *Botan. Gaz.* 96:282–297.
Keitt, G. W., E. C. Blodgett, E. E. Wilson, and R. O. Magie. 1937. *Wisc. Agr. Sta. Res. Bull.* 132:1–117.
Kent, G. C. 1946. *Iowa State Coll. J. Sci.* 20:259–263.
Keynan, A., and M. Halmann. 1961. in *Cryptobiotic Stages in Biological Systems.* N. Grossowicz, S. Hestrin, and A. Keynan, eds. Elsevier, Amsterdam, N.Y., London, pp. 64–70.
Keynan, A., and H. O. Halvorson. 1962. *J. Bacteriol.* 83:100–105.
Keynan, A., M. Halmann, and Y. Avi-Dor. 1958. *Proc. 7th Intern. Congr. Microbiol., Stockholm.* Almquist and Wiksells, Uppsala, p. 37.
Knaysi, G. 1945. *J. Bacteriol.* 49:473–493.

KNEEBONE, L. R. 1950. Ph.D. Dissert., Pennsylvania State Univ.
KNIGHT, B. C. J. G., and P. FILDES. 1930. *Biochem. J.* 24:1496–1502.
KÖHLER, E. 1956. *Ber. Deut. Botan. Ges.* 69:121–127.
KOLK, LAURA A. 1943. *Am. J. Botany* 30:317–330.
LAWRENCE, N. L. 1955. *J. Bacteriol.* 70:583–587.
LEACH, L. D. 1931. *Hilgardia* 6:203–251.
LIN, C. K. 1940. *Cornell Univ. Agr. Exp. Sta., Mem.* 233:3–33.
LING, L. 1940. *Phytopathology* 30:579–591.
LOPRIORE, G. 1895. *Jahr. Wiss. Bot.* 28:531–626.
LOWTHER, C. 1950. *Phytopathology* 40:590–603.
MCCORMICK, J. 1965. *J. Bacteriol.* 89:1180–1185.
MACHLIS, L., and ESTHER OSSIA. 1953. *Am. J. Botany* 40:465–468.
MAGIE, R. O. 1935. *Phytopathology* 25:131–159.
MAINS, E. B. 1924. *Proc. Indiana Acad. Sci.* 1923:133–135.
MANDELS, G. R., and R. DARBY. 1953. *J. Bacteriol.* 65:16–26.
MANDELS, G. R., and ANNA B. NORTON. 1948. *Quart. Gen. Lab. Res. Rept., Microbiol. Ser.* No. 11:1–50.
MARLOTH, R. H. 1931. *Phytopathology* 21:169–198.
MARUYAMA, Y., K. HAYASHI, and F. KOGANÉ. 1961. *Ann. Rept., Inst. Food Microbiol.* 14:49–52.
MELANDER, L. W. 1935. *J. Agr. Res.* 50:861–880.
MELHUS, I. E., and L. W. DURRELL. 1919. *Iowa Agr. Exp. Sta. Res. Bull.* 49:114–144.
MOL, J. H. H. 1957. *J. Appl. Bacteriol.* 20:454–459.
MUNDT, J. C., C. J. MAYHEW, and G. STEWART. 1954. *Food Technol.* 8:435–436.
MURRELL, W. G. 1961. *Symp. Soc. Gen. Microbiol.* 11:100–150.
MURTY, G. G. K., and H. O. HALVORSON. 1957. *J. Bacteriol.* 73:230–234.
NAGHSHI, J., J. W. White, JR., S. R. HOOVER, and J. J. WILLAMAN. 1945. *J. Bacteriol.* 49:563–574.
NIEMANN, E. 1956. *Phytopathol. Z.* 28:113–166.
NUTMAN, F. J., and F. M. ROBERTS. 1961. *Trans. Brit. Mycol. Soc.* 44:510–520.
O'CONNOR, R. J., and H. O. HALVORSON. 1961. *J. Bacteriol.* 82:706–713.
OHYE, D. F., and W. J. SCOTT. 1953. *Australian J. Biol. Sci.* 6:178–189.
OHYE, D. F., and W. J. SCOTT. 1957. *Australian J. Biol. Sci.* 10:85–94.
PALMITER, D. H. 1934. *Phytopathology* 24:24–47.
PLATZ, G. A. 1928. *Iowa State Coll. J. Sci.* 2:137–143.
POWELL, J. F. 1951. *J. Gen. Microbiol.* 5:993–1000.
PULSELLI, A. 1928. *Boll. R. Staz. Patol. Veg.* N. S. 8:50–85.
RABIEN, H. 1928. *Arb. Biol. Reichsanst. Land-Forstwirtsch.* 15:297–353.
REYNOLDS, H., A. M. KAPLAN, F. B. SPENCER, and H. LICHTENSTEIN. 1952. *Food Res.* 17:153–167.
RIEMANN, H. in *Spores II.* H. O. Halvorson, ed. Burgess Pub. Co., Minneapolis, pp. 24–58.
RIEMANN, H., and J. ORDAL. 1961. *Science* 133:1703–1704.
ROBBINS, W. J., VIRGINIA W. KAVANAGH, and F. KAVANAGH. 1942. *Botan. Gaz.* 104:224–242.
ROTH, N. G., and D. H. LIVELY. 1956. *J. Bacteriol.* 71:162–166.
SCHAFFNIT, E. 1926. *Ber. Deutsch. Botan. Ges.* 44:151–156.
SHEPHERD, C. J. 1962. *Australian J. Biol. Sci.* 15:483–508.
SIANG, W. N. 1956. *Res. Studies State Univ. Washington* 24:291–306.
SIBILIA, C. 1928. *Boll. R. Staz. Patol. Veg. N.S.* 88:235–247.
SIGGERS, P. V. 1947. *Phytopathology* 37:855–864.
SINGH, B. 1940. Ph.D. Thesis, Univ. of London.
SIZER, I. W. 1941. *J. Bacteriol.* 41:511–527.
SMART, R. F. 1937. *Am. J. Botany.* 24:145–159.
SNELL, W. H. 1922. *U.S. Dept. Agr. Bull.* 1053:1–47.
SNOW, D. 1949. *Ann. Appl. Biol.* 36:1–13.
SPAULDING, P. 1922. *Bull. U.S. Dept. Agr.* No. 957.
STAKMAN, E. C., R. C. CASSELL, and M. B. MOORE. 1934. *Phytopathology* 24:874–889.
STOCK, T. 1931. *Phytopathol. Z.* 3:231–239.
SUSSMAN, A. S. 1953*a*. *J. Gen. Microbiol.* 8:211–216.
SUSSMAN, A. S. 1953*b*. *Am. J. Botany* 40:401–404.
SUSSMAN, A. S. 1954. *J. Gen. Physiol.* 38:59–77.
SUSSMAN, A. S. 1965. in *Encyclopedia of Plant Physiology.* A. Lang, ed., Vol. 15. Springer-Verlag, Berlin, pp. 933–1025.

SUSSMAN, A. S., J. R. DISTLER, and J. S. KRAKOW. 1956. *Plant Physiol.* 31:126–135.

TERUI, G., and T. MOCHIZUKI. 1955. *Technol. Rept. Osaka Univ.* 5:219–227.

THIEL, A. F., and F. WEISS. 1920. *Phytopathology* 10:448–452.

THORLEY, C. M., and J. WOLF. 1961. in *Spores II.* H. O. Halvorson, ed. Burgess Pub. Co., Minneapolis, pp. 1–13.

TOGASHI, K. 1930. *Bull. Imp. Coll. Agr. Forestry, Marioka* 15:1–76.

TOGASHI, K. 1931. *Bull. Imp. Coll. Agr. Forestry, Marioka* 16:1–178.

TOGASHI, K. 1949. *Biological Characters of Plant Pathogens Temperature Relations.* Meibundo, Tokyo, 478 pp.

TREADWELL, P. E., G. J. JANN, and A. J. SALLE. 1958. *J. Bacteriol.* 76:549–556.

UPPAL, B. N. 1926. *Phytopathology* 16:285–292.

VAN ARSDEL, E. P., A. J. RIKER, and R. F. PATTON. 1956. *Phytopathology* 46:307–318.

VAN SUMERE, C. F., C. VAN SUMERE-DE PRETER, and G. A. LEDINGHAM. 1957. *Can. J. Microbiol.* 3:761–770.

VARY, J., and H. O. HALVORSON. 1965. *J. Bacteriol.* 89:1340–1347.

VAS, K., and G. PROSZT. 1957. *Nature* 179: 1301–1302.

WALKER, J. C. 1921. *J. Agr. Res.* 20:685–721.

WEBB, R. V. 1921. *Ann. Missouri Botan. Gard.* 3:283–341.

WEIMER, J. L. 1917. *Cornell Univ. Agr. Exp. Sta. Bull.* 390:509–549.

WEIMER, J. L. 1924. *J. Agr. Res.* 9:421–444.

WEIMER, J. L. 1926. *J. Agr. Res.* 32:97–132.

WILKINS, W. H. 1938. *Trans. Brit. Mycol. Soc.* 22:47–93.

WOLF, J., and S. A. Z. MAHMOUD. 1957*a*. *J. Appl. Bacteriol.* 20:124–136.

WOLF, J., and S. A. Z. MAHMOUD. 1957*b*. *J. Appl. Bacteriol.* 20:373–383.

WOLF, J., and C. M. THORLEY. 1957. *J. Appl. Bacteriol.* 20:384–389.

WOOD-BAKER, A. 1955. *Trans. Brit. Mycol. Soc.* 38:291–297.

WYNNE, E. S., and J. W. FOSTER. 1948. *J. Bacteriol.* 55:61–68.

WYNNE, E. S., and K. HARRELL. 1951. *Antibiot. Chemotherapy* 1:198–202.

WYNNE, E. S., D. A. MEHL, and W. R. SCHMEIDING. 1954. *J. Bacteriol.* 67:435–437.

WYNNE, E. S., W. R. SCHMEIDING, and G. T. DAYE, JR. 1955. *Food Res.* 20:9–12.

YANAGITA, T. 1957. *Arch. Mikrobiol.* 26:329–344.

YARWOOD, C. E. 1936. *Phytopathology* 26:845–859.

CHAPTER 9

Physiological and Biochemical Changes Occurring During Germination and Outgrowth

GERMINATION IS an irreversible process in which a number of simultaneous events take place. Over-all, initiation is usually followed by the swelling of the spore, and either rupture or absorption of the spore coat. The germ cell elongates and eventually divides into vegetative cells. A number of physiological features are associated with germination, including the loss of viability in reponse to environmental stress, the loss of refractility of the spore, an increase in permeability, a loss of spore components, and increased respiratory activity.

Therefore, the early stages of germination are primarily a period of degradative reactions. As indicated in Chapter 6, when germination is carried out in a medium supporting both growth and vegetative reproduction, RNA and protein synthesis occur during the second stage of germination. In this chapter some of the chemical changes occurring during germination will be discussed as well as the activation of a number of enzyme systems dormant in the intact spore.

Removal of the Spore Coat

BACTERIA

A number of stages in the germination process have been described in Chapter 6. The accumulating evidence that these stages are under physiological control has led to increasing efforts to describe the biochemical events accompanying each of these stages. From cytological studies of germination (Chapter 4) one of the most prominent morphological events in the early stages of germination is the removal of the spore coat, either by rupture or by absorption of the spore coat. In a few cases, the regions of the spore from which the vegetative cell emerges have been identified. As shown in Figure 9.1, the spores of *Bacillus megaterium* have a polar knob and a ridge or groove circumscribing the major

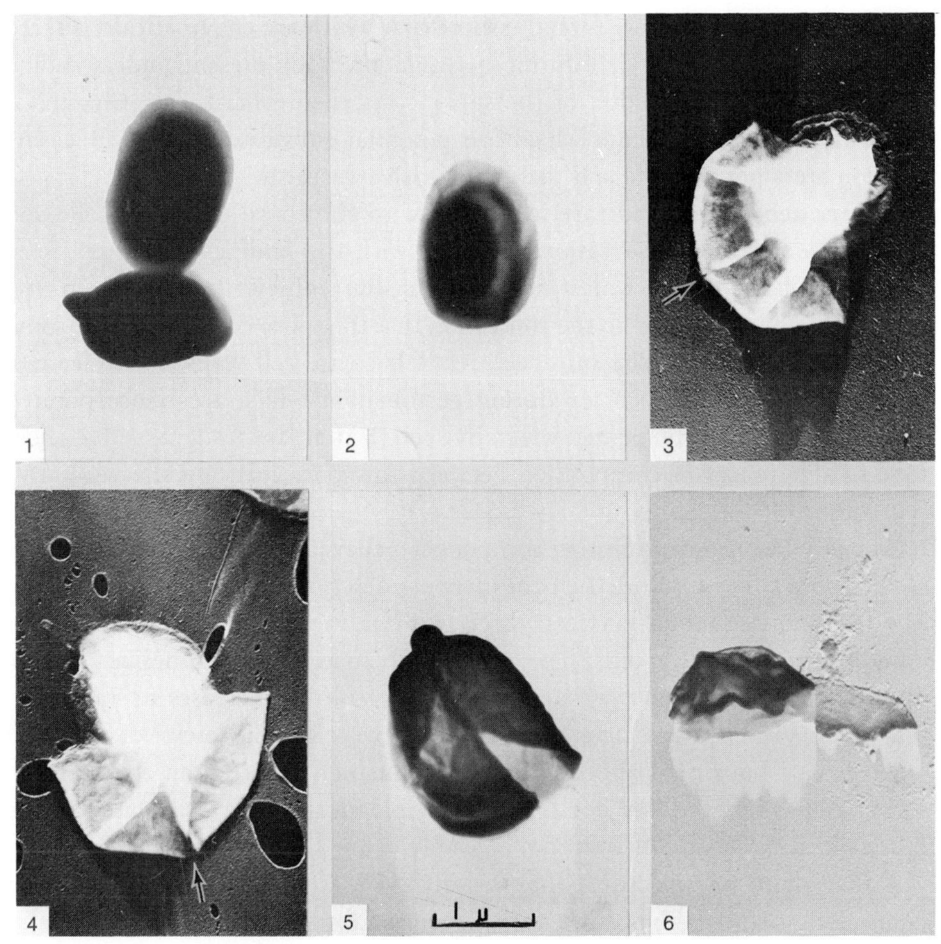

Figure 9.1 Electron micrographs of *Bacillus megaterium*. 1. Resting spores. 2. Spores germinated for 10 minutes. 3, 4. Spores germinated for 50 minutes showing emergence of the new cell and the split in the spore coat. 5. Empty spore case of an emerged cell, 60 minutes. × 7400. 6. Empty spore case of a resting spore obtained by grinding with glass beads. × 12,500. (Data from Levinson and Wrigley, 1960.)

equator of the spore case (Levinson and Wrigley, 1960). During germination, the rupture of the spore coat appears to follow the equatorial ridge or groove. This may be the region of weakness or greatest susceptibility to enzyme attack. Spores which are germinated either by physiological means or broken with glass beads show splits along the same ridge. A similar observation has been made by Fitz-

James and Young (1959) in *B. megaterium.* A new vegetative cell emerges, rupturing the outer spore coat near the equatorial portion.

A variation occurs during the germination of cysts of *Azotobacter vinelandii* (Wyss et al., 1961) which are surrounded by a barklike coat (exine). During germination, the central body of the cyst enlarges, followed by rupture and eventual shedding of the exine.

What are the chemical sites on the spore coat which are enzymatically altered in the emergence of the cell during germination? Our present understanding of the chemical composition of the spore coats is summarized in Chapter 2. The two main components which are potential substrates for the releasing reaction are a polypeptide and the cystine-rich structures.

At least ten amino acids are associated with the spore coat (Bernlohr and Sievert, 1962). These observations, coupled with the findings of Vinter (1962) that an inhibitor of cell wall synthesis (penicillin) inhibits the formation of a rigid spore envelope, lead to the conclusion that the spore coat has at least some structures analogous to the substructures of bacterial cell walls. The release of mucopeptides from the cortex during germination which are reincorporated into walls of the newly formed vegetative cell (Vinter, 1965) suggests that there may be differences in composition between the spore coat and the vegetative cell wall.

Probably the most interesting component believed to be in the outer layers of the spore is the disulfide-rich components described by Vinter (1959, 1960). The free spores contain between three to five times more cystine than their homologous vegetative cells. The cystine-rich material is synthesized during sporulation at the same period in which the culture increases its radiation-resistance (Vinter, 1961). This same material may be the source of potential —SH groups known to appear during germination (Mortenson and Beinert, 1953). Could a series of S—S bonds be responsible for the contractile nature of the spore which, following its splitting, is readily opened? Several observations suggest that the S—S structures may be involved. Reducing agents have been found both to spare the heat-activation required for rapid germination and also to inhibit the reaction in which activated spores return to a dormant state (Keynan et al., 1964). Gould and Hitchins (1963) observed that spores of *Bacillus cereus*, following treatment with various reducing agents, became sensitive to lysozyme. The mucopeptide and cell wall peptides are presumably protected. A reasonable working hypothesis would be that one of the first steps in germination is an enzymatic splitting of the disulfide bonds following activation of an enzyme in the spore (see Chapter 10). This leads to exposure of other coat components, activation of the lytic system, and subsequent swelling and changes in permeability.

The general problem of the release of intracellular macromolecular structures (viruses, spores, toxins, and so on) from bacterial cells has been the subject of increasing interest in recent years (for review see Welsch, 1958). These processes are associated with the activity of lytic enzymes which are active against vegetative cells and cell walls. Most of these are analogous to lysozyme (Richmond, 1959), although a nonspecific lytic agent has been reported in a strain of *B. cereus* which leaves at least a part of the cell wall structure intact (Norris, 1957). Similarly, lytic systems have been reported in bacterial spores (Strange and Dark, 1957) which differ in their *p*H optimum and activation by Co^{++} from the analogous enzyme in vegetative cells (Work, 1959). It is clear that a number of lytic systems are present in vegetative cells and possibly also in spores. Only a few of these have been purified to any extent, and their mechanism of action can only be inferred at this time. Therefore, it is uncertain how many of these are involved in liberating the emerging cell from its spore case. The autolytic system described by Norris (1957) is particularly interesting since it does not bring about a complete dissolution of the wall but breaks its continuity, exposing the underlying protoplasmic membrane. The picture of germination shown in Figure 9.1 indicates a similar phenomenon in which a partial digestion or weakening of the spore coat permits the escape of the germinated cell.

FUNGI

Most fungi germinate through the protrusion of a germ tube, an example of which is found in Figure 5.13. Depending upon the nature of the spore, the wall layers may or may not become part of the developing vegetative cell. Thus, conidia of *Neurospora* bulge at one end prior to germination and the hyphal wall that forms upon germination is continuous with that of the spore (A. Miller, unpublished). On the other hand, the outermost walls of the ascospore of this organism are not incorporated into the wall of the vegetative hypha (Figure 5.13). Thick-walled resistant cells, like the spores of smuts, teliospores of rusts, and ascospores of several species usually follow the latter pattern of germination.

Slime molds differ in the manner in which the spore case is disrupted during germination. For example, in the cellular slime molds germination involves a splitting, or rupture, of the spore case. However, in the case of *Acytostelium leptosomum* (Raper and Quinlan, 1958) and *Dictyostelium polycephalum* (Raper, 1956), the capsule-shaped spore is surrounded by a thin cellulose wall. During germination, the release of the myxamoebae is preceded by a swelling of the spore content and an apparent dissolution of the spore wall material.

Among the aquatic phycomycetes germination most often takes the form of the release of flagellated or amoeboid cells so that the spores can be considered to act as sporangia. In fact, there are instances in which the spores of a single organism can produce either a germ tube or motile cells. Such is the case with conidia of *Phytophthora infestans* in which the morphogenetic control is exerted by water which, when present in limiting amounts, induces the formation of germ tubes (Hickman, 1958). In *Albugo candida*, the more usual type of oospore germination is in the form of a sessile vesicle through which zoospores escape. However, under certain conditions, an exit tube is formed, at the end of which the vesicular zoosporangium appears (Vanterpool, 1959).

"Secondary" spores, which must germinate again (sporidia), may be produced upon the germination of some types of spores. Thus, spores of *Ustilago hordei* produce sporidia when germinated on water, but branched germ tubes when exposed to 95–100 percent relative humidity (Clayton, 1942). The reverse effect of water is demonstrated by teliospores of *Puccinia malvacearum* which produce promycelia with sporidia in moist atmospheres but germ tubes of indefinite length in water (Hawker, 1950). Quinary conidia may be formed from other conidia in *Entomophthora*, depending upon the physical and nutritional environment (Prasertphon, 1963).

Pathogens have evolved other means of germination, including the formation of appresoria, infection pegs, and so on (Gäumann, 1950).

Physiological Changes

RESPIRATION

Bacteria

The dormancy of the bacterial spore is perhaps best characterized by its absence of metabolic activity. Early reports on the metabolic activity of spores have varied considerably, largely depending on the extent to which metabolically active germinative forms have been removed. Vegetative cells of *Bacillus* have Q_{O_2} values of about 60–100. For example, a Q_{O_2} of 2.4 in the presence of glucose has been reported in a preparation of *B. megaterium* spores containing approximately 10 percent germinating cells (Levinson and Hyatt, 1955). Crook (1952), using a microrespirometer and a well-washed suspension of spores of *B. subtilis*, found a Q_{O_2} of less than 0.3. Unfortunately, he did not report the percentage of germination.

When precautions are taken to prepare fresh-washed suspensions of spores, no oxygen uptake can be detected in the presence of glucose (Spencer and Powell, 1952; Church and Halvorson, 1957; Halvorson and Church, 1957*b*). These findings, as well as some of the factors affecting the respiratory activity of spores of *B. cereus* strain T, are summarized in Table 9.1. Spores were washed 12–15 times until they were freed of germinating cells. When dormant cells were tested at high densities, there was no detectable oxygen uptake after 60 minutes in the

Table 9.1 Respiratory Activity of Spores and Vegetative Cells of *Bacillus cereus* Strain T on Glucose

Organism	Q_{O_2} (30°C)
Vegetative cells	60–100
Spores	
Dormant	$\leqq$ 0.05
Heat-shocked	20
Aged, heat-shocked	50
Germinated	50–70

SOURCE: Church and Halvorson, 1957.

presence of glucose. Based on the limits of the manometric techniques employed, the Q_{O_2} of dormant spores was estimated to be less than 0.05. The vegetative cells had a Q_{O_2} of 60–100. When spores were heat-shocked for one hour at 65°C, their Q_{O_2} on glucose was 20. Similar elevation in respiratory activity occurred when spores had been stored for 4 months in the deep freeze. Activation of the dormant glucose-oxidizing system was also observed when spores were germinated either by the addition of L-alanine or by high concentrations of glucose (Church and Halvorson, 1957; Murrell, 1955; Murty and Halvorson, 1957). Levinson and Hyatt (1955) have shown that germination leads to full metabolic activity under nutritional conditions where outgrowth of the germinated cells and presumably, protein synthesis, is insignificant. Heat-shocked spores were shown to germinate rapidly, the rate of germination being almost directly proportional to the rate of oxygen consumption in the presence of glucose (Levinson and Sevag, 1953). Manganese played an important role in stimulating oxidation and germination.

Germination increases the glucose oxidizing activity of aerobic spores. First, an activation of the dormant enzyme system takes place as is evident not only from studies on heat-activation but also from analysis of extracts of intact spores (Halvorson and Church, 1957*b*; Doi et al., 1959). Similar conclusions were arrived at by Rode and Foster (1960) who showed that abrading spores with glass beads led to active respiration of spores of *B. megaterium* (Figure 9.2). Similar results were found when spores were treated with *n*-dodecyl amine (Rode and Foster, 1961). Thus, spores have negligible, if not completely inactive, respiration. These spores contain metabolic systems for glucose metabolism which can be activated either by heat, chemicals, aging, or germination. The second feature which is evident occurs during the later stages of outgrowth. From the kinetic studies on respiration following germination (see Chapter 5), Levinson concluded that there were a number of stages observable in the respiratory changes during germination. These were characterized by different

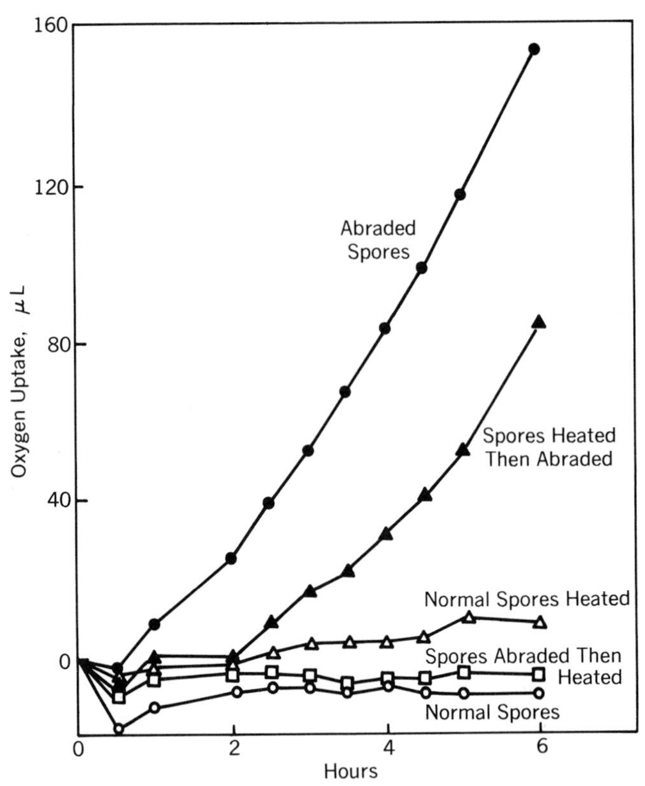

Figure 9.2 Oxidation of glucose by various types of spore suspensions. The abraded spores were prepared by agitation with glass beads in a Mickle disintegrator for 24 minutes at 4°C. Where indicated, spores were heated for 20 minutes at 65°C. (Data from Rode and Foster, 1960.)

linear increases in rate corresponding to the phases of germination, swelling, emergence, elongation, and cell division. Qualitative changes are also observed during this period. For example, Miwatani (1957) observed that after 5 or 6 hours following the initiation of germination of spores of *B. cereus*, the appearance of the cytochrome system could be detected in the vegetative cells. By the use of inhibitors, Hachisuka et al. (1958) concluded that the later stages of germination and outgrowth were dependent upon a cytochrome-linked respiratory system.

Studies on the changes in the metabolism of germinating spores of anaerobic bacteria have received little attention. As will be discussed later in this chapter (p. 252), both vegetative cells and germinated spores of *Clostridium botulinum* may contain a functional Embden-Meyerhoff pathway for glucose fermentation. The prominence of amino acids as germinating agents in anaerobic spores (Table 7.5) and the dependence of vegetative cells of these organisms on amino acid fermentation (Strickland reactions) for carbon and energy point out the need for studies on amino acid metabolism during germination. In one of the few studies available, Costilow (1962) observed a number of amino acid fermentations leading to CO_2 and H_2 in germinating spores of *C. botulinum* 62-A. During germination, the rate of amino acid fermentation increased; this rise was inhibited by chloramphenicol, an inhibitor of protein synthesis.

Another example of a dormant respiratory system has recently been reported by Dworkin and Niederpreum (1964). They observed that microcysts of the fruiting myxobacterium, *Myxococcus xanthus*, lacked respiratory activity on amino acids in spite of the presence of an active oxidative particulate fraction (Table 9.2).

Table 9.2 Comparison of Respiratory Activities of Vegetative Cells, Microcysts, and their respective Particulate Fractions

	Q_{O_2}
Intact cells[a]	
Vegetative cells	12.0
Microcysts	0
Cell-free particles[b]	
Vegetative cells	29.0
Microcysts	23.0

SOURCE: Dworkin and Niederpreum, 1964.
[a] 2 percent Casitone as substrate. Each Warburg flask contained 15.0 mg dry weight of washed vegetative cells or 7.5 mg dry weight of washed microcysts.
[b] 5μMoles NADH as substrate. Warburg flasks contained either 4.5 mg vegetative cell particle protein or 3.5 mg microcyst particle protein.

Fungi

As in the case of bacterial endospores, the spores of fungi usually show a marked increase in respiratory activity during germination. The data in Table 9.3 show examples of this kind. Such data were first obtained for fungi by Goddard (1935) and Goddard and Smith (1938) with ascospores of *Neurospora tetrasperma.* These cells remain dormant unless a heat-shock or chemical treatment is applied, after which they will germinate, utilizing endogenous substrates for energy (Sussman, 1961). Almost immediately upon being activated by heat, ascospores of this organism respire at an increased rate that may be twenty to thirty times that of the dormant organism, as the data in Tables 9.3 and 9.4 reveal. That this is also the case when furfural is used to break the dormancy of cells is illustrated in Figure 9.3, which also discloses that both oxygen uptake and carbon dioxide evolution are stimulated upon activation. This has also been shown to be the

Table 9.3 Respiratory Changes in Germinating Fungal Spores

Organism	Resting: Q_{O_2}[a]	Resting: Q_{CO_2}[b]	Resting: R.Q.	Germinating: Q_{O_2}[a]	Germinating: Q_{CO_2}[b]	Germinating: R.Q.	Reference
Phycomyces blakesleeanus, incubated 100 minutes	1.9	—	1.0	11.4	—	1.0	Rudolph, 1961
Neurospora tetrasperma, ascospores, incubated 4 hours	0.4	—	0.6	15–25	—	0.65	Holton, 1961
Puccinia graminis tritici, uredospores, incubated 72 hours	1.6	1.0	0.65	1.4	1.0	0.70	Shu et al., 1954
Aspergillus oryzae, conidia incubated 3 hours	1.26	—	1.4–2.2	2.17	—	0.6–1.0	Terui and Mochizuki, 1955
A. niger, conidia, incubated for 6 hours	0.4	—	—	1.8	—	—	Yanagita, 1957
Myrothecium verrucaria, conidia, incubated 2 hours	1.0	—	—	75	—	—	Mandels, 1963

[a] Q_{O_2} = $mm^3 O_2$/hour mg dry wt.
[b] Q_{CO_2} = $mm^3 CO_2$/hour mg dry wt.

case for ascospores of *N. crassa* that have been activated by chemicals (Emerson, 1954). Moreover, as the data in Table 9.4 show, there are changes in the fermentative capacity of these cells, as expressed in terms of carbon dioxide produced under anaerobic conditions.

Table 9.4 Comparison of Respiratory Rates of Dormant, Activated and Germinating Ascospores of *Neurospora tetrasperma* at 26°C

	Respiratory Rates: Dormant	Activated 1–2 hours after Activation	Germinating 3–5 hours after Activation
Q_{O_2}[a] ($mm^3 O_2$/hour mg dry wt)	0.21–0.59	4.5–10.9	16.4–24.2
Q_{CO_2}[b] ($mm^3 CO_2$/hour mg dry wt)	0.13–0.36	—	10.0–13.8
R.Q.[b]	0.57	—	0.59
Anaerobic CO_2 as $Q^{N}_{CO_2}$[a]	0.03	5.0–10.9	1.0–2.0

[a] Data of Goddard, 1935.
[b] Data of Holton, 1961.

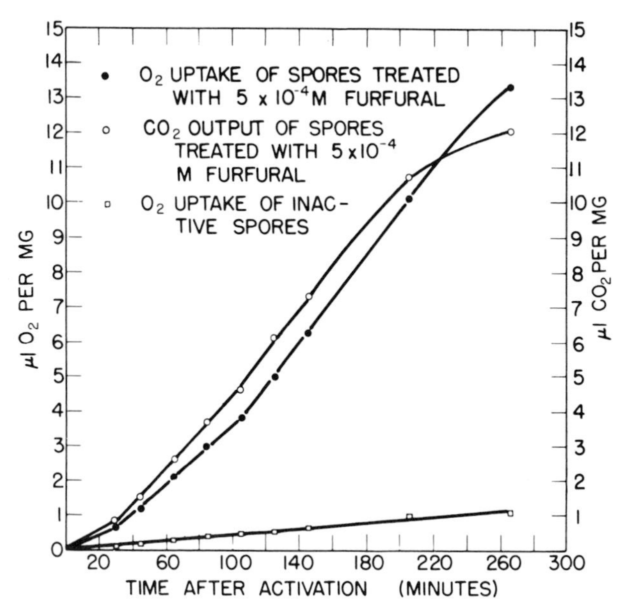

Figure 9.3 Respiratory changes induced by activation of ascospores of *Neurospora crassa* by furfural. (Sussman, 1953, courtesy *Amer. J. Bot.*)

Interesting parallels to these events are to be found during the germination of spores of *Phycomyces blakesleeanus*, as demonstrated in the work of Halbsguth and Rudolph (1959) and Rudolph (1960, 1961). Thus, heat-activation is required in order to ensure maximum germination of these spores, and both increased oxygen uptake and carbon dioxide production result.

Similar respiratory changes have been described for the germination of conidia of *Myrothecium verrucaria* (Mandels and Norton, 1948; Mandels and Darby, 1953), *Aspergillus oryzae* (Terui and Mochizuki, 1955), and *A. niger* (Yanagita, 1957). In these spores, as with those of *Phycomyces*, exogenous substrates are required, in contrast to the ascospores of *Neurospora* which germinate even in distilled water. Moreover, the kinetics of the respiratory measurements varied in *A. oryzae* where the composition of the medium determined the shapes of the curves obtained. Nevertheless, the kinetics of oxygen uptake during germination were similar enough in several of these cases to permit a mathematical description in the form:

$$y = b + \frac{kt^2}{2}$$

which can be fitted to parabolic curves (Mandels et al., 1956).

Uredospores of *Puccinia graminis tritici* have appeared to be an exception to the rule that respiratory increases are expected during germination (Table 9.3). In this case, Shu et al. (1954) observed that both the amount of respiratory activity, and the R.Q. of ungerminated and germinating spores were equivalent. Inasmuch as the respiration of the germinating spores was measured 3 days after incubation was begun, transitory increases in rate may have been missed. As a matter of fact, recent data suggest that when these spores are activated with pelargonaldehyde, there is a rapid increase in respiratory metabolism which is succeeded by a period during which the rate diminishes to approximately that of the resting spore (Allen, 1963).

A second exception occurs in the macroconidia of *Fusarium solani* f. *phaseoli* (J. C. Cochrane et al., 1963). Dormant spores of this organism oxidize acetate, malonate, and ethanol by way of the tricarboxylic acid cycle and the glyoxylic acid cycles. During germination, the respiratory rate of cells provided ethanol (Cochrane et al., 1963*a*) or mannose (Cochrane et al., 1963*b*) is not increased, whereas that of cells given glucose rises more than twofold. Slight increases are obtained when cells are germinated on fructose or trehalose (Cochrane et al., 1963*b*).

SWELLING

Bacteria

One of the most popular methods for following the germination of bacterial spores has been to measure the loss of refractility accompanying this process (Chapters 5 and 7). The loss in refractility parallels the swelling of the spore and an increase in the volume of the spore. The low water content of spores has been previously described in Chapter 2. Although the water content of spores is not known with any precision, it is presumably very low, based on the measurements of refractive index. The refractive index of a series of spore suspensions range from 1.5–1.54 (Ross and Billing, 1957). Similar measurements for vegetative cells were 1.39–1.40. Spores, therefore, are similar to dehydrated proteins like casein, wool, and leather. Thus, the uptake of water into such a system could well explain the swelling observed.

The view that the spore protoplasm is a highly condensed waterproof system has been presented (Powell and Hunter, 1956) and various workers have attempted to provide mechanisms by which a dry or semi-dry environment could be created in an aqueous medium. Prominent among these is the possibility that chelation of DPA with metals (calcium) and spore peptides could lead to a contractile state and subsequent loss of water (Rode and Foster, 1960; Lewis et al., 1960). If an anhydrous region of the spore exists, it certainly must represent only a small fraction of the total volume of the spore. From the studies of Gerhardt and Black (1961) and of Murrell and Scott (1958), no more than 30–40 percent of the spore is dry. On the basis of H_2^3O exchange experiments (Murrell, unpublished), the actual figure may, in fact, be much less. What may be the situation is that the spore is accessible to water but actually contains a relatively low content of water—possibly due to the compressed contractile nature of the cortex (Lewis et al., 1960; Alderton and Snell, 1963). Swelling may be due more to increasing the water content than to the entry of water into an anhydrous environment. This conclusion is supported by the interesting findings of Hitchins and Gould (1964). These workers isolated cores from *Bacillus subtilis* spores. Isolated cores underwent a reversible, *p*H-dependent swelling. Calcium prevented the swelling of cores at neutral *p*H; this protection could be reversed by DPA or ethylenediamine–tetraacetate. The isolated cores therefore provide a model system for examining the contractile nature of the cytoplasm in dormant spores. One might hope that with this system it will be possible to test the hypothesis of Warth et al. (1963) that the mucopeptide cortex behaves like a weak cation-exchange resin and that the spore calcium could cause the cortex to contract during sporulation.

Whatever the basis of the low water content of bacterial spores, germination is accompanied by a number of measurable changes in both the density and water content of the spores (Gerhardt and Black, 1961). The diffusible volume for water rises from 67–76 percent upon germination and the diffusible volume for

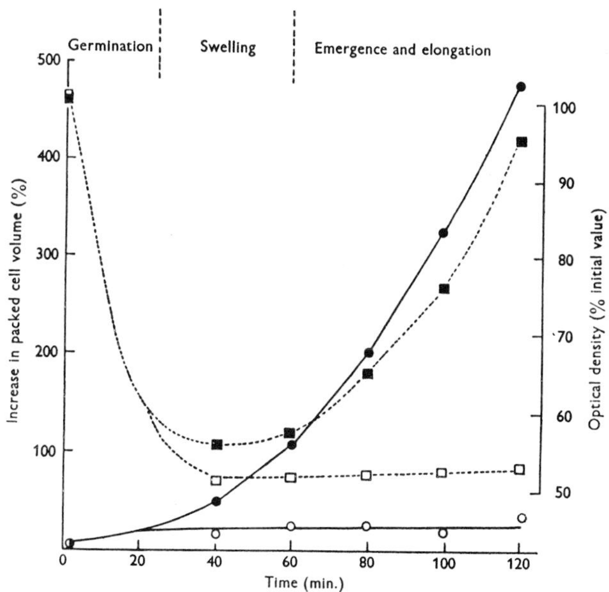

Figure 9.4 Effect of nisin on the increase in packed cell volume of *Bacillus subtilis* spores during germination. The initial packed cell volumes were 3.1 percent. Legend: ——— packed cell volume; - - - - - optical density; ●, ■, absence of nisin; ○, □, presence of 0.5 μg nisin/ml. (Data from Hitchins et al., 1963, courtesy *Jour. Gen. Microbiol.*)

glucose rises from 40–51 percent. In addition, the density of the bacterial spore in the dormant spore decreases from a value of 1.28 to 1.11 gm/ml following germination. Measurements of the water content by three different methods of desiccation demonstrated that for spores it was 64.8 percent and for germinated cells 73.0 percent.

The swelling of the bacterial spore following the uptake of water would certainly be expected. There have been, however, few quantitative studies of the increase in size of the spore during swelling to see whether these correlate precisely with the added water uptake. One such study was reported for spores of *B. subtilis* by Hitchins et al. (1963). During the initial drop in optical density accompanying germination, there was only a 20 percent increase in the packed cell volume (Figure 9.4). A second postgerminative swelling occurred after 25 minutes. Nisin, an inhibitor of coat rupture, but not of germination (Campbell and Sniff, 1959), had no effect on germinative swelling but inhibited post-germinative swelling. Similar results were observed when aeration was made limiting. Examination of cell dimensions showed that germinative swelling was largely due to the increases in the breadth of individual spores (about 40 percent). The authors suggested that the weakening of the coat, accompanying loss of DPA, calcium, and spore mucopeptide, was the initial event. Swelling of the cortex could explain the changes in cell shape which initially occur. On the other hand, postgerminative swelling apparently requires energy and this swelling may be due to synthesis—coupled with water uptake and elongation.

Fungi

Swelling of fungus spores is sometimes, but not always, a characteristic of the germination process. In the case of *Myrothecium verrucaria*, the progress of germination has been successfully followed by measuring the degree of swelling of conidia (Mandels and Darby, 1953). Other conidia that have been found to germinate in this manner are those of *Curvularia brachyspora*, *Penicillium expansum*, *Aspergillus fumigatus*, *Pullularia pullulans*, *Trichoderma viride*, and *Alternaria tenuis*. On the other hand, spores of several other of the Fungi Imperfecti do not swell perceptibly, nor do heavy-walled spores like the ascospores of several genera.

EXCRETION OF CELL MATERIALS

Bacteria

When bacterial spores germinate, a considerable amount of organic matter leaches out of the cell. Powell and Strange (1953) have demonstrated that a 30 percent decrease in the dry weight of spores of *Bacillus subtilis* and *B. megaterium* occurs during germination. During the same period there is an increase in the total amino nitrogen in the medium. Approximately 50 percent of the germination exudate was identified as calcium DPA. As mentioned in Chapter 5, the release of both calcium and of DPA has been used as a method of following the kinetics of germination of spores. The germination exudate also contains a hexosamine-containing hexapeptide (10–15 percent of the solid exudate), which has since been identified as muramic acid. In addition, 14 amino acids were demonstrated in the exudate, of which glutamic acid and lysine were the major constituents (Lee and Ordal, 1963). Some of the amino acids liberated undoubtedly arise from the free amino acid pool present in spores (Young, 1959). Increases in the alanine content of the medium accompanying germination have been reported by O'Connor and Halvorson (1960). In this case it was suggested that the endogenously liberated alanine could serve as a further germination stimulant.

Rode and Foster (1961) have compared the chemical changes following the germination of spores of *B. megaterium* induced either with inosine and alanine or by alkyl primary amines. Spores germinated with *n*-dodecylamine lost 45–55 percent of their dry weight whereas those induced with alanine and inosine lost 32 percent of their dry weight. Almost all of the calcium DPA was removed. They further analyzed the amino acids released and found that $\frac{1}{3}$ of those released were of a high enough molecular weight to be nondialyzable. In the *n*-dodecylamine-treated spores, a considerable quantity of protein (5.5 percent of the spore weight) was present in the germination exudate.

We have already discussed the situation involving the cystine-rich structures in spores which are converted to—SH groups during germination. The outer regions of the spore contain the disulfide-rich materials and are not hydrolyzed during germination (Vinter 1960). It is of interest that Lee and Ordal (1963) failed to detect S-amino acids in the germination exudate, which confirms Vinter's observations. A further description and quantitative measurements of this material should be very informative.

If identical fundamental changes are involved in the release of spore components upon germination, then one would expect that various germinating stimulants should lead to a loss of similar cell components. Riemann (1963) has analyzed the excretions of amino acids and peptides from spores of a putrefactive anerobe, 3679H, germinated by calcium DPA and EDTA. Similar excretions were observed with both EDTA- and calcium DPA-induced germination and have been found with other *Bacillus* spores. The total amount of exudate, as well as the dialyzable fraction, was greater in the case of spores germinated with EDTA than those germinated with calcium DPA.

Various physical treatments can, in fact, simulate the changes occurring during germination. An example of this has been demonstrated by Lund (1961). He observed that when spores are heated sufficiently to be killed, this process was followed by an excretion of DPA and other cell components. As shown in Figure 9.5, the excretion of DPA continues after the spores have been heated. Addition of

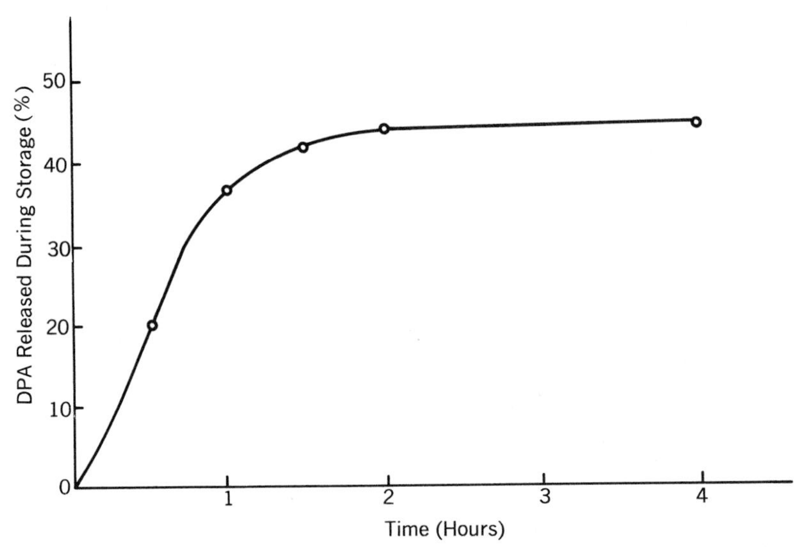

Figure 9.5 The release of DPA from spores to the supernatant liquid. The release of DPA during storage at 35°C after the spore suspension had been heated for 2.5 hours at 85°C, causing a 99.9 percent loss of viability. DPA plotted as percent of total released during incubation. During heating 38 percent was released. (Data from Lund, 1961.)

L-alanine and adenosine caused a significant increase in the rate of DPA excretion, even though the spores were nonviable. A comparison of some of the other spore components is shown in Table 9.5. Of particular interest is the finding that hexosamine and muramic acids are not released during heating, but subsequent incubation at 20°C permits the release of these materials at a slower rate than DPA and to a lesser extent than when release is induced by germination. The depolymerization of these components occurs after heating but whether the release of these agents is induced by the heating or by the appearance of spore components (L-alanine, and so on) in the suspending medium is not clear. It is evident that a characteristic pattern of loss of spore components accompanies this process. It is possible that the spore is altered by heating in such a way that the initiation of depolymerization take place.

Changes in phosphorus components of the spore during germination of *B. cereus* and *B. megaterium* have been studied by Fitz-James (1955). He observed that when spores were inoculated into media capable of supporting growth that the protein-bound phosphorus initially decreased and this decrease was paralleled by an increase in the acid-soluble fraction as labile phosphorus. The labile

Table 9.5 The Excretion of Spore Components During Germination or in Heated Spores of *B. cereus*

Treatment of the Spore Suspension	Percent of the Total Amount in the Spore Released to the Supernatant: Nitrogen	DPA	Muramic Acid	Hexosamine
Germination[a]	21[b]	95	56	34
Heated only[c]	5	26	0	0
Heated then incubated (1 hour at 30°C)	10	71	21	14
Heated then incubated in the presence of the germinating system for 1 hour at 30°C[b]	32[b]	99	49	35

SOURCE: Lund, 1961.
[a] Heat shocked at 65°C for 10 minutes, 0.28 m*M* adenosine and 15.5 m*M* L-alanine added, then incubated 1 hour at 30°C.
[b] Where the germination inducing reagents were added, the nitrogen content of the supernatant liquid was so great it was necessary to measure loss of nitrogen from the spores by difference in nitrogen content of the washed spores before and after treatments.
[c] Heated 2.5 hours at 85°C. The loss of viability was 99 percent.

phosphorus was tentatively identified as polymerized metaphosphate. During germination, the labile phosphorus was incorporated into ribose nucleic acid (for further discussion see page 234). As shown in Figure 9.6, the increases in DNA phosphorus were not evident until at least 20 minutes after the initiation of germination. When germination was carried out in media containing only alanine, adenosine, and glucose, nucleic acid synthesis did not take place, but only a rise in the acid-soluble phosphorus was found paralleling a fall in the phosphorus of the residue fraction.

Fungi

Unlike bacterial endospores, DPA has not been reported to accumulate in fungus spores, or in the medium during germination. Although the materials that do accumulate in the medium during the germination of fungal spores have not been studied in great detail, some appear to be characteristic of this process. Acetaldehyde and ethanol have been found to accumulate in the medium immediately after the start of the germination of *Neurospora* ascospores (Figure 9.7). However, the release of these substances is restricted at about the time when the germ tube has protruded, signaling a reduced rate of aerobic fermentation (Sussman et al., 1956). Similarly, acetaldehyde and ethanol accumulate during the germination of spores of *Phycomyces blakesleeanus*, as described by Rudolph

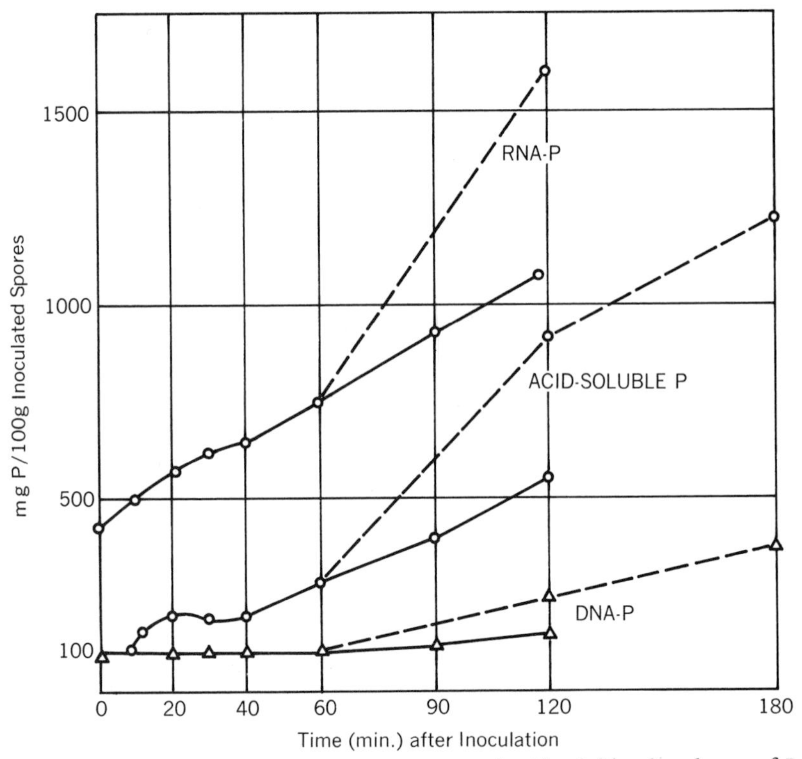

Figure 9.6 The increase in RNA, DNA, and acid-soluble phosphorus of *B. cereus* spores germinating in heart infusion broth. Series A (solid lines) the original thick culture (2.7 mg spores/ml) and series B (dotted line) subcultured at 60 minutes (0.54 mg spores/ml). (Data from Fitz-James, 1955, courtesy *Can. J. Microbiol.*)

(1961). Biotin is released by spores of *Myrothecium verrucaria* (Mandels, 1955).

During germination the exchange of labeled phosphate in conidia of *Aspergillus niger* with unlabeled phosphate in the medium (Nishi, 1961) and the release of polyphosphate (Yanagita et al., 1961) has been observed. During the germination of these spores that is induced by L-alanine, pyruvate, CO_2, and NH_3 accumulate (Hoshino et al., 1962).

Enzymes are released during germination from fungus spores, including invertase from *Myrothecium verrucaria* spores (Mandels, 1956), and "cytase" from *Botrytis* spores (Brown, 1917). Moreover, when spores utilize insoluble substrates like lignin and cellulose during germination, it is likely that they release extracellular enzymes. Inorganic substances have been found to accumulate in the medium during the germination of ascospores of *Neurospora tetrasperma*, including Ca^{++} and Na^{+}, whereas Mg^{++} and K^{+} were not released at this time. However, K^{+} did accumulate when EDTA was used to inhibit germination (Sussman, 1954). These data are presented in detail in Table 2.7 (page 36).

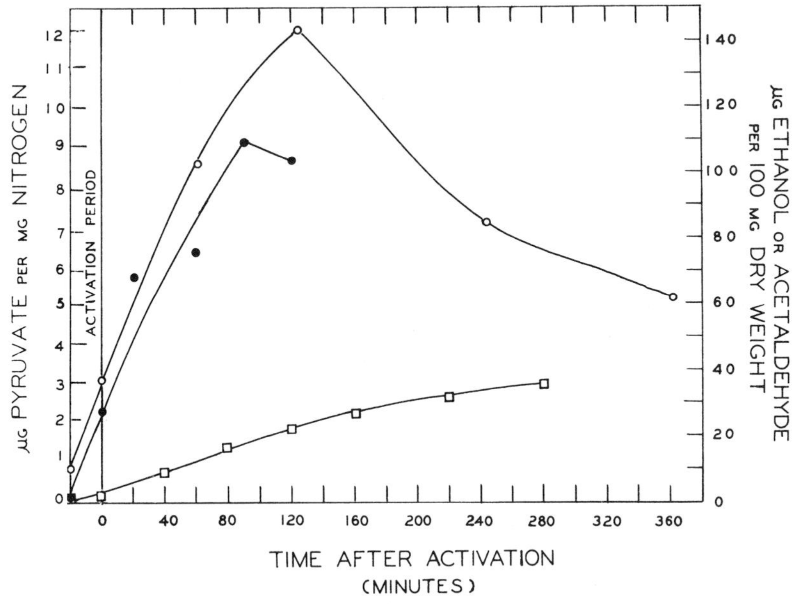

Figure 9.7 Metabolic intermediates that accumulate during the germination of ascospores of *Neurospora tetrasperma*. Ethanol and acetaldehyde analyses were of the suspending medium whereas the pyruvate was determined in cell extracts. Legend: open circles, pyruvate; solid circles, ethanol; squares, acetaldehyde. (After Sussman et al., 1956.)

PERMEABILITY

Germination, particularly of bacterial spores, is characterized by swelling, uptake of water, and increases in permeability. The changes in permeability have been discussed in Chapters 2 and 3 and will not be further detailed here.

Changes in Cellular Composition and Metabolism

SYNTHESIS OF MACROMOLECULES

Bacteria

The conversion of a spore to an actively growing vegetative cell can be viewed as a model system in differentiation. As discussed in this chapter and in Chapter 2, this transition involves structural changes as well as changes in enzyme patterns. The problem can be defined as a programming of the newly emerging cell to synthesize a different spectrum of proteins.

The first stages of germination do not involve protein synthesis. Chloramphenicol, an effective inhibitor of protein synthesis, has no effect on the loss of heat resistance when spores are incubated in L-alanine and adenosine. However, the incorporation of amino acids into proteins during the latter stages of outgrowth is sensitive to chloramphenicol. Supporting data come from studies on the nutritional dependence of outgrowth. Hyatt and Levinson (1957) observed that outgrowth and the increase in respiratory activity of the germinating spore required the addition of a source of sulfur for the synthesis of the S-amino acids. The early stages of germination can therefore be considered as a period of degradative reactions, whereas the secondary phases involve the biosynthesis of macromolecular components for the newly emerging vegetative cell.

An understanding of this unicellular morphogenetic process during outgrowth is only beginning to receive attention at the molecular level. From what has been previously discussed, this period is undoubtedly one in which controls of specific protein synthesis predominate. Based on our current understanding of the mechanism of protein synthesis, proteins are synthesized on nonspecific ribosomal particles in response to a specific tape, messenger RNA (mRNA). This RNA species turns over rapidly in vegetative cells, has a base composition of DNA, and in combination with ribosomal particles leads to the formation of functional aggregates (polysomes). One of the primary controls is exercised at the level of transcription: the expression of DNA sequence in terms of an mRNA molecule. In sporulation and germination the changes in cellular composition are best understood by a selective control of gene expression. Sporulation involves the expression of unique spore phenotypes (DPA, disulfide-rich structures, and so on), whereas germination is a return to vegetative phenotypes. Considering the question of outgrowth, two obvious possibilities exist:

1. The dormant spore contains stable mRNA molecules for the synthesis of vegetative enzymes.
2. One of the early steps in germination and outgrowth is the synthesis of vegetative mRNA.

The available evidence, although fragmentary at this time, favors the second hypothesis. This is evident from the effect of actinomycin D, which inhibits mRNA synthesis but not its function (protein synthesis) in many systems including *Bacillus* sp. (Levinthal et al., 1962). Higa (1964) and Kobayashi et al. (1965) observed that actinomycin D had no effect on the initial stages of germination (loss of heat-resistance, loss of refractility, and so on) but completely inhibited protein synthesis in the latter stages. When actinomycin D was added later during outgrowth, protein synthesis was inhibited only after a lag period. These findings suggest that the spore may be devoid of stable mRNA and that protein synthesis occurs only following mRNA synthesis.

The kinetics of nucleic acid synthesis during germination support this view (Figure 9.6). Fitz-James (1955) observed that when spores were placed in a germination medium permitting vegetative multiplication RNA phosphorus increased shortly after germination whereas DNA phosphorus increased only after a lag period. Similar results were reported by Woese (1961) with spores of *B. subtilis* as shown in Figure 9.8. Net RNA increases were observed as early as 20 minutes after germination had started whereas net DNA rose after 2 hours and cell division occurred at 3 hours.

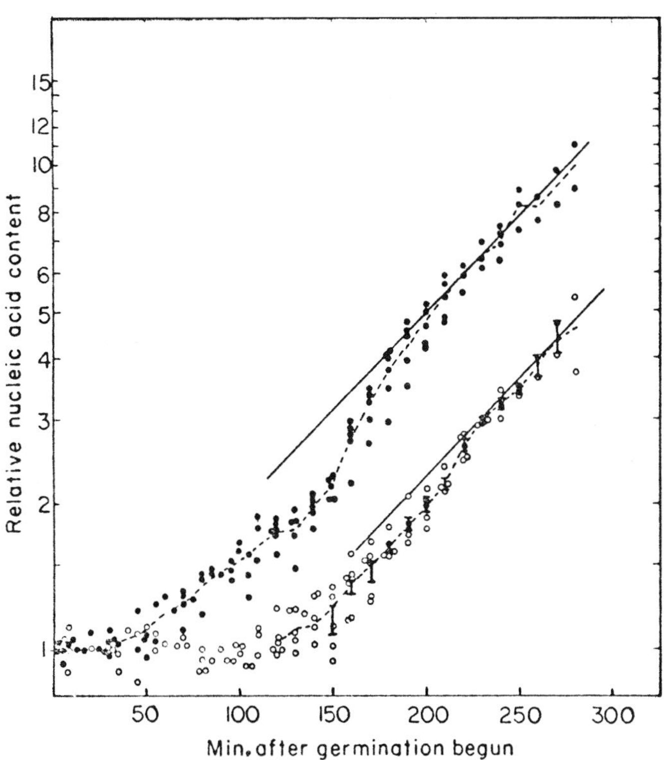

Figure 9.8 Total RNA (closed circles) and DNA (open circles) of a culture of germinating *Bacillus subtilis* as a function of time in germination. The RNA or DNA content of the resting spore is considered to be one unit. Solid lines are parallel to the growth of the culture. (Data from Woese, 1961.)

A stable mRNA fraction for sporulation was proposed by del Valle and Aronson (1962) based on the fact that actinomycin D had no effect on the sporulation process after a certain amount of RNA synthesis had occurred and also by the persistence of an RNA species formed early in sporulation which hybridizes with DNA of sporulating cells (Aronson, 1964). Also, significant RNA turnover occurs during germination, suggesting that a fairly large labile RNA fraction may be present in spores (Woese and Forro, 1960). However, Doi and Igarashi (1964) have questioned the possibility that the mRNA formed during sporulation survives in dormant spores. They found that, on the basis of base ratios and elution patterns from methylated albumin-kieselguhr columns, the RNA components of spores differ quantitatively and not qualitatively from those at other stages.

The primary difference between the RNA content of spores and vegetative cells was an enriched content of soluble RNA (sRNA) in spores (Doi and Igarashi, 1964; Balassa, 1963). The absence of mRNA in spores is supported not only by the sensitivity to actinomycin D, stated above, but also by the absence of polysomes in spores (Kobayashi et al., 1965).

The deficiency of mRNA in dormant spores is further indicated by analysis of the ribosomal components (Woese et al., 1960). Spores of *B. subtilis* contain ribosomal particles with sedimentation constants primarily of 50 *S* and 68 *S*. On the other hand, vegetative cells contain ribosomes with higher sedimentation constants (up to 99 *S*), presumably polysomes. Germination and outgrowth are characterized by increases in both unusually small ribosomal classes and in the heavy ribosomal (polysome) class. The presence of high concentrations of the chelating agent (DPA) in germinating spores may influence ribosomal stability and explain the results of Woese et al. (1960).

During the conversion of a spore to a vegetative cell, a high degree of order is observed. The initial events in germination occur rapidly in all cells in the population, and lead to a culture which, following outgrowth, divides synchronously

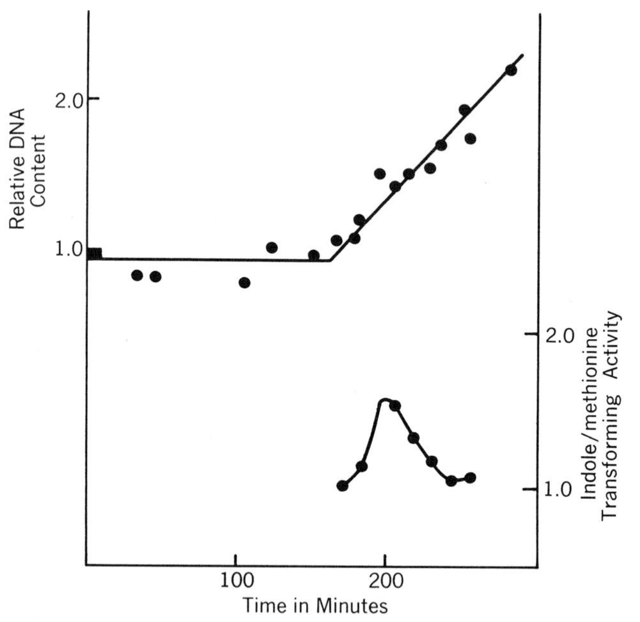

Figure 9.9 *Top:* Relative DNA content as a function of time in a germinating *B. subtilis* spore suspension. *Bottom:* Indole/methionine transformation ratios in the DNA lysates obtained at various times from the germinating spore suspension. The indole/methionine ratio for the first sample has been set at 1.0 and subsequent ratios have been normalized to this. (Data from Wake, 1963, courtesy Academic Press, Inc., Publishers.)

for several generations. RNA and protein synthesis begin a few minutes after the onset of germination; however, there is no DNA synthesis until 80–100 minutes later (Woese and Forro, 1960; Kobayashi et al., 1965). During this period new protein species appear in an ordered fashion. During outgrowth and during the first division cycle the synthesis of several enzymes commences at a specific time and each proceeds for only a fraction of the generation time (Steinberg et al., 1965; Kobayashi et al., 1965). Since the mRNA formed during outgrowth has a half-life of only a few minutes, differences in the time of synthesis of specific enzymes and proteins must be attributed to the time of transcription of the corresponding genomes. The synthesis of DNA during outgrowth is also ordered (Wake, 1963). In germinating spores of *B. subtilis*, DNA synthesis did not start until after 160 minutes (Figure 9.9) and then doubled in 90 minutes. Transforming activities for indole and methionine markers in DNA lysates obtained at various times show that the expression of each is nonrandom. Indole is copied before the methionine marker in agreement with the genetic map of Yoshikawa and Sueoka (1963).

Fungi

In *Aspergillus niger* the sequence of events occurring during germination is analogous to those observed in bacteria (Figure 9.10). During the stages occurring up to the inception of mycelial growth, loss of heat-resistance is followed by decreases in polyphosphate and subsequent synthesis of macromolecules (Yanagita et al., 1961).

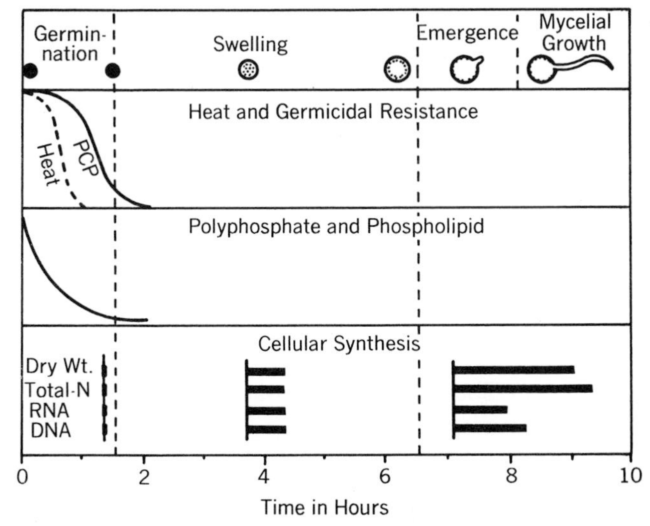

Figure 9.10 Diagrammatic representation of course of growth of *Aspergillus niger*. In bottom figure, each bar represents comparative rates of synthesis, assuming unity at the swelling phase. (Data from Yanagita et al., 1961.)

According to Yanagita (1957), RNA synthesis begins about 3 hours after the start of the incubation of conidia of *Aspergillus niger*, whereas DNA and protein synthesis begin somewhat later. These activities are accompanied by considerable uptake of inorganic phosphate and by increases in dry weight, volume, and total nitrogen (Figures 6.3 and 6.11). These data have been corroborated by Nishi (1961) who found, in addition, that although the turnover of RNA increases during the germination of these spores, that of DNA remains unchanged, even though it duplicated a few hours after incubation was begun. Takebe (1960) has found that choline sulfate accumulates in sizable amounts in conidia of *A. niger* and is one of the sources of sulfur in the synthesis of proteins during germination. The newly synthesized protein is primarily soluble (Hoshino, 1961), although the spore coat of dormant spores has the highest incorporating activity for amino acids in subcellular systems.

Whether germination of *A. niger* spores involves initially mRNA synthesis, as in bacteria, is not yet clear. That such might occur is indicated by the fact that during germination the nucleotide ratio of RNA changes: the ratio of purine to pyrimidine drops from 1.20 to nearly 1 (Table 9.6). Changes in enzymatic patterns

Table 9.6 Nucleotide Composition of RNA's Extracted from Germinating Spores of *Aspergillus niger of* Different Ages

Time of Cultivation (hours)	Adenylic Acid	Guanylic acid	Uridylic Acid	Cytidylic Acid	Ratios: Purine/Pyrimidine	Ratios: 6-Amino/6-Keto
0	1.00[a]	1.22	0.94	0.91	1.20	0.88
2	1.00	1.14	1.10	0.94	1.05	0.87
4	1.00	1.28	1.21	1.18	0.96	0.88
6	1.00	1.17	1.12	0.97	1.02	0.87

SOURCE: Hoshino et al., 1962.
[a] Numbers indicate relative values of amounts of nucleotides, taking those of adenylic acid as unity.

during this period are suggested by the observation that germinating cells have a higher dependence upon the hexosemonophosphate shunt pathway (Maruyama, 1957).

In conidia of *A. nidulans*, Shepherd (1957) found that protein nitrogen rose from 26 percent in the spore to 36 percent in the mycelium. Early in the germination period the RNA content of the conidia actually fell and that of DNA and lipid nitrogen showed no change. However, immediately before protrusion of the germ spore, a slow increase in RNA and protein occurred. Rapid synthesis of nucleic acids and protein did not occur until the vegetative phase of growth began. Protein synthesis during germination also has been shown to occur in

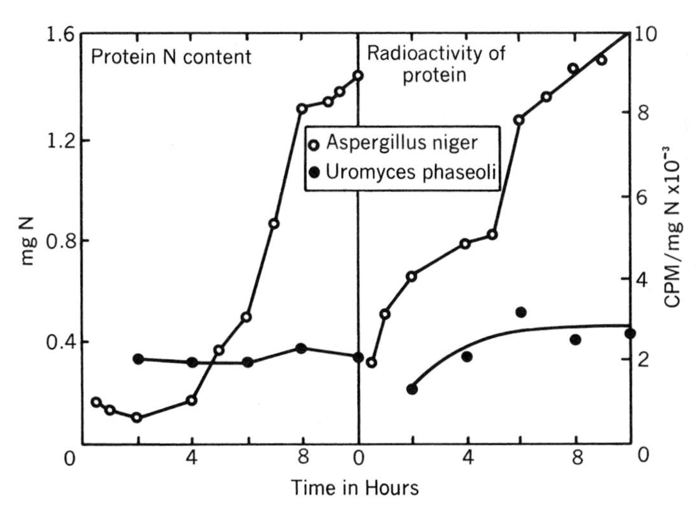

Figure 9.11 Protein synthesis and assimilation of acetate C^{14} into protein of conidia and uredospores by fungus spores during germination. (Staples et al., 1962, courtesy Boyce Thompson Institute for Plant Research.)

conidia of *Glomerella cingulata, Neurospora sitophila,* and *Aspergillus niger* (Figure 9.11) by Staples et al. (1962).

In ascospores of *Neurospora crassa* there is evidence that mRNA is not stored. Growing hyphae, resting conidia, and dormant ascospores contain the same population of ribosomes (Henney and Storck, 1963*a*) and of total, ribosomal, and sRNA (Henney and Storck, 1963*b*). However, dormant spores do not contain polysomes; these appear in the early stages of germination (Henney and Storck, 1964). Presumably, then, germination is accompanied by mRNA synthesis and subsequent banding of ribosomes (polysomes).

The nuclear cap of zoospores of aquatic fungi has been found by Lovett (1963) to be a "package" of ribosomes. Inasmuch as this cap breaks down very soon after the start of germination, it is tempting to assign it a role in this process. Thus, the cap might serve as a reservoir of RNA and protein or, alternatively, as a preformed source of programmed ribosomes which could initiate protein synthesis soon after germination commences. However, these possibilities have not been tested and further work with the Phycomycetes is needed to extend the generality of the observations discussed.

By contrast, uredospores of rusts do not synthesize proteins during germination. This was shown first by Shu et al. (1954) with spores of the wheat stem rust (*Puccinia graminis tritici*). Similar results (Figure 9.11) have been obtained with uredospores of *P. helianthi, P. sorghi,* and *Uromyces phaseoli* by Staples et al. (1962). Although no net synthesis of protein occurs in such spores, there is some turnover inasmuch as labeled amino acids are incorporated into the proteins of rust spores (Staples et al., 1962) and into the carbon of the cell (Shu et al., 1956).

These results suggest that obligate parasites may be deficient in the ability to synthesize proteins, at least during the stages of uredospore germination in rusts. On the other hand, these spores appear to be able to form at least 11 amino acids from sucrose (Kastings et al., 1959).

Changes in phenotype and RNA base ratios during the transition from dormant to vegetative systems are not restricted to microbial systems. In the dwarf bean, *Phaseolus vulgaris*, germination leads to an increase in the level of phytase and acid phosphatase (Gibbins and Norris, 1963) and in peanuts and the castor bean, enzymes of the glyoxylate cycle develop during germination (Marcus and Velasco, 1960). In a number of cases, changes in the RNA base ratios during germination have been observed. For example, Oota and Takata (1959) fractionated RNA from hypocotyls and cotyledons of seeds of *Vigna sesquipedalis* and observed differences in their base ratios and RNA/protein ratios. Further work on peanut seeds (Marcus and Feeley, 1964) reveals that whereas unimbibed peanut seeds incorporate amino acids only slowly into proteins, imbibition greatly increases this activity. Experiments suggest that an active mRNA is formed following activation. This process may be a general phenomenon in seeds and other dormant systems.

CHEMICAL CHANGES IN STRUCTURAL COMPONENTS

Bacteria

The structure and composition of bacterial spores is discussed in Chapter 2. A number of these structures are unique to the spore state, and therefore are properties which are lost during the germination and outgrowth phases.

The first of these components to be lost is the spore coat itself. As was discussed in Chapter 2, the understanding of the chemical nature of this loss is dependent upon our ability to separate chemical components of the spore coat from other fractions. Employing EDTA and heat to prevent autodegradation, and electron microscopy to follow the fractionation procedure, Warth et al. (1963) have identified most clearly the nature of the coat material. This material consists of electron-opaque outer coats, laminated inner coats, cortical material and a layer, possibly the germ cell wall, attached to the inner surface of the cortex. The presence of hexosamine peptides in fractions rich in spore coats from mechanically disintegrated spores, and the release of peptide and hexosamine from this fraction by the action of lysozyme, led originally to the view that spore coats were composed of these peptides (Powell and Strange, 1956; Salton, 1956). However, when these spore integuments were treated either with lysozyme or allowed to autodigest, the cortical structure and the cortical membrane have almost been completely degraded. The soluble material released consisted chiefly of alanine, glutamic acid, DAP, glucosamine, and muramic acid (Warth et al., 1963). The insoluble residue following hydrolysis contained the normal spectrum of amino acids found in proteins. Snoke (1964) reported similar results in studies of spore coats of *Bacillus licheniformis*. The outer coat is therefore protein in nature, whereas the muramic acid is located internally.

A second structure which is altered is the cystine-rich structure reported in several species of the genus *Bacillus* by Vinter (1960). This component, which is lost during germination and, therefore, is presumably on one of the outer layers of the spore, contains five to seven times the sulfur content of the corresponding vegetative cells (Chapter 3). It is thought that these cystine-rich structures play a role in the radiation-resistance of the spore. Germination is accompanied by an increase in the SH groups present (Mortenson and Beinert, 1953; Widra, 1956). These findings suggested that a splitting of the S—S bond to SH groups is part of the process of rupture of the outer spore coats and the emergence of the vegetative cell.

Bott and Lundgren (1964) recently extended these studies to two strains of *B. cereus*. Sporulation led to an approximately two and a half-fold increase in disulfide content. In contrast to the findings of Vinter, radiation-resistance was correlated with an increased SS/SH ratio rather than the disulfide content. Direct potentiometric titrations revealed that spores have negligible amounts of SH material, whereas this represents about 35 percent of the S of vegetative cells.

Bacitracin has been suggested to be a component of the walls of spores of *Bacillus licheniformis* (Bernlohr and Novelli, 1963). However, there is conflicting evidence as to whether it is an integral component of isolated spore coats (see Chapter 2). That other antibiotics may be found to be present in spores and not in vegetative cells is suggested by the work of Balassa et al. (1963) who have found such a material in *B. subtilis* as well.

A fourth interesting component which changes during germination was reported by Mayall and Robinow (1957). They described the presence of a cortex region which lies inside the spore coat (illustrated in study by Warth et al., 1963; Figure 2.8) and occupies approximately 50 percent of the volume of the spore. This cortex is a highly organized layer which, when stained with lanthanum, shows a visible fine structure. This region is laminated and occupies approximately 83–87 percent of the space within the spore coat. During the initial stages of germination the cortex is transformed into a highly porous spongework of delicate fibers. At this time treatment with acid no longer discloses an orderly array of concentric layers characteristic of the cortex (Mayall and Robinow, 1957). The thickness of the layers rapidly decreases until at the end of 1 hour, only remnants of it can be detected clinging to the cell wall of the emerging vegetative cell. The cortex, therefore, is destroyed during the early stages of germination. Similar structures have been observed in spores of *B. polymyxa*

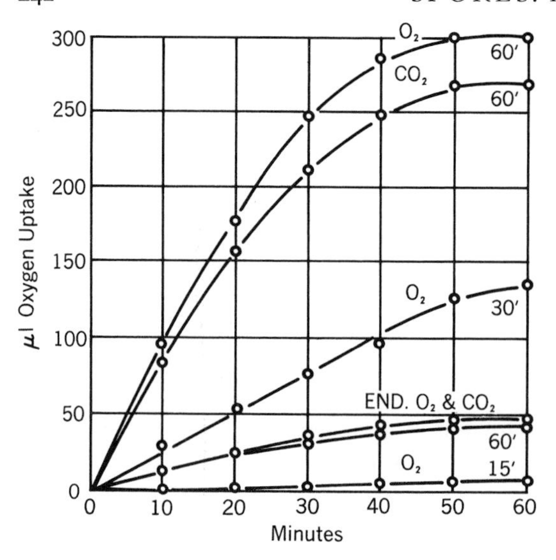

Figure 9.12 Effect of heat on glucose oxidation by intact spores (4 months old) of *Bacillus cereus* strain T. Spores were heated at 65°C. (Data from Church and Halvorson, 1957.)

(Vanden Hoof and Aninger, 1956) and in spores of *Clostridium welchii* (Smith and Ellner, 1957). Some of the chemical exudate released during germination may, in fact, originate from the cortex region. From the above discussion (see also Chapter 2) the hexosamine, peptide, and presumably DPA (Fitz-James, 1962) are concentrated in the cortex region. Moyshological changes in the cortex during germination may be seen in Figures 3.5 to 5.10.

Fungi

Structural changes during fungal spore germination include the softening of the plug through which the germ pore of germinating ascospores of *Neurospora* protrudes (Figure 5.13). The chemical nature of the plug is unknown, although it is known to be soluble in sodium hypochlorite (Lowry and Sussman, 1958).

Although unaccompanied by pictures of spores, Nishi's (1961) data on the decrease in phospholipid during germination of conidia of *Aspergillus niger* suggest that changes occur in membrane structure. Also, considerable turnover of hexosamine was demonstrated in the several spores studied by Staples et al. (1962). The data on the changes in structural components of fungal spores during germination are too incomplete to suggest any patterns.

METABOLIC PATTERNS

Bacteria

Over a decade ago it was thought by several workers that bacterial spores were devoid of enzymatic activity. As has previously been discussed, the respiratory activity of a spore is low, but not completely absent. During germination the metabolic activity of the spore rapidly increases to a point where it approaches that of the vegative cell. Inasmuch as these early stages of germination do not involve protein synthesis, it is clear that a number of enzymes pre-exist in the spore in a dormant or inactive form.

In recent years considerable effort has been undertaken to characterize the enzymatic pattern of spores and to compare these with the parent vegetative cells. More than 50 enzymes have been detected in spores and, undoubtedly, the true number approaches that of the vegetative cell. Measurements of the enzymatic content of spores are somewhat complicated by the fact that a number of the activities are masked and require activation of the spore before they can be adequately measured. The recognition of the dormant enzymes and the use of improved methods for rupturing spores have permitted a more extensive analysis of the enzyme content. The enzymes of the spores fall into three groups: (a) enzymes which are active in the intact spores; (b) enzymes whose activity *in vivo* requires some treatment to be manifest; (c) enzymes which can be demonstrated only in disrupted spores. These will be discussed later.

The biochemical changes occurring both in the period of outgrowth following germination as well in the process of sporulation can be understood by comparing the enzyme pattern of spores and vegetative cells. Table 9.7 summarizes those enzymes which have been identified and assayed under optimal conditions both in spores and in homologous vegetative cells of *Bacillus*. The changes in

Table 9.7 Comparison of the Enzymes of Vegetative Cells and of Spores of Bacteria

Enzyme	Organism	Units of Enzyme:[a] Veg. Cell	Spore
Enriched in Spore			
Adenosine deaminase	*Bacillus cereus*	0.021	0.093
Ribosidase	*B. cereus*	0	0.146
Alanine racemase	9 strains *Bacillus*	1–4	10–84
Pyrophosphatase	*B. megaterium*	0.070	1.88
Soluble $NADH_2$ oxidase	*B. cereus*	0.018	0.078
Glutamo-transferase	*B. cereus*	0.16	0.22
Decreased in Spore			
Glutamic transaminase	*B. mycoides*	0.049	0
Catalase	*B. cereus*	321	16.5
DAPA decarboxylase	*B. sphaerius*	1.25–1.87	0.25–0.50
Particulate $NADH_2$ oxidase	*B. cereus*	6.58	0.024
$NADH_2$ cytochrome *c*-reductase	*B. cereus*	0.98	0.06
Diaphorase	*B. cereus*	1.87	1.47
Succinic cytochrome *c*-reductase	*B. cereus*	0.55	0
Glutamine synthetase	*B. cereus*	0.63	0.23
Acetokinase	*B. cereus*	0.19	0.06

Source: Halvorson, 1963.
[a] μ moles/hour/mg dry weight cells.

Table 9.8 Comparative Activities of Enzymes in Extracts of Vegetative Cells, Spores, and Germinated Spores of *Clostridium botulinum* 62-A

Enzymes or Systems	Relative Activities in Extracts: Vegetative Cells: Glucose Adapted	Vegetative Cells: Non-adapted	Spores Germinated in: Trypticase	Spores Germinated in: Trypticase + CAPC[a]	Spores
Glucokinase[b]	0.25–0.44	0	0	0	0
Phosphohexoseisomerase, phosphofructokinase, and aldolase[c]	0.63	0.19	0.11	0.04	0.04–0.08
Aldolase[c]	1.60–1.85	0.75–0.80	0.50	0.09	0.06–0.11
Aldolase, 3-phosphoglyceraldehyde dehydrogenase[d]	4.2–4.6	1.0–1.4	0.9–1.1	0.6–0.8	0.4–0.5
Phosphoglyceromutase, enolase, and pyruvate kinase[e]	0.30	0.14	0	0	0
Lactic dehydrogenase	0	0	0	0	0
Alcohol dehydrogenase[f]	0.13	0.07	0	0	0
Phosphoroclastic reaction[g]	0.50–0.58	0.50–0.58	0	0	0
Acetokinase[h]	2.0–2.5	1.7–2.0	0.2–0.3	0.2	0.2
Phosphotransacetylase[f]	20	19.3	2.3	1.3	1.1
Coenzyme A transphorase[f]	3.0	2.7	1.4	0.9	0.9
Diaphorase[f]	0.5–0.65	0.54–0.63	0.58–0.60	0.25	0.20–0.40
Reduced diphosphopyridine nucleotide oxidase[f]	0.01–0.02	0.03–0.04	0.025	0.04	0.04–0.06

SOURCE: Simmons and Costilow, 1962.
[a] CAPC = chloramphenicol.
[b] Expressed as μmoles of glucose phosphorylated per hour per mg of protein.
[c] Expressed as μmoles of fructose-1,6-diphosphate split per hour per mg of protein.
[d] Diphosphopyridine nucleotide reduction at 340 mμ; change in OD $\times$ 10^2 per minute per mg of protein.
[e] Expressed as μmoles of pyruvate formed per hour per mg of protein.
[f] Change in OD per minute per mg of protein.
[g] Expressed as μmoles of acetyl phosphate formed per hour per mg of protein.
[h] Expressed as μmoles of acetyl phosphate formed per minute per mg of protein.

enzymatic constitution that occur are both qualitative and quantitative. Ribosidase is present in spores, but not in vegetative cells, whereas the reverse is true of glutamic transaminase and succinic cytochrome-*c* reductase. Five enzymes are present in higher concentrations in the spore than in vegetative cells, whereas seven enzymes are present in lower concentration in the spores.

The information available on the comparative enzyme patterns of spores and vegetative cells of *Clostridium* is very limited. Simmons and Costilow (1962) examined a number of enzyme activities in vegetative cells, spores, and germinated spores of *C. botulinum* (Table 9.8). Since glucose inhibits sporulation, the most meaningful comparisons are between enzyme activities in spores and vegetative cells which are not adapted to glucose utilization. Several trends are apparent. In general, spores have lower enzyme levels than do vegetative cells and germination leads to increased enzyme activity. In one case, $NADH_2$ oxidase, spores have equivalent or higher enzyme levels than are present in vegetative cells.

ENZYMES ACTIVE IN INTACT SPORES

Since germination is under physiological regulation (Chapter 10), one would expect that certain enzymes would be active in the intact spore, whereas others may be activated only during germination. The enzymes active in the intact spores would be expected to be protected against thermoinactivation and other unfavorable environmental conditions, whereas enzymes which are active only following germination may be protected by the same mechanism that protects passively transferred enzymes.

A number of enzymes have been identified in intact dormant spores. Halvorson (1958) proposed the following characteristics for those enzymes active in the intact bacterial spore without requiring special treatment.

1. They are heat-resistant and generally they will tolerate a temperature of 80°C for 30 minutes.
2. The activity is about as high in the intact spores as it is in the germinated spore or the spore extracts.
3. They remain heat-resistant after germination.
4. Their activity is greater in the spore than in the vegetative cell.

The enzymes fulfilling these requirements are listed under group A in Table 9.9.

Table 9.9 Enzymes Active in Intact Bacterial Spores

Enzyme	Reference
A	
Alanine racemase	Stewart and Halvorson, 1953
Catalase	Reuhle, 1923; Murrell, 1955; Lawrence and Halvorson, 1954
Adenosine ribosidase	Powell and Hunter, 1956; Lawrence, 1955; Nakata, 1956, 1957
B	
Adenosine deaminase	Powell and Hunter, 1956; Nakata, 1956, 1957
Proteolytic enzymes	Levinson, 1957
Pyrophosphatase	Levinson, 1957
L-Alanine dehydrogenase	O'Connor and Halvorson, 1960

The first enzyme which was clearly demonstrated in resting, intact bacterial spores was alanine racemase (Stewart and Halvorson, 1953). This enzyme is specific for alanine, requires pyridoxal phosphate and converts either D- or L-alanine to a racemic mixture.

Alanine racemase is heat-resistant and widely distributed among species of *Bacillus* (Church et al., 1954). It was found that very little, if any, of the enzyme could be detected in vegetative cells. However, enzyme activity appeared at the early stages of sporulation, and the maximum activity could be demonstrated only when spores initially appeared. Disruption of the spores did not increase the enzyme activity. The enzymes in both spores and debris were heat-resistant (Stewart and Halvorson, 1954). However, in extracts the soluble alanine racemase was heat-sensitive and, therefore, similar to the analogous enzyme in vegetative cells.

Alanine racemase is probably associated with an outer spore coat or exosporium. Berger and Marr (1960), in examining the kinetics of sonic disruption of spores of *B. cereus*, found that alanine racemase was removed from spores at the same time as hexosamine (probably the hexosamine peptide), adenosine deaminase, and the exosporium. Viability disappeared and the cytoplasm was removed only after more extended sonic disruption.

Similar properties have been described for both catalase (Ruehle, 1923; Murrell, 1955; Lawrence and Halvorson, 1954) and adenosine ribosidase (Powell and Hunter, 1956; Lawrence, 1955; Nakata, 1956, 1957) of spores. The enzymes are heat-resistant and enriched in bacterial spores. In spore extracts both a particulate heat-resistant enzyme and a soluble heat-sensitive enzyme can be recognized (Sadoff, 1960; Nakata, 1956). During germination the heat-resistant enzymes persist, and the heat-sensitive ones are presumably synthesized by the vegetative cell. Sadoff (1961) has purified and compared the catalase from spores (heat-resistant) and vegetative cells (heat-sensitive). The two were immunologically indistinguishable. From studies on the kinetics of inactivation by heat, and hydrogen bond-breaking agents (guanidine), he concluded that the spore catalase was less firmly coiled than the enzyme from vegetative cells. Campbell (1964) arrived at a similar conclusion to explain the heat stability of α-amylase from obligate thermophilic strains of *B. stearothermophilus*. In both these cases heat-resistance is an integral feature of the tertiary and, possibly, primary structure of the enzyme itself.

In addition to the enzymes listed in group A (Table 9.9), other enzymes have been recognized in intact, dormant spores which fulfill some, but not all, of the requirements of this class. These are listed in group B (Table 9.9). Three of these enzymes, adenosine deaminase, pyrophosphatase and L-alanine dehydrogenase are active in spores which have been activated at 65°C, but are heat-sensitive in extracts of spores. The proteolytic enzyme is active against gelatin at elevated temperatures (Levinson, 1957) and may be heat-stable. However, its activity is greater in spore extracts, possibly reflecting the greater availability of substrate for the enzyme.

The L-alanine dehydrogenase is of particular interest to the mechanism of L-alanine-induced germination. This will be discussed in Chapter 10. The enzyme has been isolated (O'Connor and Halvorson, 1961) and, under conditions precluding germination (Murty and Halvorson, 1957), has been shown (Halvorson and Church, 1957; O'Connor and Halvorson, 1960) to be active in dormant spores. However, when spores are activated by heat, or germinated, the rate of deamination and the K_m of the enzyme for L-alanine indicate that either the enzyme is further activated or substrate accessibility is improved (O'Connor and Halvorson, 1960).

In addition, glucose dehydrogenase is heat-resistant in spore extracts (Doi et al., 1959; Bach and Sadoff, 1962). However, this enzyme is inactive in the intact spore.

ENZYMES INACTIVE ONLY IN DORMANT SPORES

Bacteria

The majority of the enzymes present in bacterial spores are inactive and can be recognized only after activation by prolonged heat treatment, aging, germination, or mechanical rupture. With few exceptions, the enzymes activated are heat-sensitive and thus their resistance *in vivo* to heat activation treatment must be due to some generalized mechanism for heat stability (see Chapter 3) rather than to an intrinsic property of the enzymes themselves.

One of the first and most dramatic example of inactive (dormant) enzyme systems in spores is the oxidation of glucose. As previously mentioned in this chapter, dormant bacterial spores are devoid, or nearly so, of respiratory activity. Church and Halvorson (1957) and Murrell (1955) demonstrated that activated spores of *B. cereus* oxidize glucose in the absence of detectable germination. Extended heat-treatment of aged spores of *B. cereus* strain T activated the systems for glucose oxidation and for endogenous respiration (Figure 9.12). Freshly harvested spores showed relatively little activity, whereas storage at $-20°C$ for 4 months or longer permitted maximal glucose oxidizing capacity after heat-treatment (Table 9.10). The total respiratory activity observed after heat-activation was similar to that observed during spore germination (Church and Halvorson, 1957; Hachisuka et al., 1956).

Murrell (1955) observed that glucose oxidation could be activated in spores of *B. subtilis* by incubating them in the presence of L-alanine. When thick spore suspensions (2×10^9 spores/ml) were employed, the concentration of L-alanine controlled the rate of glucose oxidation. In spores of *B. cereus* strain T (Murty and Halvorson, 1957), exposure to L-alanine at elevated temperatures reduced the

Table 9.10 Effect of Aging at −20°C on Glucose Oxidation by *Bacillus cereus strain T.*

Storage at −20°C (months)	Heat-Activated (65°C for 60 minutes)	Total Oxygen Uptake in 60 Minutes: Exogeneous Q_{O_2} (N)	Endogeneous Q_{O_2} (N)
0	−	0	0
0	+	6	0
1	+	6	0
4	+	29	5
24	+	33	5
48	+	30	5
48	−	0	0

SOURCE: Church and Halvorson, 1957.

temperature requirements for the activation of glucose oxidation and *p*-fluorophenylalanine inhibited the stimulation of glucose activation by L-alanine. Adenosine has also been reported to activate glucose oxidation in unheated spores of *B. cereus* strain T (Church and Halvorson, 1957).

The number of enzymes activated in dormant spores is undoubtedly large and may reflect a general unmasking of cytoplasmic proteins. Glucose oxidation, as described earlier, involves a large number of enzymes. In addition to glucose oxidation, heat-activation leads to the oxidation of gluconate, α-keto gluconate, pyruvate, and acetate (Halvorson and Church, 1957*b*). Falcone and Caraco (1958) observed transaminase activities in intact spores only after heat-activation. The activities were similar to those observed in spores germinated with L-alanine. L-Alanine dehydrogenase activity is also elevated in spores following heat-treatment (O'Connor and Halvorson, 1960).

The dormancy of spore enzymes is also evident from analysis of spore extracts. Glucose dehydrogenase from dormant spores has only 25 percent of the activity of activated spores. Heat-activation prior to rupture increases the activity by 250 percent (Halvorson and Church, 1957*b*). Similar findings have been reported for a CoA kinase (Krask, 1957) and a pyrophosphatase (Levinson et al., 1958).

One of the interesting differences between spores and vegetative cells concerns the electron transport system. The main pathway of electron transport in vegetative cells proceeds by a particulate cytochrome system while activated spores primarily utilize a soluble flavoprotein oxidase for terminal oxidation (Doi and Halvorson, 1961). These findings support the previous observations that spores of *Bacillus* differ from the vegetative cells in cytochrome content (Keilin and Hartree, 1949) and cyanide-sensitivity (Spencer and Powell, 1952; Nakada et al., 1957; Hachisuka et al., 1956).

That spores and vegetative cells differed in their electron transport systems was first suggested by Keilin and Hartree (1947) who found that spores had less than 6 percent of the cytochrome present in vegetative cells. Hachisuka and coworkers (1956) observed similar differences and found that germination of the spore resulted in increased activity of the cytochromes. Spencer and Powell (1952) found that the total flavin content, on the other hand, does not vary during germination. Nakada and co-workers (1957) observed that spores are less sensitive to cyanide than are vegetative cells and that germination is accompanied by cytochrome synthesis. The low content of cytochromes and the presence of a cyanide-resistant respiration suggested that spores utilize primarily a flavin system for respiration. This conclusion is supported by the data in Table 9.7.

The electron transport particles of vegetative cells of *B. cereus* (Doi and Halvorson, 1961) had a normal complement of cytochromes characteristic of other systems and similar to that observed in other strains of *Bacillus* (Smith, 1954). Absorption peaks at 600, 556, 550, 510–530, 440, and 426 mμ were observed in these particles which correspond to cytochrome-*a*, cytochrome-*b* type, cytochrome-*c* and the β- and Soret bands. Schaeffer (1952) observed absorption peaks at 600, 554–556, 548 and 528 mμ in *B. cereus*.

When spore particles of *Bacillus* (Doi and Halvorson, 1961) were examined spectroscopically, no cytochrome bands could be detected. Only some flavin absorption was observed in the difference spectrum of spore particles. When whole spores were examined microspectroscopically, a faint absorption was found in the cytochrome-*b* region. The activity of other spore enzymes also differs from that of vegetative cells. Succinic cytochrome-*c* reductase, for example, is completely absent in the particle fraction from spores. In addition, the spore particles contain a diaphorase which, in contrast to that from vegetative cells, cannot use ferricyanide as the electron acceptor. It appears, therefore that spores contain altered or immature electron transport particles.

Bacillus spores, on the other hand, contain four times as much soluble $NADH_2$ oxidase than is present in the vegetative cells. The soluble $NADH_2$ oxidase of spores of *B. cereus* (Doi and Halvorson, 1961) is similar to the $NADH_2$ oxidase of vegetative cells of *B. subtilis* (Lightbown and Kogut, 1959). Both enzymes are stimulated by FMN. The electron transport system for spores and vegetative cells is illustrated in Figure 9.13.

Two factors contribute to the dependence of the spore on an electron transport system mediated by $NADH_2$ oxidation. The first of these is the induction of $NADH_2$ oxidase. Szulmajster and Schaeffer (1961) observed that during the critical presporulation period there was enhanced activity of $NADH_2$ oxidase in "wild" (SP^+) strains. This increase in $NADH_2$ oxidase activity was not found in a series of asporogenous mutants (SP^-) incubated under similar conditions (Table 9.11). Transformation from sporogenous strains restored both the activity of the

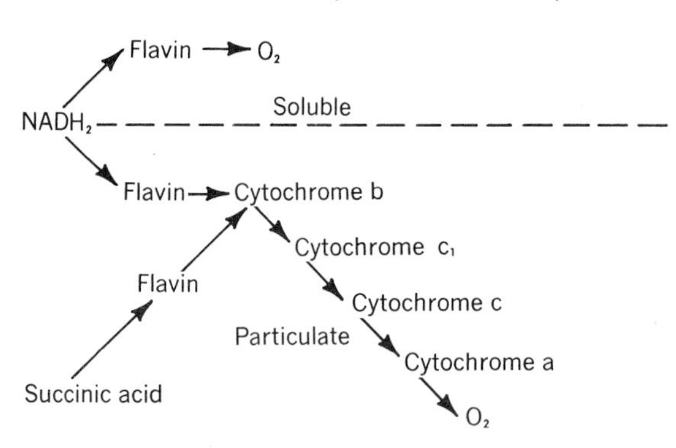

Figure 9.13 The soluble and particulate electron transport system of spores and vegetative cells. (From Halvorson et al., 1961.)

enzymes and the sporulation process. In *B. megaterium*, Tinelli (1955) observed that when sporogenous and asporogenous mutants were cultured under identical conditions, the rise in respiratory activity which normally precedes spore formation was not observed in the asporogenous culture.

Table 9.11 Comparison of Specific Enzymes Involved in the Electron Transport System

		Strains:				
Enzyme	Acceptor	Try^+ Sp^+	Try^- Sp_3^+	Try^- Sp_3^-	Try^- Sp_4^-	Try^- Sp^- (12 ultra-violet abortive)
$NADH_2$ Oxidase	Air	4.27	4.1	Tr	0.09	0.4
$NADH_2$ Dehydrogenase	Fe $(CN)_6^{\equiv}$	3.9	4.1	0.3	0.3	Tr
Diaphorase	2, 6-dichloro-phenol indophenol	13.2	14.3	2.65	1.7	3.0
$NADH_2$ Reductase	Cytochrome *C*	7200	6940	950	130	75
Cytochrome-oxidase	O_2	0	0	0	—	2000

SOURCE: Szulmajster and Schaeffer, 1961. Courtesy Academic Press, Inc., Publishers.

The second factor is the absence in the spore of functional oxidative particles which are the primary site of oxidative metabolism in the vegetative cell. The absence of cytochromes and certain enzymes from the spore particles suggests that the particles may be incomplete products of synthesis rather than derived from functional products of the vegetative cell. These particles are normally attached to the cytoplasmic membrane of the vegetative cell (Marr, 1960). The absence of functional particles in the spore is probably attributable to their origin because the inner membrane of the spore is not derived from the cytoplasmic membrane of the vegetative cell. During germination the inner membrane of the spore actually becomes part of the cell wall of the newly formed vegetative cell (Chapter 5). A new cytoplasmic membrane is formed and subsequently, functional oxidative particles appear. The lack of functional particles in the spore may, therefore, reflect the absence of the cytoplasmic membrane. It would be of interest to follow the spore particle during germination and outgrowth to see whether the newly formed vegetative cell synthesizes cytochrome on these incomplete particles or builds a completely new particulate unit. In any event, the changes in the electron transport system during sporulation, germination, and outgrowth provide an interesting problem in structure and function in cellular differentiation. A means through which terminal oxidation may be involved in dormancy is suggested in Chapter 10 (page 280).

Quantitative modifications in the pathway of glucose metabolism are also associated with sporulation and germination. Vegetative cells of *Bacillus* have been shown to contain a complete glycolytic system, together with enzymes of the hexosemonophosphate pathway (Dedonder, 1952; Keynan et al., 1954; Pepper and Costilow, 1964). In dormant and activated spores of *Bacillus*, there is some dispute over the relative function of these pathways. One approach has been to examine the mechanism of glucose metabolism in extracts of bacterial spores. An examination of some of the individual reactions demonstrated in extracts of spores of *B. cerus* strain T by enzyme purification and end-product analysis (Halvorson and Church, 1957*b*; Doi et al., 1959) are shown in Figure 9.14. Glucose

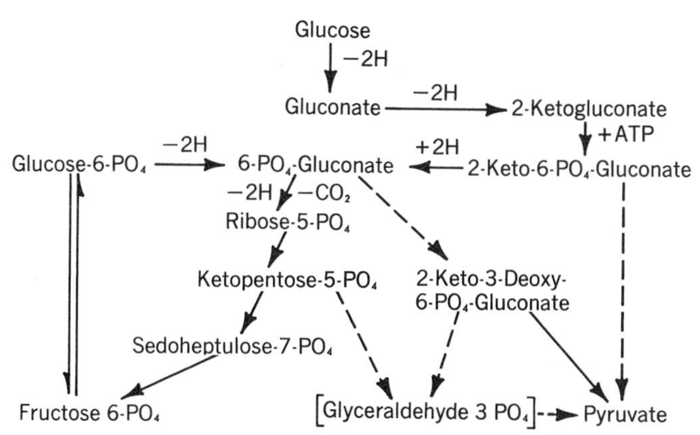

Figure 9.14 Pathways of glucose oxidation in spore extracts. Legend: ——, reactions demonstrated; - - - - -, probable reactions. (Data from Doi et al., 1959.)

is initially oxidized to gluconate by a soluble $NADH_2$-linked glucose dehydrogenase. This enzyme (Bach and Sadoff, 1960) and a heat-resistant catalase (Sadoff, 1960), were both absent in vegetative cells but appeared 3 to 4 hours prior to the development of mature spores. Gluconate is converted to 2–ketogluconate by an NAD-linked system which in turn is phosphorylated to 2–keto–6–phosphogluconate by an ATP-requiring 2–ketogluconate kinase. 2–Keto–6–phosphogluconate is reduced in part to 6–phosphogluconate by an $NADH_2$-requiring 2–keto–6–phosphogluconate reductase and in part to pyruvate by an as yet unidentified pathway. Spore extracts contain a complete functional hexosemonophosphate shunt leading to triose formation, which in turn is converted to pyruvate.

On the other hand, there is conflicting evidence concerning the presence of enzymes of the glycolytic (Embden-Meyerhoff) pathway in extracts of spores of *B. cereus* strain T. Doi et al. (1959) failed to detect enzymes involved in the formation of glucose 6–phosphate (hexokinase or phosphoglucomutase), fructose–1, 6–diphosphate (phosphohexokinase) or triose phosphate (aldolase). Goldman and Blumenthal (1964) have reported traces of hexokinase and aldolase and elevated levels of phosphohexokinase in extracts of the same organism. These findings, particularly in the case of aldolase and hexokinase, leave doubts as to the presence of *all* of the functional enzymes of glycolysis in extracts of these spores.

A second approach to the analysis of the pathways of carbohydrate metabolism in intact cells is to examine the behavior *in vivo*. From such studies, Amaha and Nakahara (1959) have suggested that spores of *B. coagulans* var. *thermoacidurans* contain a glycolytic system. Goldman and Blumenthal (1960, 1961, 1963, 1964) have attempted to measure the pathways operative in spores on the basis that via glycolysis, CO_2 is derived from C_3 and C_4 of glucose whereas by the hexosemonophosphate shunt, CO_2 is derived (by one turn of the cycle only) from C_1. Based on these considerations, Goldman and Blumenthal have attempted to evaluate the activity of these pathways during various stages of development in *B. cereus* strain T. Their conclusions are summarized in Figure 9.15. Vegetative cells operate almost exclusively via the glycolytic pathway, whereas in spores only 75 percent of the glucose was metabolized by this pathway. Completely germinated spores utilized about 20 percent of glucose via the hexosemonophosphate pathway and this dropped to 10 percent in the swollen elongated spore. By the first cell division, the percentage of glucose metabolized by this pathway was close to that found in cells in the logarithmic stage. Alternative approaches will be necessary before one can resolve contradictions from *in vivo* and *in vitro* studies. In the former case, it should be pointed out that several difficulties are encountered in the use of the radioactive CO_2 recovery from specifically labeled glucose as a measure of the participation of pathways in metabolism. These include:

1. The use of this technique *requires* knowledge of the number and type of pathways operative. For example, the Entner-Doudoroff pathway (also seen in Figure 9.14) predicts that CO_2 would be derived from C_1 and C_4 of glucose.
2. When multiple pathways are operative, the use of this technique to measure the

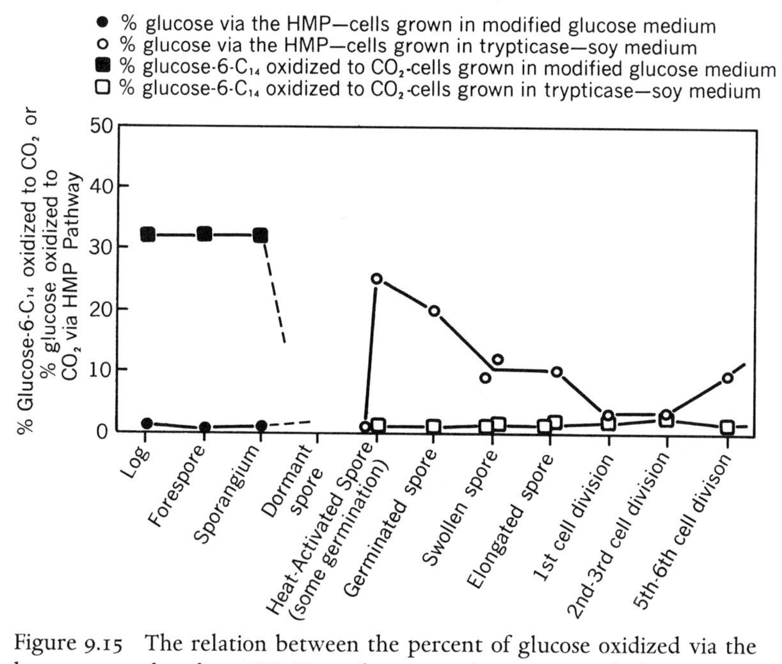

Figure 9.15 The relation between the percent of glucose oxidized via the hexosemonophosphate (HMP) pathway or the percent of glucose-6-C^{14} oxidized to CO_2 as a function of the stage of development in spores of *B. cereus*. (Data from Blumenthal, 1961.)

extent of pathways has been seriously challenged on theoretical grounds (Katz and Wood, 1963).

3. Carbon dioxide recoveries are also dependent on the pathways for oxidation of C_3 and C_2 compounds. There exists some doubt over the roles played by the tricarboxylic acid and the glyoxylic acid cycles in spores.

Dormant and germinating bacterial spores are capable of oxidatively decarboxylating pyruvate to acetate and subsequently oxidizing acetate to CO_2. Based largely on inhibitor studies and on enzymes analysis, Hanson et al. (1963*a*, *b*) concluded that the glyoxylic acid cycle predominated in vegetative cells and that the enzymes of the tricarboxylic acid cycle developed during sporulation in *B. cereus* strain T. Consistent with this, Megraw and Beers (1964) observed high levels of isocitratase and malate synthetase (key enzymes of the glyoxylic acid cycle) in rapidly growing vegetative cells but reduced levels in cultures entering sporulation or in acetate-grown cells. Goldman and Blumenthal (1964), studying $C^{14}O_2$ recovery from glucose-6-C^{14}, concluded that the terminal respiratory systems for acetate oxidation were present in vegative cells but absent in spores. The terminal respiratory activity, as well as that of fumarase (Goldman and Blumenthal, 1963), did not return to normal levels until several generations following germination. The lack of pyruvate and acetate oxidizing systems raises the question of the origin of α-keto acids for amino acid and protein biosynthesis during germination. On the other hand, Church and Halvorson (1957) reported a particulate tricarboxylic acid system for pyruvate oxidation in extracts of spores of *B. cereus* strain T.

In any event, the data indicate that quantitative and perhaps qualitative changes in the pathways of glucose metabolism occur during both sporulation and the later stages of germination.

The induction of the germination of spores by a number of nucleotides, for example, adenosine and inosine, has led to a search for enzymes active on these compounds. The observation that inosine serves as a more effective germinating agent than adenosine led to the discovery of an adenosine deaminase which converts adenosine to inosine, and a heat-stable hydrolytic nucleoside ribosidase which cleaves ribosides into the free base and ribose (Lawrence, 1955; Powell and Hunter, 1956). Krask and Fulk (1959) demonstrated that these extracts also contain a magnesium-activated ribokinase which in the presence of ATP converts ribose to ribose 5-phosphate. In addition, they have found that some of the ribose is converted to ribose inosine phosphate from adenosine, by nucleoside phosphorylase, which is converted to ribose 5-phosphate by an active phosphoribomutase. Srinivasan and Halvorson (1961) observed a phosphorylation of inosine to inosinic acid and an exchange of P^{32} into nucleotides during germination of spores of *B. cereus*.

From the preceding discussion, it is clear that spores and vegetative cells of bacteria differ in their enzyme patterns. Spores may contain certain enzymes which are unique either to the sporulation or germination process and may be absent in the vegetative cells. In addition, it is conceivable that spores contain enzymes which are passively transferred from the vegetative cell. One example of this is the penicillinase which is present in spores only from penicillin-induced vegetative cells (Harrell and Halvorson, 1955). In any event, the spores contain the genetic information and presumably the enzyme-forming systems for the enzymes present in the vegetative cells and these systems must be passed through the spore.

Fungi

A summary of the stages that ensue between the activation and germination of *Neurospora* ascospores is provided in Table 9.12. Alterations in each of four physiological markers are used as a means of defining these stages. It will be noted that, counting the dormant stage, at least five recognizably different stages exist. Undoubtedly, overlap between these exist in that certain biochemical processes are probably common to several stages. Nevertheless, these serve to define the minimum number of steps in the germination process whose origin and basis must be understood.

The definition of stages is possible in the case of other fungi as well. In the case

Table 9.12 Summary of the Stages Between Activation and Germination and the Physiological Markers Which Characterize Them in *Neurospora tetrasperma*

		Physiological Marker:			
Condition of Spores	Minutes after Activation	Q_{O_2}	R.Q.	Thermo-resistance	Deactiv-ability at 4°C or in N_2
Dormant	—	0.3	0.6	+	−
Activated:					
Stage #:					
1	0–20	0.5–4	1.2	+	+
2	30–60	4–10	1.0	−	+
3	60–150	15–30	1.0	−	−
Germinating	150	30	0.6	−	−

SOURCE: Sussman, 1961.

of conidia of *Aspergillus niger*, Yanagita (1957) and Yanagita et al. (1961) distinguished between the stages of "endogenous" and "exogenous" swelling on the basis that carbon dioxide was necessary for the latter but not for the former (Figure 9.10). Furthermore, the "exogenous" phase was temperature-sensitive, whereas the "endogenous" was not. A similar suggestion was made for spores of *Mucor rouxiana* and *M. hiemalis* by Wood-Baker (1955), except that oxygen was required for the second phase but not for the first. Differing metabolic requirements served to distinguish the early stages in the germination of conidia of *Myrothecium verrucaria* which could swell in yeast extract alone, but needed further supplements in order to progress further (Mandels and Darby, 1953).

1. *Respiratory and Other Enzymes*

As was indicated previously in this chapter, the most characteristic response of fungus spores to activation is increased respiratory capacity. Therefore, a key question is the nature of the restriction upon the metabolism of dormant cells which limits the rate of respiration. The enzymes of spores and vegetative stages have been compared in Table 9.13 in order to help explain this block.

Quantitative and qualitative differences exist in the enzyme complements of resting spores and other stages, and it can be seen that enzymes may be enriched as well as reduced in activity in spores. It seems likely that cytochrome *c* oxidase is not limiting the metabolism of the ascospores of *Neurospora*, conidia of *Glomerella cingulata*, or basidiospores of *Schizophyllum commune* (Niederpruem, 1964). In all these cases, the activity of this terminal oxidase is greater in the spores than

Table 9.13 Enzymes Found in Spores and Other Stages in the Development of Fungi[a]

Organism and Stage	Enzyme (Relative activity percent)			Reference
Enzymes Enriched in Spore				
Neurospora crassa	NAD-nucleotidase			Zalokar and Cochrane, 1956
Conidia, resting	100			
Mycelium, 6 hours	37			
Mycelium, 14 hours	1			
Mycelium, 72 hours	15			
N. tetrasperma	Cytochrome oxidase			Holton, 1960
Ascospores, resting	100			
Mycelium, 43 hours	20			
Mycelium, 68 hours	39			
Mycelium, 89 hours	21			
Glomerella cingulata	Cytochrome oxidase			Sussman and Markert, 1953
Conidia, resting	100			
Mycelium, 48 hours	53			
Mycelium, 96 hours	48			
Mycelium, 215 hours	50			
	Catalase			
Aspergillus niger	Whole cells	Disrupted cells		Bhatnagar and Krishnan, 1960*a*
Conidia, resting	72	100		
Conidia, germinating 12 hours (no germ tubes)	16	40		
Enzymes with Decreased Activity in Resting Spores				
Glomerella cingulata	Tyrosinase			Sussman and Markert, 1953
Conidia, resting	13			
Mycelium, 143 hours	32			
Mycelium, 215 hours	100			
Mycelium, 288 hours	32			
Neurospora crassa and *N. tetrasperma*	Tyrosinase	Trehalase	Invertase	Sussman et al., 1956, and Sussman, unpublished; Hill and Sussman, 1964
Ascospores, resting	0	0.88	0.7	
germinating 2 hours	—	3.20	0.9	
Conidia, resting	22	108.0	26.0	
Mycelium, 96 hours	100	80.0	18.0	
Mycelium, 648 hours	—	100.0	100.0	
N. crassa	Tryptophan synthetase	Succinic dehydrogenase		Zalokar, 1959
Conidia, resting	58	11		
Mycelium, 8 hours	73	105		
Mycelium, 30 hours	109	109		
Mycelium, 96 hours	100	100		

Table 9.13 (*Continued*)

Organism and Stage	Enzyme (Relative activity percent)			Reference
N. crassa	Aldolase	β-Galactosidase		Zalokar, 1959
Conidia, resting	31	16		
Mycelium, 8 hours	59	1		
Mycelium, 30 hours	107	4		
Mycelium, 96 hours	100	100		
Puccinia graminis tritici	Cytochrome-*c* oxidase	$NADH_2$ cytochrome-*c* reductase	Succinic cytochrome-*c* reductase	
Uredospores, resting	56	38	31	White and Ledingham, 1961
Uredospores, germinated	100	100	100	
Ustilago maydis[b]	Triose PO_4 dehydrogenase	Isocitric dehydrogenase	Malic dehydrogenase	Gottlieb and Caltrider, 1963
Teliospore, resting	15	43	19	
Teliospore, germinating				
6 hours	30	64	21	
12 hours	100	100	100	
Aspergillus niger	Aldolase	Phosphoglucomutase	Phosphohexoisomerase	Bhatnagar and Krishnan, 1960*b*
Conidia, resting	0	0	0	
Conidia, germinating (12 hours) no germ tubes	0	0	0	
Conidia, germinating (18 hours) no germ tubes	13	26	100	
Conidia and hyphae, germinating 24 hours	100	100	—	
A. niger	Pyrophosphatase	Polyphosphatase	Polyphosphate kinase	Nishi, 1960
Conidia, resting	18	21	43	
Conidia, germinating (7 hours)	100	100	100	
A. niger	Pyrophosphatase	Glycerophosphatase		Bhatnagar and Krishnan, 1960*b*
Conidia, resting	0	2		
Conidia, germinating (6 hours)	5	3		
Conidia, germinating (14 hours)	62	46		
Conidia, germinating (20 hours with germ tubes)	100	93		

Table 9.13 (*Continued*)

Organism and Stage	Enzyme (Relative activity percent)	Reference
Pencillium griseofulvum	Proteinase	Morton et al., 1960
Conidia, resting	0	
Conidia, germinating (8 hours), swollen, no germ tubes	4.6	
Conidia, germinating (12 hours), germ tubes	15	
Mycelium (20 hours), branches beginning	16	
Mycelium, (20–28 hours), rapid growth	45	
Mycelium (42 hours)	100	

[a] Relative activities were computed from the original data.
[b] In addition, considerable activity of the following enzymes was found after 12 hours but none in resting teliospores, or in those germinated for only 6 hours: transketolase, transaldolase, aconitase, fumarase.

in vegetative stages. Even in the case of the uredospores of *Puccinia graminis tritici*, where more cytochrome oxidase is found after germination, White and Ledingham (1961) have concluded that the enzyme is not limiting. Moreover, catalase is in excess in resting conidia of *Aspergillus niger*, so this oxidase seems not to be the reason for the relatively low metabolism of these spores. Although tyrosinase is lacking entirely in ascospores of *Neurospora*, or is in diminished titer in conidia of *Neurospora* and *Glomerella cingulata*, the role of this enzyme in respiratory metabolism is not established, so its significance to dormancy is uncertain. However, up to now, terminal oxidases have not been shown to play a direct role in the transition from the dormant to the vegetative state of fungus spores.

On the other hand, White and Ledingham (1961) suggest that the rate at which cytochrome *c* is reduced may be a limiting factor in the respiration of uredospores of *Puccinia graminis tritici*. In this case, germinating spores show an increase in cytochrome *c* reductase (Table 9.13). Cytochrome *c* may be increased in concentration during the germination of ascospores of *Neurospora*, according to Holton (1961). Thus, although cell-free extracts of dormant cells required the addition of exogenous cytochrome *c* for cytochrome oxidase activity to be manifested, extracts of other stages possessed an endogenous supply of the enzyme.

Differences between resting spores and other stages are to be found at the other end of the sequence of steps concerned with respiratory metabolism—that is, in glycolysis. For example, Kornfeld and Knight (1962) found that xylose reductase could not be induced in dormant spores of *Penicillium chrysogenum*, whereas abundant enzyme was formed by germinating ones. Moreover, Zalokar (1959) has shown that aldolase activity is low in conidia compared to the mycelium of *Neurospora crassa*. Also, β-galactosidase activity is lower in these conidia than in mycelium that is 96 hours old, but younger mycelium show even less of the enzyme than do the spores. In the smut *Ustilago maydis*, germination of teliospores is characterized by the appearance of key enzymes of both the hexosemonophosphate shunt and the tricarboxylic acid cycle (Table 9.14).

Table 9.14 Comparison of Specific Activities of Enzymes in Teleospores of *Ustilago maydis* at Different Phases of Germination

Enzyme	Specific Activities 0 hours	(Units/mg Protein): 6 hours	12 hours
Isocitrate dehydrogenase	0.006	0.009	0.014
Malic dehydrogenase	0.046	0.051	0.241
Triose phosphate isomerase	0.32	0.83	1.3
6-phosphogluconic dehydrogenase	0.014	—	0.027
Aconitase	0	0	160
Fumarase	0	0	240

SOURCE: Gottlieb and Caltrider, 1963.

Recently, Hill and Sussman (1964) have shown that high trehalase levels are present at all stages of the life history of *Neurospora* except in the dormant ascospore (cf. Table 9.13). Inasmuch as trehalose is the most important substrate of the germinating ascospore (Figure 9.16), it is likely that the metabolic block in these cells is associated with the metabolism of this sugar. It should be noted that lipid serves as the major endogenous substrate during dormancy and in the later stages of germination (Figure 9.17).

As was shown in Figure 9.3, as soon as activation occurs, the respiration of ascospores increases dramatically, and the R.Q. (Table 9.4) rises, suggesting that a sugar (trehalose) is being metabolized. During the first 2 hours after activation, evidence for a fermentative type of metabolism is found in the release of acetaldehyde, ethanol, lactate, and pyruvate (Sussman et al., 1956). However, after this time, these fermentation products are no longer accumulated in large amounts and the R.Q. decreases to about 0.6 again, signaling a changeover to lipid metabolism, unless an exogenous source of sugar is provided. Concomitantly, the full complement of acids of the Krebs cycle appears, suggesting that a strongly oxidative type of metabolism is evolved, in contrast to the fermentative system described in the preceding material. These suggestions are supported by the results of experiments with poisons such as fluoroacetate, which extended the time during which acetaldehyde was released, and stopped germination, presumably through interference with the condensing enzyme step in the metabolism of tricarboxylic acids. The metabolic steps in the transformation of ascospores from primarily fermentative organisms to strongly oxidizing ones based on the Krebs cycle are outlined in Figure 9.16. As Rudolph (1961) points out,

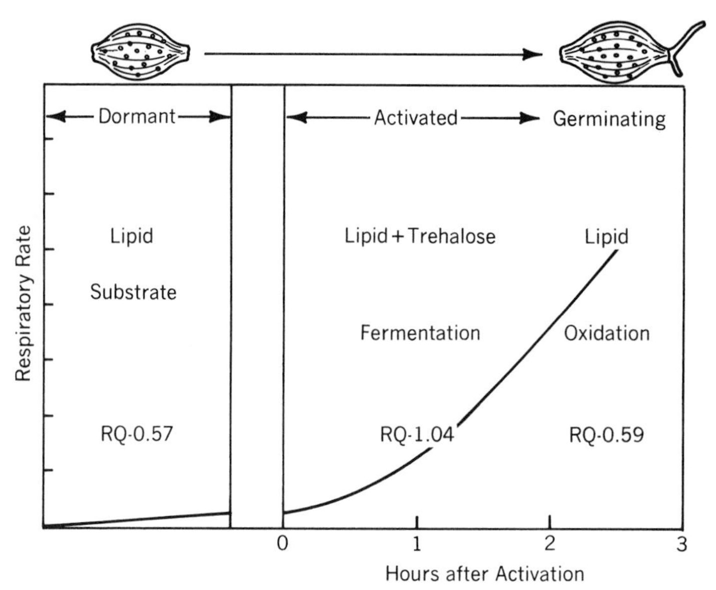

Figure 9.16 Summary outline of metabolic events during the germination of ascospores of *Neurospora*. (Sussman, 1961.)

it is still not clear whether a difference in the enzymatic pattern of the spores, or in substrates at the several stages explains these observations.

Striking parallels exist between the metabolic events described for *Neurospora* and those reported for sporangiospores of *Phycomyces blakesleeanus* by Halbsguth and Rudolph (1959) and Rudolph (1960, 1961). The spores of *Phycomyces* differ from the ascospores of *Neurospora* in requiring an exogenous energy source in addition to other metabolites. By contrast, the ascospores of *Neurospora* can germinate in distilled water and, in fact, are permeable to only a restricted group of chemicals (see Chapter 3). Nevertheless, despite these differences, many metabolic parallels exist. Thus, after a heat-shock of a few minutes at 54°C, carbon dioxide evolution is increased markedly over that of resting cells. In addition, oxygen uptake is enhanced, but less markedly than in the case of carbon dioxide. Concomitantly, acetaldehyde and ethanol production are stimulated for a period of about 30 to 50 minutes, after which their release is restricted. As in the case of *Neurospora*, fluoroacetate extends the time during which fermentation products are formed, as well as inhibiting germination. Several other inhibitors were used by Rudolph (1961) as well, with results that are consistent with the suggestion that the increased formation of pyruvate soon after activation results in the accumulation of acetaldehyde, which serves as a hydrogen acceptor, resulting in the formation of ethanol. However, a change in the pathway of terminal oxidation occurs soon afterwards (possibly induction of the Krebs cycle) so that electrons are transferred to oxygen. Such a transition from a fermentative type of metabolism to terminal oxidations based upon oxygen is very reminiscent of that which has been proposed for *Neurospora* ascospores, and argues for some generality in the mechanism. However, it should be pointed out that in neither case has the activity of the enzymes of the Krebs cycle been measured directly, so that acceptance of this model must await such data. Another instance in which a glycolytic metabolism is followed by a more aerobic type may be that of germinating spores of *Fusarium solani* (Cochrane et al., 1963*b*).

Germinating uredospores of *Puccinia graminis tritici* have been shown to synthesize chitin (Shu et al., 1954), trehalose, and other sugars and sugar alcohols (Reisener et al., 1962), and amino acids (Kastins et al., 1959). Although such spores can incorporate amino acids into proteins, they lack the ability to effect a net synthesis of amino acids or proteins (Shu et al., 1954). Other uredospores for which no net synthesis of proteins could be found included those of *Puccinia helianthi*, *P. sorghi*, and *Uromyces phaseoli* (Staples et al., 1962 and Figure 9.11), despite the ability of these spores to synthesize amino acids and sugars.

On the other hand, spores of saprophytes, including conidia of *Glomerella cingulata*, *Aspergillus niger*, and *Neurospora sitophila* have been shown to incorporate C^{14}-labeled acetate into amino acids and proteins (Staples et al., 1962). Moreover, experiments with S^{35} have revealed that germinating spores of *A. niger* form sulfur-containing amino acids from choline sulfate and at least one other compound which accumulates in resting spores (Takebe and Yanagita, 1959; Takebe, 1960). Alanine-glutamic transaminase was found by Takebe and Yanagita to be lacking in dormant spores of this fungus but to appear at the time of germination.

It has been claimed by Newburgh and Cheldelin (1958) that spores of the smut, *Tilletia caries*, differ from the vegetative mycelium in the way that glucose-1-C^{14} and glucose-3,4-C^{14} are metabolized. On the other hand, Turel and Ledingham (1959) could show no such difference with uredospores of *Melampsora lini*. However, labeling patterns alone lead to difficulties of interpretation (cf., pp. 252–253), so that these data must still be considered to be tentative.

The considerable synthetic activities of germinating spores like those of *Aspergillus niger* require the utilization of energy. Thus, as was discussed, RNA, DNA, and protein synthesis occur during the germination process, along with the synthesis of sugars and other newly formed metabolites. The source of phosphate for these syntheses in *A. niger* appears to be polyphosphates which decrease rapidly at the start of germination. Concomitantly, various nucleotides and sugar phosphates increase in the acid-soluble fraction, and ATP is the principal product derived from the polyphosphate (Nishi, 1961). Phospholipid in germinating spores decreases in parallel with the diminution in the amount of polyphosphate, and glycerophosphate appears to be its main product. These observations are supported by Nishi's (1960) previous findings that pyrophosphatase and a β-glycerophosphate-hydrolyzing enzyme (Table 9.13), as well as polyphosphatase, increase markedly early in germination. Therefore, it is likely that the primary phosphagens which serve as energy sources during the early stages of the germination of these spores are ATP and β-glycerophosphate. Polymetaphosphate has also been reported to disappear during the germination of conidia of a related organism, *A. nidulans* (Shepherd, 1957).

Some scattered observations suggest that there are cases where enzymes of similar function but different properties exist in spores and vegetative cells. This is the case for ascorbic oxidase in *Myrothecium verrucaria* in which conidia have a different form of the enzyme than hyphae (White and Smith, 1961). More recently, Solomon et al. (1964) have studied the acid and alkaline phosphatases and nonspecific esterases of *Dictyostelium discoideum*. Only three different acid phosphatases and esterases were found in the spores compared with five and seven to ten, respectively, that appeared in zymograms of migrating pseudoplasmodia and culminating stages. As for alkaline phosphatase, two bands appeared in spores, migrating pseudoplasmodia and culminating stages, but only one wider band could be seen in vegetative and aggregating myxamoebae. It is important to note the possibility that cases may be found where qualitative differences between enzymes of similar function may be found to exist in spores and vegetative stages *in the absence of significant quantitative ones*. The relevance of such changes to dormancy and germination remains to be assessed.

2. *Substrates for Germination*

The fact that spores of many fungi contain fatlike droplets which appear to coalesce when germination occurs suggested to Kordes (1923) that lipids serve as an important reserve material during that time. However, the qualitative nature of these observations, and recent data (discussed below) suggest that this question must be re-examined.

First of all, it is necessary to distinguish between those fungus spores that require an exogenous source of energy before germination can proceed, and those that do not. Among the former are the conidia of *Fusarium* which, despite the fact that they contain about 20 percent lipid, still require a carbohydrate before they will germinate (V. W. Cochrane et al., 1963*a*, *b*; J. Cochrane et al., 1963). Similarly, conidia of *Myrothecium verrucaria*, which have sufficient endogenous reserves to germinate (about 20 percent of their dry weight) still require exogenous substrates (Mandels, 1963). The R.Q. of conidia of *Aspergillus oryzae* during germination was markedly affected by the substrate in which the spores were germinated. Thus, when a basal medium containing glucose was used, the R.Q. remained close to 1.0, after falling from initially higher levels. In Koji extract the R.Q. fell to about 1.0 initially, then rose to 1.2 where it remained for several hours. However, in peptone, the R.Q. remained below 0.8, suggesting that the nature of the substrate determines the type of metabolic pattern in this case.

Similarly, starved conidia of *Cochliobolus miyabeanus* appear to utilize a variety of exogenously added sugars for their germination, along with an endogenous glucan, although no studies of respiratory metabolism and incorporation were carried out (Oku, 1960).

Among those spores that do not require exogenous substrates for germination are uredospores of rusts. For example, Shu et al. (1954) have shown that only endogenous fats and proteins furnish the substrate for germinating uredospores of *Puccinia graminis tritici.* In fact, sugars and sugar alcohols accumulate in these spores at this time (Reisener et al., 1962) although it is not yet certain that some of these are not used during germination. Flax-rust uredospores (*Melampsora lini*) also metabolize fats during germination but a shift in the R.Q. suggests that a carbohydrate also may be used as a substrate (Frear, 1960). When conidia of *Cochliobolus miyabeanus* germinate in distilled water, carbohydrate reserves are the primary substrate for germination (Oku, 1960). These disparate results may be explained in terms of the data obtained with ascospores of *Neurospora tetrasperma* by Lingappa and Sussman (1959). In these spores, lipids are utilized by

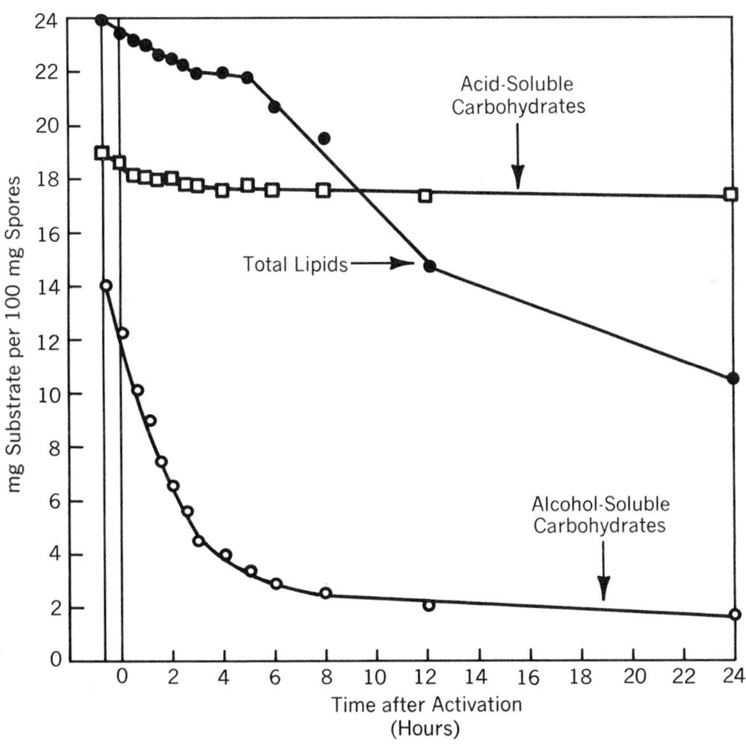

Figure 9.17 Effect of activation upon the amount of lipids and carbohydrates in ascospores of *Neurospora tetrasperma.* Ascospores were heat-activated and germination began about 2.5 hours after activation and was complete about 4 hours after. (Data of Lingappa and Sussman, 1959, courtesy *Plant Physiol.*)

dormant spores but trehalose is the major substrate of germinating ones. However, lipids continue to be used, even while the sugar is still present, and become the sole source of energy when trehalose is exhausted (Figure 9.17). Therefore, it may be that most spores require simultaneous utilization of lipids and carbohydrate, but the data are still too scattered to warrant the generalization.

General Metabolic Characteristics of Dormant Systems

A review of the metabolism of dormant spores of bacteria and fungi reveals only a few characteristics in common. The most important similarity is the low rate of respiration of dormant cells of microbes. In fact, low respiratory rates characterize diapausing insects (Lees, 1961) and dormant seeds (Klein, 1961; Mayer, 1961) as well, and so this phenomenon appears to be widespread. Therefore, questions basic to many dormant systems include the nature of the metabolic block, the mechanism of its removal, and the steps which lead to the formation of the vegetative organism.

Comparisons of the enzymatic constitution of dormant and germinating spores of bacteria have revealed that the cytochromes are absent from the former. By contrast, cytochrome oxidase and cytochrome *c* have been shown to be present in some, but not all, fungus spores, and in microcysts of *Myxococcus xanthus* (Dworkin and Niederpruem, 1964), and the restriction to respiration in these cells appears not to be due to these enzymes. A more promising explanation in some fungi, at least, may reside in the means through which reducing power is generated for terminal oxidations.

Of potential general significance in dormancy is the presence, or absence, of the Krebs cycle in fungus spores. In the case of dormant spores of *Neurospora* and *Phycomyces*, such a system appears to be lacking and it will be important to test the generality of these observations with other spores. Dormant seeds also show very little Krebs cycle activity, as judged by the performance of isolated mitochondria. Such mitochondria are increasingly active, however, as germination proceeds and Mayer (1961) proposes that activation (by thiourea) results in the faster operation of energy-releasing processes through the Krebs cycle.

As for the biochemical basis of dormant animals, it is likely that, in higher ones at least, effects upon the nervous system must be sought as the primary event in triggering development. An example of this kind is provided by diapausing insects in which evidence has accumulated to show that the brain probably is the site of activation (Lees, 1961).

Despite the uniqueness of the nervous system to animals and its probable involvement in dormancy, at least one biochemical mechanism may be common to some microbes and animals. This involves the metabolism of the sugar trehalose, whose role in the dormancy of ascospores of *Neurospora* was described above. It has been known for some time that many fungi accumulate this sugar during fruiting and that spores often are a site of accumulation. Thus, spores of the slime mold *Dictyostelium discoideum* (Clegg and Filosa, 1961), the ascomycete *Neurospora* (Sussman, 1961), basidomycete *Puccinia graminis tritici* (Reisener et al., 1962) and the imperfects *Penicillium chrysogenum* (Ballio et al., 1964) and *Myrothecium verrucaria* (Mandels, personal communication) have been shown to contain trehalose. However, it is likely that a more widespread role for this substance will be found inasmuch as it serves as the precursor of glycogen prior to pupation in several insects (Wyatt and Kalf, 1957), and in the eggs of the brine shrimp (Clegg, 1962), both of which are stages that are dormant.

The question of the degree of heterotrophy of spores, as compared with other stages, is pertinent to the data in this chapter. As was pointed out earlier, the previously held notion that bacterial endospores do not contain enzymes obviously is untenable. The data in Table 9.7 are not sufficient to decide whether bacterial spores are more heterotrophic than vegetative cells, but the situation is clearer in the fungi. Thus, the data in Table 9.13 suggest that dormant fungus spores have less enzymatic potential than germinating ones, or than the mycelium. Even when enzymatic activities are enhanced in fungus spores, they are present at other times in the life history of the organism, although reduced in activity. Further evidence on this subject is provided by Vezina and collaborators (1963) who have worked on the transformation of steroids by fungi. In typical transformations of this kind, three or more products are formed by the mycelium of the fungi which catalyze these reactions. However, only one product is formed with this same substrate in the presence of spores. Furthermore, the enzymes catalyzing steriod transformations appear to be formed in the mycelium and excluded from some spores. Finally, spores that do not contain these enzymes cannot be induced to synthesize them. The significance of the increased heterotrophy of fungus spores will be discussed in Chapter 11.

REFERENCES

Alderton, G., and N. Snell. 1963. *Biochem. Biophys. Res. Comm.* 10:139–143.

Allen, P. J. 1963. Personal communication.

Amaha, M., and T. Nakahara. 1959. *Nature* 184:1255–1256.

Aronson, A. I. 1964. *Bacteriol. Proc.* p. 96.

Bach, J. A., and H. L. Sadoff. 1960. *Bacteriol. Proc.* p. 65.

Bach, J. A., and H. L. Sadoff. 1962. *J. Bacteriol.* 83:699–707.

Balassa, G. 1963. *Biochim. Biophys. Acta* 72: 497–500.

Balassa, G., Helene Ionesco, and P. Schaeffer. 1963. *Compt. Rend. Acad. Sci. (Paris)* 257:986–988.

Ballio, A., V. Di Vittorio, and Serene Russi. 1964 *Arch. Bioch. Biophys.* 107:177–183.
Berger, J. A., and A. G. Marr. 1960. *J. Gen. Microbiol.* 22:147–157.
Bernlohr, R. W., and G. D. Novelli. 1963. *Arch. Biochem. Biophys.* 103:94–104.
Bernlohr, R. W., and C. Sievert. 1962. *Biochem. Biophys. Res. Comm.* 9:32–37.
Bhatnagar, G. M., and P. S. Krishnan. 1960*a*. *Arch. Mikrobiol.* 36:131–138.
Bhatnagar, G. M., and P. S. Krishnan. 1960*b*. *Arch. Mikrobiol.* 36:169–174.
Bhatnagar, G. M., and P. S. Krishnan. 1960*c*. *Arch. Mikrobiol.* 37:211–214.
Blumenthal, H. J. 1961. in *Spores II.* H. O. Halvorson, ed. Burgess Pub. Co., Minneapolis, pp. 120–126.
Bott, K. F., and D. G. Lundgren. 1964. *Radiation Res.* 21:195–211.
Brown, W. 1917. *Ann. Botany* 31:489–498.
Campbell, L. L. 1961. in *Spores II.* H. O. Halvorson, ed. Burgess Pub. Co., Minneapolis, pp. 195–197.
Campbell, L. L., and E. E. Sniff. 1959. *J. Bacteriol.* 77:766–770.
Church, B. D., and H. Halvorson. 1957. *J. Bacteriol.* 73:470–476.
Church, B. D., H. Halvorson, and H. O. Halvorson. 1954. *J. Bacteriol.* 68:393–399.
Clayton, C. N. 1942. *Phytopathology* 32:921–943.
Clegg, J. S. 1962. *Biol. Bull.* 123:295–301.
Clegg, J. S., and M. F. Filosa. 1961. *Nature* 192:1077–1078.
Cochrane, Jean C., V. W. Cochrane, F. G. Simon, and Jane Spaeth. 1963. *Phytopathology* 53:1155–1160.
Cochrane, V. W., S. J. Berry, F. G. Simon, J. C. Cochrane, C. B. Collins, J. A. Levy, and P. K. Holmes. 1963*a*. *Plant Physiol.* 38:533–541.
Cochrane, V. W., J. C. Cochrane, C. B. Collins, and F. G. Serafin. 1963*b*. *Am. J. Botany* 50:806–814.
Costilow, R. N. 1962. *J. Bacteriol.* 84:1268–1273.
Crook, P. G. 1952. *J. Bacteriol.* 63:193–198.
Dedonder, R. 1952. *Proc. 2nd Intern. Congr. Biochem., Paris*, p. 77.
Doi, R. H., and H. Halvorson. 1961. *J. Bacteriol.* 81:642–648.
Doi, R. H., and R. T. Igarashi. 1964. *J. Bacteriol.* 87:323–328.
Doi, R. H., H. Halvorson, and B. D. Church. 1959. *J. Bacteriol.* 77:43–54.
Dworkin, M., and D. J. Niederpruem. 1964. *J. Bacteriol.* 87:316–322.
Emerson, M. R. 1954. *Plant Physiol.* 29:418–428.
Falcone, G., and A. Caračo. 1958. *7th Intern. Congr. Microbiol.*, p. 34.
Fitz-James, P. C. 1955. *Can. J. Microbiol.* 1:502–519.
Fitz-James, P. C. 1962. *8th Intern Congr. Microbiol.*, p. 16.
Fitz-James, P. C., and I. E. Young. 1959. *J. Bacteriol.* 78:755–757.
Frear, D. S. 1960. *N. Dakota Farm Res.* 21:18–23.
Gaumann, E. A. 1950. *Principles of Plant Infection.* English Edn. Crosby Lockwood, London, 543 p.
Gerhardt, P., and S. H. Black. 1961. *J. Bacteriol.* 82:750–760.
Gibbins, L. N., and F. W. Norris. 1963. *Biochem J.* 86:67–71.
Goddard, D. R. 1935. *J. Gen. Physiol.* 19:45–60.
Goddard, D. R., and P. E. Smith. 1938. *Plant Physiol.* 24:241–264.
Goldman, M., and H. J. Blumenthal. 1960. *Biochem. Biophys. Res. Comm.* 3:164–168.
Goldman, M., and H. J. Blumenthal. 1961. *Can. J. Microbiol.* 7:677–679.
Goldman, M., and H. J. Blumenthal. 1963. *J. Bacteriol.* 86:303–311.
Goldman, M., and H. J. Blumenthal. 1964. *J. Bacteriol.* 87:377–386.
Gottlieb, D., and P. G. Caltkider. 1963. *Nature* 197:916–917.
Gould, G. W., and A. D. Hitchens. 1963. *Nature* 197:622.
Hachisuka, Y., N. Asano, M. Kaneko, and T. Kanbe. 1956. *Science* 124:174–175.
Hachisuka, Y., K. Sugai, and N. Asano. 1958. *Japan. J. Microbiol.* 2:317–325.
Halbsguth, W., and H. Rudolph. 1959. *Arch. Mikrobiol.* 32:296–308.
Halvorson, H. in *The Bacteria.* I. C. Gunsalus and R. Y. Stanier, eds., vol. 4. pp. 223–264.
Halvorson, H., and B. D. Church. 1957*a*. *Bacteriol. Rev.* 21:112–131.
Halvorson, H., and B. D. Church. 1957*b*. *J. Appl. Bacteriol.* 20:359–372.
Halvorson, H., R. O'Connor, and R. Doi. 1961. in *Cryptobiotic Stages in Biological Systems.* N. Grossowicz, S. Hestrin, and A. Keynan, eds. Elsevier, Amsterdam, N.Y., London, pp. 71–96.
Halvorson, H. O. 1958. *The Physiology of the Bacterial Spore.* Tech. Univ. of Trondheim, Norway.

HANSON, R. S., V. R. SRINIVASAN, and H. O. HALVORSON. 1963*a*. *J. Bacteriol.* 85:451–460.

HANSON, R. S., V. R. SRINIVASAN, and H. O. HALVORSON. 1963*b*. *J. Bacteriol.* 86:45–50.

HARRELL, W. K., and H. O. HALVORSON. 1955. *J Bacteriol.* 69:275–279.

HAWKER, LILIAN. 1950. *Physiology of Fungi.* Univ. of London Press, London,. 360 pp.

HENNEY, H., and R. STORCK. 1963*a*. *Science* 142:1675–1676.

HENNEY, H., and R. STORCK. 1963*b*. *J. Bacteriol.* 85:822–826.

HENNEY, H., and R. STORCK. 1965. *Proc. Nat. Acad. Sci. U.S.* (In press.)

HICKMAN, C. J. 1958. *Trans. Brit. Mycol. Soc.* 41:1–13.

HIGA, A. 1964. *Ph.D. Thesis.* Mass. Inst. Technol.

HILL, E. P., and A. S. SUSSMAN. 1964. *J. Bacteriol.* 88:1556–1566.

HITCHINS, A. D., G. W. GOULD, and A. HURST. 1963. *J. Gen. Microbiol.* 30:445–453.

HOLTON, R. W. 1960. *Plant Physiol.* 35:757–766.

HOSHINO, J. 1961. *Ann. Report Inst. Food Microbiol., Chiba Univ.* 14:53–58.

HOSHINO, J., A. NISHI, and T. YANAGITA. 1962. *J. Gen. Appl. Microbiol.* 8:233–245.

HYATT, M. T., and H. S. LEVINSON. 1957. *J. Bacteriol.* 74:87–93.

KASTINGS, R., A. J. MCGINNIS, and W. C. BROADFOOT. 1959. *Nature* 184:1943.

KEILIN, D., and E. F. HARTREE. 1947. *Antonie van Leeuwenhoek, J. Microbiol. Serol.* 12:115–128.

KEILIN, D., and E. F. HARTREE. 1949. *Nature* 164:254.

KEYNAN, A., H. J. STRECKER, and H. WALSCH. 1954. *J. Biol. Chem.* 211:883–891.

KEYNAN, A., Z. EVENCHIK, H. O. HALVORSON, and J. W. HASTINGS. 1964. *J. Bacteriol.* 88:313–318.

KATZ, J., and H. G. WOOD. 1963. *J. Biol. Chem.* 238:517–523.

KLEIN, S. 1961. in *Cryptobiotic Stages in Biological Systems.* N. Grossowicz, S. Hestrin, and A. Keynan, eds. Elsevier, Amsterdam, N.Y., London, pp. 175–190.

KOBAYASHI, Y., W. STEINBERG, A. HIGA, H. O. HALVORSON, and C. LEVINTHAL. 1965. in *Spores III.* H. O. HALVORSON, Ed., Amer. Soc. for Microbiol. pp. 200–212.

KORDES, H. 1923. *Botan. Archiv.* 3:282–311.

KORNFELD, J. M., and S. G. KNIGHT. 1962. *Mycologia* 54:407–414.

KRASK, B. J. 1957. in *Spores.* H. O. Halvorson, ed. Am. Inst. Biol. Sci., Wash. D.C., pp. 135–143.

KRASK, B. J., and G. E. FULK. 1959. *Arch. Biochem. Biophys.* 79:86–90.

LAWRENCE, N. L. 1955. *J. Bacteriol.* 70:577–582.

LAWRENCE, N. L., and H. O. HALVORSON. 1954. *J. Bacteriol.* 68:334–337.

LEE, W. H., and Z. J. ORDAL. 1963. *J. Bacteriol.* 85:207–217.

LEES, A. D. 1961. in *Cryptobiotic Stages in Biological Systems.* N. Grossowicz, S. Hestrin, and A. Keynan, eds. Elsevier, Amsterdam, N.Y., London, pp. 120–131.

LEVINSON, H. S. 1957. in *Spores.* H. O. Halvorson, ed. Am. Inst. Biol. Sci., Wash. D.C., pp. 120–135.

LEVINSON, H. S., and M. T. HYATT. 1955. *J. Bacteriol.* 70:368–374.

LEVINSON, H. S., and M. G. SEVAG. 1953. *J. Gen. Physiol.* 36:617–629.

LEVINSON, H. S., and A. S. WRIGLEY. 1960. *Science* 131:1382.

LEVINSON, H. S., J. D. SLOAN, and M. T. HYATT. 1958. *J. Bacteriol.* 75:291–299.

LEVINTHAL, C., A. KEYNAN, and A. HIGA. 1962. *Proc. Nat. Acad. Sci., U.S.* 48:1631–1638.

LEWIS, J. C., N. S. SNELL, and H. K. BURR. 1960. *Science* 132:544–545.

LIGHTBOWN, J. W., and M. KOGUT. 1959. *Biochem. J.* 73:14–15.

LINGAPPA, Y., and A. S. SUSSMAN. 1959. *Plant Physiol.* 34:466–472.

LOVETT, J. S. 1963. *J. Bacteriol.* 85:1235–1246.

LOWRY, R. J., and A. S. SUSSMAN. 1958. *Am. J. Botany* 45:397–403.

LUND, A. 1961. in *Spores II.* H. O. Halvorson, ed. Burgess Pub. Co., Minneapolis, pp. 49–58.

MANDELS, G. R. 1955. *Am. J. Botany* 42:921–929.

MANDELS, G. R. 1956. *J. Bacteriol.* 71:684–688.

MANDELS, G. R. 1963. *Ann. N.Y. Acad. Sci.* 102:724–739.

MANDELS, G. R., and R. T. DARBY. 1953. *J. Bacteriol.* 65:16–26.

MANDELS, G. R., and A. B. NORTON. 1948. *Quart. Gen. Lab. Res. Rept.* Microbiol. Ser. 11:1–50.

MANDELS, G. R., H. S. LEVINSON, and M. T. HYATT. 1956. *J. Gen. Physiol.* 39:301–309.

MARCUS, A., and J. FEELEY. 1964. *Proc. Nat. Acad. Sci., U.S.* 51:1075–1079.

MARCUS, A., and J. VELASCO. 1960. *J. Biol. Chem.* 235:563–567.

MARR, A. G. 1960. in *The Bacteria.* I. C. Gunsalus and R. Y. Stanier, eds. Academic Press, N.Y., vol. 1, pp. 443–468.

MARUYAMA, Y. 1957. *Ann. Rept. Inst. Food Microbiol.* 10:33.

MAYALL, B. H., and C. ROBINOW. 1957. *J. Appl. Bacteriol.* 20:333–341.

MAYER, A. M. 1961. in *Cryptobiotic Stages in Biological Systems.* N. Grossowicz, S. Hestrin, and A. Keynan, eds. Elsevier, Amsterdam, N.Y., London, pp. 191–201.

MEGRAW, R. E., and R. J. BEERS. 1964. *J. Bacteriol.* 87:1087–1093.

MIWATANI, T. 1957. *Japan. J. Bacteriol.* 12:283–289.

MORTENSON, L. E., and H. BEINERT. 1953. *J. Bacteriol.* 66:101–104.

MORTON, A. G., A. G. F. DICKERSON, and D. J. F. ENGLAND. 1960. *J. Exp. Botany* 11:116–128.

MURRELL, W. G. 1955. *The Bacterial Endospore.* Univ. of Sydney, Sidney, Australia.

MURRELL, W. G., and W. J. SCOTT. 1958. *Proc. 7th Intern. Congr. Microbiol., Stockholm*, p. 26.

MURTY, G. G. K., and H. O. HALVORSON. 1957. *J. Bacteriol.* 73:230–234.

NAKADA, D., A. MATSUSHIRO, M. KONDO, K. SUGA, and K. KONOSHI. 1957. *Med. J. Osaka Univ.* 7:809–818.

NAKATA, H. M. 1956. M.S. Thesis, Univ. of Illinois.

NAKATA, H. M. 1957. in *Spores.* H. O. Halvorson, ed. Am. Inst. Biol. Sci., Wash., D.C., pp. 97–103.

NEWBURGH, R. W., and V. H. CHELDELIN. 1958. *J. Bacteriol.* 76:308–311.

NIEDERPRUEM, D. J. 1964. *J. Bacteriol.* 88:210–215.

NISHI, A. 1960. *J. Biochem. (Tokyo)* 48:758–767.

NISHI, A. 1961. *J. Bacteriol.* 81:10–19.

NORRIS, J. R. 1957. *J. Gen. Microbiol.* 16:1–8.

O'CONNOR, R. J., and H. HALVORSON. 1960. *Arch. Biochem. Biophys.* 91:290–299.

O'CONNOR, R. J., and H. HALVORSON. 1961. *Biochim. Biophys. Acta* 48:47–55.

OKU, H. 1960. *Cell Physiol.* 1:231–239.

OOTA, Y., and K. TAKATA. 1959. *Physiol. Plantarum* 12:649–656.

PEPPER, R. E., and R. N. COSTILOW. 1964. *J. Bacteriol.* 87:303–310.

POWELL, J. F., and J. R. HUNTER. 1956. *Biochem. J.* 62:381–387.

POWELL, J. F., and R. E. STRANGE. 1953. *Biochem. J.* 54:205–209.

POWELL, J. F., and R. E. STRANGE. 1956. *Biochem. J.* 63:661–668.

PRASERTPHON, S. 1963. *J. Insect Pathol.* 5:318–335.

RAPER, K. B. 1956 *J. Gen. Microbiol.* 14:716–732.

RAPER, K. B., and M. S. QUINLAN. 1958. *J. Gen. Microbiol.* 18:16–32.

REISENER, H. J., H. R. GOLDSCHMID, G. A. LEDINGHAM, and A. S. PERLIN. 1962. *Can. J. Biochem. Physiol.* 40:1248–1251.

RICHMOND, M. H. 1959. *Biochim. Biophys. Acta* 33:92–101.

RIEMANN, H. 1963. Ph.D. Thesis, Copenhagen.

RODE, L. J., and J. W. FOSTER. 1960. *Proc. Nat. Acad. Sci. U.S.* 46:118–128.

RODE, L. J., and J. W. FOSTER. 1961. *J. Bacteriol.* 81:768–779.

ROSS, K. F. A., and E. BILLING. 1957. *J. Gen. Microbiol.* 16:418–425.

RUDOLPH, H. 1960. *Planta* 55:424–437.

RUDOLPH, H. 1961. *Planta* 57:284–312.

RUEHLE, G. L. A. 1923. *J. Bacteriol.* 8:487–493.

SADOFF, H. L. 1960. *Bacteriol. Proc.*, p. 65.

SADOFF, H. L. 1961. in *Spores.* H. O. Halvorson, ed. Burgess Pub. Co., Minneapolis, pp. 180–194.

SALTON, M. R. J. 1956. in *Bacterial Anatomy.* 6th Symp. Soc. Gen. Microbiol., E. T. C. Spooner and B. A. D. Stocker, eds. Cambridge Univ. Press, London, pp. 81–110.

SCHAEFFER, P. 1952. *Biochim. Biophys. Acta* 9:261–270.

SHEPHERD, C. J. 1957. *J. Gen. Microbiol.* 16:i.

SHU, P., K. G. TANNER, and G. A. LEDINGHAM. 1954. *Can. J. Botany* 32:16–23.

SHU, P., A. C. NEISH, and G. A. LEDINGHAM. 1956. *Can. J. Microbiol.* 2:559–563.

SIMMONS, R. J., and R. N. COSTILOW. 1962. *J. Bacteriol.* 84:1274–1281.

SMITH, A. G., and P. D. ELLNER. 1957. *J. Bacteriol.* 73:1–7.

SMITH, L. 1954. *Bacteriol. Rev.* 18:106.

SNOKE, J. E. 1964. *Biochem. Biophys. Res. Comm.* 14:571–574.

SOLOMON, ELDRA P., E. M. JOHNSON, and J. H. GREGG. 1964. *Devel. Biol.* 9:314–326.

SPENCER, R. E. J., and J. F. POWELL. 1952. *Biochem. J.* 51:239–245.

SRINIVASAN, V. R., and H. O. HALVORSON. 1961. *Biochem. Biophys. Res. Comm.* 4:409–413.

STAPLES, R. C., RIKSH SYAMANANDA, VIVIAN KAO, and R. J. BLOCK. 1962. *Contrib. Boyce Thompson Inst.* 21:345–362.

STEINBERG, W., H. O. HALVORSON, A. KEYNAN, and E. WEINBERG. 1965. *Nature.* (In press.)

STEWART, B. T., and H. O. HALVORSON. 1953. *J. Bacteriol.* 65:160–166.

STEWART, B. T., and H. O. HALVORSON. 1954. *Arch. Biochem. Biophys.* 49:168–178.
STRANGE, R. E., and F. A. DARK. 1957. *J. Gen. Microbiol.* 17:525–537.
SUSSMAN, A. S. 1953. *Am. J. Botany* 40:401–404.
SUSSMAN, A. S. 1954. *Mycologia* 46:143–150.
SUSSMAN, A. S. 1961. *Quart Rev. Biol.* 36:109–116.
SUSSMAN, A. S., and C. L. MARKERT. 1953. *Arch. Biochem. Biophys.* 45:31–40.
SUSSMAN, A. S., J. R. DISTLER, and J. S. KRAKOW. 1956. *Plant Physiol.* 31:126–135.
SZULMAJSTER, J., and P. SCHAEFFER. 1961. *Biochem. Biophys. Res. Comm.* 6:217–220.
TAKEBE, I. 1960. *J. Gen. Appl. Microbiol.* 6: 83–89.
TAKEBE, I., and T. YANAGITA. 1959. *Plant and Cell Physiol.* 1:17–28.
TERUI, G., and T. MOCHIZUKI. 1955. *Tech. Rept. Osaka Univ.* 5:219–227.
TINELLI, R. 1955. *Ann. Inst. Pasteur* 88:364–375.
TUREL, F. L. M., and G. A. LEDINGHAM. 1959 *Can. J. Microbiol.* 5:537–545.
DEL VALLE, M. R., and A. I. ARONSON. 1962. *Biochem. Biophys. Res. Comm.* 9:421–425.
VANTERPOOL, T. C. 1959. *Can. J. Botany* 37:169–172.
VAN DEN HOOF, A., and S. ANINGA. 1956. *Antonie van Leeuwenhoek, J. Microbiol. Serol.* 22:327–330.
VEZINA, C., S. N. SEHGAL, and K. SINGH. 1953. *Appl. Microbiol.* 11:50–57.
VINTER, V. 1959. *Nature* 183:998–999.
VINTER, V. 1960. *Folia Microbiol. (Prague)* 5:217–230.
VINTER, V. 1961. in *Spores II.* H. O. Halvorson, ed. Burgess Pub. Co., Minneapolis, pp. 127–141.
VINTER, V. 1962. *Folia Microbiol.* 7:115–120.
VINTER, V. 1965. in *Spores III.* H. O. HALVORSON, Ed. *Amer. Soc. for Microbiology.* Ann Arbor, pp. 25–37.
WAKE, R. G. 1963. *Biochem. Biophys. Res. Comm.* 13:67–70.
WARTH, A. D., D. F. OHYE, and W. G. MURRELL. 1963. *J. Cell Biol.* 16:593–609.
WELSCH, M. 1958. *J. Gen. Microbiol.* 18:491–497.
WHITE, G. A., and G. A. LEDINGHAM. 1961. *Can. J. Botany* 39:1131–1148.
WHITE, G., and F. G. SMITH. 1961. *Nature* 190:187–189.
WIDRA, A. 1956. *J. Bacteriol.* 71:689–702.
WOESE, C. R. 1961. in *Spores II.* H. O. Halvorson, ed. Burgess Pub. Co., Minneapolis, pp. 59–69.
WOESE, C. R., and J. R. FORRO. 1960. *J. Bacteriol.* 80:811–817.
WOESE, C. R., R. LANGRIDGE, and H. J. MOROWITZ. 1960. *J. Bacteriol.* 79:777–782.
WOOD-BAKER, AUDREY. 1955. *Trans. Brit. Mycol. Soc.* 38:291–297.
WORK, E. 1959. *Ann. Inst. Pasteur* 96:468–480.
WYATT, G. R., and G. F. KALF. 1957. *J. Gen. Physiol.* 40:833–847.
WYSS, O., M. NEUMANN, and M. D. SOCOLOFSKY. 1961. *J. Biophys. Biochem. Cytol.* 10:555–565.
YANAGITA, T. 1957. *Arch. Mikrobiol.* 26:329–344.
YANAGITA, T., I. TAKEBE, A. NISHI, and N. SHIMIZU. 1961. *Ann. Rept. Inst. Food Microbiol. Chiba Univ.* 14:47–48.
YOSHIKAWA, H., and N. SUEOKA. 1963. *Proc. Nat. Acad. Sci., U.S.* 49:559–564.
YOUNG, E. 1959. *Can. J. Microbiol.* 5:197–202.
ZALOKAR, M. 1959. *Nature* 183:1330.
ZALOKAR, M., and V. W. COCHRANE. 1956. *Am. J. Botany* 43:107–110.

CHAPTER 10

Mechanisms of Dormancy

THE DEVELOPMENT of the dormant state results from a morphological change in vegetative growth involving structural and chemical changes in the composition of the cell. The dormant organism can remain viable for prolonged periods under severe environmental conditions and when activated and exposed to appropriate conditions, will rapidly initiate germination. Germination is probably one of the best examples of trigger mechanisms known in biology.

The following questions can be raised concerning the dormant state, based upon the stages that are to be considered:

1. What is the mechanism through which dormancy is established and maintained?
2. What is the nature of the activation process?
3. What is the sequence of events involved in germination and what are the determinants of these?

It may be important to note that probably no one mechanism could regulate all the above phenomena described above. As will be demonstrated, the initial steps in germination may differ, depending upon the nature of the germinating stimulant, the organism under examination, and the prior history of the sporulation process. Also, the degree of dormancy for a given spore preparation depends upon the germination stimulant employed (Keynan et al., 1961). This concept of dormancy is, therefore, not a general one characterizing the state of a given spore suspension, but is dependent on the germination stimulant employed.

Mechanisms of Establishment and Maintenance of Dormancy

Hints as to the mechanism through which dormancy is established may be obtained from the data in Chapter 7 which reveal the means through which it is disrupted. The varied nature of these treatments suggests that there may be different mechanisms involved and some of these possibilities will be discussed in the framework of the types of dormancy described previously (Chapters 2 and 9).

CONSTITUTIVE DORMANCY

Innate properties of the cell determine this type of dormancy. Therefore, all restraints upon development which originate within the spores themselves are included in this category. This definition differs from that used for "rest" by workers in the field of seed germination in that permeability barriers are included in the scope of constitutive dormancy. The several types of constitutive dormancy will be discussed in detail in the following sections.

Permeability

A classic explanation of dormancy has been that a permeability barrier must be overcome before germination can be induced. Some of the observations that have lent credence to this suggestion include those of Brierley (1917), with ascospores of *Onygena equina*, Gwynne-Vaughan and Williamson (1933) with ascospores of *Ascophanus* and Stüben (1939) with resistant sporangia of *Blastocladiella stubenii*. In each of these cases it was shown that a dormant period was circumvented, or markedly curtailed, when resting stages were produced under conditions that resulted in the formation of thin-walled spores. Furthermore, Blackwell (1935) and McKay (1939) drew attention to the fact that the oospores of *Peronospora schleideni* seem to germinate only after much of the thick outer wall has been autodigested. Also, the "cracking" of the outer wall of the sporangia of *Allomyces* (Machlis and Ossia, 1953) and of *Blastocladiella* (Cantino, 1951) must precede germination of these organs. However, the differences in the permeability of thin and thick-walled spores, or of "cracked" and "uncracked" sporangia, were not investigated so that the correlation is still incomplete.

This question was studied in some detail in ascospores of *Neurospora tetrasperma* and the first possibility investigated was that permeability to water was restricted in the dormant ascospore and that activation was accomplished by a change which permitted water to enter or leave. That this hypothesis is not tenable was shown by experiments in which ascospores were suspended in concentrated glycerol solutions. Under these conditions, even dormant cells quickly become shrunken and an air bubble appeared, suggesting that water can leave the cell freely (Sussman and Lowry, unpublished). The reciprocal experiment was also performed in which it was shown that the cells that had been dehydrated in glycerol would regain their turgor when resuspended in water. Furthermore, it was established that the cells were completely germinable, even after being dehydrated and rehydrated so that the ready exit and entrance of water occurred while the cells were alive. This is somewhat different from the situation in *Erysiphe graminis* discussed by Yarwood (1950) for, in this case, only a restricted amount of water is lost before germination. However, the inability of these spores to germinate on the host does not seem to be related to the permeability to water but rather, to the presence of an inhibitory principle that restrains development (Brodie and Jones, 1946).

Inasmuch as ascospores of *Neurospora tetrasperma* can germinate in deionized water (Sussman, 1954), it is unlikely that changes in permeability to dissolved substances are involved in their dormancy. Nevertheless, experiments did show that distinct changes do occur at about 150 minutes after the spores are activated. Thus, it is only after this time that Ca^{++} and Na^{+} ions are released from the cell and EDTA becomes toxic. Furthermore, other substances, including glucose, pyruvate, cysteine, and toxic cations do not appear to penetrate the cell until that same time (Sussman et al., 1958; Lowry et al., 1957). These results show that permeability differences between dormant and activated ascospores of *Neurospora* do occur but appear to be secondary in that they follow, rather than induce, the initial steps in the activation process.

Conidiospores of *Phycomyces blakesleeanus* which have been activated by acetate have been shown by Borchert (1962) to undergo a drastic change in permeability to heavy metals. This is in contrast to heat-activated conidiospores, which change only after an hour following treatment. However, the changes in the permeability of these spores to glucose, phosphate, or other metabolites were not studied, so the physiological significance of these observations remains in question.

Other observations have suggested that alteration of the cell wall is a prerequisite for germination in some species. As long ago as 1871, Janczewski suggested this possibility as a result of his work which showed that ascospores of *Ascobolus furfuraceus* germinated after passage through the mucous membranes of the stomach of living animals. Such treatment resulted in the dissolution of the violet exosporium, as well as in several changes in the brown inner wall. That the passage of certain basidiospores through the digestive tract of slugs aids germination was shown by Voglino (1895) while deBary (1884, 1887) reported that ascospores of *Onygena cervina* required passage through an owl, and hair as a substrate, in order to germinate. Peptic enzymes were reported to facilitate the germination of ascospores of *Onygena equina* (Ward, 1899; Brierley, 1917) although the latter author pointed out that germination would occur even in the absence of such treatment if the spores were stored for 9 months. The spores of *Coprinus sterquilinus* were germinated successfully after treatment with saliva, gastric juice, pancreatic juice, and extract of horse dung, but it is probable that the last of these materials was sufficient in itself (Baden, 1915). Although none of the enzymes tested by Lowry et al. (1957) induced the germination of ascospores of *Neurospora tetrasperma*, lysozyme increased their sensitivity to furfural, one of the chemicals that does accomplish their activation. For example, after 8 hours of treatment with this enzyme, only 8 percent germination was obtained in $1 \times 10^{-3}M$ furfural, compared with 80 percent in the control. An effect of lysozyme upon the spore surface was clearly indicated but, as in all the other cases discussed, no definitive evidence has been adduced to relate the breaking of dormancy to a change in permeability.

This conclusion appears to hold for bacterial spores as well. Gerhardt and Black (1961) have studied this question most extensively and have concluded that dormant spores of *Bacillus cereus* strain T are not selectively permeable to the chemicals which induce germination, such as glucose and L-alanine. Thus, trioses, pentoses, hexoses, and oligosaccharides which do not activate showed similar space values (R^w) for uptake. The rate of uptake of glucose, alanine, and adenosine was unaffected by mild heating, or by presentation in combination instead of singly. Germination does result in changes in the permeability of bacterial spores but these do not appear to be associated with the breaking of dormancy.

Anhydrobiosis

Although anhydrobiosis has been one of the most popular mechanisms invoked to explain dormancy in bacteria in recent years, it is increasingly evident that the majority, if not all, of the spore volume is permeable to water (Black et al., 1960; Murrell and Scott, 1959; Murrell, 1961). Lewis et al. (1960) have suggested that the cortex may be a compressible structure which when ionically bonded (for example, with calcium) may reversibly contract (cf. Chapter 9).

As far as fungi are concerned, anhydrobiosis has not been used very often, if at all, to explain dormancy. The work of Sussman and Lowry which has been discussed would tend to eliminate this possibility in *Neurospora* ascospores at least. In this case, it was shown that water can enter or leave dormant ascospores unrestrictedly. It is worth noting that the spores of *Erysiphe polygoni* and of related organisms require very low humidities to germinate (Brodie and Neufeld,

1942). In this case, hydration may *prevent* development, instead of fostering it, as the anhydrous core and related theories would require. Therefore, it is reasonable to conclude that there is little evidence to support the concept that anhydrobiosis is the determinant of dormancy. Rather, dehydration probably is one of the structural features of spores which enhances survivability and may have been selected for on that basis.

Self-Inhibitors of Germination

The fact that high concentrations of certain spores germinate less well than low concentration has led to the suggestion that self-inhibitors are present in these organisms. As early as 1910, Edgerton had observed that when more than 12–15 conidia of *Colletotrichum lindemuthianum* were used per drop of inoculum, the germination percentage was drastically reduced. Wallace and collaborators (1911) noted that crowding has a deleterious effect upon conidia of *Sclerotinia fructigena* and that an inhibitory factor could be found in the water in which the spores had germinated. That strong self-inhibition is shown by conidia of *Botrytis cinerea*, which could be reversed by organic acids, was shown by Brown (1922). Other organisms in which similar effects of crowding have been reported include *Tilletia tritici* (Riehm, 1923), *Diaporthe sojae* (Lehman, 1923), *Botrytis allii*, and *Cephalosporium roseum* (McCallan, 1930), *Gloeosporium kawakami* (Yoshii, 1933), *Coccomyces hiemalis* (Keitt et al., 1937), *Neurospora crassa* (Ryan, 1948), *Fusarium caeruleum* (Boyd, 1952), *Erysiphe graminis* (Domsch, 1954), *Glomerella cingulata* (Richardson and Thorn, 1962), and *Peronospora manshurica* (Pederson, 1961; Dunleavy and Snyder, 1963). In the latter case, both the conidia and oospores form inhibitors which may be identical (Dunleavy and Snyder, 1963).

Rusts have provided some of the most detailed information on self-inhibitors. Thus, Ezekiel (1930) first reported this phenomenon in uredospores of *Puccinia graminis trictici*, followed by Allen (1955), Yarwood (1956), and Van Sumere et al. (1957). Similar observations have been made on uredospores of *Uromyces phaseoli* (Wilson, 1958), and *Puccinia coronata* (Irvine, 1963).

Observations of other kinds have led to similar conclusions. For example, spores of several myxomycetes do not germinate within the sporangium on agar plates, even under high humidities. However, if any of three species of *Didymium* were grown with a certain bacterium (possibly a mixed culture) as the substrate, the spores germinated *in situ* under the same conditions (von Stosch, 1935).

Bacterial spores show similar effects according to Halvorson (1959). Working with spores of *Bacillus cereus* he found that when 10^8 spores per milliliter were suspended in 10 percent skimmed milk solution, only 10 percent germination occurred. When 10^6 spores per milliliter were used, 90 percent germinated. On the other hand, Halvorson cites the case of *B. megaterium* which germinates more completely in higher concentrations of spores.

1. *Chemical Nature of Self-Inhibitors.* Allen (1955) was the first to study the properties of the inhibitory materials and he was able to demonstrate that the germination of uredospores of *Puccinia graminis tritici* was inhibited across an air gap by emanations from actively metabolizing spores. Floating these *en masse* aerobically for 8–24 hours precludes such inhibition. The water in which the spores have been floated contains the inhibitor but it does not accumulate anaerobically. The possibility that carbon dioxide is the inhibitor has been ruled out in this case but must be considered a possibility in other instances where this gas prevents germination in low concentrations (Stock, 1931; Magie, 1935).

A similar inhibitor has been described by Forsyth (1955). It was found that viable uredospores would not germinate in closed Warburg vessels but that a high percentage would do so in open containers. The effect of the inhibitor could be overcome by the use of a large volume of water, relative to the weight of spores, by placing a silver nitrate solution in the center well or by the introduction of acetone or ammonia vapor into the atmosphere of the flask. A parallel between the inhibitory activity of trimethylethylene and that of the natural inhibitor was found and similar means of counteracting their inhibitory effects were noted. The possibility that trimethylethylene is, in fact, the natural inhibitor was strengthened by the close similarity of their absorption spectra in acetone. Cyclohexene inhibits germ tube growth also but shows formative effects as well. This fact, taken together with an absorption spectrum that does not resemble that of the natural inhibitor, would appear to eliminate this substance as the self-inhibitor. Trimethylamine has been isolated from spores of *Tilletia tritici* and shown to inhibit germination in low concentrations (Ettel and Halbsguth, 1963). These workers suggest that this substance is the endogenous inhibitor of smut spores.

Nonvolatile inhibitors which can be isolated from unredospores of *Puccinia graminis tritici* have been described by Van Sumere et al. (1957). Among those that were inhibitory at concentrations lower than 400 μg/ml were *p*-hydroxybenzoic acid, ferulic acid, vanillic acid, and protocatechuic acid. Of these, only ferulic acid inhibited at all concentrations down to 1 μg/ml so that it may have a physiological role of significance *in vivo*. Other nonvolatile inhibitors have been described by Wilson (1958) for uredospores of *Uromyces phaseoli* in that glutamic and aspartic acids were reported to inhibit germination. However, Bell (1960) disputed this claim and reported that neutralized glutamic, aspartic, and malic acids did not inhibit uredospore germination, even at concentrations of 1000 μg/ml, whereas the native inhibitor was active at 2 μg/ml.

In the higher plants, self-inhibitors of seed germination have been found to be very widespread. Reviews of this subject include those of Evenari (1949) and Koller et al. (1962). These inhibitors are predominantly phenolic acids, their derivatives, and glycosides.

Another organism in which a self-inhibitor has been found is *Erysiphe graminis* (Domsch, 1954). The germination of conidia was inhibited by a factor that was obtained in the medium in which freshly harvested spores were suspended. It was also shown that this substance is probably not carbon dioxide and that it may have reducing groups, but otherwise its properties are unknown.

The germination of the endospores of *Bacillus subtilis* strain *globigii* may be influenced by a self-inhibitor which is a competitor of L-alanine. This self-inhibitor was not D-alanine (from action of alanine racemase), DL-serine, L-tyrosine, DPA, lactate, or pyruvate, all of which can inhibit germination (Stedman et al., 1956). However, recent work suggests that D-alanine is the inhibitor and is formed from the L-alanine used in the germination medium (Fey et al., 1964). It is possible that the oxidative breakdown products of unsaturated fats, which inhibit several species of aerobic and anaerobic spore-formers, serve as self-inhibitors, according to Roth and Halvorson (1952). This function has often been attributed to DPA itself. This view was strengthened by the findings of Young (1959) that DPA could form complexes of DPA-calcium-amino acids with a variety of amino acids and peptides. Such complexes may serve to mask enzymes of the spores, but such complexes must be specific inasmuch as several enzymes are neither inactivated nor protected against heat-inactivation by DPA (Powell, 1957). On the other hand, the soluble $NADH_2$ oxidase of spores is protected against heat-inactivation by DPA (Doi and Halvorson, 1961) and invertase is protected against irradiation damage by this substance (Braams, 1960). From studies on the release of DPA from spores (Berger and Marr, 1960; Rode and Foster, 1960*b*), and the relationship between DPA and heat-resistance (Church and Halvorson, 1959; Black et al., 1960), it appears that several forms or states of DPA may exist in spores.

2. *Relation of Self-Inhibitors to Activation Treatments.* These facts may help to explain the action of substances that induce germination. Thus, Allen (1955) showed that coumarin, dinitrophenol and 2-methyl-1, 4-naphthoquinone enhanced the germination of uredospores of *Puccinia graminis tritici* by reversing the effect of the volatile self-inhibitor discussed above. Although the mechanism of this reversal is unclear, Allen has shown that it is unlikely that a dinitrophenol-inhibitor complex is formed which prevents access of the inhibitor to the spores. Other data that might be explained by the presence of an inhibitor of this kind include the cases where paraffin or wax stimulates germination. This occurs with spores of *Phytophthora infestans* (Uppal, 1924), uredospores of *Puccinia coronata* (Melhus and Durrell, 1919), and teliospores of *P. helianthi* (Bailey, 1923). The latter author suggested that these materials might be effective because they absorbed a volatile inhibitor, thereby permitting germination to occur. It is significant that this treatment was required only when hanging-drop cultures

were used, whereas under conditions of free aeration, germination proceeded without it.

In bacteria, Harrell and Mantini (1957) observed a release of DPA during the heat-activation of spores of *Bacillus cereus* strain T. The hypothesis is therefore proposed that germination ensues only after the endogenous DPA content is first reduced to a critical threshold. The suggestion that calcium DPA complexes with amino acids and peptides (Young, 1959) and the numerous suggestions that dormancy is maintained by endogenous levels of inhibitors (Stedman et al., 1956) could be easily explained on the basis of a critical DPA threshold hypothesis. This was shown to be unlikely by the observation that in spore stocks with varying contents of DPA there was no relationship between the amount of DPA and germination (Keynan et al., 1961). In all cases, optimal germination was related to about a 10 percent loss of DPA. It is possible, however, that several reservoirs of DPA exist, only a minor fraction of which controls dormancy. Before such a possibility can be investigated, more information on the state of spore DPA will be necessary.

The presence of self-activators (Chapter 7) raises the question of the interaction between different chemicals secreted by the same cell. This is particularly the case for uredospores of rusts in which self-inhibitors have been described, as well as substances released by the cell which stimulate germination. Whether the latter operate by competing with the self-inhibitor directly, by preventing its synthesis or release, or by another means, is not known.

Metabolic Changes

1. *Bacteria.* As was outlined in Chapter 7, a wide variety of agents can act to trigger and germinate bacterial endospores. The success of these is undoubtedly dependent upon the physiological competence of the activated spore.

At least three types of germination have been described in bacterial spores. These include *physiological germination* in response to metabolizable nutrients, *chemical germination* in which the germination stimulant does not appear to be metabolized (metals, surface-active agents, or chelating agents), and *mechanical germination* in response to various mechanical treatments. In all three cases, the physiological changes and structural alterations normally occurring during germination are observed, presumably leading to the final germinated spore in each case. Although the final result of germination by these methods may be the same, the evidence suggests that the initial event, or events, in the triggering and germination process may differ. We shall, therefore, treat the known mechanisms for these three separately.

Physiological Germination. The evidence that germination in response to nutrients involves physiological reactions has been previously discussed in Chapters 6 and 9. The enzymatic nature of germination can be inferred from a number of considerations. (a) Germination agents are usually normal metabolites and in a number of cases disappear during germination. (b) Stereospecific binding sites can be recognized for germination agents which are subject to competitive inhibition. (c) The temperature-dependence of germination is that expected of an enzymatic reaction. (d) Germination can be blocked by a number of metabolic poisons.

Attempts to understand the mechanism of germination have been directed at the recognition of the primary reaction and the metabolic reactions essential to germination. This approach has led primarily in *Bacillus cereus* (Halvorson and Church, 1957; Doi et al., 1959) to a characterization of the germination agents. The common feature of the germination stimulants appears to be their metabolism rather than their structural relationships, as will be discussed in following material.

Products of hexose metabolism (pyruvate and its normal degradation products) can act as germination agents (Chapter 7). Since these early experiments of Knaysi (1945, 1948), glucose has become probably the second most commonly used germination stimulant after L-alanine. Wynne et al. (1954) found that five *Clostridium* strains readily germinate in glucose-phosphate medium, and that the germination is sensitive to the presence of oxygen. Although glucose has been reported as a stimulant for a number of aerobic bacilli (Church et al., 1954), the most commonly examined case is the germination of spores of *B. megaterium*. Spores of this organism readily germinate in glucose solutions (Powell, 1951; Levinson and Sevag, 1953; Church et al., 1954). The rate of germination is significantly stimulated by prior heat-treatment of the spores (Hyatt and Levinson, 1961). In other *Bacillus* species, the role of glucose is less clear. In *B. subtilis* (Hachisuka et al., 1954), glucose is an effective germination stimulant when used in combination with a variety of amino acids. In the absence of glucose, only about 40 percent germination was observed in the presence of amino acids alone (Hachisuka et al., 1955). Heiligman et al. (1956) reported similar results for spores of *B. coagulans*, *B. globigii*, and the anaerobic spore former, PA 3679. In *B. cereus*, glucose-induced germination was dependent upon high concentrations of glucose and was stimulated by prior heat-activation (Halvorson and Church, 1957). Wolf (1961), however, was unable to germinate spores of *B. cereus* in glucose, and similar results were observed for *B. licheniformis*.

The findings on carbohydrate-induced germination have led to the examination of the metabolism of germination agents by activated spores and extracts of activated spores. A summary of some of the individual reactions demonstrated in extracts by enzyme purification and end-product analysis is given in Figure 10.1 and discussed in Chapter 9. The compounds in large letters are primary germination agents and those underlined are less effective ones. In extracts, glucose is initially oxidized to gluconate by a soluble NAD-linked glucose

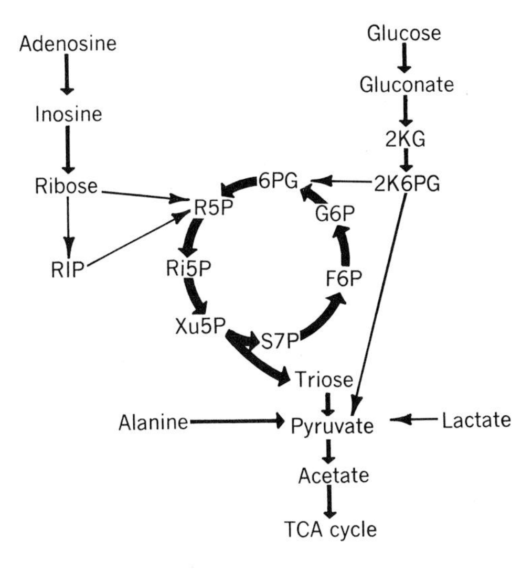

Figure 10.1 The pathway of glucose oxidation in *B. cereus* strain T spores. (From Halvorson et al., 1961.)

dehydrogenase. Gluconate is converted to 2-ketogluconate by a NADP-linked system which is in turn phosphorylated to 2-keto-6-phosphogluconate by an ATP-requiring 2-ketogluconate kinase. 2-Keto-6-phosphogluconate is reduced in part to 6-phosphogluconate by a $NADH_2$-requiring 2-keto-6-phosphogluconate reductase and in part to pyruvate by an as yet unidentified pathway. Spore extracts contain a complete functional hexosemonophosphate shunt leading to triose formation, which is in turn converted to pyruvate. Pyruvate is oxidatively decarboxylated to acetate which is then oxidized to carbon dioxide by a terminal respiratory system. Glucose, gluconate, 2-ketogluconate, pyruvate, acetate, ribose 5-phosphate and 6-phosphogluconate are all germination agents. Evidence for glycolytic activity in dormant and activated spores is contradictory (see Chapter 9).

Since Hills (1949) observed that the active germination stimulant present in yeast extract could be replaced by adenosine, considerable attention has been directed to this compound as a germination agent. Adenosine has been reported as a stimulant for most aerobic spores; exceptions have been recorded for *B. globigii* (Church et al., 1954) and for *B. subtilis* (Powell, 1957). Strain differences exist in the adenosine response. For example, Powell (1957) observed in one strain of *B. cereus* that adenosine was a stimulatory agent, whereas in another an amino acid was also required. Church (1954) found in spores of *B. cereus* strain T that elevated levels of adenosine spared the requirements for L-alanine. In this same organism adenosine requirements could be spared by xanthine, guanosine, or inosine (Lawrence, 1955). Inosine was found to be a more effective germination stimulant than adenosine for spores of *B. cereus* and *B. anthracis* (Powell and Hunter, 1955). When the spores were heat-activated for 30 minutes at 60°C, the response to adenosine was increased to that of the inosine level. These findings led to the discovery of adenosine deaminase activity in spores. This enzyme converts adenosine to inosine which is hydrolyzed by nucleoside ribosidase to the free base and ribose (Powell and Hunter, 1956; Lawrence, 1955). Ribokinase in the presence of ATP converts ribose to ribose 5-phosphate. Some of the ribose is converted to ribose 1-phosphate from adenosine by nucleoside phosphorylase which is converted to ribose 5-phosphate by an active phosphoribomutase. On the other hand, spores lack the enzymatic mechanisms for degrading cytidine and uridine (Lawrence and Tsan, 1962). Pyruvate can also be derived from L-alanine and probably also cysteine. The mechanism for these is discussed below.

Pyruvate Hypothesis. The hypothesis that in physiological germination the germination agents are metabolized to a common intermediate which is responsible for germination is supported by the finding that pyruvate may be derived from alanine, adenosine, or glucose. If germination requires the formation of products of pyruvate oxidation, one would expect that precursors of pyruvate would support a germination which is sensitive to inhibitors of pyruvate oxidation, whereas products of pyruvate oxidation would permit germination which is insensitive to these inhibitors. An example of this was observed for spores of *B. cereus* (Halvorson and Church, 1957). Germination which normally occurs in the presence of glucose, pyruvate, 6-phosphogluconate, ribose 5-phosphate, or 2-ketogluconate was inhibited by hexetidine, an inhibitor of pyruvate oxidation. The inhibition was reversed by cocarboxylase. In the presence of hexetidine, pyruvate and NH_3 accumulate. Germination in the presence of acetate, however, was insensitive to hexetidine. Similar results have been obtained with arsenite (O'Connor and Halvorson, 1959). Intermediates of the tricarboxylic acid cycle (fumaric, succinic, citric, and *cis*-aconitic acids) will also initiate germination. It is clear that germination involves the initiation of energy-yielding reactions, and that pyruvate or acetate metabolism is essential for physiological germination.

The Electron Transport System and Its Regulation by DPA. The pyruvate hypothesis, which we have just outlined, also makes germination increasingly dependent on the activation and functioning of the electron transport system of the spores. Since this system is essentially absent in the dormant spore, its activation is essential to oxidative reactions. The mechanism of electron transport in spores (see Chapter 9) is largely dependent upon a soluble $NADH_2$ oxidase. Harrell and Mantini (1957) found that both the glucose-oxidizing capacity as well as the release of DPA were proportional to the length of the heat-activation. These concurrent activations suggested that the two phenomena were closely related.

Subsequently (Halvorson et al., 1958; Harrell, 1958) it was observed in extracts of heat-activated spores that the oxidation of glucose or of $NADH_2$ could be stimulated threefold by the addition of DPA, as shown in Figure 10.2. Dipicolinic acid was not metabolized nor was the NAD-linked glucose dehydrogenase

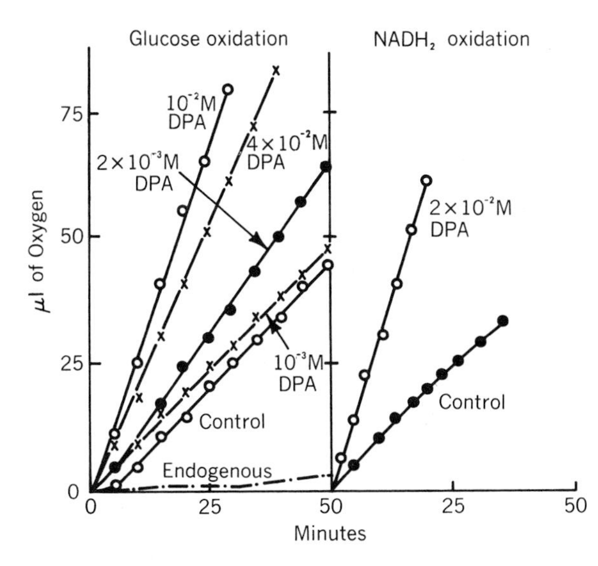

Figure 10.2 Stimulation of glucose and NADH$_2$ oxidation by dipicolinic acid. The Warburg vessels contained: glycyglycine buffer, *p*H 7.3, 75 μmoles; enzyme fraction with 4 mg protein; DPA as indicated and (a) glucose, 20 μmoles; NAD, 0.7 μmoles; (b) NADH$_2$, 10 μmoles. Final volume, 1.8 ml. Center well contained 0.2 ml of 20 percent KOH. Incubation temperature, 30°C. (Data from Halvorson et al., 1958.)

stimulated by DPA. It was apparent from these findings that DPA was acting by stimulating the electron transport system rather than at the level of substrate oxidation. Since DPA is a powerful chelating agent, and heavy metals have been implicated in controlling electron transport in other systems, it seems reasonable to suggest that it may be acting by virtue of its chelating potential. An experiment designed to test the chelation hypothesis with a soluble NADH$_2$ oxidizing system was negative (Halvorson et al., 1958). The stimulation could not be attributed to the removal of an inhibitory metal since two other chelating agents, 8-hydroxyquinoline and ethylenediamine tetraacetate did not stimulate the enzyme, and prior dialysis against DPA did not abolish its effect.

The soluble NADH$_2$ oxidase from spores has been purified twenty-fold. DPA stimulated oxygen uptake threefold while FMN stimulated oxygen uptake 9.4-fold. The lack of inhibition of the enzyme by cytochrome inhibitors, as well as the absorption spectrum of the enzyme, suggest a flavoprotein oxidase employing FMN as a cofactor.

Dipicolinic acid and FMN appear to compete for the same site (Figure 10.3). Atabrine, a flavin analog, competitively inhibits the stimulation of NADH$_2$ oxidation by either DPA or FMN. The affinity constant for atabrine is essentially the same calculated from both systems. Dipicolinic acid depresses the rate of FMN stimulation, this inhibition being reversed by higher concentrations of FMN.

Dipicolinic acid thus not only can substitute for FMN in stimulating the enzyme but also competes with FMN for the enzyme. This raises the interesting speculation that DPA, which has the pyridine ring structure in common with DPN, may act as a cofactor. If it did, one would expect that an enzyme-bound reduced form of DPA is formed. An intermediate of this type, dihydrodipi-

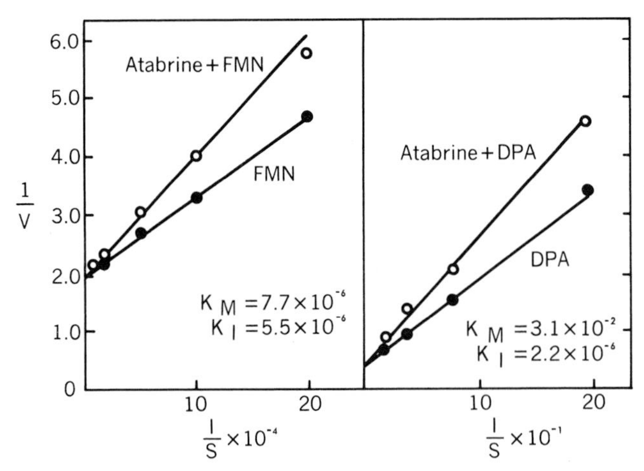

Figure 10.3 Competitive inhibition of FMN and DPA by atabrine on the soluble $NADH_2$ oxidase. Reaction mixtures contained 0.1 *M* phosphate buffer, *p*H 7.3, 5×10^{-6} *M* atabrine, 1×10^{-4} $NADH_2$, enzyme, plus FMN and DPA as indicated. Optical density changes were followed at 340 mμ at 25°C. (Data from Doi and Halvorson, 1961.)

colinic acid, has recently been postulated by Powell and Strange (1959) who suggested the following mechanism for the synthesis of DPA from diketopimelic acid (Figure 10.4).

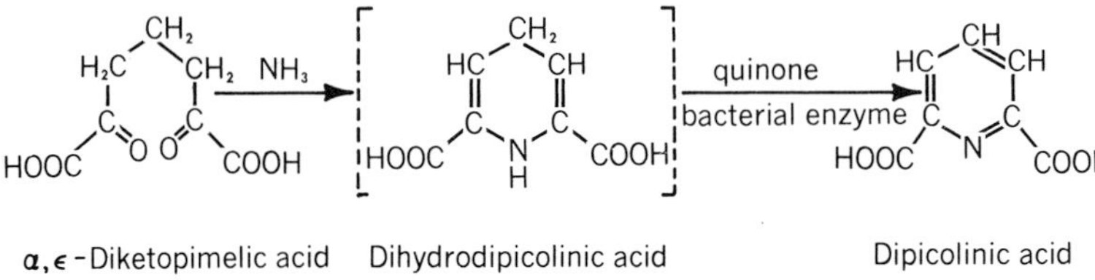

NH_3 — quinone, bacterial enzyme

α,ϵ-Diketopimelic acid   Dihydrodipicolinic acid   Dipicolinic acid

Figure 10.4 Pathway of dipicolinic acid synthesis.

Assuming that DPA can act as an electron acceptor provides an explanation for a number of phenomena associated with dormancy:

1. Bursts in respiratory activity during sporulation associated with DPA synthesis (Halvorson, 1957).
2. Anaerobic germination where DPA may act as an electron sink substituting for oxygen (Roth and Lively, 1956).
3. Rise in respiration following activation and germination (Harrell and Mantini, 1957) by stimulating the soluble oxidase pathway (Doi et al., 1959; Halvorson et al., 1958).

The Mechanism of L-*Alanine Utilization.* In bacterial spores L-alanine is one of the most widely distributed germination agents and also probably the best-studied germination stimulant (see Chapters 7 and 9).

An initial insight into the role of L-alanine was provided by Hills (1949, 1950) who found that the requirements for L-alanine-induced germination could not be replaced by related compounds, and in addition D-alanine at 0.03 times the concentration of L-alanine completely inhibited its action on spores of *B. anthracis*. The ratio of D to L-alanine which is inhibitory for germination varies with the species of spores (Murrell, 1952; Church et al., 1954; Schmidt, 1957). A similar phenomenon occurs during normal L-alanine-induced germination in that a few percent of the spores remain and do not germinate. In studying this phenomenon, Stewart and Halvorson (1953) discovered an alanine racemase which converts either D- or L-alanine to a racemic mixture. The content of this enzyme varies considerably in different spore species (Stewart and Halvorson, 1953; Church et al., 1954) which may provide an explanation for the different sensitivities to D-alanine.

The stereospecificity of the L-alanine triggering is not as rigid as was first suspected. Schmidt (1957) observed that the L-alanine-induced germination of spores of *B. subtilis* is inhibited by D-valine and by D-serine. In this same organism, Hills (1949) also observed that glycine, DL-methionine, DL-cysteine, or DL-valine at relatively high concentrations inhibited the action of L-alanine. Krask (1961) observed in *B. cereus* spores that L-alanine-induced germination was inhibited by L-cysteine but was stimulated by D-cysteine. Woese and co-workers (1958) were the first to systematically examine the specificity of the L-alanine trigger by determining the effect of substitutions in the L-alanine molecule on both the ability of the compound to initiate germination or to inhibit germination of *B. subtilis* spores in a medium containing salts, Mn^{++}, glucose, and the L-alanine analogs. Germination, as measured by the decrease in optical density, was initiated by L-alanine, L-α-NH_2-isobutyric acid, L-α-NH_2-*n*-butyric acid, L-norvaline, L-valine, L-isoleucine, and L-cysteine. Beta and γ-amino acids (especially β-alanine) are also active germination agents. Similar results have been reported by Schmidt (1958). Woese et al. (1958) found that in order to induce germination, the carboxyl and amino groups of L-alanine had to be free. Increased chain length led to decreased effectiveness. Electron negative groups on the —CH_3 portion of the L-alanine molecule (L-serine and L-cysteine) could be tolerated. The D-isomers of the germination stimulants, as well as glycine, ethyl, and methyl esters of L-alanine and some L-amino acids were able to inhibit the L-alanine-induced germination. D-Alanine had a higher binding constant with the spore than did L-alanine. In general, amino acids which are structurally related to L-alanine can serve as germination agents supporting the earlier findings (Hachisuka et al., 1955; Wynne, 1957) whereas D-analogs of these compounds inhibit germination (Wynne, 1957).

O'Connor and Halvorson (1961) have extended the findings of Woese et al. (1958) on the specificity of the L-alanine-induced germination. The germination of *B. cereus* spores was followed in a minimal system in which the supply of carbon and energy for germination was dependent solely upon the L-alanine analog added. Of 36 alanine analogs tested, only L-alanine, L-α-NH_2-*n*-butyric acid and L-cysteine initiated germination. Substitutions of the carboxyl, amino, or α-H led to inactive compounds. A number of compounds were found to be competitive inhibitors of L-alanine and L-α-NH-*n*-butyric acid-induced germination. These include the D-enantiomorphs of the germination agents as well as glycine, L-norvaline, L-cysteine, L-isoleucine, L-valine, L-threonine, and L-serine.

The prominent role played by L-alanine is understandable because it represents one of the most direct precursors of pyruvate among the germination agents. Numerous workers have observed that during L-alanine-induced germination, the amino acid disappeared from the medium. From studies with N^{15}-or C^{14}-labeled alanine, O'Connor and Halvorson (1959) demonstrated that alanine was deaminated to pyruvate and ammonia. The initial stages of germination led to the highest recovery of specific activity in pyruvate and ammonia. During the later stages of germination the isotope was diluted with endogenous L-alanine. The equimolar pyruvate and ammonia recovery suggests that compounds identical to, or closely related to, alanine are released during germination. Approximately 90 percent of the alanine metabolized was derived from endogenous sources. As discussed above, alanine deamination correlates well with the rate of L-alanine-induced germination in spores which have been heat-activated for various lengths of time. These findings indicate that the deamination of L-alanine is one of the early steps in L-alanine-induced germination.

Analysis of the spores indicated that L-alanine deamination could be accounted for by the activity of the L-alanine dehydrogenase. This enzyme carries out an NAD-linked deamination of L-alanine to pyruvate and ammonia. D-Alanine dehydrogenase has been purified and characterized from *B. cereus* (O'Connor and Halvorson, 1961), and *B. subtilis* (Yoshida and Freese, 1964). The affinity constant for substrates and products as well as the other collective data on its properties identify the enzyme as having the same characteristics as those reported in *B. subtilis* vegetative cells by Pierard and Wiame (1960), in *B. cereus* vegetative cells (O'Connor and Halvorson, 1961), and in *Mycobacterium* by Goldman (1959). The equilibrium constant of the spore and vegetative enzyme

$$(K_{eq} = 1.36 \times 10^{-14})$$

is in favor of amination. In vegetative cells this enzyme undoubtedly plays a primary role in the synthesis of L-alanine from ammonia and pyruvate.

If the L-alanine dehydrogenase catalyzes the initial step in germination, then it should be (a) inhibited by D-alanine and (b) active on L-alanine analogs which act as germination agents. In Table 10.1 are shown some of the L-amino acids which initiate germination and ammonia production by intact spores.

Table 10.1 Rate of Ammonia Release from L-Amino Acids

L-Amino Acids	Rate of ammonia release (μmoles/hour)
Alanine	2.46
Valine	1.42
Cysteine	1.12
Serine	0.82
Threonine	0.56
Isoleucine	0.46
Leucine	0.37

SOURCE: H. Halvorson et al., 1961.
Clean, heat-activated spores (25 mg) were incubated at 30°C in Conway diffusion units containing 5 μmoles of the indicated amino acid in 2 ml of 0.067 *M* phosphate buffer, *p*H 7.0. Corrections were made for endogenous (amino acid omitted) release of ammonia. Thirteen other l-amino acids were not deaminated.

Deamination of L-alanine as well as other L-amino acids is competitively inhibited by the D-isomers. Furthermore, the specificity of L-alanine dehydrogenase mirrors that of L-alanine-induced germination (Woese et al., 1958; and O'Connor and Halvorson, 1961). Some of the substrate specificities of analogs substituted in the β-carbon are shown in Table 10.2. When the L-alanine molecule is substituted on either the carboxyl, amino, or α-hydrogen positions, it loses all of its effect as a substrate of the enzyme and as a complexant of the enzyme. The structural changes which retain activity are those involving substitutions of the methyl group of L-alanine. L-Alanine and L-α-amino-*n*-butyric acid are the most effective substrates. Increasing the chain length beyond three carbons reduces the effectiveness of analogs as complexants and as substrates. When the methyl group of L-alanine is substituted by hydrogen, a competitive inhibitor is formed. In all cases, the D-isomers of effective substrates are competitive inhibitors of L-alanine deamination.

The findings which have been discussed support the hypothesis that L-alanine dehydrogenase is essential for germination initiated by L-alanine. This conclusion is based on the following:

1. Alanine deamination is an essential but not sufficient step for germination. The enzyme accounts for all of the deaminating capacity of crude spore extracts.
2. Complexants of the enzyme inhibit both L-alanine deamination and germination of the spores.
3. Heat-activation enhances both the expression of the enzyme *in vivo* and L-alanine-initiated germination.
4. The physical constants for germination (K_s) initiated by L-alanine analogs (with the exception of L-cysteine) are similar to those of L-alanine dehydrogenase.

Table 10.2 Comparison of L-Alanine Analogs as Germination Agents and Substrates of L-Alanine Dehydrogenase[a]

Substitutions on the β-carbon	Percent Rate of L-Alanine: Substrate	Germination[b]
None	100	100
$—CH_3$	32	65
$—CH_2CH_3$	17	70
$—CH_2SCH_3$	0	12
$<^{CH_3}_{CH_3}$	2.8	60
$<^{CH_2CH_3}_{CH_3}$	4	60
$—CH<^{CH_3}_{CH_3}$	4.4	10
$<^{CH_3}_{OH}$	0	0
—OH	2.5	0
—Phenyl	0	0

SOURCE: O'Connor and Halvorson, 1961.
[a] Specificity of alanine dehydrogenase expressed as V_M determined by incubating dehydrogenase at 25°C with 2 μmoles of NAD and L-alanine analogs, as indicated, in 0.1 *M* carbonate-bicarbonate buffer, *p*H 9.4. Reaction rates were measured by spectrophotometric determination of $NADH_2$ formation at 340 mμ.
[b] Specificity of germination taken from studies on *B. subtilis*.

The hypothesis described above has recently been questioned on several grounds. First Hsu (1963) reported that other amino acids in addition to L-alanine, such as L-α-NH_2-*n*-butyric acid, and L-cysteine induce germination when added singly to a spore suspension. Unfortunately these studies were carried out with aged (7-year-old) spore stocks in contrast to the fresh spore stocks employed by O'Connor and Halvorson (1961). Aging is known to alter the germination requirements, and as shown by Hsu (1963), to lead to a spore preparation containing elevated levels of free amino acids, including alanine. In contrast to the findings of others (Krask, 1961; O'Connor and Halvorson, 1961) with fresh preparations of this same organism, L-cysteine was almost inactive as a germination agent. Until further biochemical studies, including the role of endogenous amino acids in germination, are available, the significance of these findings to the role of L-alanine dehydrogenase in germination must remain in doubt. The more serious question has been raised by the findings of Park and Freese (1964) and Freese (1965). These workers isolated mutants of *B. subtilis* 168 which are low in or devoid of L-alanine dehydrogenase activity. Spores produced from these mutants germinate rapidly in the presence of calcium DPA or L-alanine. Either these spores have derived an alternate pathway for L-alanine utilization, or L-alanine dehydrogenase is not involved in L-alanine-induced germination, or only a small fraction of the enzyme present in spores actually participates in the initiation of germination. Since only a few molecules of L-alanine are apparently involved in the initiation process (Harrell and Halvorson, 1955), it is of considerable interest to determine whether these spores are *devoid* of the enzyme or contain low levels of enzyme. Until direct assays of L-alanine dehydrogenase in spores from these mutants are available, the L-alanine dehydrogenase must still remain as the most likely route of L-alanine-induced germination.

In vegetative cells, alanine dehydrogenase is the primary route of alanine synthesis. Therefore, the deamination of L-alanine by this enzyme in spores can be accomplished only if the end-products are removed in a sufficiently rapid manner to drive the reaction. Pyruvate metabolism has been demonstrated in spore extracts, although the rate of this reaction is very slow. The oxidation of $NADH_2$ by the DPA-stimulated soluble $NADH_2$ oxidase seems a more likely method of driving alanine deamination.

Several lines of evidence support the view that L-alanine deamination is driven by $NADH_2$ oxidation. First, the rate of deamination of L-alanine by dialyzed extracts of activated spores was found to be stimulated threefold by DPA (O'Connor and Halvorson, 1960). Dipicolinic acid has no effect on L-alanine dehydrogenase; its effect is presumably in the recycling of $NADH_2$ to NAD, thus depressing the level of $NADH_2$ in extract. Secondly, if the rate of recycling of $NADH_2$ *in vivo* is linked to the DPA content, then one would expect that L-alanine-induced germination would be restricted in spores low in DPA. An example of this is shown in Figure 10.5 with spores that contain only 2.3 percent DPA (Keynan et al., 1961). Dipicolinic acid dramatically stimulates the rate and amount of L-alanine-induced germination, whereas DPA alone has no effect on the spores. Germination in the presence of DPA and L-alanine is inhibited by D-alanine, suggesting that germination is triggered by the L-alanine dehydrogenase. In spores with normal DPA content, the DPA released by heat activation may play the same role as the DPA added exogenously to low-DPA spores.

The mechanism of L-alanine-induced germination can be summarized as follows. Heat-activation leads to an increase in the maximum rate of germination and a decrease in the L-alanine requirements for germination (O'Connor and Halvorson, 1961). The biochemical events underlying this are not clearly understood. Heat-activation could influence L-alanine-induced germination by releasing an endogenous stimulant, altering the properties of L-alanine dehydrogenase, modifying the rate of reactions linked with L-alanine dehydrogenase ($NADH_2$ oxidation), altering permeability or removing an inhibitor of germination. Of

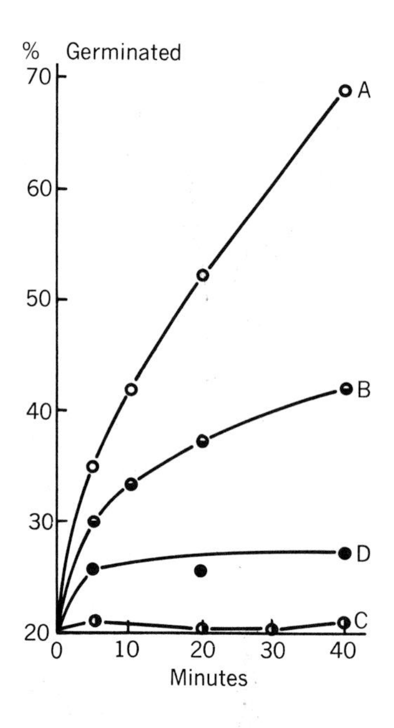

Figure 10.5 Kinetics of DPA stimulation of L-alanine-induced germination. Low DPA spores were heat shocked for 15 minutes at 65°C and resuspended in 0.2 *M* Tris buffer (*p*H 8) containing the following additions: A, 10 mg/ml L-alanine and 4×10^{-3} *M* DPA; B, 10 mg/ml L-alanine; C, 4×10^{-3} *M* DPA; and D, 10 mg/ml L-alanine, 15 mg/ml D-alanine, and 4×10^{-3} *M* DPA. Incubation temperature, 30°C. (Data from Keynan et al., 1962.)

these possibilities several would seem unlikely on the basis of available evidence. The release of endogenous germination stimulants during heat-activation should cause spontaneous germination, which is not observed in spores of *B. cereus*; however, it has been reported in spores of *B. megaterium* (Powell and Strange, 1953). Also, alteration of the permeability of spores is negligible since germination involves only slight changes in the diffusible spore volume (Black et al., 1960). The more likely explanation is that $NADH_2$ recycling is accelerated by heat-activation. The apparent change in the overall K_s and V_m for L-alanine germination with heat-activation may, therefore, reflect the stimulation of the $NADH_2$ oxidase by the DPA released during heat-activation, which in turn promotes alanine deamination.

Mechanism of Cysteine-Induced Germination. Of amino acid-induced germination, in addition to L-alanine, the effect of D- and L-cysteine is particularly interesting. An insight into the effect of these agents on the germination of spores of *B. cereus* has been obtained from the work of Krask (1961).

(1) D-*cysteine*—Krask (1961) reported that D-cysteine stimulates L-alanine-induced germination although D-cysteine itself is not a germination stimulant. Nonheat-activated spores have an absolute requirement for D-cysteine in order to germinate in low levels (5 μmoles/ml) of L-alanine (O'Connor and Halvorson, 1961). The effect of D-cysteine on nonactivated spores is particularly interesting in that the germination rate is independent of L-alanine concentration (0.0005 *M* to 0.1 *M*) in the presence of 0.0005 *M* D-cysteine. Without D-cysteine, the germination rate is highly dependent on L-alanine concentration over this range.

In this respect, D-cysteine resembles heat-activation in that much lower concentrations of L-alanine are required when D-cysteine is added.

(2) L-*cysteine*—Woese et al. (1958) observed that spores of *B. subtilis* rapidly germinate in the presence of L-cysteine, glucose, and Mn^{++}. Krask (1961) has examined more directly the role of L-cysteine in the germination of spores of *B. cereus*. He found that L-cysteine was a more effective germination agent than L-alanine and germination in the presence of L-cysteine was accompanied by the production of hydrogen sulfide.

The effect of D-cysteine on L-alanine-induced germination is particularly interesting since D-cysteine has the highest affinity constant for alanine dehydrogenase (O'Connor and Halvorson, 1961) and on this basis would be presumed to be an inhibitor of L-alanine-induced germination. Krask (1961) has proposed an explanation for this phenomenon. He suggests that the stimulation by D-cysteine is due to the inhibition of L-alanine racemase, thus prohibiting the racemization of L-alanine to the inhibitory D-isomer. Evidence supporting this conclusion was obtained from germination initiated by D-alanine. D-Alanine inhibits L-alanine-induced germination, but D-alanine alone supports a slow rate of germination. The characteristics of the rate curve suggest a prolonged lag, presumably enabling the formation of L-alanine from D-alanine, and a germination response to the formed DL-alanine. D-Cysteine inhibits D-alanine germination, stimulates the inhibitory effects of D-alanine on L-alanine-induced germination, and inhibits the extracted alanine racemase activity (Krask, 1961). Therefore, alanine racemase may serve as a regulatory system for controlling the intracellular level of L-alanine thereby controlling the rate of L-alanine activity and over-all germination. The induced germination in response to L-cysteine is more complicated and cannot be directly explained on the basis of the L-alanine dehydrogenase. Not only is the rate of germination of spores of *B. anthracis* and *B. cereus* more rapid in the presence of L-cysteine than in the presence of L-alanine, but also the end-products are not those expected from the alanine dehydrogenase. Krask (1962) has demonstrated that intact spores and spore homogenates release hydrogen sulfide from L-cysteine. Although L-alanine dehydrogenase has weak activity on L-cysteine (1 percent of the rate on L-alanine), no hydrogen sulfide is detected. The liberation of hydrogen sulfide suggests the presence of cysteine desulfhydrase (Kallio, 1951).

Germination initiated by L-cysteine is inhibited by D-alanine, L-alanine, and D-cysteine (Krask, 1961). The inhibition by D-cysteine is competitive. The rate of germination in the presence of L-alanine and L-cysteine is slower than in the presence of either germination agent alone. These observations can be explained on several grounds. L-Cysteine has been demonstrated as a complexant of L-alanine dehydrogenase (O'Connor and Halvorson, 1961). Also, L-alanine has been demonstrated to be an inhibitor of the cysteine desulfhydrase (Fromageot and

Grand, 1943; Kallio and Porter, 1950). Thus, the L-alanine-induced germination would be inhibited by L-cysteine and the L-cysteine-induced germination, proceeding presumably by a cysteine desulfhydrase, would be inhibited by L-alanine. Although it has not been demonstrated, it is possible that following the removal of hydrogen sulphide L-cysteine could serve as a precursor of pyruvate.

CHEMICAL GERMINATION. The initation of germination by agents which are not metabolized has been termed *chemical germination*. This definition does not imply that the germination process does not have a physiological basis. As will be demonstrated in several instances, the chemical triggering agent serves to activate endogenous physiological events which lead ultimately to germination. Others, such as the germination induced by polyamines and organic solvents, may have an alternative mechanism.

Germination Triggered by Inorganic Ions. Of the inorganic ions that have been shown to influence the germination of *Bacillus* species, manganese and inorganic phosphate are the most prominent. The stimulation of germination by manganous ions (Levinson and Hyatt, 1955; Levinson and Sevag, 1953) has been shown by Levinson (1957) to differ from that caused by L-alanine and adenosine in that the manganese-stimulated germination is much slower. These observations have led Levinson to examine spores for manganese-stimulated enzymes. He has reported that in ruptured spores there is accumulation of free amino acids by the action of a proteolytic enzyme. Extracts of these spores stimulate the germination of intact spores. In addition, intact or ruptured spores hydrolyze gelatin, leading to the liberation of amino acids. Examination of the exudates of spores suggests that proteolytic enzyme(s) may be acting upon the exosporium which is rich in L-alanine. Alanine has been identified as a product of manganese-stimulated protease activity. Since the spore material itself can serve as a substrate of this enzyme, manganese-stimulation may be viewed as autogermination in which the spore creates its own stimulus for germination.

A second manganese-stimulated enzyme is pyrophosphatase. This enzyme has been identified in extracts of spores of *Bacillus megaterium* by Levinson (1957). Without the addition of manganous ions, there was little or no enzymatic activity. Cobalt and zinc showed a small amount of activation. Since after germination there is a great reduction in the amount of demonstrable pyrophosphatase, it is suggested this may play a role in the germination process. Fitz-James (1955) has demonstrated that spore coats of *B. megaterium* are rich in phosphorus which is acid- and alkali-insoluble. This phosphorus fraction accounts for about 60 percent of the total phosphorus of *B. megaterium* spores. The phosphorus residues of the spores may well be subject to parallel breakdown during germination and contribute also to the phosphate requirements for germination in a manner analogous to that of the protease discussed above.

A number of ions have been shown to be germination stimulants in *B. mega-*

terium. In the Texas strain, a large number of inorganic salts (Figure 10.6) or salts of organic acids were effective in combination with L-alanine and inosine (Rode and Foster, 1962*a*). Inosine could be by-passed by ammonium propionate or

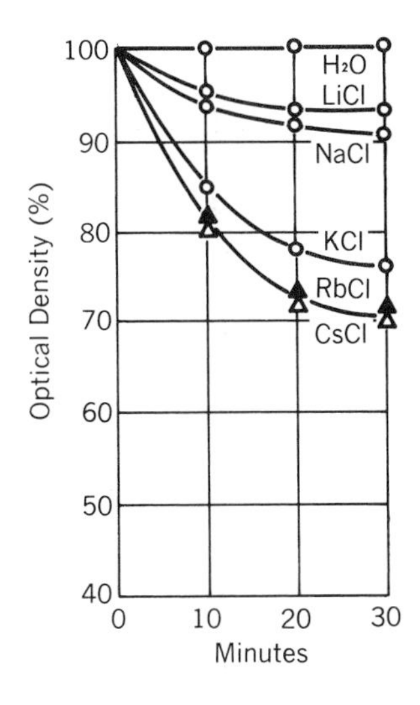

Figure 10.6 Germinative activities of inorganic salts for spores of *Bacillus megaterium Texas*. The suspensions contained L-alanine, 0.00025 *M* and inosine, 0.0001 *M*. Equivalent concentrations of Cl^- throughout. (From Rode and Foster, 1962*a*.)

salts of DPA and L-alanine could be replaced by a number of amino acids in combination with suitable ions. Salts of *n*-hexylamine and *n*-heptylamine by-passed both the L-alanine and inosine requirements. In spores of *B. megaterium* QMB1551, a glucose-type germination system, a number of salts alone were germination agents, although glucose could increase the rate of germination. The nature of the cation appeared to play the determining role. These observations have led Rode and Foster to conclude that the primary role in germination is played by inorganic ions rather than organic compounds. Although inorganic ions play a role in the germination of other spores as well (Rode and Foster, 1962*c*), the stereospecificity of organic germination agents and the metabolic dependence of germination suggest that the situation is more complicated and inorganic ions may possibly be required for binding of organic germination stimulants to some spore-specific site.

The other commonly examined inorganic ion is phosphate, which also functions only in combination with other germination stimulants. The requirements for phosphate are variable. For example, glucose-germination is accelerated by the addition of phosphate (Knaysi, 1945), whereas optimal germination induced by L-alanine can take place in the absence of phosphate (O'Connor and Halvorson, 1961). These findings may be understood if the metabolism of some germination agents requires the formation of phosphorylated intermediates, as in the case of glucose. The demonstration of P^{32} uptake into nucleotides during germination (Srinivasan and Halvorson, 1961) further supports this view.

Germination Induced by Chelating Agents. Brown (1956) observed that spores of the putrefactive anaerobe PA 3679, the NCA strain, as well as the mutant strain 8, could be germinated with a chelating agent, EDTA. The germinated ions were viable and apparently passed through the same stages of germination as those induced by a physiological germinating agent. These observations led Riemann (1961) and Riemann and Ordal (1961) to study a broader spectrum of chelating agents. Germination in response to chelating agents is highly specific, for example, Brown (1956) found for germination of PA 3679 that 2-2′, 2′-dipyridyl, ethylenediamine tetraacetate, sodium carbonate, 8-hydroxyquinoline, oxyaoxalic acid, glycylglycine, and citrate were inactive. Riemann (1961) obtained similar results; however, he reported that sodium bicarbonate gave some germination of putrefactive anaerobe S217 and that PA 3679 would germinate slightly in the presence of tripolyphosphate.

The most active chelating agent in inducing germination is calcium dipicolinate. This agent triggers the germination both of aerobic and anaerobic spores. As shown in Table 10.3 the 1:1 chelate of calcium and DPA is the most active.

Table 10.3 Germination of PA 3679 NCA Spores (#VIII) with 10 mM Tris Buffer, Different Concentrations of $CaCl_2$ and 33.3 mM EDTA, or DPA, *p*H 7.0

Concentration $CaCl_2$	Percent germination[a] in 45 minutes at 35°C: 33.3 mM EDTA	33.3 mM DPA
100 mM	0	98
50 mM	0	99
33.3 mM	0	98
16.7 mM	2	4
11.1 mM	8	15
0 mM	30	34

SOURCE: Riemann, 1961.
[a] Based on refractility.

The stimulating effect of calcium seems to be rather specific and calcium could not be replaced by a variety of other metals. Germination led to a change in optical density, excretion of peptides and amino acids, as well as ammonia and to the loss of heat-resistance.

Evidence supporting the physiological nature of calcium DPA-induced germination is summarized in Table 10.4. Although calcium DPA-induced germination is unaffected by the stereospecific inhibitors of alanine- and cysteine-induced germination, all three are sensitive to mercuric chloride, low *p*H, and to inhibitors of pyruvate metabolism (ethyl pyruvate) and electron transport (atabrine). The kinetics of calcium DPA-induced germination indicate a long lag

Table 10.4 Inhibition of the Germination of *B. cereus* Spores[a]

Inhibitor	L-Alanine-Induced Germination	Calcium DPA-Induced Germination	L-Cysteine-Induced Germination
D-Alanine	0.2	No inhibition[b]	0.03
Glycine	0.04	No inhibition[b]	0.04
D-Cysteine	Stimulation	No inhibition[c] —	0.03
Ethyl pyruvate	0.01	0.01	0.01
Atabrine	0.001	0.001	0.001
H_gCl_2	0.001	0.01	0.001
Low *p*H (*p*H 4.0)	0.001	0.001	0.001

SOURCE: Keynan and Halvorson, 1962.
[a] Molar concentration for complete inhibition.
[b] Normal germination rates as compared to controls in the presence of three times more inhibitor than necessary to give total inhibition of L-alanine-induced germination.
[c] Normal germination rates as compared to controls in the presence of five times more inhibitor than necessary to give total inhibition of L-cysteine-induced germination.
L-Alanine (0.1 *M*) and L-cysteine (0.03 *M*)-induced germination were carried out at 30°C. Germination was considered to be inhibited completely when no change in optical density occurred during 45 minutes.

followed by a rapid decrease in optical density. The latter was found to be relatively temperature-independent, and, as shown by Riemann and Ordal (1961), was inhibited by temperatures at which L-alanine-induced germination is optimal. When the temperature was lowered, the germination lag in response to calcium DPA was greatly extended. The temperature relationship between 8–20°C is characteristic of an enzymatic reaction and has a ΔH of 14,500 cal/mole which is similar to that observed for the rate of L-alanine-induced germination.

Several properties of the lag period are evident from the experiments of Riemann and Ordal (1961). They observed during the lag period a loss of refractility, a decrease in heat-resistance and a release of peptides. Since calcium is generally believed to be involved in heat-resistance, one would expect the release of endogenous calcium during the lag period. To test this, the release of calcium-45 was examined. The results (Keynan and Halvorson, 1962) indicate that calcium excretion starts immediately after the addition of calcium DPA and precedes any other measurable changes.

One further feature was observed. Although spores low in DPA have a poor response to L-alanine unless exogenous DPA is added, calcium DPA leads to rapid germination. The DPA-stimulation of L-alanine-induced germination is sensitive to D-alanine, indicating it is acting via the L-alanine dehydrogenase.

Figure 10.7 shows a diagrammatic description of the interrelationship between the germination pathways. Dipicolinic acid has been shown to stimulate the $NADH_2$ oxidase activity: L-alanine triggering is thus dependent upon its reaction. L-alanine triggering also releases internally bound DPA of spores (Powell and

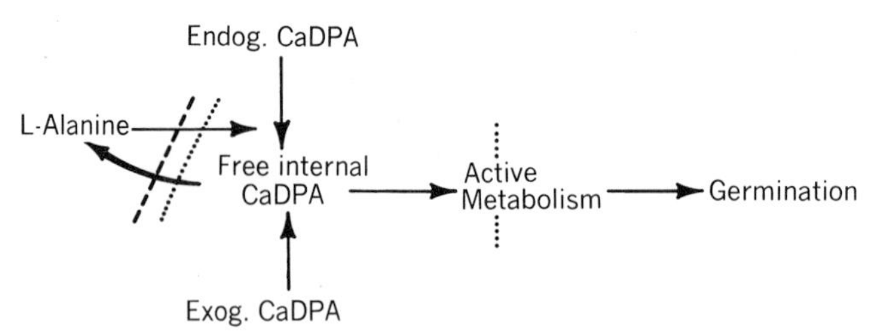

Figure 10.7 Interrelationship between L-alanine and calcium DPA-induced germination. The sites of actions of inhibitors of germination are indicated by a dashed line for stereospecific inhibitors and a dotted line for metabolic inhibitors.

Strange, 1953). Therefore, a type of feedback stimulation of germination can be envisaged. One might assume that exogenous calcium DPA activates the release of endogenous L-alanine. That this is unlikely is shown by the fact that calcium DPA-induced germination is unaffected by stereospecific inhibitors of L-alanine- and L-cysteine-induced germination. These findings lead to the conclusion that added calcium DPA acts in the same way as endogenously released calcium DPA. Dipicolinic acid itself appears to have at least two functions: (a) it drives the L-alanine dehydrogenase and (b) it induces a metabolically dependent germination, independent of the L-alanine trigger mechanism.

Germination Induced by Surface-Active Agents. Rode and Foster (1960*a, b, c*) have studied the induced germination of both *Bacillus* and *Clostridium* species by a wide variety of surface-active agents. They found that nearly all of the cationic and anionic surfactants were effective, whereas the nonionic and antibiotic polypeptide surfactants were not. Treatment with a surface-active agent led to a release of DPA, to an increased stainability, and to a loss in heat-resistance. These changes are very similar to those occurring in the early stages in germination and suggest some structural alteration in response to the surface-active agent leading to an active germination process. Whether this process leads to autogermination has not been clarified at the present time. Loss of DPA has also been reported in response to hydrogen peroxide, heat, and electrodialysis (Rode and Foster, 1960*b*).

In the case of germination induced by long-chain alkyl amines, such as *n*-dodecyl amine, the changes corresponding to germination are accompanied by a rapid loss in viability.

Rode and Foster (1961) have interpreted their collective data on the effect of surface-active agents to support the concept that the prime event in germination is a breaching of a permeability barrier in the dormant spore. This leads to a release of calcium dipicolinate, mucopeptides, and an increase in metabolic activity. Whether the proteolytic enzyme, as well as the pyrophosphatase- and alanine-induced systems are activated by these treatments is not yet known.

MECHANICAL GERMINATION AND HEAT.—Rode and Foster (1960*d*) reported that when spores of *Bacillus megaterium* were abraded with glass beads, 80–90 percent of the remaining viable spores germinated. The germinated spores had lost their DPA and peptides, were stainable, heat-sensitive, and oxidized glucose. Although the alteration of the spore in response to mechanical abrasion is not clear, most likely the outer surfaces have been weakened or broken. This process, which may be taking place enzymatically in physiological germination, sets in motion the same sequence of events characteristic of germination in response to specific stimulants. The major changes may, in fact, have a physiological basis. A parallel example has been reported in which the loss of viability of *Escherichia coli* in the sonic disintegrator has, in part, an enzymatic basis (Rotman, 1958).

An example of a reaction intimately linked with alanine deamination which may conceivably be affected by heat-activation, is $NADH_2$ oxidation. This reaction, catalyzed by an FMN-requiring $NADH_2$ oxidase, is stimulated by DPA (O'Connor and Halvorson, 1961), apparently due to $NADH_2$ recycling. The change in the over-all K_s and V_m for L-alanine-germination upon heat-activation may, therefore, reflect the stimulation of the oxidase by the DPA released during heat shock, which in turn promotes alanine deamination.

Heat-activation may act as a more general metabolic stimulant. For example, dormant spores of *Bacillus cereus* have no demonstrable endogenous or exogenous glucose respiration, but after 1 hour of heating at 65°C show optimal respiratory activity (Church and Halvorson, 1957). Similar results have been observed for transaminase activity (Falcone and Caracõ, 1958), deamination of L-alanine (O'Connor and Halvorson, 1959), and L-alanine liberation (Falcone and Caracõ, 1958; Levinson and Hyatt, 1955; O'Connor and Halvorson, 1959). When spores are frozen in distilled water (Murty and Halvorson, 1957) or frozen in the dry state (Church and Halvorson, 1957) for 4 to 6 months, the glucose oxidative capacity is about five times that of freshly harvested spores. In addition, prior heat-activation of spores before disruption leads to increases in the number of enzymes in the extracts (Church and Halvorson, 1955; Levinson et al., 1958).

2. *Fungi.* Although considerable information is available on the biochemistry of germinating stages (Chapter 9) of fungi, there is relatively little reported on the activation stage *per se*. Therefore, much of what follows will be largely restricted to ascospores of *Neurospora*, for which some data exist.

The first attempt to analyze the metabolic changes in fungus spores during germination was that of Goddard and Smith (1938). They showed that the anaerobic carbon dioxide production of ascospores of *Neurospora tetrasperma* increased in proportion to the number of germinating cells. The presence of the enzyme pyruvic carboxylase was inferred from experiments in which pyruvic acid reversed the toxicity of fluoride for anaerobic carbon dioxide production. On the other hand, dormant cells were considered to lack this enzyme because endogenously added pyruvate failed to stimulate the fermentative release of carbon dioxide. On this basis it was suggested that the metabolic block that imposed dormancy upon these ascospores was due to the lack of pyruvic carboxylase whose presence in activated cells permitted germination to proceed. This suggestion was examined by Sussman et al. (1956) who determined the pyruvic carboxylase activity of dormant, activated, and germinating spores and showed that extracts prepared from all of these sources contained the enzyme. Although the activity of the dormant cell extracts was lower than that in the other cases, it was sufficient to account for observed rates of carbon dioxide evolution in activated spores. In addition, it was shown that the coenzyme, diphosphothiamine, was present in almost equivalent amounts in dormant as well as germinating spores. Holton (1958) has subsequently shown that the carboxylase of these spores decarboxylates stoichiometric amounts of pyruvate and releases acetaldehyde as a product. On the other hand, he was not able to demonstrate the presence of a pyruvic oxidase system in any of the types of preparations he tested.

A more likely mechanism to explain dormancy in ascospores of *Neurospora* has recently been proposed on the basis of work on the endogenous substrates utilized by dormant and germinating cells. It has been shown (Lingappa and Sussman, 1959) that the ethanol-soluble carbohydrate fraction of these spores is not utilized except after the spores are activated (Tables 10.5 and 10.6). By contrast, the endogenous lipids are utilized by dormant and activated cells as well.

Table 10.5 Carbohydrate Fractions of Dormant and Activated Ascospores of *Neurospora tetrasperma*

Time after Activation (hours)	Ethanol-Soluble Carbohydrates (mg)	Acid-Soluble Carbohydrates (mg)	Total Carbohydrates (mg)
Dormant	14.0	19.4	33.4
0	12.1	18.6	30.7
0.5	10.4	18.2	28.6
1	8.9	18.1	27.0
1.5	7.4	18.0	25.4
2	6.5	18.1	24.6
2.5	5.6	17.8	23.4
3	4.4	17.8	22.2
4	4.0	17.6	21.6
5	3.3	17.8	21.1
6	2.8	17.6	20.4
8	2.6	17.6	20.2
12	2.1	17.4	19.5
24	1.9	17.5	19.4

SOURCE: Lingappa and Sussman, 1959.
All values expressed per 100 mg ascospores (dry wt).

Table 10.6 Changes in the Endogenous Substrates of Dormant Ascospores of *Neurospora tetrasperma*[a]

Age of Ascospores	Ethanol-Soluble Carbohydrates (mg)	Acid-Soluble Carbohydrates (mg)	Total Lipids (mg)	Germinability (percent)
Two years old (harvested 1956 and stored at 4°C in air)	13.6	19	21.4	82
One month old (harvested 1958 and stored at 4°C in air)	14	19	24	94
One month old (stored at 4°C then shaken 15 days in water at 21°C)	14	19	23.4	93
One month old (stored at 4°C then shaken 40 days in water at 20°C)	14	—	21	96

SOURCE: Lingappa and Sussman, 1959.
[a] All values are expressed per 100 mg ascospores (dry wt).

These workers discovered that the sugar in the ethanol-soluble carbohydrate fraction is trehalose, a nonreducing disaccharide, which comprises 14–15 percent of the cell's dry weight. Consequently, it has been proposed that the key to the activation of these spores lies in the means through which trehalose is utilized.

Several mechanisms can be proposed to explain these data, including the following:

1. An enzyme which is responsible for the breakdown of trehalose is synthesized when dormancy is broken.
2. An inhibitor of this enzyme is destroyed when the spores are activated.
3. A precursor of the enzyme forms trehalase after activation, in a manner analogous to the trypsinogen-trypsin transformation.
4. Trehalose and the enzyme which catalyzes its degradation are separated spatially in the cell and activation brings them together.

With these possibilities in mind, the trehalase activities of dormant and germinating ascospores were determined (Hill and Sussman, 1964) and it was found that there is only a four-fold increase in trehalase activity in extracts. Therefore, unless there is another means whereby these ascospores utilize trehalose, the *de novo* synthesis of trehalase cannot explain the activation process. Compartmentalization of the enzyme and substrate in dormant cells would appear to be the most likely hypothesis at the moment and recent experiments support this idea (Budd et al., 1966).

Subsequent steps in the development of activated ascospores have been discussed in the previous chapter. As a result of the acquisition of the ability to metabolize trehalose, a strongly fermentative type of metabolism ensues, accompanied by a gradual increase in respiratory capacity which reaches its peak after enzymes of the tricarboxylic acid cycle become functional (Sussman, 1961*a*).

An energy dependence for germination has been suggested for the macroconidia of *Fusarium solani* f. *phaseoli* (J. C. Cochrane et al., 1963). In this organism, a carbon source, a nitrogen source and an unknown factor in yeast extract are required for germination. Ethanol or acetoin will replace the yeast extract. Glucose is utilized by an aerobic pathway; during germination a weak glucose fermentation is acquired (V. W. Cochrane et al., 1963*a*). Ethanol depressed endogenous respiration and accelerated the rate of glucose oxidation (Cochrane et al., 1963*b*). Based on the analysis of products of acetate-2-C^{14}, they concluded that both a tricarboxylic acid cycle and a glyoxylic acid cycle were operative. Acetate, however, does not replace ethanol as a germination stimulant. One possible explanation for the role of ethanol is that germination is limited by the availability of amino acids. The synthesis of amino acids may in turn depend upon the supply of active acetaldehyde from ethanol. A further study of the mechanism of conversion of ethanol to acetate in the macroconidia may provide further insight into the role of ethanol in germination. In this connection, the stimulatory effect of acetaldehyde upon the germination of spores of *Phycomyces* (Rudolph, 1961) suggests a parallel mechanism.

In one case, a strong parallelism has been suggested between the mechanism of germination in bacteria and fungi. Conidiospores of *Aspergillus niger* require L-alanine in addition to guanine and glucose for complete germination, although mycelial growth occurs abundantly with ammonia as a sole source of nitrogen (Yanagita, 1957; Nishi, 1961). Carbon dioxide is required for the initiation of germination (Yanagita, 1957; Rippel and Bortels, 1927). Hoshino et al. (1962) have investigated the fate of L-alanine during germination. Employing uniformly and C-1-labeled alanine, they observed that radioactivity is incorporated into various cell constituents after a 30 minute lag. The incorporated radioactivity is almost exclusively from carbons 2 and 3 of alanine. Radioactivity in CO_2 was derived from all three carbon atoms. Extracts of either dormant or activated spores contain a system which actively deaminates L-alanine to pyruvate and NH_3. Pyruvate is subsequently decarboxylated to CO_2 and a 2-carbon fragment.

Hoshino et al. (1962) concluded that the enzyme responsible for deamination of alanine was an NAD-linked L-alanine dehydrogenase. Alanine deamination proceeded equally well under aerobic or anaerobic conditions, making unlikely the possibility that an L-amino acid oxidase was involved. The enzyme had a *p*H optimum around 11; like L-alanine dehydrogenase, however, an NAD or NADP requirement could not be demonstrated. The enzyme deaminating alanine is present in the soluble fraction (Hoshino, 1961) but has not as yet been further characterized.

The role of CO_2 in conidiospore germination is less clear. When CO_2 is eliminated from the germination medium, the swelling of conida is not observed (Yanagita, 1957). Employing $C^{14}O_2$, Yanagita (1963) observed that CO_2 was rapidly incorporated by dormant spores into the acid-soluble fraction primarily as ATP, whereas during germination, C^{14} was incorporated into proteins and nucleic acids. Among the various substances required for germination, $P^{32}O_4{}^{\equiv}$, $S^{35}O_4{}^{=}$ and C^{14}-alanine were incorporated after a lag, whereas CO_2 incorporation proceeds without a lag period at the start of germination.

In this organism germination may require the formation of ATP for either energy or for nucleic acid synthesis. In the latter case, a change in the purine/pyrimidine ratio as well as a rapid labeling of the RNA fractions (Hoshino et al., 1962; Yanagita, 1963) is indicative of mRNA synthesis. The carbon of ATP is derived in part from CO_2 (exogenous or derived from alanine) and the phosphorous from polyphosphate and phospholipid breakdown during germination (Nishi, 1961).

As in the case of bacteria, alternative means exist for the activation of fungus spores. For example, the dormancy of sporangiospores of *Phycomyces blakesleeanus* can be broken by treatment at 50°C for three minutes (Sommer and Halbsguth, 1957), incubation in 0.1 *N* acids, surface-active agents and 0.1 *M* ammonium acetate (Sommer and Halbsguth, 1957), acetate and other organic acids (Robbins et al., 1942), autoclaved glucose solutions (Sommer and Halbsguth, 1957), or acetaldehyde (Rudolph, 1961). Another instance is that of ascospores of *Neurospora* which can be activated by heat (60° C), furfural and certain heterocyclic analogs, and several aliphatic ethers, alcohols, and esters (Sussman, 1961*b*). Therefore, we must inquire whether the mechanisms of activation by these diverse means are identical.

There are less data on this subject for fungi than there are for bacteria. In fact, only the cases mentioned above have been studied in any detail. In the case of *Phycomyces*, Borchert (1962) has discovered that the permeability of the spore changes much more drastically and rapidly when acetate is used as the activator than when heat is used for this purpose. Furthermore, he has described a "small vacuole" stage in the activation process which appears to be characteristic of acetate-activated spores. These observations suggest that there are definite differences in at least a few of the steps leading to activation and germination in response to different activators.

This question was approached by Sussman (1961*b*) who compared the response of *Neurospora* ascospores to heat- or furfural-activation. These differences are outlined in Table 10.7 which discloses that, whereas heat-activated cells are inhibited by $NaHSO_3$ and NaN_3, furfural-activated cells are not. Similarly cyanide reversibly deactivates heat-treated spores but not those incubated in furfural. Moreover, aging affects the response to furfural but has much less effect upon the response of the cells to heat. Finally, the concentration of spores has no effect upon the percentage germination of heat-activated spores but affects chemically treated ones. Therefore, it is likely that differences in the effects of

Table 10.7 Differences Between Ascospores of *Neurospora* That Have Been Heat- or Chemically-Activated

Effect	Activated by: Heat	Furfural
Poisoned by $NaHSO_3$	+	−
Poisoned by NaN_3	+	−
Reversible deactivation by CN^- or 4°C	+	−
Influence of concentration of spores	−	+
Loss in activation ability with age	−	+

SOURCE: Taken from Sussman, 1961*a*. Courtesy *Quart. Rev. Biol.*

these two methods of activation exist in both *Phycomyces* and *Neurospora* but the exact nature of these is unknown.

Interrelations Between Types of Constitutive Dormancy

When the mechanisms of constitutive dormancy are classified and separated as we have done, it is possible to overlook combinations between these. Thus, specific self-inhibitors may work by inhibiting enzymatic reactions in the cell, thereby involving metabolism in the mechanism. Again, several structural barriers have been suggested to act as restraints upon development in the maintenance of the dormant state. These include the exosporium, cortex, and cysteine-rich structures (Chapters 2 and 8). It is possible that these function to keep a low internal content of water, reduce the intracellular passage of large molecules, as well as in the case of the cysteine-rich structures, to provide a basis for radiation-resistance. All three of these could be broken by the triggering of digestive enzymes. The protease and the pyrophosphatase are possible candidates. The cysteine-rich structures are an interesting example. Since germination is accompanied by the appearance of —SH groups (Vinter, 1962), the breaking of this structure may be linked to the supply of reducing agents (for example, $NADH_2$) and, thereby, to the release of the metabolic enzymes involved in electron transport.

Dormancy itself may not be specific. The term *dormancy* is usually employed to describe either the failure of spore preparations to respond to germination stimulants or the physiological state in which the mechanism responsible for germination is inhibited. This generalization cannot be uniformly applied, since the degree of dormancy of a suspension of spores differs, depending upon the germinating agent employed. Compared to spores with normal DPA levels, low DPA spores are less dormant when measured by the criterion of heat-induced germination, and are equally dormant when calcium DPA is used as the germinating agent (Keynan et al., 1962). Differential effects are also observed regarding the heat-activation necessary to give maximal rates of germination. In spores with normal DPA levels, heat-activation is necessary for both L-alanine- and L-cysteine-induced germination (Keynan et al., 1962; Krask, 1961) but not for calcium DPA-induced germination. Dipicolinic acid may be part of the system responsible for the dormant state, since the amount of heat-activation necessary for optimum germination is dependent upon the DPA content of the spores (Keynan et al., 1961). As shown in Figure 7.3, the heat-activation requirements for L-alanine-induced germination increase with increasing contents of DPA.

EXOGENOUS DORMANCY

Unfavorable physical or chemical conditions of the environment can delay the development of organisms in a seasonal, as well as irregular, manner. An example of seasonal dormancy is the response of higher plants to temperature variations in temperate regions. However, nonseasonal fluctuations in humidity, inhibitory principles, and in other environmental variables also may affect development. As was noted in Chapter 1, this form of dormancy often is called *quiescence* and has been described for diverse organisms. This form of dormancy is most important for vegetative stages and spores that are not constitutively dormant. However, even spores that have an endogenously imposed dormant period may have dormancy reimposed by environmental factors under certain conditions (cf. pages 309–311).

Inhibitors

1. *Soil*

HISTORY AND DISTRIBUTION. That fungistatic principles exist in soils has been abundantly confirmed. Many of these data are reviewed in the book by Garrett (1956), and in the proceedings of the recent *Symposium on Biological Control* (Baker and Snyder, 1965). One of the first reports of toxic materials in soil is that of Greig-Smith (1912) who observed that Australian soils yield extracts that are toxic to *Serratia marcescens* and other bacteria. The leaf litter of several tree species in Sweden exerts a repressive effect upon mycorrhizal fungi and bacteria, according to Melin (1946) and Melin and Wiken (1946). American subsurface soils contain inhibitors, according to Newman and Norman (1943) and materials toxic to *Helminthosporium sativum* and other fungi are described for several different Canadian soils by Simmonds et al. (1950). To further establish the ubiquity of these inhibitory materials in soils, Stover (1955) reported that spores of *Fusarium oxysporum* f. *cubense* did not germinate in raw Honduran soils, while Jackson (1958) showed similar effects upon 11 of 19 fungi tested. That extracts of pine litter and lysimeter water, as well as soil, contain fungistatic principles was shown by Vinter (1955) in Germany; and Pochon and Barjac (1952) have shown that extracts of French peat soils inhibit some bacteria strongly, especially *Azotobacter chroococcum*. Thus, a wide geographical distribution of factors inhibitory to microorganisms is demonstrated by these data. Are these materials limited to a few types of soils, or are they of more general occurrence?

That widely different types of soils demonstrate inhibitory effects has been suggested. Thus, peat soils (Pochon and Barjac, 1952), subsoils (Newman and Norman, 1943), leaf litter (Melin, 1946; Winter, 1955), and other sources were used in the work mentioned above. Moreover, Dobbs and Hinson (1953) have shown that conidia of *Penicillium frequentans* are completely inhibited on every sample of fresh soil tested, including those from forest, grasslands, cultivated gardens, bottom mud, and subsoil. More recently, Lingappa and Lockwood (1961) have shown the presence of soil fungistasis in loam, muck, and hardwood soils, using several fungi and different techniques. On the other hand, the inhibitory factor in the Nigerian soils studied by Jackson (1958) was confined to the upper 40 cm of soil, and Dobbs et al. (1960) recently have found that soils fluctuate in their ability to inhibit. Therefore, it is likely that soils differ in their content of these factors and the techniques for observing these effects undoubtedly influence the results (Lingappa and Lockwood, 1963).

Reversibility of the inhibition by soil factors is necessary if they are to play a role in dormancy. Bacteriostatic factors have been described by Waksman and Woodruff (1942) and Winter et al. (1960), so that organisms affected in this way could develop after the disappearance of the inhibitor, or the appearance of substances which reverse its effect.

Fungistatic principles are widely distributed and often these appear to be specific for spores. The observations of Dobbs and Hinson (1953) established the presence of a "widespread fungistasis" as a result of the use of the spores of several species. The reversibility of the inhibition of these spores has been demonstrated by Dobbs and Hinson (1953) and Jackson (1960). Spores have been used in most of the work on this subject but it is known in the case of several basidiomycetes that mycelium is affected as well (Dobbs et al., 1960). In either case, a state of exogenous dormancy can be induced by the fungistatic principle in soil. If, as seems likely (Burges, 1960; Chapter 3), spores of most fungi survive longer than mycelium, then the former are of greater importance in survival under these circumstances.

MEANS OF REVERSAL. As Garrett (1956) has pointed out, the ecological significance of the "widespread fungistasis" may be in the survival value that accrues to an organism if it is restrained from germinating until substrate is available. In fact, it has been shown by Dobbs and Hinson (1953) and others that a substrate itself (glucose) may serve to overcome the fungistatic principle in unsterilized soil. Reversal of the inhibition may be accomplished by the following treatments (Dobbs and Hinson, 1953; Brian, 1960):

1. Heat-treatment (autoclaving), or prolonged drying.
2. Extraction with organic solvents.
3. Treatment with citrate-phosphate, but not with water, hydrochloric acid, or phosphate buffer.
4. Addition of nutrients to soil, including glucose (Dobbs and Hinson, 1953; Jackson, 1958) and other sugars (Jackson, 1960), "crude glucose", particulate crude organic materials like soy-bean meal (Chinn and Ledingham, 1957), and peptone (Lingappa and Lockwood, 1961).
5. Growth in the vicinity of roots (Jackson, 1957), probably in response to leakage of organic compounds (Rovira, 1956).
6. Addition of charcoal to soil.

NATURE OF FUNGISTATIC PRINCIPLE. No clear-cut evidence exists which distinguishes between the lack of an essential metabolite(s) or the presence of an inhibitor, according to Brian (1960). The data are thoroughly reviewed in this paper and the view that an inhibitor is formed is favored. The basis of this conclusion is the fact that soil extracts often stimulate fungus spores (Dobbs and Hinson, 1953; James, 1958; Park, 1956; Lingappa and Lockwood, 1961). Moreover, spores of fungi which germinate readily in water are inhibited by soil (Dobbs and Hinson, 1953).

However, the failure to extract substances with the properties which have been described leaves the evidence circumstantial. Although substances have been extracted which appear to be active (Dobbs and Hinson, 1953; Dobbs et al., 1960), the results are erratic, and the effect often slight. The possibility is suggested (Dobbs et al., 1960) that the substance is unstable and easily removed on Seitz filters but little more in the way of specific chemical information is available.

It is tempting, as Brian (1960) indicates, to explain the soil fungistasis on the basis of antibiotics. However, there is no good evidence upon which to base this conclusion, whereas there are data which suggest that antibiotic production is unlikely in the soils in which fungistasis has been detected. Nevertheless, only relatively few antibiotics have been studied in detail in nature so that the possibility exists that one or more of these can explain the effect.

Humus preparations of various kinds and soil extracts have been reported by Lingappa and Lockwood (1962) to be inhibitory to fungi. These workers suggest that materials of unknown composition were present, as well as lignin, and they note that phenolic constituents of plant materials might be involved. As the authors themselves point out, a connection of these materials with the "widespread fungistasis" is doubtful in view of the occurrence of the latter in soils low in organic matter.

Therefore, pre-existing inhibitory materials, to which the "widespread fungistasis" can be attributed, have not been unambiguously demonstrated. Another type of explanation is proposed by Lingappa and Lockwood (1961), based upon provision of substrate for the growth of competing microorganisms which produce antibiotics concomitantly with the assay of germination. According to this hypothesis, fungus spores provide nutrients to the soil in their immediate vicinity, resulting in the liberation of antibiotics by other microbes. Experiments in support of this suggestion include the incubation of agar layers upon soil at 1°C in an endeavor to permit the diffusion of pre-existing fungistatic materials into the agar, after which spores were seeded on the surface. No fungistasis could be demonstrated by this means although it was proved that the soil did not lose its fungistatic capacity by incubation at low temperatures, and that the fungistatic principle can diffuse at 1°C. Moreover, the addition of antibacterial substances resulted in a decrease in soil fungistasis but suppression was not complete. More recently, these authors, in unpublished work, claim to have demonstrated that when conidia of *Glomerella cingulata* are washed to remove nutrients on the surface, germination in natural soil is greatly enhanced (Table 10.8). Uredospores of *Puccinia glumarum* also are inhibited on natural soils, but not completely.

Furthermore, the addition of peptone to these spores caused a decrease in germination (Table 10.8), presumably by stimulating the growth of antibiotic producers. Finally, as Table 10.8 reveals, spores like the ascospores of *Neurospora* are not affected by the fungistatic principle, ostensibly because they do not liberate enough nutrients to encourage the growth of other organisms, unless peptone is added.

Much remains to be done before this theory of the mechanism of fungistasis can be accepted. First, proof of the liberation of nutrients by the spores must be presented. Then, it must be established that these are responsible for the growth of antibiotic producers. Some suggestion that spores do encourage the growth of bacteria and actinomycetes is provided by Lingappa and Lockwood (1961), but these must be identified as the source of the fungistatic principle. Finally, the ability of the organisms to form antibiotics under natural conditions in soil must be ascertained and, as Brian (1957) points out, there is considerable controversy on this point. However, these possibilities should be explored, especially since the alternate hypothesis is a pre-existing inhibitor. One example of this is available.

Table 10.8 Effect of Soils Treated in Various Ways upon Fungal Spores

Organism	Treatment	Percent Germination	
Neurospora tetrasperma, heat-activated ascospores	Water agar	80	
	Sterile soil	80	
	Natural soil	80	
	Natural soil + 0.5 percent peptone	0	
Puccinia glumarum, uredospores	Water agar	75	
	Sterile soil	75	
	Natural soil	40	
	Natural soil + 0.5 percent peptone	0	
		Washed	Unwashed
Glomerella cingulata, conidia	Water agar	98	85
	Sterile soil	98	98
	Natural soil	80	0
	Natural soil + 0.5 percent peptone	0	0

SOURCE: Unpublished data of B. T. Lingappa and J. T. Lockwood.

Buxton (1957) found that root exudates of pea culm acted differently in depressing the germination of *Fusarium* spores of different races. This inhibition appeared to be related to the resistance of the spore itself.

2. *Inhibitors in Aquatic Environments.* The existence of fungistatic principles in estuarine sediments has been reported by Borut and Johnson (1962). Thus, spores of *Aspergillus wentii, Penicillium janthinellum*, and *Zygorhynchus moelleri* germinated to an insignificant extent in untreated or filtered sea water as compared to the amount in a 3.5 percent saline solution. As Figure 10.8 shows, spores of *A. wentii* and *Z. moelleri* do appreciably better in autoclaved sea water than in raw sea water, in contrast to those of *P. janthinellum* which, if anything, germinate less well in the autoclaved medium. All of the spores mentioned, however, germinated better in sterile saline than they did in the sea water media, suggesting the presence of a fungistatic principle analogous to that found in soils.

Another phenomenon that is revealed in this work concerns the ability of vegetative stages to grow in the sea waters in which spores failed to germinate. As the authors point out, all the fungi whose spores germinated in distilled water showed such a response and small amounts of nutrients helped to overcome the toxic effect of sea water.

Almost nothing is known of the chemical identity, or source of the inhibitors in sea water and it is to be hoped that such data will be forthcoming.

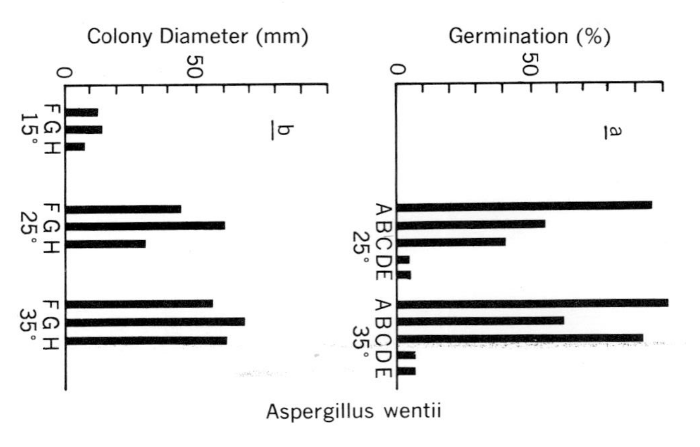

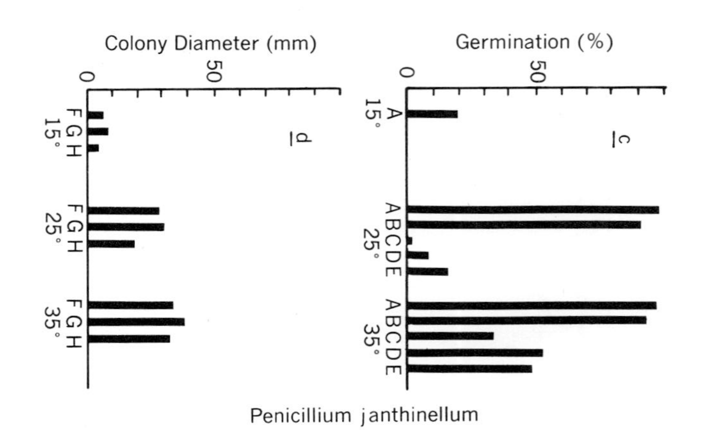

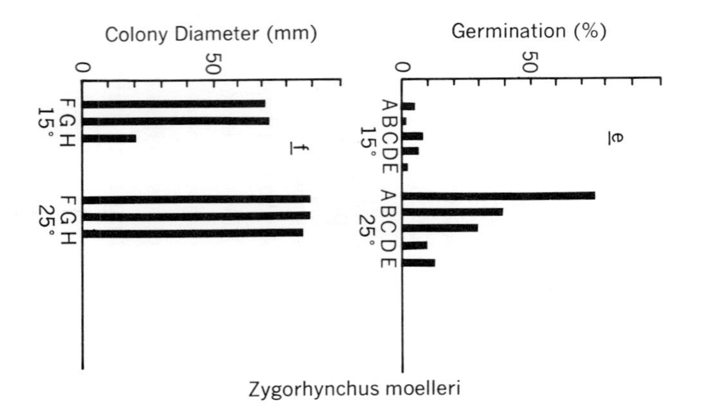

Figure 10.8 Spore germination and growth of fungi in various saline media. Legend: A, distilled water; B, 3.5 percent NaCl; C, autoclaved sea water; D, filtered sea water; E, fresh untreated sea water; F, Sabourand's agar+distilled water; G, 3.5 percent NaCl; H, raw sea water. (After Borut and Johnson, 1962, courtesy *Mycologia*, New York Botanical Garden.)

3. *Higher Plant Inhibitors.* Other substrates which serve in the germination of fungus spores in nature also contain inhibitors. Plants, as potential hosts, are included in this category and the book by Gäumann (1950) reviews some of the data which bear on inhibitory principles which contribute to their resistance to pathogens. The presence of bacterial and fungal inhibitors has been mentioned in the discussion of soil (Melin, 1946; Winter, 1955). Among the substances of natural occurrence that serve in this way are protocatechuic acid and catechol, phenols that are inhibitory to conidia of *Colletotrichum circinans* and are found in the scales of red onions (Link and Walker, 1933). Chlorogenic acid and related compounds are active both *in vitro* and *in vivo* against conidia of *Venturia inaequalis* and *V. pirina*, and phenols like pinosylvin are strongly inhibitory to conidia of *Polyporus annosus* (Rennerfelt, 1949). Because the latter substance is found in the heartwood of pine and not in that of spruce, it may account for some of the differences in the resistance of these woods to pathogens. The mustard oil (allylisothiocyanate) that is found in various plants has been shown to prevent the germination of resting spores of *Plasmodiophora brassicae* (Hooker et al., 1945; MacFarlane, 1952). More recently, Dance (1961) reported that spores of *Venturia populina* were destroyed when sprayed on shoots of aspens, whereas shoots of balsam and Lombardy poplar did not show this effect.

4. *Relation of Exogenous Inhibitors to Activation Treatments.* As was the case for the self-inhibitors discussed, it is likely that some of the requirements for germination outlined in Chapter 7 can be explained in terms of the reversal of exogenous inhibitors. The requirements for soybean meal when conidia of *Helminthosporium sativum* are germinated in autoclaved soil (Chinn, 1953) and that for glucose reported by Dobbs and Hinson (1953) for several fungi seem to fit in this category. Other means of reversing the effect of soil inhibitors have been described for spores of *Tilletia brevifaciens* (Gassner and Niemann, 1955), including treatment with inorganic salts such as Na_3PO_4, $KMnO_4$, and $MnSO_4$, as well as organic substances such as oxalate. In fact, certain of these can replace light as a stimulant of germination although low temperatures are still required. More recently, Niemann (1957) has shown that several mercury compounds also appear to reverse an inhibitory factor in soil in the case of smut spore germination. Honey-dew has been shown to contain substances that aid the germination of *Claviceps purpurea* (Garay, 1956), possibly because of its content of catalase and ergothioneine which protect the spores against hydrogen peroxide. It was also pointed out that the toxicity of certain synthetic antimetabolites was reversed by "honey-dew," although the relevance of these observations to natural systems is still in question.

Other Environmental Factors

1. *Temperature.* Reference to Table 8.1 will reveal that often the cardinal temperatures for the development of microbes is narrow. This fact is especially

relevant to the role of temperature as an inducer of exogenous dormancy in the lower ranges. Thus, even vegetative structures of microorganisms survive very well at cold temperatures (Chapter 3), so that cessation of development in the cold usually is reversible. Therefore, dormancy is induced in a manner analogous to that by which many higher plants and some animals become quiescent in winter.

Such dormancy is less likely to be induced at temperatures above the maximum because survival usually is not encountered at higher temperatures, except under dry conditions, or with certain highly resistant creatures. Nevertheless, it is likely that where survival is possible, exogenous dormancy can be induced even above the maximum temperature for growth.

2. *Relative Humidity.* It is likely that the relative humidity of an environment can determine whether or not germination will occur. The fact remains that high relative humidities are required for the development of most fungus spores, although there are exceptional organisms like the powdery mildews which can germinate in dry atmospheres (cf. Chapters 3 and 8). Consequently, if spores can withstand desiccation, low humidities can also be a means of enforcing a rest period. A mechanism whereby such resistance can be engendered is suggested by the data of Terui and Mochizuki (1955) which disclose that the Q_{O_2} of conidia of *Aspergillus niger* is greater than 5 at 100 percent relative humidity but falls to 1 at 60 percent. The exhaustion of endogenous reserves is thereby delayed and the chances for the survival of this organism are correspondingly improved under conditions of low humidity.

3. *Gas Atmosphere.* As was pointed out in Chapter 8, many microorganisms have strict requirements for certain gases. Altered levels of gases like carbon dioxide and oxygen might be expected to occur in soils that undergo seasonal changes in water level, and in certain strata of aquatic environments, and so on, so that reversible restraints upon the development of certain organisms could occur in these environments.

For example, the reversible inhibition of germination by excess concentrations of carbon dioxide has been shown in the case of certain mucors by Lopriore (1895) and for conidia of *Erysiphe graminis* by Brodie and Neufeld (1942). That this gas probably exerts a strong selective influence on soil fungi was shown by Burges and Fenton (1953) who reported that tolerant organisms populated regions of the soil that have high concentrations of carbon dioxide. Sclerotia of *Sclerotium rolfsii* fail to germinate in soils high in carbon dioxide, according to Abeygunawardena and Wood (1957), and can be induced to germinate by forced aeration of the soil.

The role of oxygen is too well known to require comment but it is likely that dormancy can be induced by the removal of this compound (see below).

4. *Induced Dormancy and Reversible Deactivation.* Environmental factors may

impose another dormant period upon spores which have had a previous state of rest disrupted. This was demonstrated by Goddard (1935) with ascospores of *Neurospora*. In this case, heat-activated spores reverted to the dormant condition after anaerobic incubation (Table 10.9). Reactivation could be accomplished

Table 10.9 Reversible Deactivation of Germination of Ascospores of *Neurospora tetrasperma*

	Time in Nitrogen after Activation	Germination	Reactivated Germination
Nitrogen series	Hours	Percent	Percent
Control (activated in air)	—	94.2	
Activated in N_2	0.0	95.9	
	0.5	96.3	
	1.0	96.7	
	2.0	74.9	
	3.0	41.1	
	4.0	2.7	
	9.0	1.6	92.5
	50.0	0.0	94.7[a]
	24.0	4.1	91.5[b]
Cyanide series (HCN = 1×10^3 M)	Time in HCN after activation		
Control (activated in air)	—	96.6	
Activated in HCN	0.0	95.6	
	0.5	93.7	
	1.0	85.6	
	1.5	75.5	
	3.0	52.8	94.5
	4.0	37.4	
	7.0	0.0	

SOURCE: Goddard, 1935, 1939.

[a] A duplicate tube was reactivated and set aside unopened for an additional 24 hours, and the data are given in the next line below.

[b] These spores have been activated three times and deactivated twice.

if the spores were heated again and provided with oxygen. Three cycles of activation and deactivation could be undergone by these spores. Also, cyanide was shown by Goddard (1939) to reversibly deactivate these ascospores. These data were corroborated and extended by Sussman et al. (1956) who showed that acetaldehyde production, a concomitant of activation and germination, is reversible under the conditions described by Goddard. Low temperatures as well as anaerobiosis will deactivate these spores, according to Sun and Sussman (1960). As shown in Figure 10.9, after incubation of heat-activated ascospores at 4°C for 48 hours, none of the spores germinated. That these could be reactivated also is

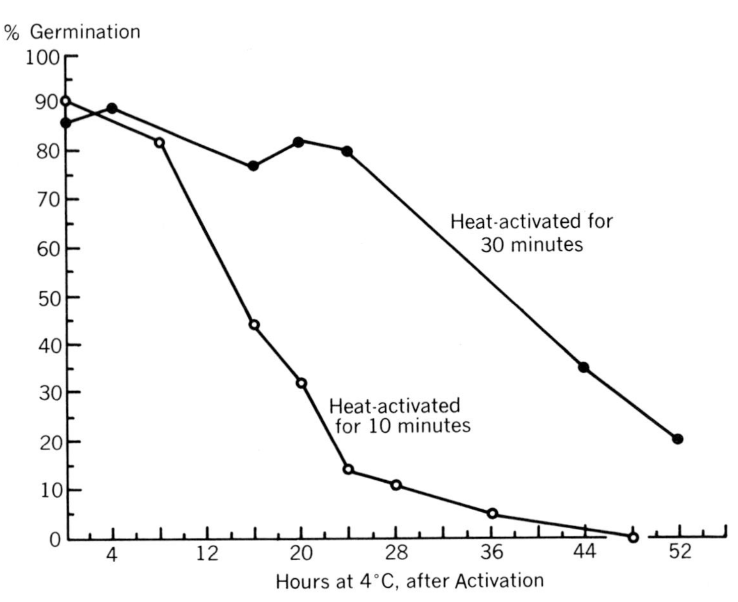

Figure 10.9 Germinability of ascospores of *Neurospora tetrasperma* after incubation at 4°C for various times. Spores were activated by heat for both 10 and 30 minutes. (From Sun and Sussman, 1960, courtesy *Amer. J. Bot.*)

shown in Table 10.10. The same effect could be demonstrated with ascospores activated in furfural. On the other hand, such spores could not be reactivated

Table 10.10 Effect of Reactivation upon Ascospores Incubated at 4°C After Their First Activation Treatment[a]

Time of Storage at 4°C (hours)	Percent Germination	
	Control Spores	Reactivated Spores
36	5	85
60	0	60

SOURCE: After Sun and Sussman, 1960.
[a] Spores were removed from 4°C, reactivated by suspension in water at 60°C for 10 minutes, and then incubated at 27°C.

with furfural although heat-treatment was effective. By contrast, the activated state was preserved at −20°C, and at 4°C when the spores were dehydrated in glycerol. Sun and Sussman suggest that a key reaction leading to germination goes more slowly at 4°C than a back reaction which causes deactivation. Furthermore, neither of these reactions can continue at −20°C, or when spores are dehydrated, so that they remain in the activated condition under these circumstances.

Analogous findings have been reported for sporangiospores of *Phycomyces blakesleeanus* by Halbsguth and Rudolph (1959). In this case, incubation at 25°C in water, or under anaerobiosis, resulted in the deactivation of heat-treated spores. Several cycles of activation and deactivation were possible, although complete inactivation was not achieved in later cycles and, beginning with the fifth activation, such treatment reduced the germination percentage. In addition, Domsch (1954) has found that an insufficient amount of oxygen will similarly affect conidia of *Erysiphe.*

Instances in which a type of dormancy is imposed that is different from that in the spores at the start are interesting variations on the theme of deactivation. Thus, Doguet (1959) has observed that spores of *Trichothecium roseum* and *Chaetoceratostoma longirostre*, exposed to sub-lethal temperatures above the maximum for growth, failed to germinate upon return to favorable temperatures. The dormancy into which they had lapsed lasted up to 17 and 32 days respectively.

Chilling of uredospores of *Puccinia graminis* var. *tritici* induces a reversible "cold-dormancy," according to Bromfield (1964). Repeated induction and reversal of the dormant condition was possible. What makes this situation different from that in *Neurospora* ascospores and *Phycomyces* sporangiospores is that activators that are usually effective in breaking the "primary" dormancy of uredospores cannot reverse cold-induced dormancy; instead, a heat shock is required (Bromfield, 1964).

Thus it is clear that environmentally induced deactivation is found in each of the major groups of fungi. In addition, Curran and Evans (1945) have observed a similar effect in bacteria. In this case, heat-activated spores were gradually deactivated during storage and could be reactivated by another heat-treatment.

Secondary sporulation, or the formation of another spore immediately after the germination of a first spore, has been known in the fungi for some time. Recently, the conditions for the formation of secondary macroconidia of *Trichophyton mentagrophytes* have been examined in detail by Chin et al. (1963) and arginine and glucose have been shown to be required. Conceivably, the formation of such spores, instead of vegetative structures, could be another means by which dormancy is induced environmentally.

The effects discussed in this section are very similar to some types of induced and secondary dormancy in seeds and vegetative propagules of higher plants. An interesting aspect of such secondary dormancy is the finding that the environmental treatments which are the inducers of this condition frequently resemble those which confer the primary dormancy that seeds develop in nature. It will be of interest to determine whether this parallel holds for spores as well.

REFERENCES

ABEYGUNAWARDENA, D. V. W., and R. K. S. WOOD. 1957. *Trans. Brit. Mycol. Soc.* 40:221–231.

ALLEN, P. J. 1955. *Phytopathology* 215:259–266.

BADEN, M. L. 1915. *Ann. Botany* 29:135–142.

BAILEY, D. L. 1923. *Minnesota Univ. Agr. Exp. Sta. Tech. Bull.* 16:1–31.

BAKER, K. F., and W. C. SNYDER. 1965. *Ecology of Soil-borne Plant Pathogens.* Univ. California Press, Berkeley, 571 pp.

BELL, A. A. 1960. *Phytopathology* (Abst.) 50:629.

BERGER, J. A., and A. G. MARR. 1960. *J. Gen. Microbiol.* 22:147–157.

BLACK, S. H., T. HASHIMOTO, and P. GERHARDT. 1960. *Can. J. Microbiol.* 6:213–224.

BLACKWELL, E. 1935. *Nature* 135:546.

BORCHERT, R. 1962. *Beitr. Biol. Pflanz.* 38:31–61.

BORUT, S., and T. W. JOHNSON, JR. 1962. *Mycologia* 54:181–193.

BOYD, A. E. W. 1952. *Ann. Appl. Biol.* 39:322–329.

BRAAMS, R. 1960. *Radiation Res.* 12:113–119.

BRIAN, P. W. 1957. in *Microbial Ecology.* 7th Symp., Soc. for Gen. Microbiol. Cambridge Univ. Press, London, pp. 168–188.

BRIAN, P. W. 1960. in *The Ecology of Soil Fungi.* D. Parkinson and J. S. Waid, eds. Univ of Liverpool Press, Liverpool, pp. 115–129.

BRIERLEY, W. B. 1917. *Ann. Botany* 31:127–132.

BRODIE, H. J., and J. F. JONES. 1946. *Can. J. Res. Sec. C* 124:318–329.

BRODIE, H. J., and C. C. NEUFELD. 1942. *Can. J. Res. Sec.* C 20:41–61.

BROMFIELD, K. R. 1964. *Phytopathology* 54:68–74.

BROWN, W. 1922. *Ann. Botany* 36:257–283.

BROWN, W. L. 1956. Ph.D. Thesis, Univ. of Illinois, Urbana.

BUDD, K., A. S. SUSSMAN, and F. I. EILERS. 1966. *J. Bacteriol.* In Press.

BURGES, N. A. 1960. in *The Ecology of Soil Fungi.* D. Parkinson and J. S. Waid, eds. Univ. of Liverpool Press, Liverpool, pp. 185–191.

BURGES, A., and E. FENTON. 1953. *Trans. Brit. Mycol. Soc.* 36:104–108.

BUXTON, N. 1957. *Trans. Brit. Mycol. Soc.* 40:145–154.

CANTINO, E. C. 1951. Antonie van Leeuwenhoek, *J. Microbiol. Serol.* 17:59–96.

CHIN, B., D. G. CARLSON, and S. G. KNIGHT. 1963. *Bacteriol. Proc.* p. 32.

CHINN, S. H. F. 1953. *Can. J. Botany* 31:718–724.

CHINN, S. H. F., and R. J. LEDINGHAM. 1957. *Can. J. Botany* 35:697–701.

CHURCH, B. D. 1954. Ph.D. Thesis, Univ. of Michigan.

CHURCH, B. D., and H. HALVORSON. 1955. *Bacteriol. Proc.* p. 41.

CHURCH, B. D., and H. HALVORSON. 1957. *J. Bacteriol.* 73:470–476.

CHURCH, B. D., and H. HALVORSON. 1959. *Nature* 83:124–125.

CHURCH, B. D., H. HALVORSON, and H. O. HALVORSON. 1954. *J. Bacteriol.* 68:393–399.

COCHRANE, J. C., V. W. COCHRANE, F. G. SIMON, and J. SPAETH. 1963. *Phytopathology* 53:1155–1160.

COCHRANE, V. W., S. J. BERRY, F. G. SIMON, J. C. COCHRANE, C. B. COLLINS, J. A. LEVY, and P. K. HOLMES. 1963*a*. *Plant Physiology* 38:533–541.

COCHRANE, V. W., J. C. COCHRANE, J. M. VOGEL, and R. S. COLES, JR. 1963*b*. *J. Bacteriol.* 86:312–319.

CURRAN, H. R., and F. R. EVANS. 1945. *J. Bacteriol.* 49:335–346.

DANCE, B. W. 1961. *Can. J. Botany* 39:875–890.

DEBARY, A. 1884. *Vergleichende Morphologie der Pilze, Mycetozoan, und Bacterien.* Engelmann, Leipzig (Engl. trans. 1887).

DEBARY, A. 1887. *Comparative Morphology, and Biology of the Fungi, Mycetozoa, and Bacteria.* Clarendon Press, Oxford.

DOBBS, C. G., and W. H. HINSON. 1953. *Nature* 172:197–199.

DOBBS, C. G., W. H. HINSON, and JOAN BYWATER. 1960. in *The Ecology of Soil Fungi.* D. Parkinson and J. S. Waid, eds. Univ. of Liverpool Press, Liverpool, pp. 130–147.

DOI, R., and H. HALVORSON. 1961. *J. Bacteriol.* 81:642–648.

DOI, R., H. HALVORSON, and B. D. CHURCH. 1959. *J. Bacteriol.* 77:43–54.

DOMSCH, K. H. 1954. *Arch. Mikrobiol.* 20:163–175.

DOGUET, G. 1959. *Bull. Soc. Botan., France* 106:177–186.

DUNLEAVY, J., and G. SNYDER. 1963. *Proc. Iowa Acad. Sci.* 69:118–121.
EDGERTON, C. W. 1910. *La. Agr. Expt. Sta. Bull.* 119:1–55.
ETTEL, G. E., and W. HALBSGUTH. 1963. *Beitr. Biol. Pflanz.* 39:451–488.
EVENARI, M. 1949. *Botan. Rev.* 75:153–194.
EZEKIEL, W. N. 1930. *Univ. Minn. Agr. Expt. Sta. Tech. Bull.* 67:1–62.
FALCONE, G., and A. CARACÕ. 1958. *7th Internat. Congr. Microbiol., Stockholm* p. 34.
FEY, G., G. W. GOULD, and A. D. HITCHINS. 1964. *J. Gen. Microbiol.* 35:229–236.
FITZ-JAMES, P. C. 1955. *Can. J. Microbiol.* 1:525–548.
FORSYTH, F. R. 1955. *Can. J. Botan.* 33:363–373.
FREESE, E., and M. CASHEL. 1965. In *Spores III*. L. L. Campbell and H. O. Halvorson, eds. Amer. Soc. for Microbiol., Ann Arbor, pp. 144–151.
FROMAGEOT, G., and R. GRAND. 1943. *Enzymologia* 11:81–86.
GARAY, A. ST. 1956. *Physiol. Plantarum* 9:344–349.
GARRETT, S. D. 1956. *Biology of Root Infecting Fungi*. Cambridge Univ. Press, London, 292 pp.
GASSNER, G., and E. NIEMANN. 1955. *Phytopathol. Z.* 23:121–140.
GAÜMANN, E. A. 1946. *Pflanzliche Infektionslehre*. Verlag Birkhauser, Basel, 611 pp. (*Principles of Plant Infection*, English edn., Crosby Lockwood, London, 1950.)
GERHARDT, P., and S. H. BLACK. 1961. *J. Bacteriol.* 82:750–760.
GODDARD, D. R. 1935. *J. Gen. Physiol.* 19:45–60.
GODDARD, D. R. 1939. *Cold Spr. Harb. Symp. Quant. Biol.* 7:362–376.
GODDARD, D. R. and P. E. SMITH. 1938. *Plant Physiol.* 24:241–264.
GOLDMAN, D. S. 1959. *Biochim. Biophys. Acta* 34:527–539.
GREIG-SMITH, R. 1912. *Zentr. Bakteriol.* 34:224–226.
GWYNNE-VAUGHAN, H. C. I., and H. S. WILLIAMSON. 1933. *Trans. Brit. Mycol. Soc.* 18:127–134.
HACHISUKA, Y. N., N. ASANO, N. KATO, and T. KUNO 1954. *Nagoya J. Med. Sci.* 17:403–411.
HACHISUKA, Y. N., N. ASANO, N. KATO, M. OKAJIMA, M. KITAORI, and T. KUNO. 1955. *J. Bacteriol.* 69:399–406.
HALBSGUTH, W., and H. RUDOLPH. 1959. *Arch. Mikrobiol.* 32:296–308.
HALVORSON, H., R. DOI, and B. D. CHURCH. 1958. *Proc. Nat. Acad. Sci. U.S.* 44:1171–1180.
HALVORSON, H. O. 1957. *J. Appl. Bacteriol.* 20:305–314.
HALVORSON, H. O. 1959. *Bacteriol. Rev.* 23:267–272.
HALVORSON, H. O., and B. D. CHURCH. 1957. *J. Appl. Bacteriol.* 20:359–372.
HALVORSON, H., R. O'CONNOR, and R. DOI. 1961. In *Cryptobiotic Stages in Biological Systems*. N. Grossowicz, S. Hestrin, and A. Keynan, eds. Elsevier, Amsterdam, N.Y., London, pp. 70–96.
HARRELL, W. K. 1958. *Can. J. Microbiol.* 4:393–398.
HARRELL, W. K., and H. O. HALVORSON. 1955. *J. Bacteriol.* 69:275–279.
HARRELL, W. K., and E. MANTINI. 1957. *Can. J. Microbiol.* 3:735–739.
HEILIGMAN, F., N. W. DESROSIER, and H. BROUMAND. 1956. *Food Res.* 21:63–69.
HILL, E. P., and A. S. SUSSMAN. 1964. *J. Bacteriol.* 88:1556–1566.
HILL, E. P., A. S. SUSSMAN, and F. EILERS. 1964. Unpublished results.
HILLS, G. M. 1949. *Biochem. J.* 45:363–370.
HILLS, G. M. 1950. *J. Gen. Microbiol.* 4:38–47.
HOLTON, R. 1958. Ph.D. Thesis, Univ. of Michigan.
HOOKER, W. J., J. C. WALKER, and K. P. LINK. 1945. *J. Agr. Res.* 70:63–78.
HOSHINO, J. 1961. *Ann. Rept. Inst. Food Microbiol. Chiba Univ.* 14:53–58.
HOSHINO, J., A. NISHI, and T. YANAGITA. 1962. *J. Gen. Appl. Microbiol.* 8:233–245.
HSU, W. 1963. Ph.D. Thesis, Univ. of Illinois.
HYATT, M. T., and H. S. LEVINSON. 1961. *J. Bacteriol.* 81:204–211.
IRVINE, B. R. 1963. *Dissertation Abst.* 23 (9): 3091–3092.
JACKSON, R. M. 1957. *Nature* 180:96–97.
JACKSON, R. M. 1958. *J. Gen. Microbiol.* 18:248–258.
JACKSON, R. M. 1960. in *The Ecology of Soil Fungi*. D. Parkinson and J. S. Waid, eds. Univ. of Liverpool Press, Liverpool, pp. 168–176.
JAMES, N. 1958. *Can. J. Microbiol.* 4:363–370.
JANCZEWSKI, E. v. G. 1871. *Botan. Ztg.* 29:257–262.
KALLIO, R. E. 1951. *J. Biol. Chem.* 192:371–377.
KALLIO, R. E., and J. R. PORTER. 1950. *J. Bacteriol.* 60:607–615.

KEITT, G. W., E. C. BLODGETT, E. E. WILSON, and R. O. MAGIE. 1937. *Wis. Agr. Sta. Res. Bull.* 132:1–117.

KEYNAN, A., and H. O. HALVORSON. 1962. *J. Bacteriol.* 83:100–105.

KEYNAN, A., W. G. MURRELL, and H. O. HALVORSON. 1961. *Bacteriol. Proc.* p. 76.

KEYNAN, A., W. G. MURRELL, and H. O. HALVORSON. 1962. *J. Bacteriol.* 83:395–399.

KOLLER, D., A. M. MAYER, A. POLJAKOFF-MAYBER, and S. KLEIN. 1962. *Ann. Rev. Plant Physiol.* 13:437–464.

KNAYSI, G. 1945. *J. Bacteriol.* 49:473–493.

KNAYSI, G. 1948. *Bacteriol. Rev.* 12:19–77.

KRASK, B. J. 1961. in *Spores II.* H. O. Halvorson, ed. Burgess Pub. Co., Minneapolis, pp. 89–100.

LAWRENCE, N. L. 1955. *J. Bacteriol.* 70:577–582.

LAWRENCE, N. L., and Y. TSAN. 1962. *J. Bacteriol.* 83:228–233.

LEHMAN, S. G. 1923. *Ann. Miss. Botan. Gard.* 10:111–178.

LEVINSON, H. S. 1957. in *Spores.* H. O. Halvorson, ed. Am. Inst. Biol. Sci., Washington, D.C., pp. 120–135.

LEVINSON, H. S., and M. T. HYATT. 1955. *J. Bacteriol.* 70:368–374.

LEVINSON, H. S., and M. G. SEVAG. 1953. *J. Gen. Physiol.* 36:617–629.

LEVINSON, H. S., J. D. SLOAN, JR., and M. T. HYATT. 1958. *J. Bacteriol.* 75:291–299.

LEWIS, J. C., N. S. SNELL, and H. K. BURR. 1960. *Science* 132:544–545.

LINGAPPA, B. T., and J. LOCKWOOD. 1961. *J. Gen. Microbiol.* 26:473–485.

LINGAPPA, B. T., and J. LOCKWOOD. 1962. *Phytopathology* 52:295–299.

LINGAPPA, B. T., and J. LOCKWOOD. 1963. *Phytopathology* 53:529–531.

LINGAPPA, B. T., and A. S. SUSSMAN. 1959. *Plant Physiol.* 34:466–472.

LINK, K. P., and J. C. WALKER. 1933. *J. Biol. Chem.* 100:379–385.

LOPRIORE, G. 1895. *Jahr. Wiss. Botan.* 28:531–626.

LOWRY, R. J., A. S. SUSSMAN, and B. VON BÖVENTER-HEIDENHAIN. 1957. *Mycologia* 49:609–622.

MACFARLANE, I. 1952. *Ann. Appl. Biol.* 39:239–256.

MACHLIS, L., and ESTHER OSSIA. 1935. *Am. J. Botany* 40:358–365.

MAGIE, R. O. 1935. *Phytopathology* 25:131–159.

MCCALLAN, S. E. A. 1930. *Cornell Univ. Agr. Expt. Sta. Mem.* 128:25–79.

MCKAY, R. 1939. *J. Roy. Hort. Soc.* 64:272–285.

MELHUS, I. E., and L. W. DURRELL. 1919. *Iowa Agr. Expt. Sta. Res. Bull.* 49:114–144.

MELIN, E. 1946. *Symbolae Botan. Upsalienses* 8:1–116.

MELIN, E., and T. WIKEN. 1946. *Nature* 158:200–201.

MURRELL, W. G. 1952. Ph.D. Thesis, Univ. of Oxford.

MURRELL, W. G. 1961. in *11th Symp. Soc. Gen. Microbiol.* Cambridge Univ. Press, London, p. 100.

MURRELL, W. G., and W. J. SCOTT. 1959. *Nature* 179:481–482.

MURTY, G. G. K., and H. O. HALVORSON. 1957. *J. Bacteriol.* 73:230–234.

NEWMAN, A. S., and A. G. NORMAN. 1943. *Soil Sci.* 55:377–391.

NIEMANN, E. 1957. *Angew. Botanik* 31:191–196.

NISHI, A. 1961. *J. Bacteriol.* 81:10–19.

O'CONNOR, R. J., and H. HALVORSON. 1959. *J. Bacteriol.* 78:844–851.

O'CONNOR, R. J., and H. O. HALVORSON. 1960. *Biochim. Biophys. Acta* 48:47–55.

O'CONNOR, R. J., and H. O. HALVORSON. 1961. *J. Bacteriol.* 82:706–713.

PARK, D. 1956. *Int. Congr. Soil Sci.* 6:23–28.

PARK, S. W., and E. FREESE. 1964. *Bacteriol. Proc.* p. 35.

PEDERSON, V. D. 1961. Ph.D. Thesis, Iowa State Univ.

PIÉRARD, A., and J. M. WIAME. 1960. *Biochim. Biophys. Acta* 37:490–502.

POCHON, J., and H. DE BARJAC. 1952. *Ann. Inst. Pasteur.* 83:196–199.

POWELL, J. F. 1951. *J. Gen. Microbiol.* 5:993–1000.

POWELL, J. F. 1957. *J. Appl. Bacteriol.* 20:349–358.

POWELL, J. F., and J. R. HUNTER. 1955. *J. Gen. Microbiol.* 13:59–67.

POWELL, J. F., and J. R. HUNTER. 1956. *Biochem. J.* 62:381–387.

POWELL, J. F., and R. E. STRANGE. 1953. *Biochem. J.* 54:205–209.

POWELL, J. F., and R. E. STRANGE. 1959. *Nature* 184:878–880.

RENNERFELT, E. 1949. *Acta Chem. Scand.* 3:1343–1349.

RICHARDSON, L. T., and G. D. THORN. 1962. *Phytopathology* (Abst.) 52:26.

RIEHM, E. 1923. *Z. Angew. Chem.* 36:3–4.

RIEMANN, H. 1961. in *Spores II.* H. O. Halvorson, ed. Burgess Pub. Co., Minneapolis, pp. 24–58.

RIEMANN, H., and J. ORDAL. 1961. *Science* 113:1703–1704.

RIPPEL, A., and H. BORTELS. 1927. *Biochem. Z.* 184:237–244.

ROBBINS, W. J., V. W. KAVANAGH, and F. KAVANAGH. 1942. *Botan. Gaz.* 104:224–242.

RODE, L. J., and J. W. FOSTER. 1960*a*. *Nature* 188:1132.

RODE, L. J., and J. W. FOSTER. 1960*b*. *J. Bacteriol.* 79:650–656.

RODE, L. J., and J. W. FOSTER. 1960*c*. *Arch. Mikrobiol.* 36:67–94.

RODE, L. J., and J. W. FOSTER. 1960*d*. *Proc. Nat. Acad. Sci. U.S.* 46:118–128.

RODE, L. J., and J. W. FOSTER. 1961. *J. Bacteriol.* 81:768–779.

RODE, L. J., and J. W. FOSTER. 1962*a*. *Arch. Mikrobiol.* 43:201–212.

RODE, L. J., and J. W. FOSTER. 1962*b*. *Arch. Mikrobiol.* 43:183–200.

RODE, L. J., and J. W. FOSTER. 1962*c*. *Nature* 194:1300–1301.

ROTH, N. G., and H. O. HALVORSON. 1952. *J. Bacteriol.* 63:429–435.

ROTH, N. G., and D. H. LIVELY. 1956. *J. Bacteriol.* 71:162–166.

ROTMAN, B. 1958. *J. Bacteriol.* 76:1–14.

ROVIRA, A. D. 1956. *Plant Soil* 7:178–194.

RUDOLPH, H. 1961. *Z. Naturforsch.* 16:611–614.

RYAN, F. J. 1948. *Am. J. Botany* 35:497–503.

SCHMIDT, C. F. 1958. in *Spores*. H. O. Halvorson, ed. Am. Inst. Biol. Sci., Wash., D.C., pp. 56–71.

SIMMONDS, P. M., B. J. SALLANS, and R. J. LEDINGHAM. 1950. *Sci. Agr.* 30:407–417.

SOMMER, L., and W. HALBSGUTH. 1957. *Forschungs ber. Wirtsch. Verkehrsministeriums Nordrhein-Westfalen* No. 411.

SRINIVASAN, V. R., and H. O. HALVORSON. 1961. *Biochem. Biophys. Res. Comm.* 4:409–413.

STEDMAN, R. L., E. KRAVITS, M. ANMUTH, and J. HARDING. 1956. *Science* 124:403–405.

STEWART, B. T., and H. O. HALVORSON. 1953. *J. Bacteriol.* 65:160–166.

STOCK, T. 1931. *Phytopathol. Z.* 3:231–239.

STOSCH, H. A. v. 1935. *Planta* (Berlin) 23:623–656.

STOVER, R. H. 1955. *Soil Sci.* 80:397–412.

STÜBEN, H. 1939. *Planta* (Berlin) 30:353–383.

SUN, CLARE Y., and A. S. SUSSMAN. 1960. *Am. J. Botany* 47:589–593.

SUSSMAN, A. S. 1954. *J. Gen. Physiol.* 38:59–77.

SUSSMAN, A. S. 1961*a*. *Quart. Rev. Biol.* 36:109–116.

SUSSMAN, A. S. 1961*b*. in *Spores II*. H. O. Halvorson, ed. Burgess Pub. Co., Minneapolis, pp. 198–213.

SUSSMAN, A. S., J. R. DISTLER, and J. KRAKOW. 1956. *Plant Physiol.* 31:126–135.

SUSSMAN, A. S., R. HOLTON, and B. VON BÖVENTER-HEIDENHAIN. 1958. *Arch. Mikrobiol.* 29:38–50.

TERUI, G., and T. MOCHIZUKI. 1955. *Technol. Repts. Osaka Univ.* 5:219–227.

UPPAL, B. N. 1924. *Phytopathology* 14:32–33.

VAN SUMERE, C. F., C. VAN SUMERE-DE PRETER, L. C. VINING, and G. A. LEDINGHAM. 1957. *Can. J. Microbiol.* 3:847–862.

VINTER, V. 1962. *Folia Microbiol.* 7:115–120.

VOGLINO, P. 1895. *Nuovo Giorn. Bot. Ital.* 27:181–185.

WAKSMAN, S. A., and H. B. WOODRUFF. 1942. *Soil Sci.* 53:233–239.

WALLACE, E., F. M. BLODGETT, and L. R. HESSLER. 1911. *Cornell Univ. Agr. Expt. Sta. Bull.* 290:163–208.

WARD, H. M. 1899. *Phil. Trans. Roy. Soc. London Ser. B* 191:269–291.

WILSON, E. M. 1958. *Phytopathology* 48:595–600.

WINTER, A. G. 1955 *Z. Pflanzenernaehr. Dueng. Boden.* 69:224–237.

WINTER, A. G., H. PEUSS, and F. SCHÖNBECK. 1960. in *The Ecology of Soil Fungi*. D. Parkinson and J. S. Waid, eds. Univ. of Liverpool Press, Liverpool, pp. 76–83.

WOESE, C. R., H. J. MOROWITZ, and C. A. HUTCHINSON. 1958. *J. Bacteriol.* 76:578–588.

WOLF, J. 1961. in *Spores II*. H. O. Halvorson, ed. Burgess Pub. Co., Minneapolis, pp. 1–13.

WYNNE, E. S. 1957. *Bacteriol. Rev.* 21:259–262.

WYNNE, E. S., D. A. MEHL, and W. R. SCHMEIDING. 1954. *J. Bacteriol.* 67:435–437.

YANAGITA, T. 1957. *Arch. Mikrobiol.* 26:329–344.

YANAGITA, T. 1963. *J. Gen. Appl. Microbiol.* 9:343–349.

YARWOOD, C. E. 1950. *Am. J. Botany* 37:636–639.

YARWOOD, C. E. 1956. *Mycologia* 48:20–24.

YOSHIDA, A., and E. FREESE. 1964. *Biochim. Biophys. Acta* 92:33–43.

YOSHII, H. 1931. *Bull. Sci. Fac. Terkult. Kjushu Imp. Univ. Fukuoka, Japan.* 4:524–544.

YOUNG, E. 1959. *Can. J. Microbiol.* 5:197–202.

CHAPTER 11

The Place of Spores in Nature

Many students of cryptobiotic stages such as spores, seeds, and cysts would agree that these structures play a role in the survival and dissemination of organisms that form them. In fact, the wide acceptance of the need for pasteurization, and of other practices in food preservation, agriculture, and medicine, implies recognition of these functions in our daily experience. However, despite this background, controversy has surrounded the biological role of spores. Thus, Knaysi (1948), in his review of bacterial spores, says flatly that, "The biological nature of the endospore has not yet been established," thereby agreeing with Lamanna (1952) and Cook (1932) who states that, "The only interpretation that can be given as yet is that they (bacteria) form spores because they form spores." Yet, later on in this same review, Cook adds that spores "are specifically produced to tide over unfavorable periods," thereby agreeing with most writers of recently published textbooks.

Several reasons can be advanced to explain the reluctance of some investigators to accept without qualification the disseminative and resting functions of spores. First, many biologists are embarrassed to accept teleological reasoning, in any form, as a basis for discussion and further research. The contradictions in Cook's arguments are ascribable, perhaps, to his belief that, "until the teleological attitude on the value of spores is discarded and spore formation is fully related to external factors, neither its value, if any, to the organism, the actual processes involved, nor its part in the life-history can possibly be known." It is worth contrasting this statement with one of Cassirer's (1950) who argues that, "The concept of purpose can never be struck out of the whole of natural knowledge and absorbed into the idea of cause. For even if it is not an independent principle for the explanation of nature, still the approach to one of her most important domains would be barred without it, and the knowledge of phenomena would therefore be incomplete and defective." Biology occupies a very different place in science than does physics, for example, in which causes alone must be sought (Krebs, 1954; Mora, 1962). This is so because much of biology is bound up with the notion of "wholeness" (Haldane, 1929), "purposiveness," or "directiveness" (Russell, 1945), which refer to the fact that most biological processes function to preserve, repair, or regenerate the whole organism. As long as teleology serves the researcher as a source of working hypotheses from which questions can be framed, and is not confused with forms of explanation, it is a valid adjunct of the research approach. Of course, the possibility always exists that a structure is simply an evolutionary "anhang" whose presence cannot be accounted for otherwise. Nevertheless, the number of biological entities lacking survival value seems to be very small so that it would be surprising if spores fit into this category. As far as the role of spores is concerned, questions will be raised here which bear on whether survival and dissemination are, in fact, engendered by their production; and, as will be seen, these questions lead directly to more detailed ones concerning the role of components of spores and their arrangement.

Another reason for doubts concerning the function of spores bears on the frequent observation that the majority of bacteria found in soil consist of nonspore formers. Although this is less true of fungi, troublesome techniques have made it difficult to judge with precision the relative amounts of spores and vegetative stages that survive in nature (Warcup, 1960). However, recent work suggests that some fungi, at least, survive mainly in the form of mycelium (Levisohn, 1955; Warcup, 1957*a*). Therefore, the argument might be that inasmuch as vegetative stages frequently survive in higher proportion than spores, spores must not be needed for this purpose. However, spores serve such a purpose in those organisms that form them and the fact that other microorganisms have become adapted to survive by other means does not vitiate the role they play for spore-formers. That the resistance of spores is a powerful factor in survival is suggested by Van Niel (1955), who points out that not a single spore-former is known that thrives in media unsuitable for the growth of nonspore-formers. Lacking this ability, spore-formers have apparently found competitive advantage in nature through the more passive means of heightened resistance to adverse influences in the environment. This is supported by measurements of growth rates which show that nonspore-forming ammonifiers grow faster than spore-formers (Chen, 1958).

In addition to enhancing survivability and disseminability, spores can, in certain cases, be considered to be timing devices which ensure that active growth occurs when conditions are most favorable. This type of ecological adaptation would confer selective advantage upon organisms whose environments undergo fluctuations in moisture, temperature, and other factors. Lees (1961) has proposed that diapause serves such a function in some insects and it is likely, as will be discussed later, that dormancy plays a similar role in microorganisms. Of course, not all of the roles discussed here are likely to be played simultaneously by a single spore. Thus, enough evolutionary advantage might be provided by any one of the roles mentioned to assure the place of spores in nature.

Finally, roles other than in survival, dissemination, and timing have been postulated for some spores. Knaysi (1948) reviews much work purporting to demonstrate that autogamic sexual processes are involved in the formation of endospores of bacteria. However, recent electron microscopic data on the formation of such spores, reviewed in Chapter 5, tends to eliminate this possibility. On the other hand, many dormant fungal spores are the result of meiotic divisions and are of significance as the start of the haploid portion of the life cycle.

Role of Spores in Survival

FACTORS INVOLVED IN SURVIVABILITY

Survivability in mixed populations such as those found in nature is the result of many interacting variables (Garrett, 1956). Among these may be some of the following:

1. Resistance to deleterious agents
2. Degradative capacity
3. Rapidity of growth
4. Nutritional status and capacity
5. Mutational capacity

For an organism to survive, it must be able to resist a number of deleterious agents, including viruses, lytic factors of several kinds, antibiotics produced by other organisms, self-inhibitors (staling factors), and autolytic principles. Resistance could be engendered by permeability barriers as well as by any other means which diminish susceptibility to the agents listed.

The ability to degrade the materials characteristic of a microbe's habitat is a necessary prerequisite to an organism's continued existence in that environment. Thus, a broad range of enzymatic capacities might be expected to enhance the survivability of an organism, all other factors being equal.

Rapid exploitation of the resources of an environment often makes the difference between success and failure in a competitive microbial society. An opportunity to develop and flourish may be fleeting if inhibitory, but slow-growing microbes can develop to the point where they produce the deleterious materials. Therefore, an organism lacking other defenses may survive by out-growing its competitors, through capitalizing first on the environmental opportunities which the community provides.

Self-sufficient nutritional status often may compensate for the lack of some other capacities which contribute to survivability. Endogenous substrates or the possession by the propagule of a capacity lacking in the organism at another stage may confer advantages in survival. These aspects of survival will be discussed below in more detail.

Because the raw material for selection in nature is furnished through mutations, organisms with a large capacity for genetic adaptation enjoy a potential advantage in survival. Changes in the genome may be reflected in changes in any of the capacities described which bear on survivability.

The result of the interaction of all the factors described and not the effect of single ones among them determines whether a microorganism will survive. Thus, an organism may be completely protected against deleterious factors in its environment, yet not be able to survive because of an insufficiency in its endogenous nutrient supply, or in synthetic capacity. Conversely, the most advantageous nutritional potential may not suffice to ensure the survival of an organism if it succumbs to the effects of antibiotics or lytic factors in the soil.

Having considered the factors involved in determining the survivability of microorganisms, it is now possible to ask about the role that spores play in aiding survival. First, do spores aid in prolonging the survival of microorganisms; and second, if they do, which aspects of survivability are enhanced by them?

RESISTANCE TO DELETERIOUS AGENTS

Many of the facts concerning the survivability of spores are provided in Chapter 3 and in Sussman (1965). These data will be reviewed briefly for several environmental factors and an attempt will be made to correlate these findings with some from experiments in which naturally occurring populations have been studied.

Reliable methods for distinguishing between vegetative and spore stages in natural habitats are basic to any evaluation of the role of spores in nature. Yet, such techniques are still not entirely satisfactory (Thornton and Meiklejohn, 1957; Warcup, 1960; Durbin, 1961), so that the interpretation of data in this field suffers. Thus, dilution plates skew the results toward the recovery of spores and spore-formers, rather than vegetative elements. Mycelia can be induced to develop more readily through the use of other techniques but, even so, the number of faster growing organisms present as spores often determines whether viable hyphae will develop. Furthermore, even storage and transport of soils affect the absolute and relative numbers of bacteria and fungi in soils (Stotzky et al., 1962). In this case, too, spore-forming bacteria survive better than do others, so that stored soils bias the results in this direction. Therefore, evidence for the survival of microbes in nature has conflicted on the question of the relative numbers of spore-formers and nonspore-formers to be found. The evidence will be reviewed in the following sections but the difficulties alluded to must be considered in evaluating these data.

Temperature

The data in Chapter 3 reveal that bacterial spores are more resistant to extremes of temperature than are their vegetative counterparts. Furthermore, dormant spores are more resistant than the vegetative stages of *Neurospora* where this comparison has been made in detail (B. T. Lingappa and Sussman, 1959).

On the other hand, there are instances where vegetative stages show remarkable resistance to extremes of temperature. Thermophilic bacteria lacking spores, as well as the blue-green algae of hot springs and snow fields, are examples of this kind. Moreover, the mycelium of *Colletotrichum lini* survives 3–4 hours at 55°C (Tochinai, 1926), and those of *Lenzites sepiara, L. lepideus, Trametes scialis,* and *T. carnea* have been reported to survive 2 hours in wood at 55°C (Snell, 1923). Where dormant spores are not produced, survival may become the function of the mycelium, or of specialized aggregates of these vegetative structures. For example, the microsclerotia of *Verticillium albo-atrum* survive exposure to 47°C for 40 minutes as compared with hyphae and conidia which tolerate this temperature only 10 minutes (Nelson and Wilhelm, 1958).

Evidence for the great survivability of vegetative stages of bacteria derives from studies of the flora of pasteurized milk in which certain nonspore-forming species constitute a majority of those found (Hammer, 1948). For example, in one experiment, of 225 unselected cultures that survived pasteurization at 62.8°C for 30 minutes, only 3 (1.35 percent) formed spores (Ayers and Johnson, 1913). Among 81 cultures isolated from laboratory-pasteurized milk were 13 spore-forming rods, 19 streptococci, 24 micrococci, 2 sarcinae and 33 nonspore-forming rods. That low temperatures can be borne with equal success by some nonspore-formers is shown by *Streptococcus lactis* which survived 111 days in liquid air (– 191°C), or 45 minutes in liquid hydrogen (– 253°C), subsequently growing as well as untreated controls (Beijerinck and Jacobson, 1908).

That the temperature-resistance of spores may confer survival value in nature upon organisms is found in the work of Borut (1960) on the fungi of desert soils. This study revealed that most of the fungi found in such habitats sporulate intensively, or possess resistant resting organs of other kinds. Furthermore, the optimum for the sporulation of all the species tested was 4 to 10°C higher than that for growth, suggesting that a selective advantage accrues to those fungi in the desert which produce spores in response to an increase in the temperature. Some representatives of the Mycelia Sterilia were found, including *Rhizoctonia* and *Sclerotium*, so that vegetative organs of some fungi survive in desert soils. Conclusions similar to those described above were reached by Nicot (1953) and Mahmoud et al. (1964), who worked with desert sands in Africa.

Similar findings have been reported for bacterial spores as a result of studies of the microbial flora of the Egyptian desert (Elwan and Mahmoud, 1960). In this work it was found that at times of drought, *Bacillus subtilis*, *B. licheniformis*, and *B. megaterium* predominated among the bacteria recovered. Nonspore-formers were recovered only occasionally.

Partial sterilization of soil has been used widely in agricultural practice and has led to experimentation on the survival of microorganisms after treatment with steam (Warcup, 1957*b*). In the case of the fungi, treatment of such a kind leads to the isolation of increased numbers of spore-formers, while reducing markedly the fungal flora of the old forest nursery soil studied. These results are shown in Table 11.1, in which it can be seen that a high proportion of ascomycetes, which appear to possess heat-resistant ascospores, are found after soil-steaming. Many of these species were recorded only rarely from untreated soils and may be suppressed by the growth of faster growing microorganisms under these conditions. Alternatively, these results may be interpreted as meaning that heat activates the ascospores of the species found after steaming so that they germinate only after such a treatment. As will be noted below, approximately the same group of organisms can be isolated from soil if it is treated with ethanol instead of heat (Warcup, 1962) and it will be of interest to learn whether these effects are due to the removal of competition, or activation of dormant spores, or to the combination of these reasons.

On the other hand, it will be noted that *Aspergillus versicolor*, *Penicillium purpurogenum*, and *Fusarium oxysporum*, none of which formed ascospores, survived 6 minutes of steaming. Moreover, *Trichoderma viride* tolerated 4 minutes of such treatment, thereby corroborating the observation of Tam and Clark (1943) that this fungus is very tolerant of heat in soil.

Radiations

The great resistance of some spores to a variety of radiations is illustrated in Tables 3.5 and 3.6, and is discussed in Chapter 3. Therefore, there is no question but that spores impart heightened radiation endurance in those organisms which form them. But, as in the case of temperature, some nonspore-formers are able to survive extremely high amounts of radiant energy. A comparison between the resistance of some spores and vegetative stages is provided in Table 3.3, in which it is revealed that *Sarcina lutea* survives exposure to greater energies of

Table 11.1 Effect of Soil-Steaming on the Isolation of Fungi from Kettering Loam[a]

Fungus	Length of Treatment (minutes)			
	0	2	4	6
Pythium sp.	4	—	—	—
Absidia cylindrospora	10	10	—	—
Mortierella spp.	10	6	—	—
Mucor spp.	7	5	—	—
Zygorrhynchus vuillemini	8	5	—	—
Fusarium culmorum	3	1	—	—
Penicillium A	6	7	—	—
P. frequentans	5	4	—	—
Sordaria sp.	1	4	2	—
Penicillium B	8	10	2	—
Penicillium C	10	10	2	—
Penicillium B_{14}	4	3	7	—
P. nigricans	10	8	9	—
Trichoderma viride	9	9	1	—
Aspergillus versicolor	1	2	1	2
Fusarium oxysporum	10	10	1	1
Penicillium purpurogenum	1	2	5	2
Aspergillus fumigatus	—	1	5	—
A. amstelodami[b]	—	—	3	—
Gymnoascus subumbrinus[b]	—	—	5	—
Gymnoascus B_{93}[b]	—	—	8	—
Penicillium D	—	—	6	—
P. luteum[b]	—	—	7	—
P. wortmanni[b]	—	—	7	—
P. ehrlickii	—	—	9	8
Total number of species isolated	31	32	22	5

SOURCE: After Warcup, 1951.
[a] Occurrence on ten soil plates.
[b] Ascosporic species.

ultraviolet light than do many spores. This is true of certain strains of other bacteria as well, including *Escherichia coli, Micrococcus piltonensis,* and *M. sphaerioides.* Nonsporing spoilage bacteria recently have been found to survive high dosages of γ-radiation. Thus, several strains of *M. radiodurans* and one of *Brevibacterium oregonium* (Duggan et al., 1962) survived dosages in the Megarad range.

However, if the data in Table 3.5 are examined, it can be seen that none of the nonspore-formers listed approach the resistance of spores of *Bacillus megaterium* and *B. cereus* to x-rays. This is in contrast to the case of ultraviolet light in which some vegetative bacteria are as resistant as spores.

One of the prerequisites for the survival of microorganisms in nature must be a means of overcoming the lethal effects of the radiant energy of the sun. As was pointed out in Chapter 2, some microbes have evolved built-in filters in the form of colored walls, or cytoplasms. Therefore, it is interesting to note in this connection that many fungal hyphae recovered in the resting state from soils are dark-brown or black (Warcup, 1960). This is, perhaps, more surprising than the fact that melanic species appear to predominate in the fungal flora of desert soils (Nicot, 1960; Borut, 1960; Durrell and Shields, 1960).

The latter workers were able to show that dark-spored species like *Stemphylium ilicis*, *Stachybotrys atra*, and *Cladosporium herbarum* survived long exposures to ultraviolet light. In a study in which the survival of fungi in soils exposed to gamma radiation was studied, it was found that colored species (Dematiaceae) were more resistant in general than uncolored ones (Moniliaceae), thereby supporting the protective function of pigmentation (Johnson and Osborne, 1964).

Melanin pigments often appear to be associated with radiation-resistance (cf. Chapter 2). Therefore, a mechanism for phenotypic adaptation to habitats with a high incidence radiation is suggested in the work of Lingappa et al. (1963) and Sussman et al. (1963). In the cases of *Pullularia* and *Cladosporium*, light induces melanization, thereby providing a model for protective "sun-burning" of some microbial species in nature. Because *Pullularia* and *Cladosporium* are frequently encountered in air (Gregory, 1961) and in desert soils (Borut, 1960), survival value may derive from an adaptation of this kind in some cases.

It is clear from that which has been discussed in Chapter 3, and in this chapter, that spores are frequently of great value in protecting microorganisms from overexposure to radiations. Although nonspore-formers may tolerate high levels of ultraviolet and γ-radiations, the resistance of spore-formers appears to be markedly higher to x-rays. One of the means through which spores may accomplish such protection is a dark wall, or cytoplasm, which serves as a filter. This is probably the case in organisms like *Neurospora* which form uncolored vegetative mycelium and black resting spores. On the other hand, the vegetative stages of other microbes may also serve in this way inasmuch as melanized resting hyphae are recovered frequently from nature. However, it should be emphasized that not all pigments function as do the melanins, for the work of Masago (1959) discloses that the pigments of *Serratia* enhance the sensitivity of this organism to ultraviolet light (see pages 40–41).

Chemicals

The suggestion was made in Chapter 2 that the exclusion of metabolites from the cell has survival value as protection against the incorporation of toxic materials in *Neurospora* ascospores. How widespread in spores is such a role of the cell surface?

Considerable data have been accumulated which show that bacterial spores are more resistant to ethylene oxide than are vegetative cells (Friedl et al., 1956; Znamirowski et al., 1960; Freeman and Barwell, 1960; Phillips, 1952). The latter found spores of *Bacillus cereus* to be between two-to-six-times more resistant to this disinfectant than are cells of *Micrococcus pyogenes* and *Escherichia coli*. That this is the case for other alkylating agents such as ethylene imine, methyl bromide, and formaldehyde, was shown by Phillips as well. Thousandfold and even greater sensitivity of vegetative cells to trichlorophenol, sodium hypochlorite, Movidyn and 4-cetyl-4-methyl morpholinium methyl sulfate was demonstrated in the same organisms by Phillips (1952).

Comparisons of the sensitivity of spores and vegetative cells of the same organism also have been made, as in the case of the effect of penicillin on certain species of *Clostridium* in which spores were at least 1000-fold more resistant to the antibiotic (Wynne and Harrell, 1951). According to Sacks (1956), penicillin and subtilin were sporostatic to a small fraction of the spores of *Bacillus stearothermophilus* but had no effect on spores of the other species of *Bacillus* that were tried. Similarly, subtilin and nisin were found by Campbell and Sniff (1959) to inhibit the outgrowth of germinated spores of *Bacillus coagulans* but were not sporocidal or sporostatic. Other chemicals, such as octyl alcohol have less effect upon dormant spores than upon germinating ones or upon vegetative cells (Halvorson, 1961). Ramseier (1960) reviews the effect of some basic antibiotics upon spore-forming aerobes and anaerobes and reports that nisin does not inhibit spores of *Clostridium butyricum*. Although some reports attest to the inhibition of some spores by such compounds (Kaufmann et al., 1955), most of the evidence suggests that they are more resistant to these substances than are vegetative stages of the same organism (e.g., Sacks, 1956).

Among the fungi, conidia of *Aspergillus niger* have been shown to be more resistant to pentachlorophenol, dehydroacetic acid, sorbic acid, phenylthiolbenzoate, butylthio-1, 4-naphthoquinone, mycelin, and eurocydin (Yanagita and Yamagishi, 1958). Furthermore, *o*-coumaric acid is more toxic to the growing mycelium of *Venturia* spp. than to spores (Flood and Kirkham, 1960), and Sawada (1959) has shown that ascospores of bakers' yeast survive higher concentrations of ethanol than do vegetative cells.

However, Foster and Wynne (1948) have reported that C_{18} acids are more inhibitory to spores than to vegetative cells of *Clostridium botulinum*. Not many instances of this kind are known for bacteria but there are several instances where fungal spores have been observed to be more sensitive than mycelial stages. Thus, the germination of the spores of *Fusarium oxysporum* f. *lycopersici* and *F. roseum* is completely inhibited by a concentration of Phygon (3,3-dichloro-1, 4-napthoquinone) below 5 ppm. By contrast, the mycelium of these fungi will grow in 100-fold greater concentrations of this substance (Deep and Corden,

1961). Another instance is that of actidione which is ten times more effective against spores of *Myrothecium verrucaria* than against mycelium (Walker and Smith, 1952). Similarly, it has been shown that mycelial fragments of *Verticillium* are much less sensitive to chlorogenic acid than are spores (McLean et al., 1961). Another claim that fungus spores are more sensitive to fungicides than is mycelium is that of Domsch (1958); these studies, in which six different assay procedures were used, revealed that the differences in sensitivities were as great as 100-fold with *Pythium* sp., *Rhizoctonia solani*, and *Fusarium culmorum*.

An interesting instance in which survival value might accrue to vegetative stages through enhanced resistance to chemicals is provided by Slotnick's (1959) work on *Bacillus*. In this case, out of eight actinomycin D-resistant isolates of this organism, *all* were asporogenous. This is a possible means through which sterile organisms gain survivability in nature.

The findings on the relative sensitivity to inhibitors of spores and vegetative stages are more discrepant in the case of fungi than bacteria. In the latter case, the bulk of the evidence supports the conclusion that spores are more resistant to the chemicals tried than are vegetative stages. On the other hand, the evidence is much more ambiguous in the fungi. The type of spore certainly is a factor that must be considered in view of the data on *Neurospora* ascospores and conidia which have been shown to differ greatly in their permeability to various substances (Chapter 2). Moreover, even closely related chemicals differ in their effects upon the different stages, as in the case of two phenols, cinnamic and *o*-coumaric acids (Flood and Kirkham, 1960). Thus, cinnamic acid inhibits the germination of conidia of *Venturia* whereas *o*-coumaric acid does not; however, the latter compound is more toxic to the growing fungus than is cinnamic acid. In view of these considerations, no generalization as to the resistance of fungus spores as compared to vegetative cells is possible at this time.

Effects of Chemicals in Nature

Is there any evidence from nature that spores endow organisms with enhanced survivability as a result of increased resistance to chemical inhibitors? The bacterial flora of a forest nursery soil was altered by formalin, according to Crump (1953), who found that such treatment increased the number of gelatin-liquefying spore-formers, among some other types of organisms. Similarly, methyl bromide fumigation of soil resulted in the recovery mainly of spore-formers (McKeen, 1954). Furthermore, as would be expected from data provided above, spore-forming bacteria and actinomycetes were found to be the most resistant organisms in soils sterilized by ethylene oxide (Clark, 1950; Allison, 1951).

Fumigation of soil has been shown to shift the balance in favor of spore-forming fungi, as well as bacteria. Thus, Wensley (1953) found that several ascomycetes, whose development is usually suppressed by penicillia and aspergilli, could be recovered after treatment with methyl bromide, propane-propene and ethylene dibromide. Ascosporic species of *Pencillium*, *Aspergillus*, *Chaetomium* and *Thielavia* are remarkably resistant to carbon disulfide, as well as to the fumigants described above. In addition, Warcup (1951) suggests that certain ascomycetes survive more readily than other fungi in mycelial zones of fairy rings because they are more resistant to antibiotics produced by basidiomycetous mycelium. Furthermore, Macfarlane (1952) claims that survival of resting spores of *Plasmodihora brassicae* is enhanced by chemical inhibitors.

However, certain fungi which do not possess resistant spores are remarkably well adapted to survive treatment with chemicals. This is true of *Trichoderma viride* which tolerates soil fumigants to a remarkable degree, as well as being able to recolonize partially sterilized soil (cf. the review by Warcup, 1957*b*). Even sterile types of fungi were recovered from fumigated soils by Wensley (1953), so that spores may help fungi to survive under such conditions but are not always essential.

Another aspect of resistance to chemicals concerns the effect of lytic factors. Such factors probably are of importance in the survivability of microorganisms and have been reported to destroy fungus mycelium (Chinn, 1953; Carter and Lockwood, 1957; Lockwood, 1960), as well as fungus spores (Lingappa and Lockwood, 1961; Leal and Villanueva, 1962). Antibiotics (Carter and Lockwood, 1957; Lockwood, 1959), as well as enzymes (Leal and Villanueva, 1962) may be involved, but the lytic principles have not been well characterized. On the other hand, the data on longevity discussed previously suggest that some propagules resist lysis over long periods of time so that survivability in some of these cases may involve resistance to lysis. In fact, studies of Iichinska (1960) suggest that spore formation may enhance survivability by protecting the cell against its own autolytic enzymes when growth is retarded because of nutrient deficiency, or otherwise. Thus, she found that asporogenous mutants of *Bacillus subtilis* and *B. megaterium* are unstable and undergo lysis very readily so that their viability is low. Furthermore, yeast spores appear to be resistant to autolysis in view of their presence in the outer autolyzed layer of old yeast colonies (Lindegren and Hamilton, 1944). Therefore, it may be that the ability of spores to survive lysis due to products of other organisms, or to its own, may contribute to their survivability. However, it should be pointed out that direct comparisons of the resistance of spores and vegetative stages to such factors have not been made so that this conclusion must be tested.

Therefore, it seems likely that spore-forming bacteria enjoy considerable selective advantage because of their resistance to deleterious chemicals. This is true in soils treated by fumigants and other chemicals and is fortified by *in vitro* studies with antibiotics such as penicillin, subtilin and nisin, which attest to the greater resistance of spores as compared to vegetative cells. Although there are many cases in the fungi where spores also appear to aid survival after treatment with chemicals, vegetative structures like sclerotia, and even mycelium, may serve as resistant structures (Warcup, 1957*a*; Hawker, 1957).

NUTRITIONAL STATUS AND CAPACITY

Under conditions where energy sources are limiting in the environment, the presence of endogenous substrates may provide the organism an advantageous start in growth. There are many fungi which germinate in distilled water but such self-sufficiency in the supply of energy sources is less characteristic of bacterial spores. For example, in the case of *Neurospora* ascospores, the lipid substratum of the dormant cells comprises more than 20 percent of the dry weight of this organism, and the carbohydrate reserve which is used during activation makes up about about 15 percent of this total (B. T. Lingappa and Sussman, 1959).

Even when there is a sufficiency of energy sources, the enhanced requirement for other nutrient materials may confer a selective advantage upon spore-formers. A case in point is that of *Ophiostoma multiannulatum* for which it has been shown that the conidia of deficient mutants are more viable than those of unmutated strains under certain circumstances (Fries, 1948). Some of these results are provided in Figure 11.1, in which a hypoxanthineless mutant was studied.

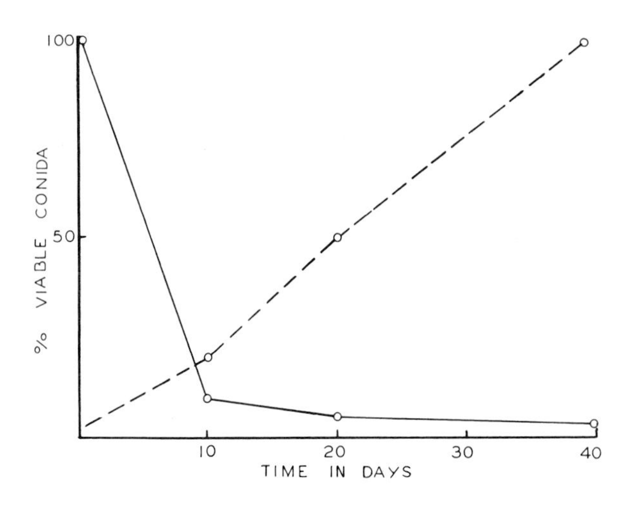

Figure 11.1 Survival of conidia of *Ophiostoma multiannulatum*. —o—, percentage living conidia of all conidia; - - - o - - -, percentage living mutant conidia of all living conidia. (After Fries, 1948.)

These results are parallel to those of Macdonald and Pontecorvo (1953) with *Aspergillus nidulans* wherein spores of a biotin-requiring mutant died rapidly in a biotin-deficient medium but the introduction of a second mutation drastically increased survival in minimal media. Such is the case for *Neurospora* also, as was demonstrated by Lester and Gross (1959) when they found that the longevity of inositolless strains was extended seventyfold if a tryptophan requirement was added to that for the vitamin. In fact, these observations are the basis for a technique evolved by these authors in which auxotrophic mutants having an amino acid, purine, pyrimidine, or vitamin requirement can be enriched in populations of irradiated conidia. Therefore, the enhanced viability of double mutants appears to be fairly general in *Neurospora*.

The effects of auxotrophy upon the survival of bacterial spores have not been studied in as great detail and it will be of interest to learn whether similar results are obtained. However, Table 7.5 reveals that endospores of bacteria have an enhanced requirement for metabolites like adenosine, serine, and other activators. Consequently, germination would be delayed in an environment lacking these substances, thereby ensuring the maintenance of the resistant spore stage until enough metabolites were available to permit continued development of vegetative cells. The fact that spores have a diminished requirement for substances like oxygen, uracil, phenylalanine, and nicotinic acid is not necessarily a disadvantage because the activation step is required to initiate germination and if adenosine, for instance, is not present, development will not begin even in the presence of uracil and the other metabolites.

On the other hand, the enhanced requirement for a metabolite by spores may work to the disadvantage of the organism. Thus, conidia of inositol- and pyridoxal-requiring strains of *Neurospora* die very rapidly when incubated on media which lack the needed metabolite, whereas those that survive fail to do so. Consequently, it is likely that the conidia of the inositol- and pyridoxal-requiring strains do not require the growth factor, whereas the vegetative stages do. The reason for this difference is not known but one possibility is that spores have a supply of the growth factor which is exhausted before vegetative growth can ensue. Another possibility is that the spores can synthesize enough of the nutrient to effect germination, after which the synthetic capacity is lost. However, no decision can be made as yet between these alternatives. In any event, advantage in these cases accrues to those organisms whose spores cannot germinate in the absence of a growth factor for which they are deficient, in that their chances for survival are increased.

These considerations lead to an interesting speculation concerning a possible beneficial effect of antibiotics upon some sensitive organisms. A model for this kind of interaction derives from the work of Strauss (1958) who found that ethionine prolonged the life of conidia of inositolless strains of *Neurospora*. The assumption therefore might be made that any means whereby the germination of "suicidal" strains of microorganisms could be reversibly delayed, in the absence of the needed metabolite, would enhance the chances of its survival.

Among the unique metabolites of bacterial spores are bacitracin in *Bacillus licheniformis* (Bernlohr and Novelli, 1963) and the unknown antibiotic formed by *B. subtilis* (Balassa et al., 1963). In the latter case, it has been shown that nonsporulating races do not form the antibiotic but they regain the capacity when they regain the ability to sporulate through transformation. Although the role of these substances is still not certain, it is possible that their release aids the germinating spore to increase its "inoculum potential" (Garrett, 1956) by suppressing the growth of competitors.

GENETIC FACTORS IN SURVIVABILITY

Formation of New Recombinants

As Gregory (1952) and Bonner (1958) have pointed out, when the life cycles of organisms that produce resistant spores are compared, genetic recombination usually is closely associated with sporulation. Such an association results in the production of spores that are very variable due to the occurrence of recombination prior to spore formation, or during germination. An obvious advantage of this system is that the greater the genetic variability of the spores, the greater the likelihood that a genotype will be found that is suited to new environmental or geographic situations.

The association of spore formation and recombination is illustrated in many of the fungi. For example, *Neurospora*, as well as many other ascomycetes, forms resistant ascospores which are the result of a meiotic division. A role that is analagous to that of ascospores is played by the resistant sporangium of many aquatic phycomycetes within which meiosis occurs prior to the release of zoospores. Among the mucors, meiosis probably occurs when a resistant zygospore germinates to form an abbreviated mycelium, from which an asexual sporangium is formed. A secondary resistant spore is to be found in the sporangium which releases asexual spores. In this case, recombinant nuclei do not become distributed through spores until after the secondary resistant spore is formed. An exception of another type is that of the teliospores of rusts which are resting spores whose germination leads to the formation of a promycelium within which meiosis occurs. Distribution of recombinant nuclei is accomplished in this case through basidiospores which are formed on the promycelium. Thus, although the site of meiosis may be removed from that where the recombinant nuclei are formed into spores, the principle that recombination is carried out in a resistant stage appears to hold for many fungi. An exception may be the rusts in which evanescent basidiospores are formed.

On the other hand, bacterial spores appear to play no special role in distributing the products of meiotic recombination. Zygote formation is transitory and not associated with spore formation. However, an interesting possibility does exist in which bacterial spores, or the ability to form them, plays a role in extending genetic versatility. Thus, Anagnostopoulos and Spizizen (1961) have noted that the peak in sensitivity to transformation in *Bacillus subtilis* occurs during pre-sporulation stages. Furthermore, strains of this organism that are unable to sporulate do not become competent. Consequently, the ability to sporulate confers a genetic advantage upon this organism by the development of transformability. In addition, it is known that bacteriophages remain latent (lysogenic) as long as their bacterial hosts continue to grow. However, they become lytic just before spores are formed, so transduction may be enhanced by the act of sporulation, inasmuch as virus is released in quantity at this time.

Sexuality may be completely absent in some organisms, yet resistant stages may be formed, as in the case of some rhizopods. At first glance, the fact that *Neurospora* and other fungi produce resistant asexual spores, as well as ascospores, might appear to be another case like that of the amoebae described above. However, new heterokaryons of different genetic constitution are formed in the macroconidia of species like *Neurospora*. When uninucleate spores (microconidia) are formed, new combinations of nuclei result upon germination, thereby producing heterokaryons of different genetic constitution. Another case than can be mentioned is *Coprinus*, in which it has been suggested that far more spores germinate and fuse with an already established mycelium than ever themselves succeed in establishing a new one (Transeau, 1949). Therefore, new recombinations may be formed by asexual fungus spores as well as by sexual ones.

An association between recombination and the formation of resistant stages occurs in other organisms as well as in the fungi, according to Bonner. Thus, he draws a parallel between the spores of fungi and those of algae and other lower plants, the cysts of protozoans and other invertebrates, and the propagules of some higher plants and animals. Therefore, there seems to be considerable generality to the role of resistant spores as the carriers of the products of recombination.

Isolation of "Fitter" Nuclei

The coexistence of numerous nuclei in the same mycelium in fungi ensures heterogeneity of the genome and the maintenance of mutant nuclei (Lindegren, 1942). Heterokaryons permit the survival of mutant genomes even under conditions where such nuclei are selected against by growth on deficient media (Davis, 1959). The maintenance of such genetic heterogeneity is, of course, advantageous as a source of variability when new environments are to be exploited. However, the perpetuation of disadvantageous mutations may reduce the survivability of the fungus in which they accumulate. Such deleterious genetic elements may be nuclear or cytoplasmic in origin (Jinks, 1959). Under these circumstances, therefore, there is selective advantage in the periodic isolation of the component genomes of a heterokaryotic organism such as occurs in the formation of microconidia of ascomycetes and some conidia of imperfect fungi. Of course, new heterokaryons may form very soon after such spores germinate, or new mutations may arise, thereby assuring the variability and benefits which have been described.

In summary, spores play two potentially important genetic roles in the fungi, including the establishment of new recombinations, and the isolation of fit nuclear types from less desirable ones. Although somatic recombination does occur in the fungi (Pontecorvo, 1956), the role played by spores in ensuring variability is important, and that which permits isolation and subsequent recombination is unique.

Summary: Longevity and Survival in Nature

Because longevity, especially under natural conditions, stems from the ability of organisms to survive in the face of a large number of interacting environmental challenges, studies of the effects of single variables probably oversimplify the issues. Therefore, an attempt will be made in this summary to analyze the role of spores in the light of what is known from the study of longevity in natural populations.

That the longevity of spores can be very great is proved by the data in Chapter 3. Examples of the kinds given there are to be found in every group of microorganisms which produces resting spores. But the obvious survivability of spores should not obscure the fact that vegetative stages also enjoy remarkable longevity. Instances of this kind are provided in Bosco's (1960) work in which cultures were examined that had been stored at room temperature in the dark for many years. Also, as can be seen in Table 3.1, nonspore-formers survived up to at least 45 years, thereby establishing the astonishing longevity of certain of these microorganisms. Therefore, it is not surprising to read that, "By far the greatest number of microorganisms found in the soil by means of the microscope consists of minute non-sporing rods and cocci. The large spore-forming bacteria such as *Bacillus megaterium* and *B. cereus* have been found in normal soil only in the form of spores which make up a very small proportion of the total bacterial flora of the soil" (Waksman, 1927). Winogradsky (1949) is in general agreement but notes that treatment of the soil in certain ways elicits the growth of more spore-forming rods and actinomycetes.

As for the fungi, the recognition of the role of vegetative stages in survival perhaps has been later than in bacteria. Recently, rhizomorphs, sclerotia, and mycelial strands in soil have been shown to yield basidiomycetes (Levisohn, 1955; Warcup, 1957*a*). The main structures of major plant pathogens and other fungi which survive in soil are listed by Wahl (1961) and Barton (1965) and these lists include several fungi which depend upon hyphal aggregates like sclerotia and rhizomorphs for survival, instead of upon spores. Although it is true that rhizomorphs, and so on, are functionally akin to spores, they often are produced *in addition to* spores and so replace the latter as resting bodies in these cases. Moreover, the ordinary mycelium of *Phytophthora* appears to survive over winter in the tissues of hosts such as potato, taro, and other plants (Hickman, 1958). Instances where parasites survive in seeds are reviewed by Barton (1965), but in many of these cases it is not known whether the mycelium or spores are the infective element. In any case, Warcup (1957*a*), who has critically reviewed the methods used for isolating fungi from soils, concludes that "resting hyphae may be more common in soil than originally considered."

Another aspect of survival that is difficult to evaluate is how far it is possible to extrapolate to nature from data accumulated in the laboratory. Thus, the great resistance of microbes is established from the experimental data given in Chapter 3, but selection may alter the organism. For example, virulent strains of *Pasteurella tularensis* can be isolated readily from certain streams in the western United States. On the other hand, when cultured strains of this bacterium are reintroduced into these streams, they rapidly disappear. Another case is that of spores of *Bacillus* sp. which are more radiation-resistant when isolated from meat or soil than when grown on the usual culture media, according to workers at the Morrill Company's laboratories. Finally, the well-known inability of *Bacillus papillae* to sporulate in the laboratory is to be contrasted with the large number of spores found in their insect hosts. Similar cases where fungi fruit in nature but not otherwise can be presented. Therefore, any conclusions to be derived from the results discussed in Chapter 3 and in this chapter must be tempered by recognition of the heterogeneity of most microbial populations and the pressures which may select during experimentation.

Nevertheless, it is likely that spores are highly resistant in nature, as well as in the laboratory. Consequently, they provide for increased survivability in those organisms which produce them. On the other hand, vegetative structures may be vital elements in the survival of nonspore-formers, as well as of some spore-formers whose spores are not resistant.

Role of Spores in Dissemination

MECHANISMS OF DISPERSAL AND DEPOSITION

Unlike many fungi, unicellular bacteria and yeasts have not evolved mechanisms to facilitate dispersal of spores in air. Although, as we shall see, the spores and vegetative cells of bacteria are admirably adapted for floating in air, no natural process capable of producing an aerosol of single bacterial cells is known. Instead, mechanical disturbances of various kinds can carry particles of soil, dust, surgical dressing, and so on, into the air along with clumps of bacteria. In addition, rain splash, breakers, and sea spray may inseminate the atmosphere with these organisms. Droplets expelled by coughing and sneezing also are responsible for forming aerosols of bacteria which are important as foci of infection (Wells, 1955).

The elevation of the sporophore of actinomycetes above the substratum permits better distribution of dry conidia, a mechanism that is employed by more elaborate organisms too. Thus, the sporangia of slime molds are admirably suited for dispersing spores into the air, as are those of other fungi, including the Peronosporales and Mucorales. Among the other dispersal mechanisms to be found in the fungi are splash-cups, explosive devices, and several other adaptations which facilitate wind dispersal of spores (Ingold, 1953, 1960). In fact, there is more diversity in such mechanisms among the fungi than in any other group of organisms excluding, perhaps, the seed plants in which many means of dispersing seeds have been evolved (Gregory, 1961).

Large spores, like the uredospores and aeciospores of rusts, and those of certain leaf pathogens, frequently are deposited by impaction. However, small dry spores, such as bacterial endospores, and the spores of *Penicillium* and *Aspergillus*, are of a size that is unsuitable for impaction so that other processes account for their deposition (Gregory, 1961). Consequently, the small spores sift through vegetation in rain, and less efficiently by other means.

DISPERSAL OF BACTERIAL SPORES

That bacterial spores are a means through which the organism is distributed aerially has been claimed by Bisset (1950). The opposing view has been stated by Lamanna (1952) on the basis of calculations deriving from Stoke's Law which is given below:

$$\text{Terminal velocity of fall} = \frac{2r^2(d_p - d_f)g}{9\eta},$$

where r = the radius of a sphere, d_p = the density of the particle, d_f = the density of the fluid, g = the gravitational constant for acceleration, and η = the viscosity of the fluid. Lamanna points out that the advantages a spore enjoys over a vegetative cell in its ability to float in quiet air probably are minimal. This can be seen from the data he assembled in Table 11.2 which shows only a small difference between the calculated terminal velocities in air of spores and vegetative cells. But Stoke's law was derived to describe the terminal velocity of smooth spherical particles and does not necessarily apply to others. Furthermore, there is reason to expect that particles of heterogeneous density in cross section, such as spores, do not obey Stoke's law. Therefore, any conclusions about biological materials, based upon this law, are liable to be uncertain unless the assumptions discussed above are met. Under these circumstances, measurements of the terminal velocity would be very useful but the conditions are difficult to

Table 11.2 Ratios of the Terminal Velocities of Various Natural Objects Predicted from Stoke's Law

	Size	Specific Gravity	Idealized Shape	Ratios of Terminal Velocities in Air: Endospore to	Vegetative Cell to
Bacillus cereus endospore	1.0 × 1.5 μ	1.2	Cylinder		
B. cereus vegetative cell	1 × 4 μ	1.1	Cylinder	3.7	
Aminitopsis vaginata spores	9.6 μ	1.02	Sphere	50	14
Timothy grass pollen	35 μ	1.0	Sphere	653	178

SOURCE: Lamanna, 1952. Courtesy *Bact. Rev.*
Bacillus cereus was chosen as a soil organism commonly found in air masses overland.
The calculations recorded have assumed a viscosity of 0.00018 poises, and a negligible density (0.0012 for dry air at 1 atm pressure and 18°C) for air. In addition, it was assumed that a cylinder would fall through air at a rate equal to that of a sphere of the same surface area.

Table 11.3 Observed Terminal Velocities of Spores and Pollens

Organism	Terminal Velocity (cm per sec.)
Bacillus subtilis, spore[a]	0.00037
Fungus Spores	
Amanita rubescens	0.15
Coprinus comatus	0.4
Helminthosporium sativum	2.0–2.78
Lycoperdon pyriforme	0.05
Pluteus cervinus	0.067
Puccinia graminis tritici, uredospores	0.94–1.25
Ustilago tritici	0.07
Pollen	
Abies pectinata	38.7
Alnus viridis	1.7
Larix decidua	9.9–22.0
Secale cereale	6.0–8.8
Pinus sylvestris	2.5

SOURCE: Gregory, 1961.

[a] Calculated by the authors, using a density of 1.28 for spores of *B. subtilis*, density of air = 1.27×10^{-3} gm per cc, acceleration of gravity = 981 cm per second^2, viscosity of air at 18°C = 1.8×10^{-4} gm/cm/second, and a radius of the spore = 0.62 μ.

standardize. Nevertheless, Gregory (1961) has assembled many such data and they are provided in Table 11.3. A comparison of Tables 11.2 and 11.3 reveals that the calculated terminal velocity of a representative bacterial endospore, subject to the reservations concerning Stoke's law which have been mentioned, is much less than that of fungus spores and pollen. In any case, organisms that have much higher terminal velocities, like pollen and fungus spores, are disseminated widely in the atmosphere (Schrödter, 1960; Gregory, 1961) so that bacterial endospores are not unique in being able to float in air.

What is unique about endospores, and probably most important in the dissemination of bacteria that form them, is their survivability. The greater resistance of spores, as compared with that of vegetative cells of the same organism, has been discussed previously (Chapter 3). Consequently, although it is likely, as Lamanna points out, that vegetative cells of spore-formers can be air-borne almost as readily as spores, the probability of their survival is less due to the effects of radiation, desiccation, and so on.

Evidence from Nature

During a sirocco, or "blood rain," in the vicinity of Lyons, Ehrenberg (1849) calculated that almost one ton of microorganisms per square mile were deposited (McAttee, 1917). Although this is an exaggerated example of the abundance of microorganisms in dust, the fact that bacteria are widespread in the air is well established and is reviewed in detail in a recent book (Gregory, 1961). Evidence on this score comes from the classic studies of Miquel (1883) who initiated quantitative studies of the air spora near the ground. Using a volumetric trap outdoors, he found 700–1000 bacteria per cubic meter in Parc Monsouris outside of Paris and about tenfold more in the city itself. The organisms he found included *Micrococcus* (66 percent), *Bacillus* (25 percent), *Bacterium* (6 percent) and *Vibrio* (1–2 percent). A more recent study of the air sampled on the roof of a building in Montreal, Canada, by Kelly and Pady (1953) revealed the presence of the following bacteria: aerobic spore-formers (37.9 percent), gram-positive pleomorphic rods (23.8 percent), *Micrococcus* (18.8 percent), gram-negative rods (4.8 percent) and *Sarcina* (4.6 percent). There is agreement in these studies that although many spore-formers are found, a large percentage of other bacteria exist in the air near the ground. Other examples of the dissemination of nonspore-formers in the atmosphere include the epidemics of plague, *Pasteurella pestis* (Meyer, 1961).

Some studies of organisms collected from distant areas of the earth, including the polar regions, oceans, and the upper atmosphere, are summarized in Table 11.4. Thus, the bacteria of Antarctica were studied by Darling and Siple (1941) who concluded that the majority must have come as atmospheric dust, although some probably were brought by man and migrating animals. Several spore-

Table 11.4 Some Evidence for the Long-Range Spread of Bacteria in the Atmosphere

Region	Organisms Found	Reference
Antarctica	*Achromobacter deliculatum, A. liquidans, Bacillus albolactis, B. fusiformis, B. mesentericus, B. subtilis, B. tumescens*	Darling and Siple, 1941
984–10,650 feet elevation over Nashville, Tennessee	Cocci, 37.7 percent; Spore-formers, 37.7 percent; nonspore-formers, 24.6 percent	Wolf, 1943
36,000–68,880 feet	Five species of *Bacillus*	Rogers and Meier, 1936
13,120 feet over Germany	Mainly spore-formers but occasionally *Sarcina lutea, Micrococcus citreus,* and *M. luteus*	Flemming, 1908
9840 feet over the North Atlantic	Viable bacteria all the way across the Atlantic	Pady and Kelly, 1954

formers were found, as well as two species of *Achromobacter*. On the other hand, Prince and Bakanauskas (1960) could find no unicellular bacteria in the air at about 83°N in the North Polar Basin, although actinomycetes and fungi were found.

Studies of the microbiology of the upper atmosphere also have revealed the presence of many spore-formers, and sometimes a preponderance of others (Flemming, 1908; Proctor, 1935; Rogers and Meier, 1936).

As for the flora over oceans, ZoBell (1946) collected rain water far over the Pacific Ocean and showed 1–10 bacteria per milliliter and no fungi to be present. Sea-water media demonstrated that gram-negative rods predominated whereas fewer than half the cultures were of spore-formers. Similarly, among the viable bacteria collected over the North Atlantic Ocean by Pady and Kelly (1954) were *Micrococcus* and *Sarcina* (41.4 percent), gram-negative rods (4.3 percent), gram-positive pleomorphic rods (20.4 percent), and aerobic spore-formers (33.2 percent).

Spore-forming bacteria appear to predominate in the flora of the air over the regions covered in Table 11.4. However, other bacteria occur frequently and are to be expected because of the extreme aerosol-stability of some nonspore-formers, including staphylococci and mycobacteria (Goodlow and Leonard, 1961). Although it is tempting to consider that the widespread dissemination of spore-formers is due to the survivability of endospores, there is as yet no direct proof that this is the case. All of the studies summarized in this review are based upon plate or broth cultures derived from the collected organisms. Therefore, some of the colonies that were counted might have arisen from vegetative cells. Unless convenient means of visualizing the collected cells are developed, this problem will remain. Other technical difficulties include the use of media which are necessarily selective for certain kinds of bacteria. Finally, as Hesse (1884) first stressed, the bacteria in the atmosphere usually exist in clumps so that each colony on a plate probably represents an undefined number of individuals, making quantitative studies difficult.

DISPERSAL OF FUNGUS SPORES

Because of their size, fungus spores can be counted directly so there is much less doubt as to their role in dissemination. Furthermore, the importance of fungi as plant pathogens has resulted in the amassing of a wealth of data on their distribution and spread. The forces whose interaction determines the transport of spores in air include gravitation, velocity of fall, horizontal air movement, atmospheric turbulence, and molecular and electrostatic forces. Although the latter are negligible under the usual circumstances in nature, the first four factors must be considered in any explanation of aerial transport. Theoretical aspects of this subject are treated in detail by Schrödter (1960) and Gregory (1961) and will not be reviewed here.

Large numbers of fungus spores are available for distribution through the air. For example, Buller (1909) calculated that a single giant puffball (*Calvatia gigantea*) can produce 7×10^{12} spores, and the smaller fruiting bodies of mushrooms (*Agaricus campestris*) release millions of spores from the hymenium. Another example is provided by Christensen (1942) who found that a field of wheat only moderately infected by the wheat rust, *Puccinia graminis*, produces at least 25 million uredospores per square meter.

The fact that fungus spores spread over long distances also is well established. Wheat rust can be used as an example here as well, due to the detailed studies of Stakman and co-workers, some of whose results are provided in Table 11.5.

Table 11.5 Data on Dissemination of Uredospores of *Puccinia graminis*[a]

Place	Approximate Distance from Source (miles)	Uredospores per sq. ft. in 48 hours
Dallas, Texas	(Source area)	129,216
Oklahoma	186	6288
Falls City, Nebraska	347	7680
Beatrice, Nebraska	521	1968
Madison, Wisconsin	601	192

SOURCE: Stakman and Hamilton, 1939.
[a] Deposition on ground, May 24–25, 1938.

Because of the circumstances at the time the study was carried out (early summer, 1938), it could be assumed that the spores collected in the various localities north of Dallas, Texas, could not have been produced locally but were spread by southerly winds.

A wider sample of fungus spores was studied by Kramer et al. (1959) with results of the kind seen in Table 11.6. These results underline the predominance

Table 11.6 Principal Fungal Constituents of Air Sampled From a Kansas Rooftop

Organisms Found	Visual Count (percent)	Viable Count (in culture) (percent)
Cladosporium	40.9	44.5
Basidiospores	24.3	—
Nonsporulating fungi	—	17.6
Alternaria	3.4	12.6
Yeasts	7.3	8.4
Penicillium	—	6.1
Aspergillus	—	5.4
Smuts	5.9	—
2-Celled hyaline	4.4	—
Fusarium	2.9	—
1-Celled hyaline	1.4	—
Cercospora	1.0	—

SOURCE: Kramer et al., 1959.

of fungus spores over vegetative stages in the atmosphere. On the other hand, yeasts were found, as were nonsporulating fungi whose presence was recognized only in the cultures prepared from the collected material. In the latter case it is possible that the medium was unfavorable for spore formation, so it is not certain that vegetative cells were the source of the inoculum.

Evidence for the long-distance transport of fungi also comes from studies of airborne organisms over the North Polar Basin (83°N) by Prince and Bakanauskas (1960). Viable microorganisms were sought near sea level and a small number of cultures of *Penicillium viridicatum* were obtained, along with some actinomycetes, but no bacteria.

The upper atmosphere was studied by Flemming (1908) who found *P. crustaceum* and some yeasts up to 13,000 feet. Fungi also were found by Rogers and Meier (1936) between 36,000 and 68,800 feet during the descent of the balloon *Explorer II*. The relation between microbial concentration and air mass was studied by Pady and Kelly (1954) and Pady and Kapica (1955) at altitudes between about 8,900–10,000 feet in flights between Montreal, Canada, and London, England. Among the fungi found were: *Cladosporium* (82.3 percent), *Alternaria*

(2.6 percent), *Pullularia* (2.3 percent), yeasts (2.1 percent), *Penicillium* (1.6 percent), *Botrytis* (1.5 percent) and nonsporulating colonies (3.2 percent). These studies establish that viable fungi occur at altitudes up to 10,000 feet across the North Atlantic, although bacteria were much fewer in number.

Oceanic spora were investigated by Sreeramulu (1958) with the finding that 5–50 miles at sea, *Cladosporium* and smut spores, along with colored basidiospores, were the most commonly found fungus propagules. A summary of these results shows that the number of fungus spores found varied from 9.3 to 222 per cubic meter, with an average for 19 separate counts of about 69 spores per cubic meter. By contrast, the number of hyphal fragments found varied from 0.7 to 10.2 per cubic meter, with an average of 3 per cubic meter. At greater distances offshore, over the Pacific Ocean, ZoBell (1942) could find only a few fungi and both he and Sreeramulu conclude that oceans are a barrier to the transport of spores.

These results establish that fungus spores predominate over vegetative cells as components of the atmospheric flora. This conclusion can scarcely be doubted due to the accumulation of data obtained in many different parts of the world (Gregory, 1961) which reveal the presence of hyphae in only small amounts. Yeasts are distributed widely in the atmosphere, presumably as vegetative cells, but again are only a small proportion of the atmospheric flora. By reason of the varied mechanisms for making them airborne, and their ability to float and to survive in air, spores are the most effective means of dispersal for the fungi.

Role of Spores as Timing Devices

Dormant spores can be considered to be timing devices which ensure that active growth occurs when conditions are most favorable. This type of adaptation would confer selective advantage upon organisms whose environments undergo fluctuations in moisture, temperature, light, and in other factors which affect survivability. Lees (1961) has proposed that diapause serves such a function in some insects and it is likely that dormancy plays a similar role in microorganisms. In the latter, timing can be considered to occur at two stages of development, including spore formation and germination, so that this subject will be discussed under these headings.

TIMING IN SPORULATION

A generalization which appears to hold for a variety of microorganisms is that a reduction in the supply of certain nutrients induces sporulation, whereas the presence of glucose, and related hexoses, suppresses this process. It is to be noted that vegetative growth must be promoted on relatively rich media until competence to sporulate is achieved, after which induction by "starvation" may be accomplished.

That the growth of bacteria in a rich medium often favors vegetative growth and delays sporulation of bacteria has been discussed in an extensive review by Foster (1956). Thus, the general experience of bacteriologists is that spores appear after the logarithmic phase of growth, when nutrients are exhausted and that their development may be hastened by employing a dilute medium of the same composition. Moreover, "endotrophic sporulation," or the suspension of bacteria, just prior to the time of maximum growth, in distilled water or buffer is effective in eliciting spore formation. Although nucleotides and other metabolites are released from autolyzing cells under these conditions, it is still very likely that other nutrients are in low supply.

Similarly, a large body of data suggests that sporulation in yeasts (Miller, 1959), some mucors (Bartnicki-Garcia and Nickerson, 1962), and other fungi (Hawker, 1957) is favored by dilution of the medium, or deprivation of nutrients, after growth has occurred. In fact, even media upon which depauperate growth has been made from the start will enhance the fertility of interallelic crosses in *Neurospora* (Ishikawa, 1962).

Therefore, it is possible that there has been selection for strains of microorganisms which respond to unfavorable environmental situations by the production of spores. To the extent that this generalization holds, the induction of spore formation represents a timing device which introduces a phase of the life cycle which usually is suited to tide the organism over the unfavorable period. The exceptions are not numerous enough to invalidate the rule, which holds with surprising generality.

Of course, other stimuli are known to induce sporulation in slime molds and other fungi, notably light (Gray, 1953; Hawker, 1957; Cantino and Turian, 1959) and carbon dioxide (Hawker, 1957; Cantino and Turian, 1959). The selective advantages of these environmental stimuli are not clear but it is reasonable to expect that benefits similar to those discussed for nutritional stimuli accrue to organisms employing light and other environmental cues.

TIMING AND GERMINATION

Dormant spores could be considered as representing a simple timing system in which an arresting device must be overcome by an activator. Arrest is accomplished by the types of dormancy described in Chapter 10, and activation by the means discussed in Chapter 7. In the following material we will explore instances in nature where spores appear to abet survival by acting as timing devices.

Mechanisms of Arrest

1. *Chemical.* Two types of chemical arrest have been described in Chapter 10,

including self-inhibitors, and those produced outside the spores. These will be discussed separately.

SELF-INHIBITORS. As was shown in Chapter 10, many microorganisms can form self-inhibitors. These substances may function to restrain the germination of spores produced on the outside of hyphae, like the conidia of *Glomerella* (Lingappa and Lockwood, 1963) and *Erysiphe graminis* (Domsch, 1954), or spores which are produced within containers, like those of slime molds (von Stosch, 1935). In either case, it is likely that the prevention of the germination of spores at the place of their production assures their dissemination to new environments and subsequent mixing of gene pools by the formation of heterokaryons and sexual reproduction. On the other hand, ascospores of *E. cichoracearum* (Schnathorst, 1959) and of the Laboulbeniales (Benjamin, 1963), are known to develop within the ascus so that a form of "vivipary" does exist in the fungi.

EXOGENOUSLY PRODUCED INHIBITORS. The work of Macfarlane (1952) suggests that any of several means of suppressing the germination of resting spores of *Plasmodiophora brassicae*, including the presence of inhibitors, enhanced the survival of these spores. Although no mechanism was proposed to explain these results, in this case at least, survival value was attached to *sensitivity* to a fungistatic principle. A similar argument has been applied to explain the role of the widespread fungistasis in soil but until the mechanism of this effect is better understood conclusions must be tentative. An assumption that is basic to the suggestion that the presence of inhibitors enhances survival is that there is discontinuous production of these inhibitors so that development is possible at certain times. That the suppression of germination by the widespread fungistasis may indeed have selective value is suggested by the data which are presented on page 303.

2. *Temperature.* The data in Tables 7.1 and 7.3 disclose that temperature can be an important means of restraining development. Unless the proper temperature is furnished the spores listed in these tables, the dormant condition is maintained. In most cases this means that continued incubation of spores at temperatures which are optimal for vegetative development will delay their germination. Furthermore, it often follows that exposure to extremes of temperature results in activation of spores.

Is there any ecological and selective advantage in such a generalized difference between the temperature requirements for activation and vegetative growth? One possibility is that extreme temperatures serve as cues which anticipate seasonal changes. For example, basidiospores of *Flammula alnicola*, a fungus causing decay of conifers in Canada, require storage at $-7°C$, followed by incubation at higher temperatures, in order to develop (Denyer, 1960). These requirements restrict infection to the spring season. Moreover, these spores cannot survive temperatures usually found around the aboveground parts of the host so that its infections are restricted to roots because of the milder temperatures which exist in soil during winter. Consequently, the initiation of the development of this fungus is timed to coincide with the beginning of growth of the host, and with the start of the relatively short warm season in Canada.

This situation is to be contrasted with that in another wood-rotting basidiomycete, *Fomes ignarius* var. *populinus*, whose spores are capable of germinating at any temperature encountered during the growing season, but fail to do so below 15°C (Good and Spanis, 1958). Therefore, it is adapted to germinate rapidly during the summer, at which time sporulation is at its minimum. It is difficult in this case to see any selective advantage in the timing of spore germination, but the complexity of the host-parasite interaction, and the fact that germination is only the first step in the process, makes it highly likely that many other factors must be taken in account.

Other exceptions to the generalization that spores act as timing devices exist, including the cases of spores of *Rhizopus delemar* and *Peronospora parasitica* because intermediate temperatures are required for their germination, whereas their vegetative development is favored by thermophilic and psychrophilic conditions respectively. Nevertheless, these spores may still play a role in timing development within the ecological niches favored by these organisms. However, this speculation is not worth pursuing in the absence of further data. In any event, the conclusion is still favored that the optimal development of many microorganisms requires exposure of spores to extremes of temperature, followed by incubation at intermediate ones.

Role of Activators

The data in Chapter 7 on "triggers," reveal a bewildering array of activators which overcome the arresting devices discussed earlier. It is pertinent to ask what purpose in nature is served, if any, by the evolution of these differing requirements for germination.

1. *Chemical Activators.* Spores of pathogens frequently germinate in response to secretions from host plants, according to Garrett (1956), who has reviewed the extensive literature. Examples of this kind are to be found in Table 7.12, including the germination of spores of *Erysiphe polygoni*, *Botrytis cinerea*, and *Claviceps purpurea*. Propagules other than spores, like sclerotia of *Sclerotium cepovorum*, also fail to germinate except in the presence of substances diffusing from roots of its host *Allium* (Coley-Smith and Hickman, 1957). Many of the defined activators listed in Table 7.5 are produced by higher plants and it is possible that some of these potential hosts secrete the substances which induce the germination of parasites. One such case is that of rice, which produces glutamine on the surface of its leaves, thereby stimulating the germination of spores of the causative agent of the "blast" disease, *Piricularia oryzae* (Suryanarayan, 1958).

Activators may affect the spore directly or alter its environment in a way which permits germination, but the exact mechanism through which they work in nature most often is not known. An interesting case which illustrates the pitfalls in extrapolating from *in vitro* experiments to natural conditions is that of the bean root rot fungus, *Fusarium solani* F. *phaseoli*, which was studied by Schroth and Snyder (1961). Chlamydospores of this fungus germinate in distilled water, sterile soil, and water agar, *but not in field soils*. In the latter instance, exudates from bean plants induce germination, so it is suggested that the nutrients secreted by the host are needed to overcome the widespread soil fungistasis which is introduced on page 301. According to these authors, the chlamydospores remain dormant and survive in the rhizosphere of nonhost plants until they come in contact with exudates from beans, thereby establishing a possible role for the widespread soil fungistasis.

Mycorrhizal fungi have been shown to require exudates from living roots in order to germinate. In the case of *Russula adusta* and *R. sanguinea*, only pine roots served as a source of the activator but tomato roots were effective with *R. fragilis* (Melin, 1955). In other cases, germination can occur in the absence of plant extracts but is enhanced in their presence in *Boletus luteus* and *B. piperatus*. Again, the mechanism in nature may be difficult to determine with certainty. Thus, Mosse (1963) has shown that spores of another mycorrhizal fungus, *Endogone*, may be induced to germinate by the addition, under aseptic conditions, of water-soluble substances released by a mixed population of soil microorganisms in a soil-agar plate. Therefore, the observation that exudates from wounded roots frequently induce increased germination may not always indicate direct action of the exudates upon spores: rather, the growth of soil microorganisms may be enhanced, thereby resulting in the liberation of the actual activators secondarily.

Self-stimulators are another class of activator whose role may be assumed in certain cases. Thus, spores of the commercial mushroom germinate only poorly unless transferred to media upon which its mycelium has been grown (Ferguson, 1902; de Zeeuw, 1943). It is possible in this case that the cue to germinate serves to assure continued growth in an environment favoring the organism.

Otherwise, the role in nature of many chemical activators can only be guessed. Such treatments as passage through animals, the use of diffusates from other microorganisms, and soil extracts need investigation from this standpoint. Furthermore, decoy plants are known to induce the precocious germination of pathogens in soil by producing activators similar to those in host plants (Garrett, 1956), and it is possible that microorganisms serve such a role as well.

2. *Temperature.* The need for heat-activation by many bacterial and fungus spores is strikingly evident from the data in Table 7.1. Burned-over areas in southern Asia are covered with the pink conidia of *Neurospora*, according to

Went (1901), so it is possible that the activation of ascospores by heat accounts for this "bloom". Selective value surely accrues in such cases due to the great survivability of ascospores as compared with conidia and vegetative stages (Y. Lingappa and Sussman, 1959). Nevertheless, there is reason to question whether this explanation holds in nature. Thus, ascospores of *Neurospora* are known to be activated by chemicals such as furfural, as well as by heat (Chapter 7). However, their responsiveness to chemicals diminishes during aging (Sussman, 1953; Emerson, 1954), but can be recovered by heat-treatments at lower temperatures than those which activate such spores (Sussman, 1954). These temperatures are of the order of 44°–50°C (Figure 11.2), and are much more

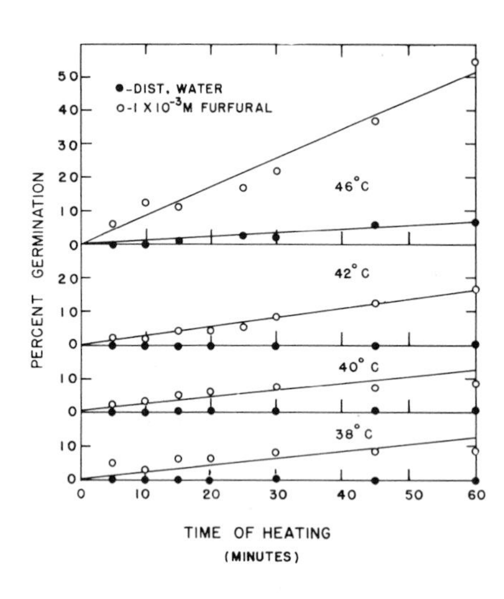

Figure 11.2 Effect of exposure to temperatures from 38°–46°C upon the response of ascospores of *Neurospora tetrasperma* to furfural (1×10^{-3} *M*). Ascospores were used 28 months after harvest. (Taken from Sussman, 1954, courtesy *Mycologia*, New York Botanical Garden.)

common in nature than are those required for activation. In fact, furfural and related heterocyclic activators are among the most ubiquitous compounds in nature, inasmuch as they are breakdown products of pentosans which are components of the walls of higher plants. Therefore, it is likely that compost piles, and similar areas of active microbial decomposition, are the source of both chemical activators and the slightly elevated temperatures needed to ensure maximal response to the chemicals. It is pertinent to note that the fungi whose spores are activated by heat are mainly coprophilous ascomycetes, and that *Phycomyces*, one of the few phycomycetes on the list, also inhabits dung (Table 7.1). Such a habitat probably yields abundant furfural, as well as forming enough heat to sensitize the spores, so that the source of the fungus makes reasonable the suggestion as to the type of activation which occurs in nature. Whether activation is a cue for the most propitious moment to germinate on the natural substrate (dung, grass, and so on) remains to be learned.

This discussion again highlights the complications which arise when extrapolation to nature from laboratory experiments is attempted. In this case, the combination of chemical activator and heat is the most likely means through which dormancy is broken in nature, rather than either treatment alone. Thus, the interaction of activators must be studied, as well as their separate effects. Finally, the habitats of microorganisms in nature, and their response to these environments, must be known before the selective advantage of the characteristic in question can be analyzed meaningfully.

Comparative Physiology of Activation

Starting with the types of activators required by the different dormant organisms, a host of questions may be raised. Why is light so infrequent a cue for germinating microbes, whereas higher plants and many animals frequently use this environmental factor as a signal? What is the nature of the activators in soil extracts, diffusates, and products of the metabolism of microorganisms and other creatures? Which mechanisms of arrest and activation are common to many organisms and which differ? How do the environmental cues in sporulation and germination correlate with the phenology of the dormant organisms in question? Many of the answers must be deferred until the intricacies of regulatory and control systems within single organisms are better understood. The rest must await solution of the questions of regulation and control among populations of organisms.

REFERENCES

ALLISON, L. E. 1951. *Soil Sci.* 72:341–352.

ANAGNOSTOPOULOS, C., and J. SPIZIZEN. 1961. *J. Bacteriol.* 81:741–746.

AYERS and JOHNSON. 1913. *U.S. Dep. Agr. B.A.I. Bull.* 161.

BALASSA, G., HÉLÈNE IONESCO, and P. SCHAEFFER. 1963. *Compt. Rend. Acad. Sci. (Paris)* 257:986–988.

BARTNICKI-GARCIA, S., and W. J. NICKERSON. 1962. *J. Bacteriol.* 84:829–840.

BARTON, LELA. 1965. in *Encyclopedia of Plant Physiology*. A. Lang, ed. Springer Verlag, Berlin, pp. 1058–1085.

BEIJERINCK, M. W., and M. H. JACOBSON. 1908. *Proc. 1er Congres Int. ou Froid, Paris*, p. 9.

BENJAMIN, R. R. 1963. Personal communication.

BERNLOHR, R. W., and G. D. NOVELLI. 1963. *Arch. Biochem. Biophys.* 103:94–104.

BISSET, K. A. 1950. *Nature* 166:431–432.

BONNER, J. T. 1958. *Am. Naturalist* 92:193–200.

BORUT, SHIRA. 1960. *Bull. Res. Council of Israel* (D) 8D:65–80.

BOSCO, G. 1960. *Nuovi Annali di Igiene e Microbiologia* 11:227–240.

BULLER, A. H. R. 1909. *Researches on Fungi.* Longmans, Green, N.Y., pp. 153–178.

CAMPBELL, L. L., and ESTHER E. SNIFF. 1959. *J. Bacteriol.* 77:766–770.

CANTINO, E. C., and G. F. TURIAN. 1959. *Ann. Rev. Microbiol.* 13:97–124.

CARTER, H. P., and J. L. LOCKWOOD. 1957. *Phytopathology* 47:169–173.

CASSIRER, E. 1950. *The Problem of Knowledge.* Yale Univ. Press, New Haven, 334 pp.

CHEN, WEN-H. 1958. *Dokl. Mosk. Sel'skohoz. Akad.* [*Biol. Abst.* 44:1212 (96425)].

CHINN, S. H. F. 1953. *Can. J. Botany* 31:718–724.

CHRISTENSEN, J. J. 1942. in *Aerobiology*. S. Moulton, ed., pp. 78–87. Am. Assoc. Sci. Pub. #17, Wash., 289 pp.

CLARK, F. E. 1950. *Soil Sci.* 70:345–349.

COLEY-SMITH, J. R., and C. J. HICKMAN. 1957. *Nature* 180:445.

COOK, R. P. 1932. *Biol. Rev. Camb. Phil. Soc.* 7:1–23.

CRUMP, L. M. 1953. *Rept. Rothamstead Exp. Sta. for 1952*, p. 58.

DARLING, C. A., and P. A. SIPLE. 1941. *J. Bacteriol.* 42:83–98.

DAVIS, R. H. 1959. *Genetics* 44:1291–1308.

DEEP, I. W., and M. E. CORDEN. 1961. in *Biological Investigations for secondary school students*. Am. Inst. Biol. Sci., Biol. Sci. Curr. Study, Boulder, Colo.

DENYER, W. B. G. 1960. *Can. J. Botany* 38:909–920.

DOMSCH, K. H. 1954. *Arch. Mikrobiol.* 20:163–175.

DOMSCH, K. H. 1958. *Plant and Soil* 10:114–131; 132–146.

DUGGAN, D. E., A. A. ANDERSON, and P. R. ELLIKER. 1962. *Bacteriol. Proc.*, p. 22.

DURBIN, R. D. 1961. *Botan. Rev.* 27:522–560.

DURRELL, L. W., and LORA M. SHIELDS. 1960. *Mycologia* 52:636–641.

EHRENBERG, C. G. 1849. *Passatstaub und Blutregen*. Kg. Akad. Wiss. Berlin, 192 pp.

ELWAN, S. H., and S. A. Z. MAHMOUD. 1960. *Arch. Mikrobiol.* 36:360–364.

EMERSON, MARY R. 1954. *Plant Physiol.* 29:418–428.

FERGUSON, M. C. 1902. *U.S. Dept. Agr., Bur. Plant Ind. Bull.* 16:1–40.

FLEMMING. 1908. *Z. Hyg. Infekt. Kr.* 58:345–385.

FLOOD, A. E., and D. S. KIRKHAM. 1960. in *Phenolics in Plants in Health and Disease*. J. B. Pridham, ed. Pergamon Press, N.Y., 131 pp.

FOSTER, J. W. 1956. *Quart. Rev. Biol.* 31:102–118.

FOSTER, J. W., and E. S. WYNNE. 1948. *J. Bacteriol.* 55:495–501.

FREEMAN, M. A. R., and C. F. BARWELL. 1960. *J. Hyg.* 58:337–345.

FRIEDL, J. L., L. F. ORTENZIO, and L. S. STUART. 1956. *J. Assoc. Off. Agr. Chemists* 39:480–483.

FRIES, N. 1948. *Physiol. Plantarum* 1:330–341.

GARRETT, S. D. 1956. *Biology of Root Infecting Fungi*. Cambridge Univ. Press, London, 292 pp.

GOOD, H. M., and W. SPANIS. 1958. *Can. J. Botany* 36:421–437.

GOODLOW, R. J., and F. A. LEONARD. 1961. *Bacteriol Rev.* 25:182–187.

GRAY, W. D. 1953. *Mycologia* 45:817–824.

GREGORY, P. H. 1952. *Trans. Brit. Mycol. Soc.* 35:1–18.

GREGORY, P. H. 1961. *The Microbiology of the Atmosphere*. Interscience Publ., N.Y., 251 pp.

HALDANE, J. S. 1929. *The Sciences and Philosophy*. Hodder and Stoughton, London, 344 pp.

HALVORSON, H. O. 1961. in *Cryptobiotic Stages in Biological Systems*. N. Grossowicz, S. Hestrin, and A. Keynan, eds. Elsevier, Amsterdam, N.Y., London, pp. 32–63.

HAMMER, B. W. 1948. *Dairy Bacteriology*. 3rd ed. John Wiley, N.Y., 593 pp.

HAWKER, LILIAN E. 1957. *The Physiology of Reproduction in Fungi*. Cambridge Univ. Press, London, 128 pp.

HESSE, W. 1884. *Mitt. Kais. Gesundheitsamte* 2:182–207.

HICKMAN, C. J. 1958. *Trans. Brit. Mycol. Soc.* 41:1–13.

IICHINSKA, EVA. 1960. *Microbiology (Mikrobiologiya—Transl'n), AIBS* 29:147–150.

INGOLD, C. T. 1953. *Dispersal in Fungi*. Oxford Univ. Press, London, 197 pp.

INGOLD, C. T. 1960. in *Plant Pathology*. J. H. Horsfall and A. E. Dimond, eds., vol. 3. Academic Press, N.Y., pp. 137–168.

ISHIKAWA, T. 1962. *Neurospora Newsletter #2*, p. 19.

JINKS, J. L. 1959. *Heredity* 13:525–528.

JOHNSON, L. F., and T. S. OSBORNE. 1964. *Can. J. Botany* 42:105–113.

KAUFMANN, O. W., Z. J. ORDAL, and H. M. EL-BISI. 1955. *Food Res.* 19:483–487.

KELLY, C. D., and S. M. PADY. 1953. *Can. J. Botany* 31:90–106.

KNAYSI, G. 1948. *Bacteriol. Rev.* 12:19–77.

KRAMER, C. L., S. M. PADY, C. T. ROGERSON, and L. G. OUYE. 1959. *Trans. Kans. Acad. Sci.* 62:184–199.

KREBS, H. A. 1954. *Bull. Johns Hopkins Hosp.* 95:45–51.

LAMANNA, C. 1952. *Bacteriol. Rev.* 16:90–93.

LEAL, J. A., and J. R. VILLANUEVA. 1962. *Science* 136:715–716.

LEES, A. D. 1961. in *Cryptobiotic Stages in Biological Systems*. N. Grossowicz, S. Hestrin, and A. Keynan, eds. Elsevier, Amsterdam, N.Y., London, pp. 224–225.

LESTER, H. E., and S. R. GROSS. 1959. *Science* 129:572.

LEVISOHN, I. 1955. *Nature* 176:519.

LINDEGREN, C. C. 1942. *Iowa State J. Sci.* 16: 271–290.
LINDEGREN, C. C., and E. HAMILTON. 1944. *Botan. Gaz.* 105:316–321.
LINGAPPA, B. T., and J. T. LOCKWOOD. 1961. *J. Gen. Microbiol.* 26:473–485.
LINGAPPA, B. T., and J. T. LOCKWOOD. 1963. Unpublished results.
LINGAPPA, B. T., and A. S. SUSSMAN. 1959. *Plant Physiol.* 34:466–472.
LINGAPPA, Y., and A. S. SUSSMAN. 1959. *Am. J. Botany* 46:671–678.
LINGAPPA, Y., A. S. SUSSMAN, and I. A. BERNSTEIN. 1963. *Mycopathol. Mycologia Appl.* 20:109–128.
LOCKWOOD, J. L. 1959. *Phytopathology* 49:327–331.
LOCKWOOD, J. L. 1960. *Phytopathology* 50:787–789.
MACDONALD, K. D., and G. PONTECORVO. 1953. *Advan. Genet.* 5:142–238.
MACFARLANE, I. 1952. *Ann. Appl. Biol.* 39:239–256.
MAHMOUD, S. A. Z., M. A. EL-FADL, and M. KH. ELMOFTY. 1964. *Folia Microbiol.* 9:1–8.
MASAGO, H. 1959. *Ann. Phytopathol. Soc. Japan* 24:97–103.
MCATTEE, W. L. 1917. *Monthly Weath. Rev., Wash.* 45:217.
MCKEEN, C. D. 1954. *Can. J. Botany* 32:101–115.
MCLEAN, J. G., D. J. LE TOURNEAU, and J. W. GUTHRIE. 1961. *Phytopathology* 51:84–89.
MELIN, E. 1955. *Uppsala Universitets Araskrift* 3:1–29.
MEYER, K. F. 1961. *Bacteriol. Rev.* 25:249–261.
MILLER, J. J. 1959. *Wallerstein Lab. Commun.* 22:267–283.
MIQUEL, P. 1883. *Les Organismes Vivants de l'Atmosphere.* Paris, 310 pp.
MORA, P. T. 1962. *Am. Scientist* 50:570–575.
MOSSE, BARBARA. 1963. in *Symbiotic Associations.* P. S. Nutman and B. Mosse, eds. Cambridge Univ. Press, London, pp. 146–170.
NELSON, P. E., and S. WILHELM. 1958. *Phytopathology* 48: 613–616.
NICOT, MME. J. 1953. *Brief Account of Fungic Microflora Found in Desert Sands.* Unesco/NS/AZ/149.
NICOT, MME. J. 1960. in *The Ecology of Soil Fungi.* D. Parkinson and J. S. Waid, eds. Liverpool Univ. Press, Liverpool, pp. 94-97.
VAN NIEL, C. B. 1955. *J. Gen. Microbiol.* 13:201–217.
PADY, S. M., and C. D. KELLY. 1954. *Can. J. Botany* 32:202–212.
PADY, S. M., and L. KAPICA. 1955. *Mycologia* 47:34–50.
PHILLIPS, C. R. 1952. *Bacteriol. Rev.* 16:135–138.
PONTECORVO, G. 1956. *Ann. Rev. Microbiol.* 10:393–400.
PRINCE, A. E., and S. BAKANAUSKAS. 1960. in *Scientific Studies on Fletcher's Ice Island.* T–3, 1952–1955, vol. 3. Geophysics Res. Directorate, Air Force Cambridge Res. Center, Air Res. and Dev. Command, USAF, Bedford, Mass., pp. 92–94.
PROCTOR, B. E. 1935. *J. Bacteriol.* 30:363–375.
RAMSEIER, H. R. 1960. *Arch. Mikrobiol.* 37:57–94.
ROGERS, L. A., and F. C. MEIER. 1936. *Nat. Geog. Soc. Stratosphere Series* 2:146–151.
RUSSELL, E. S. 1945. *The Directiveness of Organic Activities.* Cambridge Univ. Press, London, 196 pp.
SACKS, L. E. 1956. *J. Bacteriol.* 70:491–497.
SAWADA, SACHIKO. 1959. *Ecol. Rev.* (*Mt. Hakkoda Botan. Lab., Tohoku Univ.*) 15:23–25.
SCHNATHORST, W. C. 1959. *Phytopathology* 49: 464–468.
SCHRÖDTER, H. 1960. in *Plant Pathology.* J. H. Horsfall and A. E. Dimond, eds., vol. 3. Academic Press, N.Y., pp. 169–227.
SCHROTH, M. N., and W. C. SNYDER. 1961. *Phytopathology* 51:389–393.
SLOTNICK, I. J. 1959. *J. Bacteriol.* 78:893–895.
SNELL, W. H. 1923. *Am. J. Botany* 10:399–411.
SREERAMULU, T. 1958. *J. Indian Botan. Soc.* 37:220–228.
STAKMAN, E. C., and L. M. HAMILTON. 1939. *Plant Disease Reptr., Suppl.* 117:69–83.
STOSCH, H. A. VON. 1935. *Planta* (Berlin) 23:623–656.
STOTZKY, G., R. D. GOOS, and M. I. TIMONIN. 1962. *Plant Soil* 16:1–18.
STRAUSS, B. S. 1958. *J. Gen. Microbiol.* 18:658–669.
SURYANARAYANAN, S. 1958. *Current Sci.* 27:447–448.
SUSSMAN, A. S. 1953. *Am. J. Botany* 40:401–404.
SUSSMAN, A. S. 1954. *Mycologia* 46:143–150.
SUSSMAN, A. S. 1965. in *Ecology of Soil-Borne Plant Pathogens—Prelude to Biological Control.* K. F. Baker, and W. C. Snyder, eds. Univ. Calif. Press. pp. 99–109.
SUSSMAN, A. S., Y. LINGAPPA, and I. A. BERNSTEIN. 1963. *Mycopathol. Mycologia Appl.* 20:307–314.

TAM, R. K., and H. E. CLARK. 1943. *Soil Sci.* 56: 245–261.

THORNTON, H. G., and JANE MEIKLEJOHN. 1957. *Ann. Rev. Microbiol.* 11:123–148.

TOCHINAI, Y. 1926. *J. Coll. Agr. Hokkaido Sapporo Univ. (Japan)* 14:171–236.

TRANSEAU, E. N. 1949. *Am. J. Botany* 36:596–602.

WAHL, I. 1961. in *Cryptobiotic Stages in Biological Systems.* N. Grossowicz, S. Hestrin, and A. Keynan, eds. Elsevier, Amsterdam, N.Y., London, pp. 107–119.

WAKSMAN, S. A. 1927. *Principles of Soil Microbiology.* Williams and Wilkins, Baltimore, 897 pp.

WALKER, A. T., and F. G. SMITH. 1952. *Proc. Soc. Exp. Biol. and Med., N.Y.* 81:556–559.

WARCUP, J. H. 1951. *Ann. Botany* (London) 15:305–318.

WARCUP, J. H. 1957*a*. *Trans. Brit. Mycol. Soc.* 40: 237–262.

WARCUP, J. H. 1957*b*. *Soils and Fertilizers* 20: 1–5.

WARCUP, J. H. 1960. in *The Ecology of Soil Fungi.* D. Parkinson and J. S. Waid, eds. Liverpool Univ. Press, Liverpool, pp. 3–21.

WARCUP, J. H. 1962. Personal communication.

WELLS, W. F. 1955. *Airborne Contagion and Air Hygiene: An Ecological Study of Droplet Infections.* Harvard Univ. Press, Cambridge, Mass., 423 pp.

WENSLEY, R. N. 1953. *Can. J. Botany* 31:277–308.

WENT, F. A. F. C. 1901. *Zentr. Bakteriol. Parasitenk. Abt. II* 7: 544–550; 591–598.

WINOGRADSKY, S. 1949. *Microbiologie du Sol.* Masson et Cie, Paris, 861 pp.

WOLF, F. T. 1943. *Bull. Torrey Botan. Club* 70:1–14.

WYNNE, E. S., and K. HARRELL. 1951. *Antibiot. Chemotherapy* 1:198–202.

YANAGITA, T., and S. YAMAGISHI. 1958. *Appl. Microbiol.* 6:375–381.

DEZEEUW, D. J. 1943. *Phytopathology* 33:530–531.

ZNAMIROWSKI, R., S. MCDONALD, and T. E. ROY. 1960. *Can. Med. Assoc. J.* 83:1004–1006.

ZOBELL, C. E. 1946. *Marine Microbiology.* Chronica Botanica, Waltham, Mass., 240 pp.

INDEX

Page numbers in italics refer to the illustrations.